Mahinto's *Wind Wolf Woman* will make

MW00061418

...s

Wind Wolf Woman is a difficult book to describe because it's not static...it's enlightening, entertaining, and chock full of real emotions...

—The Book Alert

Wind Wolf Woman is irrefutably, irretrievably, and irreducibly... A PAGE TURNER...

—The Las Vegas Review Journal

Wind Wolf Woman is rapid, wide ranging, overwhelming in concept, limitless in scope...

—The Wichita Falls Times

Wind Wolf Woman...written with the shyness of a brass band and the reticence of a tigress...

—The Atlanta Constitution

Wind Wolf Woman...the phony Native American facade disappears and the characters are vividly real...

—The Miami Herald

Wind Wolf Woman...captivating, raw, and sometimes charming...

—The Chicago Daily Tribune

WIND WOLF WOMAN

Published by: Taté Publishing
Las Vegas, Nevada
www.windwolfwoman.com

Art Director: Sharon Nail
Production: Richard Curtis

This novel is based on a true story. Some of the characters and places have been changed to protect the rights, privacy and identities of others.

Printed in the United States of America on acid-free recycled paper.

Publisher's Cataloging-in-Publication Data

Mahinto.
   Wind Wolf Woman: the story of a medicine woman / Mahinto.
   — 1st ed.
   p. cm.
   LCCN: 00-90453
   ISBN: 0-9677461-0-8

   1. Mahinto—Religion. 2. Women shamans—Biography. 3. Shamanism.
   4. Indians of North and South America—Religion. 5. Indian women—North America—Biography. I. Title.

      BL73.A73M342000   299'.74'092
                                                        QBI00–322

10 9 8 7 6 5 4 3 2 1

WIND WOLF WOMAN
The Story of a Medicine Woman

Mahinto

Taté Publishing
Las Vegas, Nevada
www.windwolfwoman.com

Introduction

I am a Breed and proud of it. The name Mahinto was given to me by my grandmother. It is spelled phonetically so you can pronounce it: Mah-Hen-Toh.

From birth to the age of ten years old I was raised by my grandmother, a powerful medicine woman. At her death, I was sent to live with my father who taught me some of my harshest lessons. At the age of fifteen I ran away from home and went to New York where I trained for a career in show business. My career as a performer afforded me the ability to travel throughout the world, and everywhere I travelled I made it a point to learn about the native philosophies. I have published *The Seed, Walk Your Talk, How to Deal with a Cheating Mate* and *The Medicine Bag*.

Having dedicated my life to reversing the plight of the American Indian, I battled Congress to protect the gas, oil and mineral rights of reservation lands. During these experiences my roots only grew stronger and I never ventured too far from my grandmother's blanket. I now spend my days doing what I love best—writing and teaching.

Preface

When I started to write this book little did I realize it was going to be a novel. It was not easy to relive my past and write it into a story. It has taken me years of gathering information and researching old records to attain the exactness of the material for this book. I believe that most of the human race are breeds by birth who are raised to believe in a certain culture. The beginning of my story lets you see the damage to one's life brought on by birthright, rejection and the lack of education.

Early on in life I learned the meaning of harshness and poverty, and I have spent most of my life traveling from place to place. By the time I was seven years old, I had a very inquisitive mind and asked many questions. When the adults in my life could not answer these questions books became my best friend. From the moment I learned to write, I started to secretly write about my dreams of the future. Little did I realize it would take more than dreaming to accomplish those imaginings. By the time I reached the age of ten, I had withdrawn from people and lost my original identity. By the time I reached twenty, the stage was my identity. By the time I was thirty, I was cold and indifferent like my father. By the time I was thirty-five, I found myself a lonely lost soul and went in desperate search for who I was.

It is important as you read this book to understand it embraces four generations of people, all educated in different times and ways. Four strong medicine people taught proper morals and a good spiritual belief system to the two major characters in the book, but this knowledge did not mesh into their lives until they had experienced many hard lessons.

Take my hand as you walk through the pages of *Wind Wolf Woman*, I hope to appeal to your intellect and cut to the chase of your heart all the while emphasizing that the way to knowledge is through living and experience. Life is a precious gift that must be recognized and honored in order to return to the original source of your soul and know all that you are.

Acknowledgements

I would like to extend a very special thank you to my wonderful friends who supported me during this endeavor. It was their dedication, time and effort that completed this novel. Their patience, support and understanding has no words. I humbly thank each of you: Sharon Nail, Joy Siddiqi, Frank Grundman, Ann Sims, Alan Hubbard, Marcia Pando, Vonda Elsbury, Jaeynka Postupack, George Beyer, Marion Booth-May, Laura Lee and Penny Meyer.

I would also like to extend a personal thank you to my four legged friends who are members of my household. I live with two beautiful and devoted loving friends. Shatonga Wi V (Wolf Woman) is a female wolf that is kind and understanding. Many times she has waited far too long to be fed or let out so that I could continue writing undisturbed. Shatonga knows my schedule and each day leads me into my office to ensure I turn on the computer and write. Her patience has far surpassed that of all humans that I have ever known. Her sidekick is a little black-brown terrier lovingly called "Jake the Snake." Jake offers his support by sitting patiently on the sofa listening to every word while I read out loud what I have written.

Dedication

I am honored to dedicate this book to my son, Richard Curtis, *Cetan Luta* (Red Hawk). We have walked a long road together—meeting and experiencing life as one.

Contents

1 Sunbeams Arrival ◆ 1
The Mighty Winds Sing Us into Life

2 The Quest of a Spiritual
Warrioress ◆ 32
The Heart/Mind of Nature's Medicine

3 Sunbeam Leaves the
Reservation ◆ 44
Calling In the Spirits

4 Living with Sam ◆
The Womanhood Ceremony

5 Sunny Travels ◆
The Road to Your Dreams

6 Meeko's Birth ◆
The Teachings of an Old Medicine Man

7 Medicine Wheel ◆
Walking in the Four Directions

8 Boy Training ◆
Becoming a Man

9 Meeko Learns to Fly ◆
The Eaglet Tests Its Wings

10 Vietnam ◆
Fighting a War Without Cause

11 American Indian Movement ◆
Fighting for the Rights of My People

12 Prison Life ◆
A Guest of the United States Prison System

13 Meeko Meets Sunny ◆
Meeting My Soul Mate

14 Sunny Returns to
the Reservation ◆
Traditional Marriage Ceremony

15 Honeymoon ◆
Romance, Sandy Beaches, Drums and Vudan

16 The Beginning of the End ◆
Booze, Bars, Broads, Blow, Bills, Betrayal—Bullshit

17 Sunny Returns to Sundance ◆
Feather Piercing and Pulling the Buffalo Skulls

18 Medicine Woman ◆
Picking Up Medicine Power

Glossary of Sioux Terms

Akan	Sacred, very old
Alo Wanpi	Sing Ceremony
Anpetu	Red that shines at dawn and twilight
Até	Father
Atsitsi	"Glove"; Owl
Banshee	Noisy spirit
Chachuba	Bone Marrow
Contrar-Heyoka	A person knowing something so well that they can perform it backward or forward
Dinky Dau	Vietnamese term for crazy
Eya	West Wind
Eyeska	Mixed blood
Ezonzon Wi Cha Nah He	Sunlit Soul
Gnaski	Demon
Ha Hey	A call or chant to the spirit world before prayer
Hanblecheyapi	Vision Quest, a Rite on the Pipe
Hanhepi	Darkness
Hanwi	Moon, night sun
Hau	Greeting, accept, agree
Hé aka	Male elk
Hoka Hey	Battle cry
Hu Nunpa	Spirit Bear
Hunka Até	Adopted father
Hunka Towa	Adopted child
Hunka, Hunkapi	Making of Relatives, a Rite on the Pipe
Hunkapila Kola	Adopted relative friend
Igmu	Cougar
Iktomi	Spider
Ina	Mother

Indian Time	Matching up the earth and sky maps for ceremony, or whenever I get around to it
Inipi	Sweat Lodge
Inyan	Stone People
Ishna Ta Awi Cha Lowan	Womanhood Ceremony
Iya	Evil Spirit
Keya	Turtle
Kinnikinnik	Mixture for sacred tobacco
Kola	Special friend
Ksa	Wisdom
Lela Wakan	Very sacred
Maka	Earth
Maka Ina	Mother Earth
Mato	Bear
Mica	Coyote
Mitakuye Oyasin	All my relations
Moi	Savage in Vietnamese
Niya	Sacred Breath of Life
Okaga	South Wind
Paha Sapa	Black Hills
Pejuta Wi'Inyan Wakan	Holy woman, medicine woman
Pte Oyate	Buffalo Nation
Shade	Spirit ghost
Sunka'	Phonetically pronounced Shung'
Sunka' Di Cha	Den of Wolves
Sicun	Intellect, a part of the four aspects of the soul
Sku'ya	Sweet
Stiginney	Creek dialect for Screech Owl
Sun Goes Over Down	Sunset
Sunka' Manitu	Wolf
Sunka' Tanka	Big Dog (Horse)
Sunwise	Clockwise
Taku Skan Skan	Motion in All Life Forces
Tapa Wanka Wap	The Throwing of the Ball, a Rite on the Pipe

Tatanka	Buffalo
Taté	Father of the Winds
Tob Tob	Spirit Bear, Son of Chiefs, connected to the 4 by 4 in the Inipi
Ton	The essence of everything
Tunka'shila	Grandfather
Unci	Grandmother
Unhcegila	Mastodon
Unk	Contention, passion
Unktehi	Dinosaur
Wabasha	Dakota Sioux
Wakan Tanka	Creator
Wakanka	Spirit, Seer
Wakanpi	Spirit with less power
Wakinyan	Thunderbeings
Wanagi	Spirit
Wanbli Gles'ka	Golden Eagle
Wanbli Pey'ska	Bald Eagle
Washichu	White man in short pants
Wazi	Wizard
We'cha	Raccoon
Wi	Sun
Wi Até	Father Sun
Wichasha Wakan	Holy man, medicine man
Wicahmunga	Witch
Winkté	Homosexual
Wiwanyag Wachipi	Sundance Ceremony
Yanpa	East Wind
Yaté	North Wind
Yumnimni	Whirlwind
Yupayo	Close the Door
Yuwipi	Spirit Calling Ceremony

Sunbeam's Arrival

Around midnight in late September 1935, darkness cloaked a Montana reservation as Cheering Woman, a Dakota Sioux medicine woman, awakened in confident anticipation, knowing that her son's firstborn was a girl. She dressed her tall, statuesque body warmly, then quickly brushed and braided her long salt-and-pepper hair, twisting and winding it into a crown on top of her head to frame her proud, finely chiseled features. Although in her late seventies, she still retained her youthful agility and glowed with the spirit of life.

Cheering Woman got into her old truck and drove to her son's home. When she arrived, she found Sam slumped over the kitchen table with a half-empty bottle of whiskey in one hand, while from the bedroom she heard the cries of a healthy newborn. Cheering Woman's penetrating black eyes took in her son's abject misery with a single glance. It was obvious that his manly pride had been wounded by the birth of a girl child. Sam, unable to ignore her any longer, looked up and said in a quiet monotone, "It's a girl. Found her on the front porch in a basket."

He handed his mother an envelope, adding, "This was pinned to her blanket. It's addressed to you." Cheering Woman quietly read its contents, then placed it into a leather pouch that hung from her waist.

She touched Sam's hand comfortingly and said, "Be happy my son, *Wakan Tanka* has given you a healthy child. It hurts me to see you deny your own flesh." Head bowed, he offered no response, yet his silence spoke loudly.

Cheering Woman studied him for a moment. As a child, he had been sensitive and gentle, but there had always been a wild streak hidden deep within him that could never be completely contained. The tall, muscular man now sitting before her still retained that intense, animalistic wildness. Many would call him handsome with his cool gray eyes and shiny black hair worn in waist-length braids. Yes, she thought, this son of mine can be very charming when he has a mind to please, but he is fiery tempered, unruly and sullen when he doesn't get his way.

"Sam, I have many fond memories of you and Anna, this child's mother, whom I love like my own. You have known each other since you were babies learning to walk and run together. How I loved watching the two of you explore life. It was Anna who brought this excitement to you. I remember how happy you were when you'd both run through the open fields in summer looking for abandoned baby animals to raise. By the time you were eleven anyone could see you were meant for each other.

"You were barely seventeen when I warned you not to have sex before marriage. I remember telling you then that your first child would be a girl, born to a mission. When Anna got pregnant and you two sneaked off for an abortion, she almost died, so I promised that if she kept the baby, I would raise it. I know it broke your heart when her family moved away. I also know you will always love Anna, and she will always love you. But now you are married to another. It's time to stop feeling sorry for yourself and accept this baby's existence. As Wolf Clan, I promised to raise this special born child in the old medicine way. I will guide her toward her birth purpose and awaken her powers before she reaches womanhood. Sam, proof of the undying love between you and Anna lives on in this baby girl."

Sam's eyes stung with unshed tears as he recalled his beloved Anna. He silently acknowledged his mother's words, but offered no response.

Impatient to see her granddaughter, Cheering Woman took Sam's arm and steered him to the makeshift crib. Leaning over the newborn, she picked it up with gentle hands, saying a silent prayer as she lay claim to her granddaughter's soul.

Cheering Woman walked to the window, moved the torn shade aside and let the morning sun gently touch her granddaughter's radiant skin.

"She is as beautiful as first light, just before daybreak. What are we going to name her?"

"Does it matter? It's just a girl."

Showing her annoyance at his pigheaded ways, Cheering Woman snapped, "Stop it! You know we must call her something!"

Sam's wife, Hazel, overheard Cheering Woman and entered the bedroom. Sam looked at Hazel, then muttered, "Me and Hazel haven't talked about a name. I thought maybe *you* would like to name her."

Intimidated by Cheering Woman's presence, Hazel stammered, "I thought since her mother was half white, maybe we should give her a white name."

Cheering Woman bristled. "My son, speak to your woman! This is none of her business. This child is your Indian daughter who shares in your birthright. So what if she's a mixed blood! She's not white! Besides, since neither you nor Anna wanted this child, and since I'm responsible for raising her, I will name her!"

Seeing that her harsh words were causing defiance in her son, she redirected her conversation to the baby.

"You're going to need a powerful name. Since you rode the moon's rays into life, and Father Sun touched your body this morning, you should carry a name that reflects those powers." Staring coldly at Hazel and Sam, she continued, "Because of your attitudes toward a mixed-breed female, she is already suffering from prejudice and rejection. Humor this old woman. I will take the child with me and teach her to walk in both worlds without suffering. In my time I have seen many changes take place between the Indian and the white man. I will train her to walk to serve both cultures in the medicine way."

"Hazel," said Sam, in a superior tone, "Mother is right! This is my child, so I'll name her." Leaning close, he pulled the blanket aside, gazed at the baby's little face, then softly touched her tiny chin with the back of his hand. "You may be a girl, but I'll make you a boy. I'll call you Sonny. Yep, that's what I'll call you, Sonny!"

Used to his stubborn, mulish ways, Cheering Woman smiled sweetly and then, exercising her refined ability to manipulate him, answered, "Hmm, that's good, son. I think *Ezonzon Wi Cha Nah He*, Sunlit Soul, is strong and keeps with our tradition." Looking down at the infant, she continued, "Yes, Grandchild, that is your name, but we will call you 'Sunny' to please your father and 'Sunbeam' to please Father Sun. May you become as bright as the dawn of a new day, and make your presence upon Mother Earth shine with the strength of your Father, the Sun."

Sam's expression remained stoic, but inside he swelled with admiration and pride at the strong name his daughter had been given.

"Sam, my son, I give you your daughter, Sunbeam," announced Cheering Woman as she placed the baby in his arms.

Sam stiffened with resentment as he stared into the tiny face. The baby gazed back, challenging him with unflinching gray-green eyes reminiscent of deep pools filled with hidden crystals. Acknowledging his daughter at last, he smiled and accepted the inevitable. His mother, after all, had chosen the child's direction in life before she'd been born.

Cheering Woman knew she had won another battle with her son, and leaned close to him, whispering, "This child is strong, like you. And that is good. I assure you she will walk with the old knowledge and think like an Indian."

Cheering Woman gathered up her new granddaughter and returned home, where she immediately prepared a sweat. Thus began Sunbeam's training in medicine.

Throughout early childhood, Sunbeam was isolated from outside influences, and by the age of seven she was well-steeped in the old ways. She was a small-framed child with long, dark hair that flowed down her back. At times her penetrating, expressive eyes held an extraordinary gaze. At others times, hidden behind wispy, disheveled bangs, they flashed with devilish mischief.

Strangers were often amazed at her spirited, animal-like independence. Some thought her a bit too arrogant, particularly those who saw her as another illegitimate half-breed. Others suspected that despite her mixed blood, Sunbeam could hear more than what was spoken. Cheering Woman, who knew her best, saw her granddaughter as a mild-mannered, shy little Indian girl who felt awkward in the presence of others and preferred to spend time alone in the serenity of the apple orchard behind the arbor.

One day when all the chores were completed, Cheering Woman called seven-year-old Sunbeam aside. "Grandchild, for years I've been training you to find lost objects. It's now time to honor the spiritual warrioress that sleeps within your soul."

Sunbeam frowned. She hated this game her grandmother called hide-and-seek. But knowing her determination, she gave in quietly, expressing her aggravation with a deep sigh.

"You stop that! No more fighting with me over this game! You're going to work harder at it. A lonely object has been waiting for almost three days to be found. If you fail today, you will see a night without supper. Now once again, close your eyes, still your mind, and feel the object's presence. Where is it? What is its color? What is its shape?"

After an hour of concentrated effort and more badgering from Cheering Woman, Sunbeam still had no answers.

Cheering Woman, frustrated by her granddaughter's lack of interest, scolded, "Your head is more than a hat rack. Anybody can do this! It's your lazy, scattered mind that gets in the way. But don't worry, Granddaughter, I know exactly how to fix the problem. I'm sure that if you go to bed on an empty stomach and get a good night's sleep you'll concentrate better tomorrow. By daybreak you will surely have the answer."

Sunbeam, knowing there was no hope of changing her grandmother's mind, moped around the house until early evening.

"Time for bed," announced Cheering Woman, in a spirited mood.

Sunbeam sulked off to the feather bed they shared, dramatically clutching her growling stomach, knowing that if she didn't have the answer by the following morning, her Grandmother would add another day without food to her training. As she climbed in, she recalled the words she had heard many times before: "Granddaughter, fasting is good for the soul. It makes you pay attention."

Sunbeam tossed and turned, listening to the old people who had gathered on the front porch to eat and gossip about the day's events, before finally falling asleep.

It was still dark when Sunbeam awakened. Her dreams had told her what the lonely object was! Climbing out of bed quietly, so as not to awaken her grandmother, she went to the hook where her grandmother's traveling pouch always hung. She took it down and pulled out a river stone they had found on their last outing. There it was, smooth and white, just as she had seen in her dreams. A broad smile crossed her face as she placed the stone beside her grandmother's pillow. Her work done, she climbed back into bed and fell asleep.

"Get out of bed, Granddaughter," Cheering Woman threw back the covers and tugged playfully at Sunbeam's exposed foot. She waved the stone in front of Sunbeam's face in a congratulatory manner. "I see you have finally found the lost object. Hurry, Grandchild!" scolded Cheering Woman playfully. "Your breakfast is getting cold."

Sunbeam sighed with relief and gave silent thanks to *Wakan Tanka* for helping her find the hidden object. She leapt up and confidently followed her grandmother to the sweet smells of the kitchen. Soon she was wolfing down her fry bread and scrambled eggs while Cheering Woman sipped her coffee smiling with pride.

Cheering Woman knew she had finally attracted her granddaughter's full attention. "It takes patience to learn concentration. You must focus and have a clear thought in mind. When I am no longer on this earth, you will be glad you listened to me, just as I am thankful that I listened to my grandmother."

After many more months of exposure to Cheering Woman's diligent efforts, Sunbeam became exceptionally good at hide-and-seek and came to love the game.

Not only was she refining her ability to find lost articles, but she was also learning how to find missing people.

Cheering Woman had finally decided that the best way to teach her granddaughter was through suspense and mystery—methods that seemed to keep the child's mind stimulated. "Grandchild, always be aware of what is around you," she would say. "Use your imagination to explore the mysteries that are hidden from you. Search inside for answers to your questions. Learn to recognize the difference between what you see and what you *think* you see."

As time went on Cheering Woman noticed a quiet defiance and an air of arrogance taking root in Sunbeam which was intolerable in the Sioux culture. To stop its growth, she used a firm hand, tempered with love; but controls of this sort only sparked outward rebellion.

Determined to cure this terrible disease that had infected her granddaughter's mind, the old medicine woman began to discipline her with fear, guilt and bribery, sometimes forcing her out of bed long before sunrise and engaging her in a lesson that lasted until long after dark.

The battle of wills continued for weeks until early one morning when Cheering Woman threw off Sunbeam's covers, yelling, "Get out of that bed! You're going to smell like an old bear! How can Father Sun spread his light and warmth across the earth if you don't get up to greet him? Hurry, Grandchild!" Cheering Woman glared in mock disgust before leaving the room.

Struggling to wake up, Sunbeam made her way to the kitchen and picked at her breakfast. Cheering Woman quietly sipped her coffee while waiting for her granddaughter's eyes to fully open.

"*Sku'ya*, Sweet, last night you were crying out in your sleep. Tell me about this visit to Shadow World."

Shivering in fear, Sunbeam struggled to recall her frightening dream. "I was somewhere terrible. I went to the Valley of Death, and it was dark and cold. Crying spirits with ugly faces were hanging from gnarled, dead trees. They reached out and tried to touch me."

"Uh-huh," acknowledged Cheering Woman as she nodded her head, her eyes half-closed.

Sunbeam waited in silence for what seemed like an eternity.

When she had nearly lost her patience, Cheering Woman said:

"Your vision seems to hold many fears. The spirits hanging from dead trees were earth-bound souls begging you to release them to the Other Side. When their pained faces scared you, it meant that those lost souls trusted you to take them to the light. They moaned and screamed because you were ignoring their needs. Those poor souls live in a twilight time, and it is you who must help them gain their spiritual freedom."

Sunbeam shuddered at the thought of helping ghosts, but she knew if she did not do as her grandmother instructed, those horrible faces would haunt her forever.

"A visit to Shadow World is considered a rare gift to be treated with great respect. Accidental visits to all sorts of places happen in the dream state if you do not focus on where you are going. You are responsible for this newfound knowledge. I have taught you to go to the Other Side and listen to your inner voice, but last night you acted out of fear, creating confusion. Tonight you must return and complete your mission. That is the only way to free yourself from the haunting faces of those lost souls.

"Granddaughter, you know that everything has a meaning, and your responsibility is to find that meaning. You also know you must accept the unknown when you visit Shadow World. I've told you that whatever you fear will materialize before you. Why place judgment and limitations on your thinking? Everything simply is.

"To find out the time of day, you must read shadows cast by the sun. To understand the nighttime, watch the light of the moon and the position of the stars in the heavens. Remember how we watched the birds, the animals, and the growing plants to learn the power of the seasons? Once you understand the signs of nature, you will be able to glimpse the reality behind the unknown and the unspoken. That is why I taught you to go to Shadow World."

Tired and still sleepy, Sunbeam could barely pay attention.

Cheering Woman, having surrendered her patience, rose from her chair. "My word, Granddaughter, do you think this is all I have to do in life? Many apprentices want to learn what I have to teach! You need me, Granddaughter. I don't need you! I will never play nursemaid to a slow, dull mind!"

Without warning, Cheering Woman slammed her fist on the table, knocking the dishes to the floor. "As Medicine, I demand your undivided attention! You will bring your mind into focus." She sat back down and glared intently at her granddaughter.

Sunbeam was shocked. Never before had she seen her grandmother's wrath or been the target of such temper. Not knowing how to respond to this terrible outburst, she kept her eyes glued to the floor and whimpered an apology for having taken advantage of her grandmother.

"Well, I like sharing with people who understand the importance of my teachings, and if you need cruelty to learn, then so be it. I have made a vow and I will fulfill it! I want you to know how to read the unwritten and hear the unspoken, whether it comes from the past, present, or future. Humph! Right now your unspoken fears are talking so loudly I might lose my hearing."

Sunbeam picked up the broken dishes and began to cry.

"Oh Grandmother, I'm sorry. Please don't be mad at me. I promise I'll listen."

"Go to the Grandmother Lodge and do not return until you have released those captured souls from the Valley of Death."

Still shaken, Sunbeam rushed out the back door and ran all the way to the Grandmother Lodge. It was around noon when she returned and smiled when she spotted her grandmother in the garden.

Cheering Woman looked up and said, "I see you have done well. I'm proud that you released those poor souls so they can go back home to *Tunka'shila*. Come, let's spend the rest of the day in the woods. We have medicines to gather and berries to pick."

As they walked down the familiar pathway with their buckets, Cheering Woman said, "It takes time for an unaware mind to learn the secrets hidden in plants and trees. Ah, *Sku'ya,* my purpose is to show my granddaughter that although the mind is always learning, awareness must be experienced. Look around you. Mother Earth is a garden of plenty, but it takes interest to learn her secrets."

She bent over and picked leaves from a rib-grass plant. Slowly inhaling their fragrance, she added, "We'll keep these. They're good for toothaches, although the burn from these leaves can be worse than the pain in the tooth!"

"I know, Grandmother. I remember my last toothache."

Cheering Woman stopped at the base of a large pine tree. Sunbeam watched as she peeled off the outer crust and scooped away decayed bark. She then cut a deep gash into the flesh of the tree, and took a handful of wet pulp and placed it in a special leather pouch.

"This will make a strong tea for congested lungs. It takes a good medicine person to know the best times to harvest in order to capture the powers of plants.

"Fall is the time to gather crops, pick berries and collect seeds for the coming year. Fall reminds us it's time to return home and prepare for winter. In winter we do not gather certain medicines; instead, we speak to our silence and change our thinking. It's also a time to rest by the fire in harmony with our loving families and share our experiences with younger generations.

"Ah yes, how I love springtime. That's when we clear debris from the land and the mind, recharging ourselves with new energy so that we can walk in rhythm with the sacred circle of life. Spring brings joy to people's hearts and rekindles our faith in new growth. What a miracle it is to watch the birth of new life. Why, even the budding plants and blossoming flowers tell us there is a cycle to life. Look at the sensitivity and beauty in a wildflower. Become its friend, and it will show you its sacred power to heal. It was my grandmother who taught me that spring is the time to dig for tender roots and prepare our medicines.

"Ah, Granddaughter, I know how you love summer. As we gather the fruits and vegetables from our garden, we see it's a time of plenty. *Sku'ya,* always remember to say a special prayer for the miracle of life as you play in summer's green meadows and walk in a good way. We must always appreciate the changing seasons as one of the never-ending gifts from *Wakan Tanka*. Our acknowledgment is what helps Mother Earth keep everything in harmony and balance. This goodness is what nurtures all things. Someday when you become a mother, you will nurture your children in this same way.

"They say that long ago Mother Earth and Father Sky were joined in marriage to demonstrate the bond of absolute love. Watch how they share responsibility for their children. Observe Lightning Man during a storm as he throws bolts of energy into Mother Earth's body to enrich her soil. When you witness this, think of her womb producing our foods and all the medicine plants. Without the warmth of Father Sun and the moisture from the rains, Mother Earth could not sprout new growth. Is this not proof of a great love?

"Ah, *Sku'ya*, nature is harmonious when left alone. *Wakan Tanka* is trying to teach us that everything has a place and a time. If you walk with the medicine knowledge handed down from all past generations, you will become one with the cycles of life. I now pass this on to you, and if you do not use it well, surely the old ones will grieve for Mother Earth and all her generations to come."

By late afternoon they had arrived at the blackberry patch. Sunbeam hated the stickers on the bushes, but loved eating the fresh berries. Having spent three hours in the scorching sun, she was hot and sticky and eager to get away from the aggravating gnats that swarmed around her head, she wandered off to a shady spot.

Before long Cheering Woman went to find her. Spotting her a short distance away, she quickly took in her granddaughter's berry-stained face and hands, and knew she had been putting more fruit in her mouth than in the bucket. Cheering Woman decided to arouse enough fear and doubt in her granddaughter's mind to teach her another lesson.

"Granddaughter, did you check those berries for bird marks? I hope you remembered that if the winged ones don't eat them they may be poisonous."

Terrified by the possibility that she might die, Sunbeam thrust out a handful of berries for her grandmother's inspection.

Cheering Woman examined each one with a long "hm-m-m." Then with a fiendish twinkle in her eyes, she grabbed the berries and tossed them into her mouth. Smacking her lips with pleasure, she gleefully wiped her mouth with the back of her hand.

"Grandmother, what are you doing? You've eaten my berries!"

"Ah yes, Granddaughter. The sweet taste of these berries reminds me that Mother Earth provides well for us. But you must never trust another too freely. Granddaughter, you are so easily influenced by others' opinions that one day someone is likely to take more than a handful of berries from you. Why, even I was able to trick you." Cheering Woman roared with laughter, shaking a playful finger in Sunbeam's face. "Never listen to the voice of fear, and always question another's motives. Trust what you know! Let this be a good lesson. After all, the only thing you lost today was a handful of blackberries. Tomorrow it could be your life."

Angry and embarrassed, Sunbeam tagged along as her grandmother headed for home, chuckling over her own cleverness.

They spent the evening separating the herbs and berries and preparing jars for canning. After watching her grandmother boil and test the mixtures, Sunbeam helped seal the jars. When the canning was finished, she helped her grandmother place the fresh barks and roots on drying racks.

When they had retired for the night, Sunbeam lay in the big feather bed watching the moon trace a golden arc of light across the covers.

"I'm sorry I let old trickster Coyote into my life. I promise it won't happen again."

"Sunbeam, Sunbeam. Life teaches us to respect the old ways. I stole your berries to teach you never to doubt what you already know."

Early the next morning, Cheering Woman and Sunbeam were busy gathering eggs in the henhouse when they heard a truck pull into the yard.

"Granddaughter, give me the basket and go see who's there."

Sunbeam rushed to the front of the house.

"It's Sam," she yelled over her shoulder. She approached her father, a shy smile crossing her face.

Sam tousled her hair and handed her a brown paper bag. "Open it! It's for you."

Unaccustomed to such overtures from her father, Sunbeam stared at him in disbelief. She peeked into the bag and pulled out a handmade leather sheath that contained a beautifully carved hunting knife. "Is this really mine?"

"Made it myself," bragged Sam. He explained how to take care of it as she examined the blade.

Sunny recalled that if a female received a knife from a male, it traditionally meant the relationship was severed. Was this why Sam had given her this gift?

"Since I'm not a boy and you gave me a knife, does this mean I can be a warrioress, or are you just throwing me away?"

"Hell no! Stop acting dumb. I gave you the goddamn knife to use."

Seeing tears well up in her eyes and fearing an altercation with his mother, Sam softened his approach. He took the knife and showed his daughter where he had carved her name on the handle, then added, "C'mon, Sonny, let's not talk about Indian bullshit."

Although she liked the knife, Sunbeam's feelings were hurt. "Thank you," she mumbled, sliding the sheathed knife inside her left boot.

"Good place to keep it."

They were standing in awkward silence when Cheering Woman appeared from around the side of the house.

"Good morning, Mama," Sam respectfully embraced his mother. "Gotta cup of coffee for a tired son?"

They made their way to the back porch where Sam carelessly pulled out a chair, scraping the freshly polished floor. Cheering Woman peered at him sternly and stepped into the kitchen. Stoking the fire in the old woodstove, she added water to the coffee grounds, returned to the porch, and sat down to hear the latest family gossip. When Sunbeam heard the coffee boil over she ran to the kitchen and raced back with two steaming cups, eager to catch every bit of news.

Cheering Woman studied her son's appearance with disapproval.

"You look disgusting. What's the sense of living if you don't take care of yourself? Your clothes look like you've slept in them for a month and your hair is a greasy rat's nest! People who see you look like this will think your family is trash! You tell your woman she'd better take care of you." Reaching for a hairbrush, Cheering Woman proceeded to drag it through his long hair, which she then parted down the middle and began to braid.

Sam loved the attention. It reminded him of happier days, when he was younger and still living at home. "Now, Mama, stop fussing! You know Hazel has her hands full with the new baby and all."

"Humph," Cheering Woman snorted with mock disgust, yanking his braids to emphasize her point. Sunbeam handed her six long strips of red cloth and watched her grandmother's expert fingers wrap each braid, then neatly tie it off. She stood back to admire her work, patted Sam on the head to signal that she was done, and sat back down to finish her coffee.

After breakfast Sam repaired a few items, then fixed a leak in the henhouse roof. Sunbeam followed at a safe distance, watching with curiosity.

Suddenly the old red rooster spotted Sunbeam, and with great fervor began an assault. Sam let out a hearty belly laugh as his daughter ran through the back yard kicking and shouting, trying to fend off the flogging rooster, all the while thinking with pride that his daughter could fight better than any boy.

Angry that her father had made fun of her, Sunbeam left in a huff to unravel the mystery of the knife. Sam had never given her a gift before, so why now? Nor had he paid attention to her the few times he had come to visit. There was good reason to stay away from Sam, she told herself. She had heard what people said about him when Cheering Woman was not around. He was a mean drunk who beat his wife and children, and a womanizer who made no bones about his *Wasichu* lady friends. Thankful that she did not have to see her father more than every once in awhile, Sunbeam decided to return home and hide in the henhouse until Sam's departure. When she heard his old truck leave, she joined Cheering Woman on the front porch.

"Heard the old rooster got you again today," her grandmother announced, chuckling.

"Yes, I wish that old coot would die," Sunbeam replied, spreading salve on the back of her legs.

"Humph, you watch your mouth, Granddaughter. He's a fine rooster and he does a good job around here. Look how many setting hens we have this year. You'd better pray those new chicks aren't all roosters." Cheering Woman chuckled softly and gazed at the dark clouds beginning to form overhead. "Looks like rain is coming. Can you feel the dampness in the air? Ah yes, the rains will definitely be here tomorrow."

Weeks later, dozens of baby chicks hatched. Sunbeam and her grandmother gathered up the smallest ones, placing them under heat lamps to help them survive. Before long all the chicks had grown into good-sized pullets, and were taking up a great deal of Sunbeam's time. When she wasn't chasing escapees into their pens, she was gathering eggs or cleaning the henhouse.

"Chickens are the filthiest birds in the world!" she screamed in disgust.

"Sunbeam, get over here," demanded Cheering Woman, alarm in her voice.

Thinking something terrible had happened to her grandmother, Sunbeam raced over to find her peering down into one of the outhouse holes.

"Granddaughter, how could you have done such a bad thing? I know you hate my chickens, but why in God's name did you put one down that hole?"

Sunbeam stared in horror at the young chicken submerged up to its neck in human shit making feeble attempts to flap its encrusted wings. She backed out of the privy adamantly denying that she had done such a thing.

"Granddaughter, how dare you lie to me!" Using a pole, Cheering Woman tried to rescue the chicken, but eventually gave up. "My poor little chicken will die. You come here! You put that chicken in there, and you're going to get it out!"

Grabbing Sunbeam, she shoved her, dangling by her heels, headfirst into the hole. Sunbeam's face was only inches from the foul-smelling feces as she desperately groped for something to grab onto.

Sunbeam attempted to hold her breath as the horrible stench filled her nostrils, causing her to gag. She tried repeatedly to grab the chicken, but each time she came close, it flapped its wings, showering her with slime.

"Let me up. I can't do this!" she begged, struggling against Cheering Woman's powerful grip.

"Oh, yes you can, Granddaughter! If you don't grab that chicken, I'll let go!" Cheering Woman dropped Sunbeam an inch closer to the waste to make her point, shaking her as if to let go.

Knowing her grandmother was not one to make idle threats, Sunbeam gathered her courage for a final attempt. Retching from the awful smell, she closed her eyes and then thrust her arms into the muck in search of the chicken. At last she grabbed the slippery bird, whereupon Cheering Woman pulled them both to safety, but not before the chicken flapped its wings, covering Sunbeam's face with human waste.

Cheering Woman carried her chicken to the water hose and proceeded to give it a bath. Sunbeam stripped off her clothes and waited for her turn at the faucet. When Cheering Woman finished cleaning the chicken, she set it loose and roared with laughter as it ran around the yard. Glancing over at Sunbeam, she sniffed and held her nose. "Phew! Granddaughter, you reek of shit!" She turned the hose on her granddaughter. "You'd better burn those clothes." She threw Sunbeam a towel.

"Grandmother, I swear I didn't put that chicken down the outhouse hole."

But no matter how adamantly or how often Sunbeam proclaimed her innocence, her grandmother saw her as guilty and remained amused by the consequences. The outhouse story was told many times with many embellishments as Cheering Woman continued to insist her granddaughter had committed this terrible deed. Each time the story was told, the listeners roared with hoots of laughter. Sunbeam, embarrassed over the futility of trying to prove her innocence, always slipped away when the chicken story began.

A few days later Sunbeam was sitting on the back porch staring at a tenpenny nail embedded in the wall. Hanging on the nail was Cheering Woman's most prized possession, her bullwhip, which she lovingly referred to as her 'Rope of Hope.' Many times Sunbeam had dreamed of the day she would earn the right to possess her own Rope of Hope. Each time she watched Cheering Woman flick the rawhide whip, Sunbeam's interest grew.

"One must have great honor to possess a Rope of Hope, for hidden within it are many magical secrets," Cheering Woman would always say. But each time Sunbeam asked her grandmother for one of her own, she was told, "In time, Granddaughter. You are not quite ready for such a big responsibility."

With each postponement of her dream, Sunbeam's desire doubled.

Two long years passed. Sunbeam was now nine and her grandmother had not relented. She had almost given up hope of ever having such a rope when one day while on a long walk with her grandmother, she felt a glimmer of possibility. "See how my rope makes our lives easier?" Cheering Woman whipped it onto a tree branch and picked off a piece of bark. "Someday this rope will share its secrets with you. But for now, you must be content to learn the lessons of a rope's power. When you have that knowledge, Granddaughter, you will get your rope."

Cheering Woman spread a blanket on the ground for a moment of rest. She lit her happy pipe and broke into a story about the mysterious rope. As the story ended, she gazed at her granddaughter and with a twinkle in her eye pulled a large piece of tanned cowhide from under her blanket.

"I have something very special to give you."

"Oh, Grandmother, I have waited a long time for this day." Sunbeam gently touched the hide, then held it lovingly to her heart as tears of joy spilled from her eyes.

"You have earned it, Little One. Now you must listen to the hide tell you how to catch its power. You cannot begin to cut it until you know what it is saying."

Week after week, Sunbeam took the hide to Cheering Woman and guessed at its message, only to hear, "No, Granddaughter, think again!"

Sunbeam began to sleep with the hide, hoping that her dreams might reveal its secrets. In one of her dreams she saw a rope curled in three circles on the hide, but at the very end of the dream the circles turned into snakes, coiled and ready to strike. Sunbeam snapped awake in terror and lost the answers she had been seeking.

In frustration, Sunbeam took the hide to Father River and prayed for him to intercede. Although such strong determination in one so young pleased Cheering Woman, Sunbeam brought back the wrong answer.

"Patience, Little One. Soon you will find the right way to capture the strength in this hide."

Disappointed, Sunbeam began to feel the task was hopeless. Although sensing that she was on the verge of giving up, her grandmother steadfastly refused to help.

"Granddaughter, there are many ways to capture a power, but you must penetrate your inner mind to find the right one. The hide is telling you the answer, but you are not listening. Think of the many ways my rope has shown you its power. Remember the loads of firewood it helped us bring home and the times it protected you from harm while climbing a tree or kept you from falling down a steep embankment?"

"Grandmother, I know yours works, but I can't understand this hide," pouted Sunbeam. "Maybe I'm not meant to have a Rope of Hope. I can't seem to hear anything it says." She carelessly tossed it aside.

"Granddaughter, show your respect!"

Sunbeam picked up the hide apologetically, all the while hoping her grandmother would give her the answer rather than another puzzle to unravel.

"Granddaughter, think about your dreams! Didn't you tell me that the rope curled into three circles on the hide before it turned into a snake?"

"Yes, Grandmother," Sunbeam nodded, recalling the dream in vivid detail.

"Maybe your answer was in that dream, but your fear of snakes captured the knowledge. Think again of what you already know."

Sunbeam reflected on these words. Taking the hide with her, she spent the rest of the morning under her favorite tree, letting her mind drift with the lazy clouds overhead.

Suddenly she burst through the front door yelling with excitement, grabbed her grandmother and danced her around the room.

"Grandmother, I've got the answer. I know how to cut the hide! You were right. I feared the snake and lost my thoughts."

"You don't have to tear the hinges off the door or crush my ribs to tell me what I already know."

Sunbeam ignored her grandmother's remark and explained, much to her grandmother's delight, how she would cut the hide. After gathering a pencil and other supplies, she began to draw the first circle.

"Keep the hide flat or you will surely destroy its strength. And don't stretch it! A hide that is too thin will turn on you," directed Cheering Woman.

Sunbeam cut the first circle and then two more. Oiling each one until it was pliable, she then tied them together and braided them into a rope leaving three small pieces trailing out from the end.

Cheering Woman produced a wooden handle. "Sam made this for you." Sunbeam accepted the gift and painted a small wolf in the center holding it up for her grandmother's approval. As they attached the handle to the rope, Cheering Woman smiled and said, "My, my, Granddaughter, you have made yourself a fine rope."

Stretching to release the tightness in her shoulders, Sunbeam watched proudly as her grandmother drove a tenpenny nail into the wall and hung her newly completed Rope of Hope in a place of honor.

Satisfied with the day's work, Cheering Woman wrapped her arms around her granddaughter, saying, "We've had a busy afternoon. Come, let's eat supper and get some rest."

The following morning, long before the sun had touched the earth, Sunbeam bounded out of bed, retrieved her rope from the nail and ran outside to await the sunrise. When she saw her grandmother crossing the yard, she smiled broadly and handed her the rope.

Cheering Woman checked it for strength and pliability, then shot it upward.

The rope made a whirring sound followed by a loud snap. Grinning, she handed the rope back to Sunbeam. "This rope has great power, but its secret is hidden in the touch. Feel with your heart, Granddaughter. Your accuracy depends upon speed and timing. Watch the twist of your wrist and keep the movement flowing or the rope will attack you," she concluded abruptly, her voice somewhat ominous, then promptly returned to the house.

Right away Sunbeam began to practice using her Rope of Hope. This is easy, there's nothing to it, she thought. However, by late afternoon when her arms and legs were covered with cuts and bruises, she had developed a deeper respect for Cheering Woman's skills.

For the next few months, the rope consumed Sunbeam's every waking moment. If only she could use the rope as skillfully and as well as her grandmother. With constant practice, she learned to snag branches and climb to her favorite places in trees. And by late summer, she was able to snap up a single stone with remarkable accuracy.

One afternoon Cheering Woman stepped out onto the front porch, surprised to find that Sunbeam was not practicing with her rope. Instead, she was nestled high in the old oak tree reading a book, her rope at her side.

"Maybe we should go to the woods and see what kind of expert you've become," Cheering Woman challenged.

Needing no further encouragement, Sunbeam wrapped the rope around her waist, shinnied down the tree and trailed after her grandmother, eager to show off her skills.

As they walked through the woods, Cheering Woman pointed to a fir tree. "See the wet pitch in that grand tree? It's good for chest colds and eye infections. Climb up and get some for me."

Sunbeam's eyes lit up with enthusiasm. She cracked her rope overhead, her wrist twisting in a smooth circular motion. It shot outward and wrapped itself around a low branch. Sunbeam jerked it back firmly testing for safety, then grasped the rope to pull herself up the trunk.

"Be careful, Granddaughter," warned Cheering Woman, watching her climb hand over hand up into the tree and out of sight.

Securing herself between two branches, Sunbeam pulled her knife out from her left boot and peeled away three large pitch-filled strips of bark, dropping them to the ground. She then maneuvered her way down the tree, carefully hooked the rope around a branch, swung out in a wide arc and landed near her grandmother.

"I'm impressed," Cheering Woman said, watching her granddaughter proudly curl the rope around her arm. "You're very good. Reminds me of my youth. But one should never go beyond their abilities. Knowing your limitations will help you live by your convictions."

She breathed deeply and continued, "Your rope has a beginning and an end, as does your life. The tool itself is unimportant; what matters is the completion it brings to your strengths and abilities. Study the weaknesses in your rope and you will understand your power. The rope can teach you how to keep balance in your life. A 'good' must have an 'evil,' just as an 'up' must have a 'down' and a 'hot' must have a 'cold.' To understand 'wet' we must experience 'dry.' When balanced, we cannot be consumed by ego.

"Ultimately, the Rope of Hope teaches us to master the discipline of a thought. Although everyone is born with this ability, it is activated only as one gains the knowledge to build personal power. Someday you will become the teachings of your rope. Look at how many new ideas your imagination has snared. You learned to rely on the unseen powers of your magic. I give you little in material things, Granddaughter. My legacy to you is richness of spirit."

Her grandmother's words allowed Sunbeam to see that her prize rope was merely a tool to be used for expanding her mind. Already the rope had given her clarity of focus, and she could tell that the best lessons were yet to come. As she learned to rely more on her imagination, she found that the magic in her hand would allow her to accomplish whatever she visualized.

"Sunbeam, haven't I told you that your real power rests between those ears?"

"Yes, but what if I don't want the responsibility of this power? I want to do what I feel like doing. And to tell you the truth, I don't want to stay on the reservation and teach Medicine like you."

"Oh really?" mocked Cheering Woman, sending the cold breath of old *Yata*, the North Wind, into Sunbeam's soul. "Since when is Medicine a choice? Can you dance like Grouse? Can you go to the void with Raven and create life? Or does your ego demand that you live with the illusion of Dragonfly? I ask you, Granddaughter, is this moment real, or are we dreaming it?"

"I don't know Grandmother," Sunbeam answered, hanging her head.

"Well, until you understand the lessons of the rope, let's not speak again of your responsibilities to Medicine. You may have learned a few tricks, but you have learned nothing about Medicine."

They turned and headed home with no words passing between them. Sunbeam knew she would pay dearly for her defiant attitude.

And indeed, Cheering Woman dropped Sunbeam's training and generally ignored her for the rest of the summer. As the lonely days passed one after another, Sunbeam began to realize that her success with the Rope of Hope gave her little joy compared with her grandmother's company. By fall, the monotony of her idle days had fueled a new hunger for learning Medicine.

Winter came early that year. As snow covered the ground in white silence, grandmother and granddaughter nestled by the evening fire, listening to howling winds race across the plains. Occupied with needles, beads and leather, Cheering Woman spoke often of the old ways, showing Sunbeam the meaning of each design they created. By the time spring arrived, Sunbeam felt a new respect for her people's traditions.

As if blown in by the gentle spring winds, people from miles around gathered under the arbor to seek Cheering Woman's wisdom. Her reputation as a medicine woman had extended far beyond the reservation, attracting many white people who recognized that here they could live in the old ways. Some stayed a few days or weeks, while others remained for the entire summer season. Those who stayed the longest put up tents and took part in the cooking and the daily chores.

Fall arrived, and still Cheering Woman spent long hours each day teaching and healing. One afternoon the old woman seemed more tired than usual as she sat alone in the arbor reviewing the morning's events. "Some people never seem to learn," she grumbled to herself. "They keep making the same mistakes over and over, then want a quick fix instead of first healing the lack of harmony in their lives."

Sunbeam, observing her grandmother's exhaustion and feeling a chill in the air, wrapped a shawl around the old woman's shoulders, then handed her a fresh cup of coffee. Cheering Woman lit her happy pipe, took a sip of the coffee and spoke:

"Never share your knowledge with those who stand in front of you until you know who they are. Many will think you carry the secrets of life, but do not trust the sweetness of their words until you know why they are offered. Too easily you may be woven into a usable braid by getting caught up in deception and flattery. Be careful, Granddaughter, or you may become entrapped in a prison of false self-importance. Always look at others with your heart, not your eyes. Life has its own way of staking a claim to each of your accomplishments. Failure too holds value in the school of life. But attachment to failure can become a way of life."

Sunbeam knelt at her grandmother's feet gently resting her head on the old woman's lap. Cheering Woman idly stroked the child's hair as she continued: "Little One, life is a very precious gift, and yours is just beginning. Life was born with a twin called Death. Therefore, we must accept this twin to complete the circle."

"Grandmother, please don't speak of death," begged Sunbeam. "Come, it's late. Let's go inside. You need your rest."

Suddenly Cheering Woman grabbed her chest.

"What's wrong, Grandmother?"

"Nothing, Little One, nothing! I'm just a tired old woman and you're right, I need my rest."

Sunbeam slept fitfully that night, worried about her grandmother's health. By daybreak, however, her concern lifted. As the two dressed, they heard pounding at the door.

Startled, Cheering Woman said, "Who can that be at this hour of the morning? Go see, Granddaughter." There was an edge of irritation in her voice, for she did not appreciate being disturbed before her morning preparations were completed.

Sunbeam cautiously opened the door to find Sam leaning against the wall for support. His breath reeked of stale alcohol, and she felt like vomiting. Cheering Woman, sensing that all was not well, came to the front door. Filled with disgust, she addressed her son coldly. "I see you've been drinking again."

"Get off my back, Mama!" Sam's words were slurred. "I got some problems. I need to talk with you. After all, you're a medicine woman, and I think it's time you helped your own son!"

Cheering Woman glared at him, her piercing black eyes filled with revulsion and anger. Her lips tightened into a grim line as she reached out and slapped him hard across the face.

"Watch what you say to me, my son! Now go around to the back porch. And when I get there, have your respect in order for this medicine woman," she demanded shoving him away from the door.

Sunbeam was terrified. She had never seen her grandmother in such a fury.

"Stay here, Granddaughter. I have a drunk on my hands." Cheering Woman tromped through the house gathering items she would need for a ceremony, then went out to the back porch. Sunbeam listened to her speak in a loud, harsh tone, "I hate alcohol! I have told you never to come to my home drunk. When you disrespect my home, you destroy what I stand for. And that, my son, is not allowed. When will you learn to stop drinking? Alcohol drives you to violence and craziness!"

Sam turned slowly and stared at Cheering Woman with wild, bloodshot eyes that gleamed with insanity. She grabbed his hair and jerked his head backward, forcing his mouth open. "Where is my son?" she screamed into his face, pouring a red powdered mixture into his eyes and mouth. "I know you are in there, bad *Wakanpi*, and I will never allow you to destroy my son!" Sam, coiled on the floor, howled in pain, vomit spilling from his mouth.

"Leave him, *Iya*, Evil One!" Cheering Woman raged, pouring the powder over his entire body. "Free Sam and I will free you. Otherwise, I will capture you and cause more anguish than this body can endure. If my son is destroyed in the process, then so be it!" She then began to chant over Sam's writhing body.

"You will never destroy me," growled an unfamiliar voice from deep within her son's throat.

"Watch me, Evil One," challenged Cheering Woman, chanting louder and louder as she drew a circle of red powder around Sam. "I have you, *Iya*! You are mine now. If you stay in this body, I will destroy it!" she bellowed in her Dakota tongue.

Without stopping, Cheering Woman spread a green and red mixture on Sam's forehead. The moment she removed her hands, he moaned and rolled over in a cold sweat. Satisfied that the Evil One had left her son's body, Cheering Woman nonchalantly walked into the kitchen, poured herself a cup of coffee and sat down to wait for the outcome of the ceremony.

Within an hour, Sam got up from the floor, wiping spittle from his mouth. Cheering Woman smoked him off, and then they prayed together. She put her pipe away and offered him an herbal tea. "Sam, you are my son, but I will not participate in your destruction. You know what will happen if you continue to drink. Next time, it could be your death. I love you, but I will not watch you destroy yourself. Leave my home and never again return with this Evil One in control. For if you do, I will have no son!"

Sunbeam, frightened and trembling, sat in the far corner of the kitchen, watching as Sam bowed his head in shame.

"A bad spirit controls me," he said sheepishly. "When it takes over, it makes me drink."

"You are wrong, my son," Cheering Woman answered firmly. "This bad entity lives in the bottle that you choose to drink from."

Knowing her words were true, Sam mumbled an apology, then got up and left.

Sunbeam ran to Cheering Woman. "Grandmother, who is this Evil One called *Iya* that lives in Sam?" she cried hysterically.

"Easy, Little One," soothed Cheering Woman. "Sam is a bad drunk, not a bad man. He's not in control when he drinks."

"If he knows this, then why does he drink?"

"Sam didn't used to drink; but his fears have created a world of confusion, and now he lives in a hell of his own creation. He has a serious problem, and alcohol irrigates the soil that feeds the growth of this evil seed. As a young boy your father ventured into the white system, and the more involved he became, the further he distanced himself from the old beliefs. Once he too wanted a Rope of Hope, but he was not willing to wait for the hide to speak to him. He began cutting without seeing the finished rope in his mind, and so he never learned its real power." Cheering Woman hid the bittersweet tears that flowed at the thought of Sam's wasted life.

Not wishing to intrude on her grandmother's private feelings, yet deeply disturbed by the morning's events, Sunbeam slipped quietly out the door to sit under the oak tree. An hour later, still uneasy, she sought out several elders around the camp to discuss the problem.

Late that afternoon while Sunbeam was playing with her cousin under the arbor, Cheering Woman called to her, saying, "Come, Granddaughter, we must go to the river." While gathering her ceremonial medicine bundle, she added, "Granddaughter, get some pieces of meat for an offering and bring another blanket." When all was ready, she walked toward the river, motioning for Sunbeam to follow.

Cheering Woman, having heard about Sunbeam's discussions with the elders, wanted to teach her granddaughter a lesson about the privacy of family affairs. She remained silent for some time, then spoke. "Gossip is never for the betterment of another. You must not speak to people about someone else's problems. When you know their heartache, be silent about it," she scolded.

As they neared the river, Sunbeam stopped to listen to the water crashing loudly over the rocks. Her grandmother, meanwhile, placed the sacred bundle respectfully on a blanket she had unfolded.

"This is one of the oldest medicine bundles in the area," she began. "It represents our clan and carries the power of Beaver and nearly every winged one. Granddaughter, this has been in the family for many generations. You are obligated to learn how to use it, so that someday when you carry this bundle, the power will continue for the people. The old woman carefully untied the sacred bundle, acknowledging each medicine person who had helped to build it.

"Long ago, our relatives spent time studying the power of every animal," she continued, unwrapping each piece respectfully and placing it on the blanket. After smoking off each piece in silence, she lifted the items one by one, explaining:

"This pipe represents the center of the power bundle. The owl's body signifies night wisdom, and the hawk's, the clue-finding messenger of Father Sky. The loon carries messages to all the waterfowl. This bearskin represents the land. These are very old and sacred." While unrolling an elkhide she concluded, "And this represents the sacred mountains. All these sacred articles must be handled very carefully, for they have great power."

Turning to Sunbeam, she asked, "Where is the piece of raw meat you brought, Granddaughter?" Silently, Sunbeam handed it to her and watched the old woman walk to the river bank and bury it in the soil. Returning, she filled and lit her pipe in a sacred manner, then offered it up asking *Tunka'shila* to come smoke with her.

Humbly calling each spirit by name, Cheering Woman asked for help in fighting the bad spirits of alcohol.

Sunbeam heard drums accompanying her grandmother's chant, and a sense of calm drifted over her as she listened to the cadence of the old woman's words. A soft fog soon rose from the river and enveloped Cheering Woman, who proclaimed:

"Let the power of this sacred river carry my words upon its waters as they race toward unknown destinations."

Sunbeam thought she heard a male voice speaking over her grandmother's words. At that point, Cheering Woman chanted in her native tongue:

"*Hau*, Grandfather! Hear me, Great Spirit! This is Cheering Woman. We walk as one. I stand before you as a mere human being. I am nothing without you. You are my power! I come today as a troubled child. *Tunka'shila*, give Sam the strength to reject this bad spirit. *Wakan Tanka*, guide my son back to the good Red Road. Touch him and bring peace to his heart. Help him, *Wakan Tanka*. Let all medicines come and make your presence known to him so he will call upon you to get well."

Cheering Woman sang many sacred bundle songs as her feet glided back and forth in a trance-like dance. Cradling the loon in her arms, she moved its head up and down while holding two golden eagle feathers up to Father Sky. "*Tunka'shila*, touch Sam's heart in this dreadful hour. All my relations who have gone before me, hear me in my hour of need," she beseeched, calling each by name. Turning to face the West, she continued, "Hear me, *Wanbli Gle'ska*, my brother Eagle." She then circled the eagle feathers high above her head, saying, "See your feathers? Go quickly to Father Sun. Tell the Great Chief of my most urgent message and ask him to see fit to heal Sam."

Turning to the North, she continued:

"I call upon my four-legged relations. Sacred Buffalo, heal Sam's spiritual sickness. Oh, Great Bear of wisdom, walk in front of him and protect him with your powerful medicines. Destroy the Evil One who seeks to steal his soul!"

Facing the East, she called upon the hoofed ones pleading:

"Elk, Moose, Antelope, and Deer, send your love swiftly for a fast recovery."

Offering her pipe to the South, she cried:

"Great Cougar, destroy Sam's need for alcohol. Grandfather, I humbly thank you in my hour of need. *Hau, Mitakuye Oyasin*, all my relations."

Cheering Woman concluded her prayers by offering the ashes from her pipe to the four winds. Then, her face streaked with dried tears, she gathered her medicine bundle and silently turned toward home, beckoning her granddaughter to follow.

Sunbeam's heart was heavy. She hated to see her grandmother engulfed in such sorrow. Tears stung her eyes, but instead of crying she focused her attention on the huge clumps of summer grass that lined the edge of the pathway.

As they entered the yard, Sam waved apologetically from the front porch swing. Seeing Cheering Woman he nodded in acknowledgment as Sunbeam disappeared behind the house so they could spend time alone.

Sam was thankful that his mother had accepted his silent request to join him. The two spoke in soft voices throughout the remainder of the afternoon and into the evening. As the sun set, Sunbeam served them fresh coffee and a homemade apple pie, quickly vanishing back into the house.

By the time Sam left, Sunbeam was already in bed. Cheering Woman came in and lit the oil lamp, then sat on the side of the bed and began to unbraid her hair. "Granddaughter, the Great Spirit brought Sam back to an awareness of the power in our sacred pipe. He will be leaving the reservation and moving his family to Tennessee. They will live near your Auntie Rose. She has offered him a place to raise and train his hunting dogs."

The old woman blew out the lamp and crawled under the covers. Long after Cheering Woman had fallen asleep, Sunbeam cried silently in the dark. She knew that whatever had overtaken her father was a terrible power and was saddened, yet at the same time relieved, to learn of his departure.

Sometime before daybreak, Sunbeam heard her grandmother stirring in the kitchen. She joined her at the table, hoping for more information. As tradition demanded, she waited until Cheering Woman spoke.

"Granddaughter, I need to tell you about a bad spirit called *Gnaski*. Many years ago, when white traders first came to this land, Indians met with many new problems. Wars and starvation were rampant. As time passed, the white man's gift of grain cursed our people, causing us to become a downtrodden race. Alcohol has destroyed more families than all the battles we Sioux have ever fought. Granddaughter, I predict most of our babies will be born as alcoholics." Taking a puff on her corncob pipe, she continued. "Something is different about Indians. Alcohol makes them crazy. Who knows why? All I know is this Evil One possesses Sam!

"Less than fifty years ago, a Sun Dance was held on the Fort Peck Indian Reservation. The medicine man, having little knowledge about how to run a Sun Dance, released bad medicine in the form of a demon called *Gnaski*. He appears in the flesh and is easily recognized by his hoofed feet, which he covers with a long brown trench coat. His eyes, sunk in deep red sockets, peer out from under a slouched hat. This disguise hides the burned flesh hanging from the side of his left cheek. To some people he appears as a handsome man wearing a black suit and a long, flowing black cape. In any case, when he enters a bar, he stretches out his arms and bellows in a deep, hypnotic voice:

'Welcome, my children! You all belong to me.'

"Those who see him are usually so terrified that they escape into the night. Occasionally some fool will chase him, but *Gnaski* always stays an arm's length ahead and then suddenly vanishes into nothing. Many women have danced with him, and some believe they have given birth to his children. It is said that once he touches you, he controls you for the rest of your life. Wherever he appears, a death follows in his wake, and within six months the place burns to the ground.

"While at a bar in Poplar, Montana, Sam saw this Evil One. *Gnaski* burned his image into the bar's front door to show Sam his power. We quickly moved from

Poplar, hoping Sam would escape this curse, but apparently he did not. Granddaughter, if this evil spirit ever appears to you, show no fear. If you are fearful, he will capture your soul too."

Sunbeam's eyes widened in terror. "How could this be, Grandmother? Why would people allow the Evil One to steal souls? Is that why Sam doesn't want me?"

Cheering Woman looked sorrowfully at her granddaughter. "Sam doesn't hate you. It's just that he is burdened with guilt over his past mistakes." Her voice dropping to a whisper, she continued, "I pray both of you will find a love for each other."

Sunbeam was silent, still confused about her relationship with her father.

Cheering Woman changed the subject, hoping to distract her granddaughter. "Sunbeam, can you feel the stillness?" she asked, her voice blending with the soft wind that rustled the nearby leaves. "There is a power in this stillness. I remember when silence was not a word."

The following morning, Cheering Woman asked Sunbeam to gather fall herbs with her. Taking her old hat and medicine pouches, she led her granddaughter across the overgrown fields behind the barn. The rains had been heavy for the last two weeks and the hot, humid air was filled with mosquitoes, gnats and flies, all buzzing and biting with fervor. Sunbeam complained bitterly as red welts appeared on her arms and legs. Cheering Woman handed her a sealed jelly jar filled with salve, saying, "There must be movement if life is to exist, Sunbeam. Rub this on your skin. It will ease the pain."

Over the next two hours Cheering Woman was engrossed in the peaceful beauty of the last days of Indian Summer and was oblivious to her granddaughter's complaints. As the pain of her bites eased up, Sunbeam began to play idly with her rope. While snapping leaves from a tree, she accidentally hit a bluebird. She heard it thump to the ground and saw what she had done, whereupon tears of anguish welled up in her eyes. She picked up the lifeless little bird and ran over to Cheering Woman.

"Grandmother, look what I've done. Please bring it back to life," she begged, handing the bird to her grandmother.

Cheering Woman took the bird and said quietly, "There is no putting life back into the dead, Granddaughter."

"But it was an accident," sobbed Sunbeam.

"Such things can happen, Little One, even in meaningless play. I know you didn't try to hurt the bird, but you are responsible for what you do with your rope."

"Oh, Grandmother, how could I have done such a bad thing? I've never killed anything before."

Cheering Woman dug a small hole at the base of the tree, then told Sunbeam to offer a prayer of forgiveness for what she had done. This accomplished, the old medicine woman wrapped the little body in sage and tied it in a red cloth. After placing it in the ground, Sunbeam covered it gently with dirt and marked the place with a stone.

"Come, Granddaughter, let's go home. We'll gather herbs another day."

When they reached the house, Sunbeam hung the rope on its nail, swearing never to use it again. Then she took a long walk, wanting time to herself.

Several hours passed before a concerned Cheering Woman went to look for her granddaughter. She found her sitting in an open field behind the barn, still mourning the devastating loss. She sat by her granddaughter's side and patted her arm, saying, "You must forgive yourself, Grandchild. It was an accident. Creator knows you didn't plan to kill the little bird."

Sunbeam leaned into the comfort of her grandmother's arms, and cried as if her heart would break. "Oh, Grandmother, I'm so sorry. I'm not worthy of my Rope of Hope! I'm never going to use it again."

"Now, now, Granddaughter. The rope belongs to you. Whether you use it or not, you're still responsible."

Sunbeam sat up and dried her eyes. Confused by Cheering Woman's words, she asked, "How can I be responsible if I never use the rope again, Grandmother?"

"Simple, Granddaughter. If you don't use the rope, the power you have built into it will die. Once you create something, you are responsible for its death as well as its life."

"Oh, Grandmother, what am I going to do?" wailed Sunbeam.

"Come," said Cheering Woman, "let's take a walk to think this through."

The two strolled hand in hand, listening to the birds as the wind whirled past them, informing all the little animals nearby that humans were approaching their territory. Sunbeam's head raced with thoughts of Sam and his evil spirit, Cheering Woman's heart trouble, and now the death of the little bird. What else could possibly happen? Soon they neared the gnarled trees and stagnant waters of an old lake that forever filled the air with the smell of decay. The only visible sign of life was a water moccasin swimming through the thick green algae.

Cheering Woman, cupped her hands to shade the sun from her eyes. "This poor lake is dying. It has forgotten that it needs movement to live." She jumped up and down. "Look at me. This motion proves I'm alive."

Sunbeam watched quietly, still distraught, barely moving a muscle.

"See that willow tree over there? Climb up and get me the branch closest to the lake."

Despondently, Sunbeam climbed the tree, then reached for her knife and cut the branch, letting it drop to the ground. Cheering Woman skinned the bark away and shaped one end into a perfect 'Y.'

"There is magic in this willow branch. It can find the water children that are hidden in Mother Earth's body. Come, Granddaughter. Today, I'm going to teach you how to find the secrets of movement within things you cannot see." With a mysterious tone she picked up her pace and headed across the open field. Turning to her granddaughter, who trailed along beside her, she said, "Do you remember the story of how the water children are related to Father River?

"Well, long, long ago, there was a lonely willow tree who lived among the tall trees and felt she had no purpose in life. Her swaying branches hung low, yet she wanted to be tall and strong like the towering trees overhead. The willow cried out to the other trees, pleading with them to help her grow tall and strong, but they were too tall to hear her. Drained of energy, she lost her will to live and dropped her branches into Father River remorsefully. He listened to her sad story and granted her the power to find the great underground water spirits. To this day, the branches of willow trees will point to the ground to tell us where the water children live. Now that you have shared your sadness as the willow tree did long ago, maybe she will share her secret with you."

Cheering Woman held the willow branch in front of her and began to sing as she walked across the field with Sunbeam following. "Come, little water children, where are you hiding? I want you to meet a sad friend who needs your playful glee. Come, little water children, don't be shy and please don't flee. Come, little water children, come to me." Suddenly the branch twisted downward in her hands. "Quick, Sunbeam! Come, look!" Cheering Woman exclaimed. "One of the water children heard our song, and it's telling us where it's hiding."

Sunbeam approached shyly, watching the stick point directly to the ground. Cheering Woman spoke in a low, soft voice. "Water child, this is Sunbeam." She handed the branch to Sunbeam, saying, "Take this, Granddaughter. I want you to find another water child to help you come to peace with the little bird's death."

Sunbeam took the branch, and holding it in front of her, mimicked Cheering Woman's words while she strode farther into the meadow. Two hours passed as she chanted louder and louder, but the branch did not move. Just as she was about to give up, the branch suddenly trembled and twisted in her hand, then pointed toward the ground.

"Grandmother, come see! I think I've found one."

"My word! Hush, child. Your voice could wake the dead. When are you ever going to learn to control your emotions? If you are not careful, your excitement could persuade life to return to this old lake, flooding the entire land. Now, go. I'm sure you will find many more river children before the day is over." She grinned, happy to see a smile had finally returned to her granddaughter's face.

After their picnic lunch, Cheering Woman lay down on her blanket for an afternoon nap. Hot and sweaty, Sunbeam stepped into the river to rinse off. She cupped her hands together and dipped them in the water, as an unsuspecting fish swam into them. Holding her breath Sunbeam quickly grabbed one and hurled it onto the bank, then another and another. Proud of her catch, she scooped her fish into a discarded bucket and ran back to show them to her grandmother. As Sunbeam was about to shout out her good news, she stopped and stared in amazement.

Perched on Cheering Woman's shoulder was a bluebird. When a moment later it darted off, Sunbeam approached, asking, "Grandmother, how did you get the bird to sit on your shoulder?"

"A bluebird came to tell me about the fish you caught," Cheering Woman said, laughing.

"Oh, Grandmother, don't tease. How did you call the bluebird?"

Ignoring the question, Cheering Woman stood up indicating it was time to head back home.

Sunbeam cleaned the fish, then Cheering Woman dusted them with flour and placed them in a hot skillet. After a delicious dinner, it was time for Sunbeam's favorite evening ritual. Sunbeam picked up her grandmother's hairbrush and mirror from the top of her dresser and followed her to the front porch. As they sat swinging, Cheering Woman said, "Anyone with a good heart can talk to a bird. Its spirit knows if a person is a friend or an enemy. Someday you will understand that everything is connected to *Wakan Tanka's* love. The bluebird came to tell me that the little bird you killed was very ill and wanted to return to the Other Side to end its suffering. It chose to make its departure quickly and painlessly. The little bird trusted in the power of your rope and asked the Great Spirit to allow for its return."

Sunbeam let out a great sigh of relief as the burden of the bluebird's death lifted from her shoulders. She slipped out of the swing and began to brush Cheering Woman's knee-length hair. After weaving it into braids, she tied off each one, then took the loose hairs from the brush and handed them to her grandmother. Then she sat between her grandmother's legs, gave her the brush, and closed her eyes in eager anticipation.

Cheering Woman spoke as she worked the bristles through Sunbeam's hair. "You're going to be very pretty someday. But I'm afraid your eyes will see many tears as you travel through life. Many people will admire you, and just as many will fear and hate you. Never let these hurts steal your power. Remember to accept without judgment. Things are not good, not bad, they just are. Never forget these words, no matter where life may lead you. They will build a strength in you when I am no longer here to help.

"Hmm, your hair is getting very long. I think I'll make you a scalp lock and hide power in it for you. Long ago, our strongest warriors hung a simple piece of hair from the side of the head. Wearing this scalp lock, they would strut through camp with their chins thrust slightly forward, daring anyone to dispute their power. The mere presence of a scalp lock spoke loudly to all who saw it. 'Take it if you can,' its bearer seemed to say, 'but if you lose, I will take your life, or make you my slave until you die.' Only a fool would challenge such a warrior."

Cheering Woman pulled Sunbeam's hair into her first scalp lock, slipping in a piece of her own for good measure. She chuckled, then handed Sunbeam the mirror so she could see this new power. "So, Granddaughter," Cheering Woman proclaimed. "Today you are announcing to the world that you are a bold and fearless warrioress, and that you dare anyone to tamper with your courage."

Sunbeam returned the mirror and hairbrush to her grandmother's dresser, then strutted out the back door toward the henhouse. She moved proudly, displaying her new power while challenging everything on her path. The dogs and cats understood the message and ran away, but the old red rooster crowed his defiance and approached, preparing to attack. Sunbeam thrust her chin forward and took a warrior's stance. The rooster, sensing something was unusual, retreated in defeat. Sunbeam whooped and shouted her victory all the way to the henhouse.

Cheering Woman watched the scene from her kitchen window. As Sunbeam picked up a bucket of cracked corn and began to feed the chickens, the old woman smiled and said aloud:

"Well, well, Granddaughter, you may become a good Dakota Sioux after all."

Quest of a Spiritual Warrioress

Sunbeam sat under the tallest apple tree in the orchard, her thoughts drifting toward Cheering Woman, who as always was sitting beneath the pine arbor teaching yet another group of students. For years Sunbeam had resented not only her city cousins, but people from all walks of life who returned to the reservation to learn the old traditional ways. She thought it strange that they were thrilled to be living in tents under the starry skies, cooking over open fires and bathing in cold river water. Most of the time she hated Cheering woman's apprentice, Shung', and her bossy ways, but was glad it was her job to take care of these intruders.

For as long as she could remember, Sunbeam had watched people come and go, slipping back and forth between the Red and white cultures. Just the thought seemed to leave a bittersweet taste in her mouth.

The first thing every morning, they would clamor out of their tents to fill the *Inipis,* sweat lodges. There they would pray awkwardly, searching for their roots. Seeing them hunger for this knowledge made Sunbeam realize that even at the tender age of ten, she was indeed an old spirit and wise for her years. At these times, she was thankful her grandmother had given up so much to prod, shape and mold her spiritual walk. I need to remember, she thought, to lift my hands in prayer up to *Wakan Tanka* for my grandmother's rigid training.

Although many people considered Cheering Woman a saint, others thought her a demon from hell. She was amused by their contrasting perceptions and aware that all respected her. Sunbeam took great comfort in knowing her grandmother walked her talk and held a place of honor among all the people. She was proud to be the granddaughter of such a powerful medicine woman.

Propelled by her thoughts, Sunbeam got up and headed for the arbor. As she drew near, she heard her grandmother's familiar words. "Creation is ongoing, and *Wakan Tanka* lives in everything. Everyone is born to serve and honor *Tunka'shila's* work. This is how we please the Great Spirit. And in serving the Great Mystery, we serve ourselves, for it is Creator who teaches us to live properly. This is what leads us to our spiritual happiness."

Cheering Woman spotted her granddaughter, stood up and stepped aside, leaving Shung' to complete the lesson.

"Hurry, Sunbeam, come," Cheering Woman said eagerly. "There is much work to be done before my cherished friend Madame Bianchoff arrives. Do you want your soul to die of boredom, young lady? Remember, idle hands make for a lazy mind and a grumpy soul. There's wood to chop, fires to build, medicines to prepare, sage to gather and water to haul for the *Yuwipi* ceremony tonight."

The lesson finished, Shung' approached them, whereupon Cheering Woman handed her a shopping list, saying, "Shung', hurry along to the store and take someone with you to help. I'll need you back here as soon as possible to take over my teaching duties. Madame Bianchoff should be here by early afternoon and I want to be free to spend some time with my dear friend. It's been a while since I've seen her and I want her visit to be special."

As Shung' turned to go, Cheering Woman flashed back ten years to the day when her half sister had come to live with her and help care for the infant Sunbeam. She remembered Shung' as a timid, overweight little girl who was hoping to someday become a medicine woman. Now at twenty, she was a strong, well-spoken young woman, and Cheering Woman was proud to call her an apprentice to Medicine.

Meanwhile Madame Bianchoff, a Russian ballet instructor, was driving across the western plains about four hours away from Cheering Woman's home. A smile crossed her face as she remembered when they had first met in Los Angeles during a fund-raising event to gather food and clothing for the poor on the reservation. How many boxes had she packed since then to send to that determined Indian woman who was one of her best friends? What an effort it had been to convince Cheering Woman to take a drive to see the ocean for the first time. Laughing out loud, she recalled how her friend had compared the ocean waves with the rolling wheat fields at home.

As she turned onto a one-lane road, she became immediately intoxicated, for the view was exactly as she remembered when youth had belonged to them. Father Sky still appeared to be touching the edges of Mother Earth's body and the wheat fields still rolled like ocean waves. Madame was anxious to share these rapturous thoughts with her old friend.

Sunbeam, having finished her morning chores, was bathing in the river. Cheering Woman stood on the riverbank shouting, "A dip in Father River awakens the mind and stimulates the soul. Now, get out of the water. It's important for you to spend time with Otis. He's been with me for many years, and is the best of Fire Chiefs. I want you to learn from him the sacredness in tending a fire."

Sunbeam emerged from the water, and after dressing, followed her grandmother to where Otis Lightday was building a new *Inipi*. As they approached the tall, thin elder, he acknowledged their presence with a nod.

Sunbeam remained at a respectful distance, drying her hair in the sun as the two conversed privately. Cheering Woman said quietly, "Have patience with her, my old friend. You know she is special born. I want her to find the heartbeat of everything. Please see that she makes peace with the fire people." With these words, she departed.

Otis motioned for Sunbeam to join him. She watched quietly as he drove a stake into the ground to establish the center of the fire lodge. Stepping back two feet, he drew a circle as a guide for building the rock cradle that would hold the Stone People. Moving out ten more feet, he made another circle to establish the outer wall of the *Inipi*. Once everything was in place, Sunbeam handed him the freshly cut willow branches which he shaped into an intricate perfectly round domed structure that would join the above and below powers as one.

Sunbeam helped him cover the frame with blankets and buffalo hides. Once finished, he lit a cigarette and stood back to admire a job well done. Clearing his throat, he spoke to Sunbeam in his limited English:

"To live a good life, you must have faith and build power in your beliefs. This comes when we keep good thoughts about others. *Sku'ya*, everything is related and you must respect all life forces if you are to become a part of the Great Mystery. When you give respect to everything as if it were a relative, you then can understand the power of *Tunka'shila,* Grandfather, the oldest of ancient knowledge.

"We see the trees to be a nation of people. Because these standing ones are alive, we cut them in a certain way. It is said they are *Lela Wakan*, very sacred, and that long ago the people would hear their whispering voices in prayer songs. When their wood is stacked in a reverent manner, we make a happy fire."

Moving about fifteen feet from the West Door of the new *Inipi*, Otis started to build the Old Man Four Generations fire pit. "We do these things, *Sku'ya*, because our forefathers taught us to take great care and offer respect while touching another's life. In doing so, we honor the ways of our ancestors."

As his old, wrinkled brown hands worked the small earthen mound that was to become the molehill, Otis spoke of how proper preparation and good prayers must come from a good heart. Sunbeam knelt beside him, watching him shape and mold the four horns of Old Man Four Generations. "These represent the past four generations of our people and the four generations to come. If we shape the horns in a good way, surely *Wakan Tanka* will hear our prayers and help all the children's children who are yet to come. Old Man Four Generations holds the sacred fire to heat the stones."

At this point, he set four short pieces of wood into a square foundation over the face of Old Man Four Generations. Handing him more wood, Sunbeam watched him stack the pieces west to east, then north to south, until they were four high. On top, Otis carefully placed the stones he had selected for the upcoming sweat. Using several longer pieces of wood, he arranged them in a tipi formation around the structure, saying, "Remember, everything is *Lela Wakan,"* as he stretched his arms wide to emphasize his point. "A good Fire Chief must do everything with a pure heart. A sacred fire will help the people speak the truth of their needs.

"We are the keepers of the fire, and must depend on the old ways if we are to carry the little fire of the sun that exists in each stone. In our sweats we join with the sacred little fire and connect with the forever fire of Creator. If we do our ceremonies from a loving heart, the fire people will give us their blessings." Otis placed tinder amid bits of kindling in the little opening to create a perfect flame.

"Sunbeam," he continued, "a happy fire needs to breathe plenty of good air before it can speak to us. Sadly, there are many who have never heard the sweet voice of a flame. When ignorance builds a fire, it becomes angry and gives off lots of smoke, sometimes breaking the stones. I have seen some fires so angry that they heave hot coals at people. A fire with order won't have a quarrelsome nature. It will burn in a peaceful manner, heating the stones to heal the people.

"It is the spirit of the fiery-tempered salamander that calls the fire to help us. These little people are very impatient with humans and will not speak to us unless we come right. A match cannot strike, and a flint cannot make sparks without Salamander's help."

Otis lit the tinder, providing just enough friction to send forth a soft, gentle flame. "*Sku'ya,*" he said with great seriousness, "when you touch the life of fire, never anger its spirit or it will surely cause trouble in the *Inipi.*"

Otis and Sunbeam watched the flames build their power, all the while looking for the little people in the fire. Within moments, Sunbeam excitedly pointed at the many tiny people that she could see dancing and slithering among the hot coals. Otis lifted the corner of his mouth in a knowing smile.

When the last of the stones had fallen into the glowing embers, Otis said, "Go tell Medicine the Stone People are almost ready. I hear you'll be sweating with the elders today. That is a very special gift."

Stunned, Sunbeam ran off to deliver the message to her grandmother. Upon reaching the arbor, she found Cheering Woman telling an old Indian story:

"The Stone People are our earliest record keepers…Long ago, in the time of the longhairs, the earth was dotted with boulders that had been painted red by the ancient ones. Knowing of the boulders' special powers, they hid pieces of their hair around these stones as offerings. Others offered wildflowers or small pebbles at their bases to invite the Great Spirit to speak directly to them. Even children would place small prayer stones in the lower forks of nearby trees so the spirit helpers would also speak with them.

"As you enter the *Inipi,* think of all these things. Let the sweat heal your body, mind and soul. Let the Stone People guide your breath as you humble yourself before *Wakan Tanka.* Pray from your heart and speak freely about your problems. When the sacred waters touch the stones to become *Tunka'shila's* breath, release your fears and let your breath join with these life-givers to inspire your growth. Ask the Great Spirit to help you during your upcoming *Hanblecheyapi.* After all, it is *Wakan Tanka* who will fulfill all your needs."

Cheering Woman dismissed the group and acknowledged Sunbeam's arrival with a nod. She noticed the worried look on her face and approached her, asking, "Granddaughter, what's wrong?"

"Otis told me that I might be sweating with the elders today. That scares me because they have such long, hot sweats."

"Why, Granddaughter, there's no reason to fret. Maybe they won't have that much to pray for today." Cheering Woman chuckled as she put her arm around Sunbeam, and together they walked to the new *Inipi.*

"But, Grandmother, what if they do have lots to pray for today?"

"Have faith, child! A sweat makes your spirit strong and will heal your fears," soothed Cheering Woman, as they removed their clothes and wrapped themselves in towels.

Bending down on all fours, the medicine woman entered the *Inipi*. Sunbeam followed and sat next to her grandmother, fearfully clutching her towel in an attempt to cover her nude body.

Cheering Woman burned a special mixture of herbs to prepare the little dwelling for a healing sweat. One by one, the elders entered in a sunwise manner and sat on the freshly picked sage that covered the dirt floor. Gentle smiles crossed their faces as the fragrant aroma filled their nostrils. Heads bowed, they waited in silent prayer for Cheering Woman to begin the first round of the sweat. Still apprehensive, Sunbeam bowed her head along with the others.

Otis cradled a hot ash on a piece of bark and handed it to Cheering Woman, who lit her pipe. He then sat down outside the *Inipi* door to wait. She offered her pipe up to *Wakan Tanka*, Father Sky, Mother Earth and the four directions, then smoked before passing it around to the others. When the pipe returned to her, she began singing a ceremonial song as she handed it to Shung'. At this point, Otis went to Old Man Four Generations and picked up the first hot stone with a pair of antlers to begin his return walk on the sacred *Unci,* Grandmother, and *Tunka'shila,* Grandfather, fire path. Kneeling at the opening of the *Inipi*, he passed in the stone and Shung' touched the stem of the pipe to it, a signal for Otis to place it in the sacred cradle. He then brought in six more in the same manner.

Cheering Woman began her prayer. "*Hau, Inyan*, the Stone People, you that hold our oldest of records and are the backbone of *Maka Ina*, Mother Earth. We ask you, *Inyan*, to share your sacred knowledge with the people." She then offered herbs, along with her special tobacco, to the hot stones. Otis took the pipe from Shung', refilled it and handed it to Cheering Woman then lowered the flap over the entrance, checking to make sure no light came into the *Inipi*. He then took his pipe from the top of the sweat lodge and sat down to smoke.

"*Ha-Hey, Ha-Hey, Ha-Hey, Ha-Hey*. This is Cheering Woman," she pleaded.

Reaching into the wooden water bucket, she filled the gourd dipper then offered the water to the stones. Clouds of steam blasted upward while everyone listened to the hissing voices of the stones. As the aroma of sweetgrass and sage filled the *Inipi,* everyone drew its sweetness into their lungs, stilling their thoughts.

"Today, I come to you in a most humble way," she prayed, inviting the spirits to join them. "*Hau, Wakan Tanka, Tunka'shila*. It is you who gives life to all things. I am nothing without you. I ask you to hear our voices as we speak of the needs of the people. Guide our breath and let it join you, *Tunka'shila,* as we connect to the above powers. *Hau, Wakan Tanka,* teach us how to fight the many raging battles that live within us, so we may understand our purpose in life. Let us use this sacred breath of *Tunka'shila* as we speak of our troubles. Help us to cleanse ourselves of these hurts.

"*Hau*, powers of all the sky dwellers. Help us see from far above, sharing in your powers as you take our prayers up to *Wakan Tanka*.

"*Hau, Wakinyan*, the Thunderbeings, come join us. We thank you for sending your precious rains to replenish Mother Earth, who provides for all of her children.

"*Hau*, great powers of the Day and Night, we thank you for the Two times Two, and for *Anpetu,* the red that shines before dawn. We thank you for the precious gift of the sun, whose warmth keeps Mother Earth alive. We thank you for *Hanwi*, the Night Sun, the gift of quiet time that allows us to reflect on who we are. We thank you for the morning star who helps us understand the messages you send us each day.

"*Hau*, Great *Tatanka*, sacred Buffalo, from which all things come to take care of the people.

"*Hau, Mato*, Bear, who brings the sacred medicines. Help us to heal our bodies as we purify ourselves today.

"*Hau*, Hoofed Ones, place love in our hearts and give us the speed and agility to join our brothers and sisters in their hour of need. Let the people understand the love of Great Spirit so that they may know peace in their hearts. Unite and touch the families that are being destroyed. Bring their troubled souls back to a loving and respectful way, *Wakan Tanka*.

"*Hau*, sweet South, where *Igmu*, Cougar, lives. Help us through our heartaches. Let the green medicines be understood as they grow with abundance to heal and feed the poor. Let the children of this sacred world never again feel hunger in their bellies."

Cheering Woman lit the pipe and passed it sunwise around the *Inipi* as each person offered up his voice to Great Spirit. When the pipe returned to Cheering Woman, she prayed, "*Hau, Tunka'shila*. Tomorrow we will bring you our new vision questers. Guide them, Grandfather, and help them come to you with pure hearts. *Hau, Mitakuye Oyasin,* all my relations."

Cheering Woman tapped the side of the *Inipi* signaling to Otis to lift the flap. The people, their bodies wet and glistening, sat in silence as Grandfather's breath left the sweat, allowing their prayers to ride up on the steam.

Again Otis walked the sacred pathway to bring in the stones for the second round.

"*Yupayo*, close the door," said Cheering Woman.

As Otis lowered the flap, the *Inipi* was once again consumed in a pitch-black darkness that blocked out all connection to the outside world. Again, Otis removed his pipe from the top of the *Inipi* and smoked. Then he refilled Cheering Woman's pipe and placed it in front of the molehill while waiting for the third round.

After prayers, songs, and chants, Cheering Woman tapped again on the *Inipi's* inner wall to signal Otis to open the door. Sunbeam was grateful for the fresh, cool air that swept in and caressed her skin. The elders, sensing her relief, held a gentle smile in their hearts for her approaching *Hanblecheyapi*.

Otis brought in the stones for the third round and lowered the flap. The *Inipi* grew hotter with each dipper of water as the prayers intensified. While the old ones prayed long and hard for Sunbeam, her mind dwelled on the intense heat, confirming her worst fears. As more water was added to the stones and the sweat became too demanding for her, the old people prayed hard to help her leave her body behind and go to the Great Spirit. Cheering Woman, seeing her granddaughter's dilemma, reached over and touched her to assure her that there was nothing to fear. She then tapped the side of the *Inipi* for the flap to be lifted. Again Sunbeam gave thanks for the coolness of the outside air.

Otis walked down the pathway with the last of the stones and closed the flap for the final round. Cheering Woman prayed for a very long time, pouring the water over the stones before passing the dipper. One by one, each elder took the dipper then offered a few drops of water to the hot stones. When the dipper reached Sunbeam, she hesitated. Her thirst was intense and she wanted to take a drink, but Cheering Woman, sensing her thoughts, grabbed her arm and Sunbeam contritely gave her water to the stones.

Cheering Woman took the dipper and continuously fed water to the stones, creating billowing clouds of hot steam. As the searing heat raced upward filling the *Inipi,* Sunbeam held a piece of sage close to her nose, trying to breathe. Unable to inhale, she placed her face to the ground in order to escape the burning heat. Gasping for air, she felt as if the gates of hell had opened wide and something from within had captured her lungs. In a frenzy of claustrophobia, she panicked. Cheering Woman ordered her to breathe slowly, but try as she might, Sunbeam could not inhale. Cheering Woman added more water, praying harder for her granddaughter. As the heat escalated, Sunbeam felt invisible arms reach out and clutch her body. In despair, she withered and collapsed.

"Release your mind, Granddaughter. Go from the pain and seek your peace!" commanded Cheering Woman, pulling her into an upright position as the elders loudly chanted an old prayer song. Gathering her strength, Sunbeam joined in the chant. Then more water was offered to the stones and again she felt her body being consumed by a wall of intense heat as the skin across her shoulders began to blister.

"*Hau, Wakan Tanka,* help my granddaughter get beyond her body! Give her the power to embrace you, *Tunka'shila,*" prayed Cheering Woman as Sunbeam leaned into her for support.

Suddenly Sunbeam's composure returned and her soul was lifted up to another place where a powerful wolf shade, rose from the steaming stones. Drawn to this ghost, like a moth to a flame, she remembered an old familiar promise.

"Welcome, little pup," said the shimmering wolf, rising from the steaming stones. "I see the dreamer has found her way back to me. I once promised your soul that when you were ready, I would return and walk by your side."

Sunbeam stared directly into Wolf's glowing, golden eyes as it drew her spirit into another world to the throbbing beat of distant drums.

"If life's experiences have weakened you, release the power placed in your soul from long ago," said Wolf. As these words were spoken, Sunbeam felt a wave of power enter her body and spin her downward into a spiral of darkness. "This is as far as you can go today. I, the earth teacher, will always be here to direct your destiny. From this day forward, you will walk with my powers."

Something pressed against Sunbeam's chest, causing a pleasant sensation and she watched in wonderment as liquid colors tumbled from Wolf's coat. Drawn into Wolf's body, Sunbeam looked through its eyes and saw the *Inipi* illuminated with spiritual beauty.

"Sunbeam, I ask, is this an illusion? Are you dreaming me, or am I dreaming you? Is your skin still burning, or did your mind manifest a painful experience? Create from the goodness of your heart, and fulfill the promises you made in the Spirit World. Let my visit bring you peace. I am with you always."

Suddenly Wolf was replaced by a large eye that flashed bolts of lightning. "Come, you puny thing. Come, dance with me," roared *Wakinyan*. "Your life is just beginning, and what a cowardly mockery it is! You, with no power, will ride the never-ending sacred hoops until you are worthy to experience my powers."

Sunbeam remembered her grandmother saying that *Wakinyan's* messenger was a swallow. When one appeared and turned into a spiraling tornado, she gasped as it turned back into a swallow and flew away. Wolf returned, and at this point Sunbeam could feel her body spinning over the hot stones. Wolf bared its teeth, transformed into billowing steam, and disappeared.

The elders acknowledged Wolf's presence as a vision and said in unison, "*Hau.*"

Cheering Woman closed the ceremony and Otis lifted the flap on the final round. The people moved in a clockwise manner, following Cheering Woman out of the *Inipi*. The sun touched them with gentle rays as they re-entered the outside world, standing firm on their spiritual path. Life was again serene and beautiful. And that was good.

Overwhelmed and humbled, Sunbeam stood alone, feeling the cool air on her skin and watching the steam rise off the elders' bodies as they mingled in silence. She could tell they were preoccupied with the shade's visit. Knowing she had been given something special, Sunbeam dressed and offered a silent prayer to Creator.

Otis watched her from a distance, then tilted the corner of his mouth into a smile, signaling for her to join him. As she approached, he said, "That was a hot sweat. You did good. I'm sure *Wakan Tanka* has many plans for you." He then guided her toward the fire pit signaling for Sunbeam to kneel beside the Old Man Four Generations to watch him clean the altar.

He combed through the ashes, separating them by color. "These ashes," he said, "speak to us about many things. Watch me as I use them to build Old Man Four Generation's face." Taking the gray and black ashes, he arranged them on the outer edge of the round head and down the neck to form the hair. "These gray and black ashes show that someone prayed for the dead and got their answer." Next he spread the yellow ashes over the face, saying, "These yellow ashes tell us that someone prayed for their troubled family and that love and harmony will return to them." He then used the red ashes to make two horizontal lines on each side of the face. Smiling, he told Sunbeam, "These tell us that many healings took place during the ceremony."

Crawling into the *Inipi,* he chose the first of seven stones, each of which he proceeded to set in place…two for the eyes, two for the nose holes, and three for the mouth. Standing back to get a better look at his work, Otis smiled in satisfaction.

"This is how you build the face of Old Man Four Generations, *Sku'ya*. See those white ashes? They speak of the goodness of *Wakan Tanka*. Ah yes, that was a good sweat."

For several minutes, teacher and pupil sat in stillness as Sunbeam contemplated the gift she had been given. Otis broke the silence, saying, "The shade who came to visit you was female. This she-wolf will walk with you for the rest of your life. Always keep Wolf close to your heart, so she can help you in your life's journey. Tomorrow you will begin your first *Hanblecheyapi*. If you have a vision during this time, you will carry many responsibilities for the rest of your life." He picked up a bundled pipe, walked her to the Sundance Circle and motioned for her to sit under the Tree of Life.

"*Sku'ya*, your grandmother says you might earn the right to carry a pipe after your vision quest. For now, look around the circle. The blood of many of our brothers and sisters has spilled on these grounds. That's what makes this a sacred place that must always be respected. There can be no lies between us when we sit here.

"Long ago, Creator made four supernatural powers and gave each an ability. There was *Wi,* the sun; *Taku Skan Skan*, the motion of life; *Maka Ina,* Mother Earth; and *Inyan*, the Stone People. We, the two legs, were the fifth born and the last of these creations.

"Our ways of the pipe came from White Buffalo Calf Woman. They say that she lives far beyond the stars and the gift of the pipe comes from *Até*, her father. She came to earth and taught the people the seven sacred rites on our pipe and how to use them. When her mission was done, she promised that someday she would return, telling us that until then we should walk with the pipe and use it in a good way. The first rite of the pipe is the *Keeping and Releasing of the Soul*. The second is the *Inipi*, the Rite of Purification. The third is the *Hanblecheyapi*, Lamenting for a Vision. The fourth is *Winwanyag Wachipi*, the Sun Dance. The fifth is the *Hunkapi*, the Making of Relatives. The sixth is *Ishna Ta Awi Cha Lowan*, the Preparation of a Girl for Womanhood. And the seventh is *Tapa Wanka Yap*, the Throwing of the Ball, which teaches us to become one with our universe. Always remember your power is in the pipe, and the pipe can only be as strong as the one who carries it."

Otis handed Sunbeam a golden eagle feather. "I give this to you for your *Hanblecheyapi*. The ways of *Wanbli Gle'ska*, Eagle, will give you a good life, and someday maybe you will be a strong, visionary pipe carrier."

Overwhelmed at receiving such a sacred gift, Sunbeam accepted the feather and held it gently. "*Até,* I will always honor this sacred gift. I will keep it close to my heart."

Otis smiled as they left the Sundance Circle. After following him in silence, Sunbeam made her way to the river where her grandmother was waiting.

"I see Otis gave you your first eagle feather. Granddaughter, someday you will become a strong pipe carrier. I was proud of you this morning, but you did worry me. I hope you realize that if you had tried to leave the sweat, I would have broken your arm to make you stay." Cheering Woman laughed as they waded into the river.

The mere thought of her grandmother attacking her in front of the others, caused Sunbeam's face to turn bright red in embarrassment. Meekly, she mumbled, "I was too afraid to leave, Grandmother."

"Ah yes, I believe that, Grandchild," said Cheering Woman, stepping out of the water and grabbing her towel.

Sunbeam plunged into the river, exhilarated by its coolness. She swam to a large stone, where she stretched out in the sun to reflect upon the morning's events.

It was late morning when Buffalo Man, a medicine person, summoned her to the arbor. He sat quietly for a long time, then cleared his throat as all elders do before speaking:

"Granddaughter, we have discussed the sweat. We all agree that someday you will be called upon to share the teachings of the old ways. You have known this 'up above shade' in other lifetimes and it will be Wolf who supports your human endeavors. You must accept this blessing and honor this earth teacher. Wolf will bring you good medicine during your *Hanblecheyapi*. We have agreed that we will not interfere with the guidance of this spirit helper.

"In life, Granddaughter, you may study with many good teachers and some bad ones, but it will be Wolf who leads you through your most harsh challenges. She will demand that you have a strong identity, learn to make quick, yet good decisions before acting, demonstrate courage, develop endurance and be willing to accept every challenge that comes into your life. The best teachings will come from your life experiences.

"Ah yes, Granddaughter, Wolf will tutor you in the fine art of fighting. She will teach you when it is wise to walk away from a battle, always with the promise that you will return to fight another day. If you listen to this shade, you will someday think as Wolf. We will talk more when you return from your *Hanblecheyapi*. For now, that's all I have to say."

Buffalo Man handed her a golden eagle feather. Sunbeam thanked him and left the arbor. She knew the heavy responsibility of the two sacred eagle feathers she now carried, and hoped Eagle would help her have a strong vision.

Soon afterward, she set off to join Cheering Woman under the arbor with the other vision questers. When she arrived, she heard her grandmother instructing them in the making of tobacco ties. Having completed hers the week before, she simply listened to Cheering Woman's wise words.

"Life is the perception of your reality. It is the almighty winds that sing us into life. As a dreamer, your mind must touch the sensitivity of your heart. Only then, can you become balanced in all that you are. Your vision quest may bring order into your chaotic life as you travel with the spirits.

"While making your tobacco ties, place a prayer into each one to call upon the four hundred and five spirits. This number was given to us by our ancestors who knew there are twenty wheels times twenty sub-wheels, which makes four hundred. The five opens us to the four directions, the animals, the winds and all the life forces. You must find your center in this five to receive all the gifts from the above and below powers.

"After tearing your material into two-inch squares and placing the tobacco in the center, say a prayer then fold the cloth from corner to corner. String the tobacco ties onto one long cord, and keep them about one inch apart as you move along. When you are finished, give them to Shung'."

Cheering Woman motioned for Sunbeam to follow her out of the arbor. "My friend will arrive sometime late this afternoon, and I would like to spend time with her," she explained. "I need your help preparing for the *Yuwipi*, Spirit Calling ceremony, for this evening."

As they entered the house, Sunbeam's mouth began to water as the smell of good food drifted from the kitchen. Knowing that she would be without food or water for the next four days, she grabbed a piece of buttered fry bread before going to the living room to watch Otis and three men remove all the furniture and cover the windows to black out all light.

Cheering Woman and Sunbeam sat down to make the black, yellow, red, and white flags for the ceremony. After tying a pinch of tobacco in the corner of the material, they tied each flag onto a stick. Sunbeam took four coffee cans and filled them with dirt. When she returned, she put a flag in each one and set them in the center of the room at Cheering Woman's altar. Finding nothing more to do, she went to the front porch swing to await for the arrival of Cheering Woman's friend.

Although Sunbeam barely remembered Madame Bianchoff, she immediately recognized her as the car pulled into the yard. A thin blonde woman with smooth white skin got out of the car carefully, using a cane for support from an old back injury. Sunbeam approached shyly.

Glancing around, Madame Bianchoff noted that Cheering Woman's house had not changed much since her last visit, but Sunbeam had grown. Smiling at Sunbeam, she said, "Turn around, my dear. My, you have grown into such a pretty young lady. I am thrilled that your grandmother invited me to your first vision quest."

Sunbeam smiled back, then nodded as she reached for Madame's bags. She took them into the house and set them down in the room especially prepared for their guest.

Overhearing their conversation, Cheering Woman greeted her friend. "Ah, my sister, it's so good to see you. Come." She took Madame Bianchoff's arm, guiding her to the arbor where all the food was waiting in her honor. Many old friends and curiosity seekers had gathered to see the lady who often sent Cheering Woman packages of food and clothing to distribute among the people. Throughout the afternoon, everyone enjoyed the good food and conversation, but when darkness intruded upon their celebration, the apprentices left to prepare for the night's *Yuwipi* ceremony.

Upon entering the house, Sunbeam noticed that many people had already arrived and had taken seats on the floor. She spotted Otis and quickly sat next to him. A few minutes later a large tan spider crawled onto Sunbeam's foot and she whispered, "Grandmother Spider, thank you for coming. What do you have to tell me tonight?"

Otis glanced down to see who she was talking with and said, "Well, well, I see *Iktomi*, has come to visit you. Hmm, *Sku'ya*, this could be a good sign or a bad sign. One never knows for sure if Grandmother Spider is spinning you a pretty or an ugly world. Got to watch out for that old trickster, *Iktomi*. Just remember, whatever you do to the spider's web, it will do to you. The old people say it was Grandmother Spider who wove the web that holds the earth, moon, sun, and stars in their place. They say without her web these powers would drift all over the universe."

As he finished his story, Sunbeam glanced down to find the spider had disappeared. Worried about Spider's double meaning, she said a silent prayer, asking Grandmother Spider to please spin her a pretty world. Still feeling the presence of old *Iktomi*, Sunbeam moved closer to Otis for protection.

Just then, Cheering Woman entered the room along with two apprentices who wrapped her in blankets and bound her with ropes. The signal was given to turn out the lights, and as the room became pitch-black, the Spirit Calling ceremony began.

Suddenly flashing streaks of blue light illuminated the darkness, whereupon Sunbeam silently welcomed Lightning Man to the ceremony. She heard many soft, unknown sounds as tiny sparks of light continuously danced around the room, touching all the people. Muffled whispers encompassed the entire room, when suddenly Sunbeam was hit on the head and an unfamiliar voice bellowed out her name.

Otis got up and led her through the darkness, then left her standing at the altar. An isolated haze of circling blue lights danced before her eyes, along with a floating gourd that continually touched her face.

Without warning, two more gourds appeared. Then three, four, five and six of them came into view and began to touch her entire body. Many spirits were seen around the floating, rattling gourds. A drumbeat was heard from another place and the rattles grew louder and louder as the gourds touched Sunbeam's body. A voice asked Sunbeam many questions that she did not understand. Then suddenly a large, round face encircled by blue light floated in front of her.

"My name is *Round Face Man*. I am the spirit that you asked to come and do your bidding. I am old, and I am wise. I have little patience with stupidity, and if you wish for me to serve you, you must heed my rules! I will be with you throughout your life and I will always respond to your call. Be careful what you ask for, and never use me foolishly. I am not responsible for any poorly worded instructions that you may give me. If someone or something gets destroyed while I am doing your bidding, you will pay for it, not me! Know this, I will use your energy to fulfill your requests, so each time you call upon me it will shorten your earthly life. I will be presented to you in the form of a round stone. It is the doorway to my power, so use it wisely." *Round Face Man* vanished as a frightened Sunbeam returned to her seat.

Next, many people were called forward and given answers and healings to fulfill their needs. One had been looking for her missing son who was found in a California state prison. Another, who asked about some lost legal papers was told where they could be located. Madame Bianchoff was taken to the altar where a soft bluish light encircled her body, healing her tormented lower back.

It was past midnight when the ceremony was completed. The lights were turned on, and to everyone's surprise, there sat Cheering Woman next to the folded blankets that she had been wrapped in, with the ropes placed on top, coiled in a tight circle.

As tradition dictates, everyone was then served a soup that contained an unknown meat, along with berry cobbler and plenty of black coffee. The people ate and spoke in whispers about the *Yuwipi* ceremony they had just witnessed. Before departing, many gave gifts to Cheering Woman for the ceremony. When the last guest had left, Sunbeam joined her grandmother and Madame Bianchoff on the front porch to exchange a few personal gifts of their own.

Sunbeam was handed a package, and she quickly unwrapped the soft pink paper, exposing an oblong box. Lifting the lid, she saw a pair of pink ballet slippers and squealed in delight as Cheering Woman and Madame exchanged an all-knowing look.

Thrilled with the slippers, Sunbeam tried them on, whereupon both women agreed they were a perfect fit.

"The gift is from your grandmother and me. Someday you may want to study the art of dance," said Madame Bianchoff.

Sunbeam thanked them profusely. She had always wanted such a pair of dance slippers, for she secretly dreamed of dancing someday. Then, remembering that she had to be up before sunrise, she respectfully excused herself. Sunbeam crawled into bed and lay in darkness watching the moonlit shadows of Cheering Woman and Madame Bianchoff dance in the movement of the swing. As the moon's light spilled across her bed, she thanked Wolf for coming, wondering if she was worthy of such a special gift.

She saw the North Star from the window, and thought of the great warrior Crazy Horse. Sunbeam could almost see him riding fearlessly into battle. She prayed to him for support and courage. Hoping he would come to her, she closed her eyes and focused on her upcoming *Hanblecheyapi*. She drifted into Shadow World using the lulling, sweet voices of Cheering Woman and Madame's reminiscing to still her mind. Sunbeam was nearly asleep when Cheering Woman and Madame Bianchoff started to discuss her future.

"When a child is gifted, she must have an outlet to express herself. I think it is wonderful that you have made plans for your granddaughter to explore all of her talents so that she may live comfortably in two cultures," observed Madame.

"Yes, for her to survive, I must prepare her to walk in both worlds."

"Is she as talented in Medicine as you wished her to be?"

"Oh, yes! But sometimes she's a little too arrogant."

"Together I'm sure we can direct this high-spirited child to the areas in which she is most gifted," replied Madame Bianchoff as they both chuckled. "Here are the acceptance papers for her scholarship to the finest school of the arts in New York. When she is ready, send these papers along with my letter and they will accept her," she added, handing the forms to Cheering Woman.

Cheering Woman stuck them in her pocket, and looked at her friend with a deep feeling of sincere appreciation. "You know I must make good plans for her because my time is short. My daughter, Rose, will see that my wishes for her are carried out without too much interference from her father. I hope that someday my son and granddaughter will heal what stands between them."

Madame Bianchoff smiled in agreement as they retired for the night.

Wi, the sun, was just touching the horizon when Sunbeam came out of the *Inipi.* As she and her grandmother walked up the hill to the vision quest pit, Cheering Woman handed her a round stone, saying, "This is the special stone that the spirit spoke about last night. His name is Round Face Man, and he is big medicine. This spirit has known our family for seven generations. Use him as wisely as those before you and he will serve you well. Use him foolishly and he will destroy you."

Sunbeam's eyes widened big as saucers as she listened to her grandmother's words, then she placed the stone in her medicine bag. When they reached their destination Sunbeam hesitated, then hugged her grandmother for assurance.

The pit was encircled by Sunbeam's swaying tobacco ties, and colored flags representing the four directions were flying in the wind. Sunbeam lowered herself into the pit, stripped, and covered her body with a white sheet, knowing she would be isolated from the world for the next four days. She stood facing the West, smudged herself off, then smoked her pipe.

Sunbeam spent the day in prayer, speaking to the gatekeepers of the four directions, asking the good spirits to come help her. As the day moved forward, Sunbeam's world became filled with distant familiar sounds. In the late afternoon she was glad to feel the coolness of Mother Earth's body on her skin. It was strangely quiet except for the winds that spoke to her through the rustling leaves from the nearby trees.

But as the sun fell behind the horizon, the sanctuary began to disappear. Darkness brought the cold, and many strange sounds pierced her mind. Shapeless, shadowy reflections bounced off low-hanging clouds. Her fears brought a heavy restlessness and she curled up against the earth wall of the pit, fighting feelings of terror and isolation as a deep loneliness crept into her soul.

As morning light appeared, Sunbeam breathed a sigh of relief and gave thanks to *Wakan Tanka* for the warmth of the sun that caressed her shivering body. By late afternoon on her second day in the pit, she began to feel pangs of thirst and hunger.

By the third day nausea and cramps gripped her growling stomach. As night fell, Sunbeam's world came crashing in on her. Surrendering to exhaustion, she wailed in tears as she pulled the sheet tightly around her body, hoping to fall asleep and escape the cold.

Startled, Sunbeam was awakened by a loud clap of thunder. Looking up, she saw dark, heavy clouds looming overhead, threatening rain. *Wakinyan* rumbled as Lightning Man danced boldly across the sky, touching the earth all around her. Suddenly a thunderous, deafening sound resonated across the land as she watched lightning split a tree and smash it to the ground. Fire and smoke blazed upward as pieces of the stump sat smoldering.

Scared out of her wits, Sunbeam jumped up and called out to her grandmother, but no one came to answer her pitiful plea. The angry winds joined in the destruction, ripping limbs and throwing trees to the ground. As dark clouds rolled across the sky, splattering raindrops turned into a torrential downpour. Sunbeam cowered against the earthen wall, watching Lightning Man play with the wind as it filled the air with flying debris that whipped across the pit. Alone and afraid, weeping in terror, Sunbeam prayed hard.

As the thunderstorm's momentum grew the pit began to fill with water. She desperately wanted to open her mouth and quench her thirst, but resisted the temptation. Sunbeam spent the rest of the night sitting in the cold drizzling rain, wondering if the spirits were testing her and whether she had the endurance to continue the *Hanblecheyapi* ceremony.

When a gray dawn arrived on her fourth day, she saw the pit was half full of water, and the walls were crumbling into muddy mounds of wet earth. Covered with mud and trembling with cold, she cried out to *Wakan Tanka* for mercy.

Just then something silvery slashed through the water, breaking into bubbles on the surface. Her imagination running wild, Sunbeam recalled a warning her grandmother had once given her:

"If you ever see a hairy, eyeless monster called Bog, remember to stay very still because he likes to eat children! If you anger a bog, you could be responsible for flooding the world. His body will become filled with many holes that will forever spew water, thus creating a huge flood that will destroy all life on earth."

Sunbeam screamed in terror as she fought off this fearful memory. Then, as if in a dream, she saw Cheering Woman appear from nowhere and stand above the pit. In a soothing voice, she assured Sunbeam it was not Bog. Finding comfort in her grandmother's presence, Sunbeam calmed down.

Although she remained stoic, Cheering Woman's heart was breaking over her granddaughter's pitiful dilemma, so she stayed with Sunbeam until the sun broke through the gray clouds.

"This is your fourth and final day, Granddaughter. Maybe it's not time for you to have a vision." Cheering Woman tried to sound comforting.

"No, Grandmother. I must stay until I have my vision."

"Too much is happening, Granddaughter, and you're not coping with your fears."

"Grandmother, please. I promise I will not be afraid if you let me stay until I have my vision."

"Sunbeam, that is not my decision. It is yours. If you choose to stay, I can't assist you, no matter what happens," concluded Cheering Woman. Then she turned and walked away.

The day was hot and humid, and by early afternoon Sunbeam was fighting off the mosquitoes and other swarming insects that had come to intensify her misery. Thankful for last night's rain, she covered her body with mud to protect herself from these pests, then she curled up and pressed her body against the wall in pitiful prayer.

As dawn appeared on her fifth day, Sunbeam felt the sun's warmth touch her body and thanked Creator for his mercy. But as night fell, her battle with terror returned. Many unknown spirits hovered over her like corpses, while others came unbidden from the hidden corners of her overcrowded mind. Strange things appeared and they seemed to enjoy her suffering. It was as though the beauty of the spirit world had forsaken her and she was being dragged into caverns of darkness.

Feeling deserted and lost in space and time, Sunbeam felt tears roll down her cheeks, exposing clean streaks of skin on her face. Praying fervently for guidance, she heard a wolf howl in the distance. She felt something beside her move and opened her eyes to see Wolf affectionately nipping at her. Thankful for the visit, Sunbeam reached out to touch it, only to find her hand passed through Wolf's body. She heard Wolf say, "I who protect you also watch over you. Fear will eat up the soul just as quickly as winter will eat summer. Now, focus on your purpose of becoming a dreamer!"

Sunbeam melted into Wolf's yellow-gold eyes, then suddenly she felt her body merge with Wolf, filling her with a strength she had never known. A wild freedom had her running as Wolf on tireless legs, chasing a lone deer through the mountains. Sunbeam felt such freedom and boundless joy that she never wanted to return. As quickly as the thought entered her mind, she was back in the pit, watching another spirit materialize in the far north corner.

This spirit did not have the beauty that she had just experienced as Wolf. Sunbeam screamed in horror as the soil in the pit moved in elongated, wavy lines. Once again she was gripped by a hysteria that challenged her very existence. She fell to her knees and found herself staring into the eyes of a large undulating snake.

"If you fear me so much, then why did you call me?" Snake asked nonchalantly.

Turning her face to the wall, Sunbeam answered with a trembling voice, "I didn't mean to, so please just go away."

"Well, now," said mighty Snake, "I come from the distant dimension of Upper World, and we're not so rude there. I had no plans to visit you, but it was your fear that called me! Now that I am here, what is your problem?"

"I'm afraid of you and I want you to go away."

"I wish you no harm, Little One," he hissed from his towering position. "Your mind has created this fear of me. Every world has its own perceptions and knowledge. Unlike you, I fear nothing. This allows me to move from one world to another, and as you know, we must accept our oneness with all of the Great Mystery's creations. Since I have made this trip, I will show you the flames of the firebird. Maybe it will help you find your strength," added Snake, vanishing into the wall.

Suddenly Sunbeam was immobilized and she felt the walls of the pit fill with his writhing body. Again she screamed, and again he returned. But this time he coiled his body tightly around her and began to loosen her skin.

"One must shed the old skin to find the new cycles of life. I shed your skin to fill you with the essence of my spirit. There is a wholeness in the willingness to experience. Let me prove to you that you are equal to everything in creation. I bring no harm. Ingest the poisons of your fears and eat my medicine so you will understand. This is a rare gift and I give it to few."

"Maybe you're trying to trick me because *Wi*, the Sun Chief, destroyed most of your people."

"Oh, that was long ago," said Snake. "Now I bring fire to purify your life. Why don't you quit doubting me and eat from the table of intellect, so you can receive my gifts of charisma and leadership? I am the knowledge and the resolution of your dreams. It is my gift that will allow you to accomplish your ambitions. If you accept my medicine, you will connect with the Great Spirit," he explained as he entered her body.

Reflecting on Snake's message, Sunbeam felt helpless as her lips curled back to make room for his long fangs.

"Become my magic and you will have the power of the magician. Infused with this power, you can dance in truth with the rhythm of your dreams and transform your soul into the energy of pure fire. Accept my magic and merge with the fire and rain. Only then can you stand in the two good blue days and the two good red days and survive," said Snake in a mysterious, whistling tone.

As she and Snake glided over large boulders and small stones, fear let go of Sunbeam's soul and she found a new rhythm.

"Can you feel how comfortable you are? Were not your old patterns of fear foolish? Doesn't your body feel as free as a flowing, winding river? Can't you feel our connection with the universe as we dance together?" Snake asked.

Suddenly a roaring fire was coming at them.

"Do you feel the power of the fire? Hurry, cast yourself into the eternal flame so that we may co-exist throughout eternity. Let the flames fill you with exuberance. Open your heart and receive the sparks of fire knowledge."

Then just as Sunbeam was beginning to enjoy the experience of being in Snake's world, she was abruptly flung back into the pit. Although her skin was burnt from the hot sun and her parched lips were cracked and bleeding, she felt at peace with herself.

From a foggy distance, she heard Cheering Woman's comforting words as she placed a cloth soaked with peyote on her granddaughter's swollen lips. Sunbeam sucked on the rag until she fell once more into the dream state. This time she saw another storm brewing on the horizon, but it no longer mattered. She heard thunder, and yet there was no thunder. The pit was illuminated and she perceived the ageless, outstretched wings of Eagle before her. With each step he took toward her, huge lightning bolts shot up from the ground.

Without warning, she was sucked into drenching skies, soaring from storm to storm on Eagle's back. As they flew higher and higher, his invincible wings held off the assailing winds. Before them appeared a flaming rainbow that continually dissolved and reappeared. Sunbeam marveled at all this beauty as they sped through the universe.

"Look through my eyes and see what is around you," said Eagle. "When life breaks a wing, heal it with love. Love is true power when it comes from within. Go to the highest of grounds to seek knowledge and when you become tired, go to the silence of the towering mountains to rest. Never again allow your wings to be clipped. Honor me and I will take you beyond the Beyond.

As you meet life's challenges, you will grow strong, becoming one with the sky dwellers. Only then can you be honored with a gift of many feathers. Little Eaglet, broaden your beliefs and feed your soul. We shall dance in flight again and again as you conquer your fears and self-doubt. Feel me in the shadows as well as the light, and know you are supported on the wings of Eagle. Listen for my call and we will fly through the sun."

With Eagle, Sunbeam saw brilliant colors swirling around her body creating an energy that shot upward from the core of her being. Spinning downward, she danced with the four winds, the fire, the earth and the water, each engulfing her as though the pleasure of death and rebirth were joyous.

Suddenly everything stopped and seven liquid gold circles dropped down around her body then melted into the earth. As a sacred pipe was offered, soft words echoed from somewhere deep inside. "Walk as this pipe! Remember this life is but a moment in time." Sweat poured from Sunbeam's face as she began singing the medicine songs with sacred Buffalo while dancing with *Mato*, the Bear.

Sunbeam heard Cheering Woman's voice calling to her and she slowly opened her eyes, surprised to see her grandmother standing above the pit with tears running down her cheeks. Sunbeam smiled up at her, knowing she had completed her *Hanblecheyapi*. With caring hands she was lifted from the pit and wrapped in a clean blanket, then led in silence to the *Inipi*.

In the sweat, Sunbeam spoke of her experiences to the elders, who listened intently before interpreting what she had envisioned. Buffalo Man, the oldest, said:

"Your vision tells us you will carry many responsibilities in your life. You will be tested over and over, and you will suffer because of others' lack of understanding. Never waver in your principles or beliefs. Life's experiences will become your best teacher, and with this knowledge you will build the strength to keep freedom in your soul.

"Granddaughter, always run with the freedom of the wind. Feel the river on your skin and recognize that you are searching for what most do not even know exists. Someday these lessons will direct your life and lead you to an honored place among the people. Walk with a strong heart, Granddaughter. Know that Wolf will always be by your side and Golden Eagle will always carry you on wings of love.

"Snake Medicine goes all the way back to first creation. It was *Wi* who made and destroyed Snake with fire. Snake people carry strong magic, but most often they are misunderstood. Remember to walk carefully with Snake, for his people still hold a grudge against *Wi*.

"Few can accept the power of Snake. Some think of him as good; others think of him as bad. Snake demands that you accept constant change before his power can be used on the physical plane. His touch means that you could become your own worst enemy and create harm to yourself and others. Be aware of his danger and remember that you control the direction of your life.

"*Wanbli Gle'ska,* the golden eagle, has touched you and flown into your heart. Let this sacred messenger take you far beyond what is known. Granddaughter, the old ones have always walked with you, and what I say is true. That is all I have to say," he concluded, as Cheering Woman closed the fourth round in prayer.

Otis lifted the flap of the *Inipi* and everyone crawled out followed by Sunbeam who was absorbed in thoughtful silence. She and Otis exchanged smiles before she left for a long bath in the river. Entering the water, she reflected on the words of the elders. Sunbeam knew that life would demand much of her and she would have to face the coldness and harshness of old *Yata*, the North Wind, but she felt a new power had been given to her to help her face any challenge.

After returning to the house, she sipped a cup of Cheering Woman's special herbal tea then retreated to her room to rest. As evening approached, Cheering Woman went into Sunbeam's room to bathe her sunburned skin with a cool herbal solution, saying gently, "I am very proud of you. Now get some more rest. We'll talk tomorrow." Then Cheering Woman left to spend her last night with Madame Bianchoff.

For the next few weeks Sunbeam withdrew from everyone. She spent most of her time alone thinking of her visions and the elders' predictions. Summer drew quickly to a close and Sunbeam was happy that everyone was finally going home, thankful that she no longer had to share Cheering Woman with others.

Usually Sunbeam revered seasonal changes, but this year as winter approached and the gales of *Yata* returned, she felt anger. She hated the way his bad temper seemed to intensify on these chilly, gray days and how his cold breath whipped through the trees, tearing off the remaining leaves. And to prove his power, *Yata* came one night with a mighty snowstorm that announced his determination to once again renew and reshape the Great Plains.

The snow continued to fall for days, forcing Sunbeam and Cheering Woman to stay inside close to the fire. Sunbeam, becoming restless with this forced inactivity, looked to her grandmother for new ways to occupy her time. Cheering Woman understood, and filled Sunbeam's days with beading, quilting and creating beautiful leather bags.

On one particularly harsh night, Sunbeam snuggled in the big feather bed letting her mind dance with the powers that were promised in her vision quest. Curious as to why her thoughts seemed to be consumed with dreams of *Wakinyan,* she sensed his awesome power and could almost feel his determination to purify the world. She could envision him flying over the waters, dropping his cloud robe into them as he asked the winds to help him battle the contention of the world. Oh, how she admired this *contrar* warrior who rode the spirals of the wind.

In the blink of an eye, she was riding over the eye of a hurricane. From an unknown place a deep voice spoke, saying, "Granddaughter, feel the power of stillness and find your center." Honored by these words, Sunbeam hoped that someday she too would travel to the outer edges of the world, be committed enough to become a student like *Eya*, the West Wind, and learn the *contrar* way."

Sensing the presence of Cheering Woman at the foot of the bed, Sunbeam sat up with a start. "Get out of bed, you dreamer," demanded her grandmother.

Sunbeam rubbed the sleep from her eyes and climbed out from under the warm covers. She dressed quickly as she glanced out the window to see another fresh blanket of snow covering the ground.

"Today is your naming ceremony, and we have much to do."

Sunbeam trudged to the kitchen disgruntled over another cold day. A loud knock was heard at the door and Joe LittleDog came in stomping the snow from his boots.

"I came to speak about the naming ceremony," he announced. Seconds later, Joe

LittleDog was singing Cheering Woman a song he had written for Sunbeam, all the while banging on the side of the table to keep the beat.

"I'm sure the people will like your song, Joe. Someday our children's children will sing these words," said Cheering Woman.

Joe shouted, "Sunbeam, come. I want you to go with me to the river."

Sunbeam headed for the truck happy for a chance to leave the house. When she climbed inside the cab, a black puppy snuggled close to her. She stroked its head, feeling sad over what was about to take place.

Upon arriving at the river, Joe took the puppy from the truck and painted a red circle in the middle of its forehead, then tied a string around its neck. He began to sing an old song that asked for the puppy's life. Sunbeam watched the string grow tighter and tighter around its neck as the puppy began to pull backward. Suddenly Joe gave a slight jerk and the puppy fell limp on the ground. He picked it up and placed it on the seat. As they drove home Joe observed how much the incident had caused pain for Sunbeam.

"Everything must contribute something to life. The dog is our loyal friend and helps us carry our burdens. We never forget the suffering and hunger that our ancestors endured when they were forced to eat their dogs to survive. We take the life of a puppy to remind ourselves to always remain humble as we remember our people. Without the dog, we would have starved and there would be no Sioux. So you see, we aren't called 'Arrogant Dog Eating Sioux' for nothing."

Sunbeam was still brooding when they got home, she joined the women in the kitchen and watched them prepare the ceremonial dishes. But when she saw Joe LittleDog cutting up the puppy, she went to the bedroom. When he was finished, Joe insisted that she help set up the altar. Sunbeam felt bad over the death of the puppy, but felt better around dusk when friends and relatives began to arrive. She sat near Joe's feet as he opened the ceremony with prayer. He then spoke of the old ways and added Sunbeam's vision to their oral history.

"I've written this honoring song to celebrate the person this young girl will become. It has many verses that tell the story of Sunbeam's future life and the responsibilities to her new spiritual name." He began to beat a rhythm on his small drum and sang the haunting melody. He ended the song with a prayer, saying, "Let this young girl become strong in life so that she will remember these words and sing them to her unborn children."

Joe lit his pipe and prayed again: "Her voice shall be as the wind. It will travel far and hold a powerful magic. The sound will touch all those who listen. Her voice will speak as a soothing summer breeze, but it will also foster the potential of becoming a terrible tornado. She will be loyal to the people and will nurture the masses. As surely as the wind blows across these western plains, she will touch the world. But until she can walk with honor and learn the power of her name, she will not be allowed to use it." Handing Sunbeam the head of the puppy, he added, "You will now eat the meat of the dog."

Sunbeam's stomach churned as she stared at the puppy's severed head, its swollen tongue hanging from the corner of its mouth and its eyes protruding from the sockets, but she remained expressionless. Looking up, she saw Cheering Woman's face held an authoritative look that demanded obedience.

Determined to obey, Sunbeam conformed to tradition. She brought the dog's head to her mouth, and ate ravenously, then smacked her lips to demonstrate her enjoyment while sucking the marrow from the bones. She looked around the room, and deliberately licked her fingers with feigned pleasure.

Then she calmly wrestled a queasy stomach while smugly watching the looks of disgust on the faces of many people present, who politely wrapped their pieces of dog meat in napkins to 'take home for later.'

"The head of dog will help you think and remember to honor the people. The humility of the dog will make you strong and help you remember the suffering of your forefathers," said Joe LittleDog.

After Cheering Woman closed the door behind the last guest, she expressed pride in her granddaughter.

"Grandmother, I still feel terrible about the puppy's death," Sunbeam confessed.

"Granddaughter, when you thank the puppy for its life, pray to your forefathers. They will help you understand. This ceremony showed you the importance of respecting all things. Animals are part of all creation, and they too know the importance of life and death. We always remember the four legs since they are teachers of Medicine. Trust the old ways, and don't question them.

"Remember how our great nation was once almost destroyed by the white man? Thousands died from starvation, and we were forced to eat our dogs to survive. Without the dog, the Indian would not be! Think of your ancestors! They are the hope for our young. Someday they will bring the people back together as a proud nation. Humph! As long as there is one drop of Sioux blood, we will never forget what it is to be Indian.

"Personally, I think you should be grateful the puppy was not a collie. I hear their meat is full of hair and very stringy," chuckled Cheering Woman.

"Grandmother, please! Don't joke!"

"I too once feared the responsibilities of my name, but I learned to trust in the powers that it gave to me," admitted Cheering Woman.

"What will happen if I can't fulfill the power of my name?"

"Then the name will destroy you. But have faith, Sunbeam, Creator does not give his children a task they cannot fulfill. Now, come! This old woman needs her rest."

At dawn Sunbeam awakened with a start to discover her grandmother was not in bed. She found her in the living room rocking chair holding her chest, Sunbeam helped her to bed and ran to get Shung'. By late morning, many medicine people had arrived to perform ceremonies on Cheering Woman's behalf. Shung' sent for the local doctor, who confirmed that Cheering Woman was having heart trouble again and was in need of much rest.

Auntie Rose called saying that she and Sam were coming for a visit. Their stay was hard on Sunbeam, who was extremely hurt when she learned that if her grandmother died they would not return for the funeral. She resented their coldness and swore to herself that if anything happened, she would take care of the burial.

Sunbeam began to spend most of her time with her grandmother, fluffing her pillows and lighting her happy pipe. Shung' kept a respectful distance and did the cleaning and cooking along with the many other people who came to help.

Taking her grandmother breakfast one morning, Sunbeam nervously said, "Grandmother, I had a dream last night."

Cheering Woman patted the corner of the bed, signaling her to sit, then smiled at her asking, "And what might that dream be, Little One?"

Sunbeam, feeling proud of her training, described the dream in detail:

"A boy came to visit me last night. He said we would meet someday, then handed me a picture he had painted. I didn't recognize the woman, but he said it was me when I was grown up."

"Sounds like that young boy is very serious," answered Cheering Woman, teasingly. "But, that's a good sign. Maybe I won't have to worry about you becoming an old maid," she chuckled as Sunbeam hid behind her hands with embarrassment. Then in a more serious tone, Cheering Woman added:

"I think I know of this young boy. He came to me in a dream from another time, long before you were born. You see, you have known this soul in many lifetimes. Both of you will have been trained in the traditional ways, and he will be born when you reach the age of eleven. When you are older you will meet each other in a large, noisy city. That's what came in my dream. Be careful, Granddaughter, your lives will be filled with heartache if you don't heed the old ways." Then seeing the apprehensive look on her granddaughter's face, Cheering Woman laughed, saying, "I do hope he is wise enough to allow your mustang spirit its freedom."

Sunbeam smiled at Cheering Woman's humor and replied, "I just won't go to a big city. Then I won't have to worry about it."

"Ah, Granddaughter. What a shame that such a pretty little face will someday be streaked with so many tears of sadness," Cheering Woman said, stroking her granddaughter's hair. "But through those tears, you will learn. And someday you will understand those tears served you well. You will also realize that this man brings not just heartache, but this clever coyote will teach you the best of your lessons.

"You have always loved this soul, and you will find him very pleasing to the eye. His charm will become your weakness and he will always win your attentions through flattery. His ways are good. His talents could bring much beauty to our world. You will recognize him by a rose tattoo placed between the thumb and forefinger of his left hand," she added, weaving more mystery for Sunbeam. Then Cheering Woman gently touched Sunbeam's face with both hands.

"Granddaughter, it's time I tell you other things. I'm losing the light from my eyes, and I have heard my death song. I'm ready to pass to the Other Side, and we need to speak about your life after my departure. I have prepared a good life for you after I'm gone."

Sunbeam began to weep openly at the thought of losing her beloved grandmother.

"Shush, Granddaughter," continued Cheering Woman, "I have waited for you to learn the old ways, and now it's time to accept my death. Come, let's go to Shadow World and look at your future."

Cheering Woman's gentle words guided Sunbeam's mind to colorful worlds of pure energy. As they lifted out of their bodies and into the spirit world, grandmother and granddaughter traveled across the universe at the speed of thought. Rushing through the void of darkness and into radiant light, they flew side by side into another time and place.

"Let's search the pages of time for your future," Cheering Woman instructed as they ventured far beyond the sun.

"Oh, Grandmother, I've never seen such beauty," said Sunbeam ecstatically.

"The wonders of the universe are limitless. But often the human mind has difficulty accepting that these sacred beauties exist."

Then suddenly they were back on Cheering Woman's bed. Sitting up, Sunbeam pleaded, "Grandmother, you can't leave me! I won't let you go!" Sobbing, she threw her body across Cheering Woman's thinning frame and held her tightly.

"My body may leave this earth, but my soul will live forever. You know I will always be with you. And when the time comes for you to travel to the Other Side, I'll be there to welcome you." Cheering Woman rocked Sunbeam in her arms, "After all, haven't I proven that we are just a thought from each other? You know how to pierce the invisible veil and come to me, just as I can come to you. Your life will be good. Sam, your Auntie Rose and Madame Bianchoff know of my plans. Give up this sorrow, and let's speak of all the happy times we have shared."

"Oh, Grandchild, you have been such a blessing. I have many fond memories of our time together. Do you remember the chicken in the outhouse hole?" laughed Cheering Woman.

"Grandmother, I swear I didn't put that stupid chicken down the hole!" Sunbeam, touched her heart and then the floor to prove she was swearing the truth on Mother Earth.

"Oh, yes you did, Granddaughter! You're going to have to make peace with chickens someday. Ah, but that old rooster sure taught you about courage!" She chuckled as they exchanged their respective views on the subject. "And, do you remember the only time I ever spanked you?" asked Cheering Woman. Sunbeam smiled reluctantly as they both broke into laughter.

"It was in late fall when all the apples had been picked from the orchard. You found a perfect red apple that had not been picked, hanging from the top of the tree. It was the most beautiful apple that you had ever seen. I remember how it called to you from the top of the old apple tree and how you could not resist its call. Many times I had warned you about the danger of climbing trees in the late fall, but your desire for that apple overshadowed your common sense, and you stole that tree's most prized possession. Seeing you out on the edge of that dry branch made me shiver. I yelled and you let go. My heart almost stopped beating when you tumbled to the ground. I still remember the look on your face as you lay at my feet."

Reliving the moment, Cheering Woman wiped tears of laughter from her eyes, and said, "Mercy, we were both frightened out of our wits. But when I saw you were all right, I was so angry. I couldn't believe my granddaughter would disobey me.

"You were so scared that you took off faster than a startled deer, ran to the house and dived under the bed. When you refused to come out, I became as determined as an old badger to punish you. I took my old broom and poked at you, but you just scrambled to the opposite side. Aware that it was only a matter of time before your kidneys would drive you from under that bed, I waited," she chuckled.

"When I grabbed your arm, you screamed like a demon had hold of you. But, as I've told you many times, you act silly because you have just enough white blood to confuse yourself, but not enough to harm anyone." Cheering Woman laughed.

"Oh, Grandmother, stop teasing. You like white people."

"Yes, I like all people, but I don't like the white system. Someday you will deal with that white world. Be warned, don't ever let it confuse you or I will rise from my grave and haunt you," she said, grinning. "Soon we will both be leaving the reservation. But before you go, visit the old apple tree. It will bring you many happy memories and connect you to the land. In time you will understand, my child.

"Granddaughter, you once asked me about the mark on my wrist. Today I'll teach you its meaning. Long ago when I too was ten, your great-grandmother marked me. It is to help guide you safely to the Ghost Road. There you will meet a very old and wise woman who sits in the middle of the road. She will look for a mark, and if you do not have one, she will push you from the clouds and you will wander through eternity, moaning and whistling until you find your way to the Lodge of the Pines. I'm going to give you this mark today so you can find me. It's my last gift to you."

Cheering Woman asked Shung' to bring her marking kit. Returning, Shung' smiled as she sat down to watch Cheering Woman's expert hands take Sunbeam's wrist and chart the position of the four sacred arrows. Then she drew a straight line with two steps going off to each side and said, "These arrows will protect and guide you on your final journey." Next she tattooed four dots underneath the line, adding, "These two lines and four dots are the four directions and they will tell the old woman that your people have passed this way before." As she finished, Cheering Woman turned to Sunbeam, saying, "You must promise me that you will never remove this map from your wrist."

"I promise. It's very beautiful."

"Never mind beautiful!" scolded Cheering Woman. "See how the colors on my mark have faded over the years? That's telling me it's time to go home. But I'm not leaving you unprepared. I will always be with you. Go to the apple tree and wait for me." Then she placed her hand over Sunbeam's heart, and as a happy tear ran down her cheek she said, "The beat of my heart lives within you. I will always feel everything you touch. Promise me that you will not grieve for me. Let my passage be easy as I return to *Wakan Tanka* from a very hard journey."

Crying, Sunbeam embraced her grandmother then went to the barren apple orchard feeling cold and all alone. Within three hours Cheering Woman had her last chest pain, then departed peacefully to return to the spirit world. When Sunbeam heard the final trillo from the women, she knew the spirit of her grandmother had left her body.

Soon afterward, medicine people came to pray and to prepare Cheering Woman's body to return to Mother Earth.

Four days passed as Cheering Woman's ceremonial departure was completed. Aware of Sunbeam's grief, Shung' gave her a cardboard box as Cheering Woman had instructed. After breaking the seal, Sunbeam cried when she saw her grandmother's golden eagle fan, her pipe and a doeskin wedding dress with a letter that read:

Dear Granddaughter.

When you read this, I will no longer be with you. The dress is to be worn at your wedding. Wear it with pride and never forget you are Sioux. This eagle wing holds much power. Use it well. The pipe is old and also very powerful. I've carried it since I was a little girl. It's made simple and I'd like you to leave it this way. It was carried by my great-grandmother, my grandmother and then me. Now it is yours, to continue the work for the people. Someday, Granddaughter, you will be Medicine just as your relatives were before you. I want you to go to the apple tree and smoke the pipe, so our spirits may always ride as one.

Grandmother

Her heart aching, Sunbeam carefully returned everything to the box, except the pipe, which she took with her to the apple orchard. She sat under her favorite apple tree and cried as she filled her grandmother's pipe in the traditional manner. Feeling forsaken, she smoked it, praying, "*Hau, Wakan Tanka.* My beloved grandmother has gone to be with you. She was my only family, and now I have no one!"

Suddenly a soft voice spoke from above. "Wipe your eyes, Child."

Sunbeam looked up into the radiant light and cried out with joy as she saw her beautiful grandmother sitting high in the old apple tree with the apple that Sunbeam had once stolen perched on her head as a crown.

"Oh, Grandmother, are you truly here?"

"Ah yes, *Sku'ya.* I told you I would be with you always. Let this moment live in your heart forever. Be happy that I no longer suffer." Cheering Woman smiled and held out the red apple. "Take it, my child. You've certainly earned it."

Sunbeam reached for the apple, but as her fingers touched Cheering Woman's hand, her grandmother and the apple faded from sight.

She spent the rest of the day and the night sitting under the old apple tree, mourning her grandmother's death. As the sun rose on the following morning, she watched its graceful rays paint the rolling hills with a soft rainbow of colors and knew this was a good sign. Sunbeam's heart filled with peace knowing her grandmother lived.

Sunbeam Leaves the Reservation

Sunbeam was overcome by waves of terror when Otis and Shung' dropped her off at the bus station to go live with Auntie Rose in the rural area of Red Bank, Tennessee. This small, forlorn figure sat alone on an old wooden bench, feeling extremely downhearted over being forced to leave the reservation. When the bus roared to a stop, raising a cloud of dust in its wake, her hands began fidgeting with her Rope of Hope that was tied around her grandmother's old suitcase.

The driver opened the door and called out, "All aboard."

Sunbeam boarded the bus and shyly handed him her ticket. She found a seat and tucked her suitcase under it as the bus pulled away from the station. She sat tightly pressed against the window staring out at the place she had always called home, knowing that she would surely miss the reservation way of life.

Sadness gripped her heart as the bus passed the reservation border and turned onto the open road. How would she ever survive in this strange new place without her grandmother's support and protection? The reservation represented all she knew, loved and respected. Without this connection, how would she exist in her new environment?

She thought about spring and felt a desperate loneliness. She would miss seeing the young, budding trees and the beautiful yellow sunflowers dancing tirelessly across the plains. All the seasons would come and go without her presence.

And what about living near Sam? As these thoughts surfaced, Sunbeam's sorrow turned to fear. Tears welled up in her eyes and she immediately prayed to *Wakan Tanka* to guide her through the frightening transition into the white world.

On the second day of her trip Sunbeam awakened to find the landscape had changed dramatically from rolling hills of swaying grass into fields of barley and hay. She knew nothing about this new world and marveled at its vastness. As the sun went over down and darkness cloaked the sky, Sunbeam curled up in her seat and closed her eyes. The drone of the tires racing over the pavement soothed her enough so that she could finally drift off to sleep.

As the huge bus jolted to a stop, Sunbeam awakened to see the bright sun shining over a small Midwestern town. This was the third day of traveling and the food that Shung' had packed was gone. She got off the bus to wash up and use the restroom. On her return her eyes glanced longingly at the snack bar.

The bus driver knew that look and understood the plight of reservation people. He bought a soda and a couple of sandwiches then quietly handed them to Sunbeam as she boarded the bus. She thanked him and returned to her seat, feeling grateful that someone cared enough to feed her. She ate sparingly as she stared out the window marveling at the tall buildings and the ever-increasing patches of concrete spreading before them.

When the driver informed her she would be getting off at the next stop, she was grateful that the trip was over. As she clutched her bag tightly to her side she was herded through a noisy corridor and onto a busy sidewalk. The heat and humidity blasted her face and the heavy air was hard to breathe. Sunbeam pressed her body tightly against the building trying to understand the noisy traffic and sea of angry white faces who spoke with a funny accent.

When she saw Sam's truck pull up to the curb, she felt immense relief and ran toward him. She threw her bag into the back of the truck and climbed in beside him.

"Hey, Sunny. I know I'm fucking late, but this goddamn morning traffic is heavy."

She watched in amusement as Sam cut in and out of traffic like a madman, cursing every driver on the street. Sunny was fascinated by the tall buildings. She leaned out the window and peered upward for a better view until she grew dizzy at their towering height. She was glad when they left the city behind for the green countryside. As the city gave way to country, she was amazed at the many houses surrounded by well-manicured yards and white picket fences.

"How come they got so many fences?" Sunny asked timidly.

"Hell, who cares. The fences mean keep out. White people think they own the land."

"The reservation never had fences."

As they ventured further into the countryside, well-groomed cornfields dotted the landscape as far as she could see. This graceful panorama revealed a different kind of beauty from any Sunbeam had ever known. Everything seemed to be placed exactly where it belonged. Sunny marveled at the beauty of it all, but wondered how she would ever fit into or find her place in such a controlled environment.

Sam shifted gears then turned onto a dirt road, the tires kicking up a trail of dust behind them as they sped along.

"Your Auntie Rose lives over there" said Sam. He thrust his chin toward a hillside that held a beautiful, white two-story house overlooking the valley. As they drove down the long driveway, Sunbeam was excited and curious about her new home. Covering the landscape was a sea of green grass dotted with huge shade trees. The large front yard was neatly manicured and surrounded by many colorful flowers. This was the most beautiful place she had ever seen and she quickly offered a silent prayer of thanks to Creator for her new home.

Her grandmother had often mentioned that Auntie Rose was a nurse and had been married to a doctor, but since his death she lived alone. She would have liked to have known more about Auntie Rose, but never asked since it was disrespectful to speak about such things.

Sam pulled into the back, alongside a red barn. As they got out of the truck Sunny saw Auntie Rose walking toward them with her arms out, smiling. She was happy to see her friendly face, but when Auntie hugged her, she felt awkward returning the embrace.

"I'm glad you're here. I've been waiting for you," said Auntie Rose, guiding them toward the house.

They entered a beautiful, tidy white kitchen with many colorful potted plants filling the windows. Auntie Rose poured Sam a cup of coffee and offered them freshly made doughnuts as she asked Sunny about Cheering Woman's funeral.

She answered each question carefully, remembering her grandmother did not approve of idle gossip.

"It will be nice to have someone living with me," said Auntie Rose. "Come, let me show you to your room."

Sam squirmed uncomfortably in his chair, then said, "Sunny will be staying with us for a little while, Sister. Hazel needs her help."

Auntie Rose was noncommittal and did not argue with Sam. Sunny was very disappointed and felt deeply hurt but she did not dispute their decision. As they said their goodbyes, Sam promised to let Sunny come and visit, then the two of them drove to Sam's house in silence.

Sunny was shocked when they pulled into a dirt yard and got out of the truck. Her heart sank as she saw a forlorn tarpaper shack surrounded by a graveyard of rusty old trucks, car engines and broken-down farm equipment. The makeshift barn, barely standing, was covered with freshly killed animal skins drying in the sun. Blowflies swarmed over the hides, picking at the unsalted edges as the stench of rotting flesh filled the air.

Several shabbily dressed children ranging in age from six to eight came from the barn accompanied by barking dogs that ran out from under the house. Sam set her suitcase on the ground and without a word got back into the truck and headed down the road disappearing into a cloud of raw brown dust.

Sunny stood there, mute and motionless, wondering what to do next. She picked up her suitcase and headed toward the house followed by four boys and growling dogs.

Hazel stood in the doorway with a fretting baby on her hip. She looked old and tired and Sunny was amazed to see that she was pregnant again. Hazel struggled to get the half-hinged screen door open and with a rather toothless smile said, "This one cries a lot. Think he's teething," as she wiped the infant's runny nose on her dress.

Sunny remained silent as she stepped inside.

"Don't have much to offer, but we share what we got. Come, I'll show you where to put your things."

Hazel shuffled toward the back room with the children following close behind. The room was small and dingy. The walls were lined with folded cots, while the rest of the floor space was crammed with cardboard boxes that held the children's faded clothing. Hazel pointed toward a stack of folded quilts lying in the far corner of the room and said, "You can sleep there."

Sunny set her things down and followed Hazel back to the kitchen. She sat down in a rickety chair and Hazel handed her the baby while she heated up a pot of coffee. The baby's gums were swollen and feverish. Sunny recalled her grandmother's remedy for teething babies and placing the baby on the floor, she went to the bedroom. She opened her suitcase and removed a copper penny strung on a leather thong. She came back and placed it around the baby's neck, saying, "There, he should feel better soon."

Hazel poured the coffee and sat down at the table with Sunny, asking about old friends and relatives on the reservation.

By midday everyone had been fed, and the children wanted to take Sunny around to get her acquainted with the new surroundings. After a short walk, Sunny knew there was nothing here that would remind her of the reservation. Their small creek and wooded places could never replace the old singing river and the wide-open plains. She thought of Cheering Woman and the freedom of reservation life, and was once again overwhelmed by deep loneliness and knew she was already homesick.

Even though Sunny was only ten years old, from the very beginning it was made clear that she was to help Hazel with the chores to pay for her room and board. From morning till night she cooked, cleaned, washed, ironed and took care of the vegetable garden.

At the end of each day, when all the chores were completed, the children would gather around Sunny waiting to go for a walk in the woods. They loved listening to the old Indian stories and all the secrets about nature, just as Sunny had done when her grandmother taught her on their many long walks. This created a certain warmth among them.

Weeks passed and Sunny tried to get to know her father, but he refused to acknowledge her presence. Sam ruled the family with an iron hand, expecting everyone to understand and respond immediately without hesitation or question to his grunts and glares. Sunny soon learned to read the looks and gestures of his voiceless orders. Fear was his enforcer and you either followed Sam's rules or suffered the consequences. No one dared speak in his presence except in answer to his commands. The mere idea of refusing to obey his orders was unthinkable.

Sam believed emotion was a sign of weakness, and never demonstrated any affection or allowed anyone else to show any kindness in his presence. Sunny often wondered how long she would be able to survive in the midst of this loveless void.

The rules were well established for everyone in the household except Sam. All meals were eaten in silence and no one was allowed to leave the table until Sam had completed his meal. Everyone was assigned duties in the clean up of the kitchen, except Sam. After dinner he kept everyone busy doing chores outside, sometimes till long after dark.

Late one evening Sam arrived home reeking of liquor. This was a very bad sign, and the children either scurried to their bedroom or quickly disappeared. Sunny was putting the baby to bed when he growled from behind his newspaper, "Sunny, go to the store and get me a bottle."

She reacted like a startled deer at her father's harsh command. She grabbed a jacket and hesitated at the door.

"It's getting dark. Can one of the kids go with me?"

"Fuck no! I don't give a goddamn if it is dark. I told you what to do, now go do it! And don't you ever give me any fucking back talk again. You understand me, girl?"

Sunny hurried out the door, fearful of what would happen if she waited a moment longer. Everyone was afraid for her as she ran past the window in silence. It was a cold, moonless night and she decided to take a shortcut across the back field and through the woods. As she clutched her jacket close to ward off the cold, tears of hurt and anger rolled down her face. Her heart was filled with pain at Sam's cruelty.

As she approached the clearing she could see the sawmill looming like a tortured, deformed shadow in the darkness. When she drew closer she saw several dark figures lurking around one of the logging trucks near the front entrance.

"Hey, little girl, where you going?" squawked a boisterous voice.

Sunny quickened her steps, fearing she might be their intended prey. Looking at the ground, she pulled her jacket even tighter, and started to run.

"Hey, come here, little girl. Daddy's got a nice long hot dog for you."

The meaning of his crude remark was all too clear. Heart pounding, she picked up her pace.

Other voices shouted from the direction she was headed.

"Hey, little girl, come over here. We've got something for you," they guffawed, shining the truck's bright lights into her face.

"Holy shit! That's the crazy Indian's kid! We better get the fuck outta here." The men scrambled into the truck and with tires screeching, they drove off.

Sunny was filled with terror. She ran deep into the woods and propelled back across the open pasture. She was breathless when she entered the house. Sam looked at his watch then noticed she did not have his bottle.

"Where's my goddamn bottle?"

"I didn't get to the store," Sunny whispered, eyes on the floor. Sam rose from his chair in a blinding rage as he towered over her. "There was a pack of wild dogs near the sawmill and I was too afraid so I came back!" she mumbled.

Sam stared at her in disbelief for disobeying him. "Goddamnit, girl! That's a fucking lie. I was by there earlier and there was no fucking dogs! I told you to go get me a bottle of liquor! What does a fucking bunch of dogs have to do with what I told you to do?"

Sam grabbed his coat and dragging Sunny by the sleeve he headed for the door, snarling, "C'mon, you little whore! You better be able to prove your words if you want to live."

He pushed her into the cab of the truck and drove recklessly toward the mill, circling it many times as he shined his flashlight into the surrounding woods.

"I don't see any fucking dogs! Where are they Sunny?"

"I don't know," Sunny whimpered.

"Let me tell you. There are no goddamn dogs. Tell me the fucking truth before I kill you! You lying piece of shit! You know how much I hate a liar!"

Sam slammed on the brakes causing Sunny's head to hit the windshield. Filled with wrath, he exploded as he doubled up his fist and struck her hard. Blood trickled from her mouth as silent tears ran down her face. Still not satisfied, he grabbed her by the hair, dragged her from the truck and threw her on the ground.

Sunny recoiled in pain, screaming like a wounded animal.

As the savage beating continued, he drew back his foot and kicked her viciously in the stomach. She screamed and cried and tried to crawl away, but Sam became even more outraged by her apparent cowardice. He yanked Sunny to her feet and holding her close to his face, he slapped her then threatened, "Shut your fucking mouth. Only a fool would try and run from me. If you ever try that again, I'll hunt you down and kill you. Nobody crosses me and lives to talk about it."

Sam stared coldly at her, unmoved at the sight of the blood that gushed from a deep gash across her forehead.

"You're nothing to me and you never will be! You're just another whining female and you're damn lucky I don't put you out of your misery!" he thundered, throwing her back into the truck.

Sunny remembered her grandmother's warning and recognized the Evil One in Sam. As her spirit wilted, her eyes held a blank stare and she willingly submitted, just as if she were one of Sam's hound dogs.

"There were no dogs. I was afraid to tell you about the men in the blue truck that were at the sawmill," she whimpered.

"What men?" exploded Sam. "No man would ever touch a kid that belongs to me! They know I'd kill them!"

Sam double-clutched, slammed the gears into first and spun the truck out of control. He wrestled with the steering wheel for a moment, changed gears and sped down the highway. When they arrived at the liquor store, he left the engine running and swaggered into the store.

Blood poured into Sunny's eyes. She cracked the door before Sam could return and leaned down to grab a handful of dirt to press against her forehead.

Sam threw a ten dollar bill on the counter, saying, "Gimme a quart of Jim Beam and if some assholes in a blue truck come around, tell them I'll be seeing them soon." He grabbed his change and as he strode out he cracked the seal and took a swig while heading back to the truck. Sam sucked on his bottle, letting out a sigh of relief as the warmth of the alcohol temporarily silenced him. He placed the bottle between his legs and drove home.

Sunny glanced at him from the corner of her eye sitting frozen, until Sam pulled into the yard and ordered her into the house.

Hazel gasped in horror. "Oh, my God, Sam! What have you done?"

The kids saw Sunny and quickly slipped back into their bedroom.

"It's none of your business, so shut your fucking mouth, woman! Stop her bleeding or you're gonna get the same thing!"

Looking directly at Sunny, he added, "If you ever lie to me again, I'll kill you. And don't ever act like a coward around me! If you're not brave enough to fight for your beliefs, then you're not strong enough to have a fucking belief. I walk my talk, girl, and don't you ever doubt it!" He turned like a violent tornado and left the house, slamming the door behind him.

Frantically, Hazel got a wet cloth and with shaking hands she cleaned Sunny's face, saying, "My God, how could you lie to him when you knew he was drinking? Now he's gonna get really drunk, then who knows what he'll do to the rest of us."

Hurt by Hazel's words, Sunny pushed her away and went to find her medicine pouch to get some valerian root powder. She pressed it into the open wound, then lay down on her pallet and cried.

Hours passed as Sunny listened to Hazel pacing the floor like a caged animal. Sunny felt sorry for her and got out her prairie dog tooth to pray for mercy on her behalf. The children heard her prayers and moved close, hoping that her prized tooth could stop the beatings.

A dark shadow loomed over the house as everyone waited with dread for Sam to return. An empty darkness filled Sunny's tormented soul with helplessness as she thought of what she had created for the family. This can't be happening. I know there's no love lost between Sam and me, but I think I fear him more than *Gnaski*, the devil himself.

When Sam returned shortly after midnight all the youngsters pretended to be asleep. From their bedroom they heard him alternate between demanding sexual pleasures and ruthlessly beating Hazel. Throughout the long night Hazel screamed and whimpered, begging Sam to spare the life of their unborn child.

Sunny covered her ears to block out the screams and pitiful pleas, but the horrific sounds still filtered through.

Shortly after daybreak she heard Sam get into his truck and drive away. Sunny jumped up and rushed to the kitchen. She found Hazel's unconscious naked body sprawled on the floor lying in a pool of blood, beaten beyond recognition, a lifeless infant between her legs.

Sunny grabbed a quilt to cover Hazel and called out to the children to stay in their room. Hazel stirred, then moaned slightly when Sunny cut the baby free. She cleaned the small body, then wrapped it in a blanket and handed it to Hazel who took it and held it tenderly to her bosom, wailing in anguish.

Sunny went to her room and when she returned she placed her bear necklace around Hazel's neck, saying, "Grandmother gave me this necklace, and I want to give it to you. One of the old people carved it from chokecherry wood. It'll stop your bleeding. Hold it close to your heart and it'll make you as strong as an old bear, then you can protect yourself from Sam."

She took the baby from Hazel's arms, then carried it into the woods where she dug a small grave and solemnly gave it back to Mother Earth. She placed a small stone on top, then took her pipe and prayed for the baby's soul, promising she would never forget this day.

When the ceremony was finished, she wandered through the woods searching for the herbs her grandmother had taught her to use when a child was stillborn. When she had gathered everything she needed she returned home, her heart heavy with the burden of responsibility that was more than any ten year old should have to bear.

Sunny gave Hazel a handful of dampened honeysuckle, saying, "Press it up high between your legs." She then boiled the serviceberry bark into a strong tea and gently held Hazel's head, urging her to drink. "Grandmother always told the women that this tea would flush out the body."

Sam had been gone for several weeks, but everyone behaved just as though he were there. They merely existed, nothing more. The children were quiet and subdued, always listening for the sound of Sam's truck. Hazel had slowly recovered, but was sad and melancholy, spending most of her day in the old rocking chair staring out the window. Sunny found herself furtively looking over her shoulder to make sure that Sam was not there before she said or did anything. Everyone was still being ruled by fear, and she knew if they continued living this way much longer they would become the walking dead.

Running the household became Sunny's responsibility. She cooked, cleaned and cared for the children. One by one they would join her on long walks to gather medicines from the woods. Sunny taught them to pray as her grandmother had taught her, and each day they prayed for *Wakan Tanka* to take care of their needs. Sunny found a group of willows growing down by the river and built an *Inipi*. After their first sweat her brothers sensed the true meaning of family kinship.

This day as she walked along the river, Sunny found a secluded spot that reminded her of the place where she and her grandmother had gone for ceremonial prayer. She could feel her grandmother's presence and decided to build a lean-to and a Medicine Wheel. She gathered many stones and built her secret haven then taught the children its meaning, making them promise that Sam must never know of its existence. The children loved knowing about their heritage and were eager to learn how to use the Medicine Wheel.

"It's not good to talk about others or dwell on bad things. Our grandmother always said that outside forces can take over people. We must ask her to come between us and Sam before he comes home. If we do this in a good way, *Wakan Tanka* will heal Sam. Creator will give him the strength to fight his bad spirit. When Sam returns we must forgive him."

The children listened and wanted to believe her, but their fear of Sam created much doubt in their minds.

The following morning when all the chores were finished, Sunny said, "It's time we use the old ways like our grandmother did to protect our home." Everyone watched her place strings of red tobacco ties at each corner of the house. She placed kernels of sacred corn over the doors then took a red strip of cloth and tied it to the doorknob. She burned sage and cedar to smudge the house. "These things we have done will keep the family from harm and will drive away all evil spirits." When she had finished everyone was less fearful and smiled as they talked among themselves. "Each of you must remember to pray every day to help keep our home safe and happy," reminded Sunny.

As the new season arrived the family's food supply had dwindled to almost nothing. The garden was picked clean except for a few frostbitten potatoes. Sunny spoke to Hazel about this, but she just shrugged her shoulders. She thought of walking to Auntie Rose's but was afraid that Sam might be there. Frustrated and hungry, Sunny went to her private place to pray. After she entered the Medicine Wheel, she lit her pipe and prayed. "Grandmother, please help us. There is little food and the children go to bed hungry each night. Please ask the Great Spirit to send us help."

Sunny heard a branch crack and the sound of footsteps approaching. Sam walked toward her, his face frozen into a mask of insane rage. Without a word he entered the Medicine Wheel then kicked away the stone circle. Sunny saw the Evil One staring at her through Sam's eyes. He grabbed at her pipe.

"You little bastard!"

Something snapped in Sunny. She stood up, filled with a fury that she had never known. "Beating me is one thing, but you will not destroy these sacred things." No longer caring if she lived or died, Sunny grabbed her Rope of Hope and swung it full circle over her head. With a loud snap the rope wrapped around Sam's wrist as he reached for the pipe. Sunny jerked the handle and managed to pull him to the ground.

Sam stared at her in utter disbelief, then stood up, unwrapping the rope from his arm. "Goddamn you! Who in the hell do you think you are? You're fucking dead!"

Sunny picked up her pipe and stared coldly into his eyes, her voice as hard as steel.

"As of today, Sam, if you ever touch these things again, I will take an eye or an ear from you!"

Unflinching, Sunny stood her ground until she saw a flicker of fear in Sam's eyes. He glared back at her, his eyes filled with hatred. His daughter's fearless behavior was bewildering and he could feel his mother's presence around her. Sam took two strides, toward her then turned and growled back over his left shoulder, "You do whatcha gotta do! But you better well have the balls to stand by those fucking words."

From that day forward, Sunny's relationship with Sam unfolded differently. She began to study him with emotional detachment. It took patience and self-discipline, but at last she found the key to his power had been that others feared him. Sunny knew if she appeared fearless, he had no power. Armed with this knowledge, she became the predator and Sam was her prey. Weeks went by, both knowing the game without a word passing between them.

One sunny day Auntie Rose stopped by bringing food and new clothes for the children's return to school. "Sunny, I've made arrangements for you to attend school with the others. I want all of you bathed and dressed by eight o'clock in the morning. I'll be here to drive you to school."

Everyone was thrilled with their new clothes and the prospect of returning to school. Hazel and Sunny went to the kitchen and cooked a large meal. Everyone sat in silence as they ate, enjoying how good it felt to once again have a full stomach. The children were so content they didn't even protest the community bath in the galvanized tub.

That night anxiety engulfed Sunny as she lay in bed thinking about attending a public school for the first time. She remembered how she had enjoyed her grandmother's friend teaching her to read and write in English. But the mere thought of having to spend her days shut up in one room was beyond her comprehension.

The following morning as everyone ate breakfast the boys started talking about school. They told Sunny that no matter how smart she was, she would be ignored by the teachers. They reminded her to sit in the back of the room with the other Indians. Sunny thought their statements were rather unusual but said nothing.

Arriving at school, Sunny climbed into the front seat feeling awkward in her oversized, hand-me-down dress, wishing she was in her jeans and shirt.

When they arrived at school the boys went to their assigned rooms while Sunny sat nervously in the principal's office waiting for Auntie Rose to fill out the necessary papers.

"Just another one of those good-for-nothing ignorant savage Standinghawk kids that we're forced to teach," the principal muttered just loudly enough for Sunny and Auntie Rose to hear. With cold, condescending eyes, he asked Auntie Rose, "Can she read or write?"

A wave of anger engulfed Sunny. How dare this white man treat her as if she was not there! Looking him directly in the eye, she answered, "Yes, I can read and write!"

"Although she's never been to school, she reads and writes quite well. I was told that you would give her a test to see what grade she should attend," smiled Auntie Rose.

The principal looked contemptuously in Sunny's direction and handed her a test booklet directing her to a seat in the hallway.

Sunny was nervous. What if she couldn't pass his stupid test? She should be in the fourth grade but if she did badly, she knew she would be placed in a lower grade. Remembering her grandmother's words, she called upon the spirits to give her the correct answers.

The principal seemed surprised when she handed the test booklet back to him within a few minutes. "I guess you couldn't read well enough to finish it, huh."

Sunny and Auntie Rose waited in the hall until the test was corrected. The principal walked out of the office and addressed Auntie Rose stiffly. "She'll be in the fifth grade."

Turning to Sunny, he continued, "Down the hall. Third door."

Sunny opened the door and stepped inside her new classroom. The students stared and snickered. The teacher pointed to an empty seat in the back of the room, then went on with the lesson. Sunny, determined to remain stoic as was required of a good Sioux, thrust her chin forward and walked proudly to her seat.

School was Sunny's first experience at being an Indian in a white world. The white students made it clear that to them she was just another dirty Indian. She quickly found she had nothing in common with her white classmates, and although there were a few other Indians in the school, they were not Sioux. She watched them from a distance as they watched her. After a few weeks of learning their tribal differences, they slowly became friends.

By the end of the first month, Sunny had determined that school was totally useless. The history books were written by whites and gave little information about the Indians who were erroneously portrayed as ignorant and cruel savages. Her history book said that America was discovered by a man named Christopher Columbus, but Sunny knew that the Indians lived here long before that. How could he discover America when it was never lost?

When she raised her hand to ask the teacher about this, she was severely reprimanded and was assigned to copy the entire chapter for her insolence. Sunny determined that the punishment was wrong and refused to accept any of the white man's teachings. She hated the teacher for limiting her mind, but mostly she hated the confinement of the classroom. Frequently her mind drifted out the window and back to the carefree days of reservation life.

Sunny turned to the library for a friend. She learned to love books, and finding none in her home, she spent as much time as possible reading. When she was in the library, it seemed as though Sam, the kids and Hazel would fade into the background and she could dream about all the places she would one day visit. Thomas Edison's discovery of the light bulb and his many early failures were very confusing. Why hadn't he just studied the power of the sun?

This day as she walked home from the library, she was in deep thought after reading about the Civil War. The idea of slavery sanctioned by the white man troubled her. As she entered the yard and saw Sam's truck parked by the barn, Sunny grew afraid. It had been four months since the family had seen him. She entered the house hesitantly.

"Sunny, what's all this shit? The place stinks of cedar and sage and what the fuck is all this crap hanging from the corners of the house and on the door? I told you not to teach that Indian shit around here." Sam threw the torn tobacco ties at her.

Sunny waited until he had finished, then picked them up and walked away without a word in total defiance. In this new world of hers, nothing seemed real. She had never seen anyone defile sacred objects like Sam did. Why did he continue to disrespect the oldest of universal laws? Although Sam was a Sioux, he had caught the white man's disease.

She walked along the river and as she dropped the tobacco ties into the water, her eyes stung with tears. It seemed her grandmother and the reservation were lost forever, and she no longer wanted to live.

"Where are you going, Father River? Will you take me back to the reservation so I may be among the things I know and love?" she implored as she lay down on the river bank, reflecting on her situation. She did not know which was worse, the school and its prejudices or Sam and his uncontrollable wrath.

As she lamented for some answers, many images began to melt from one vision into another. Her mind stretched until it was completely engulfed beyond the present and she begged for her earthly journey to end. As dawn broke over the horizon,

Sunny smoked her pipe and put it back in her secret place, then ran across the field to flag down the school bus.

When she got off the bus, she knew she could not face another day confined to a classroom and headed for the library. Finding comfort among the books, she was surprised when she heard the librarian mention Sam's name to another woman.

Betty, the librarian, said, "You know I've been seeing Sam for some time, and I want you to stay away from him."

Francis, an attorney's wife, looked at her coldly. "Listen, old maid, everyone knows about you and Sam. I suggest you leave him alone and never threaten me again. After all, he and I are just friends. No one controls Sam. We both know he's nothing but walking trouble and a threat to society. Sam's not called a drunken, gambling, womanizing Indian for nothing. But we both know he's good in bed." Francis laughed, then turned and walked out of the library.

Sunny's face reddened at hearing these two women discussing her father's sexual prowess which all the women in town seemed to enjoy. Their remarks were cruel and shameful. Humiliated, she had to find a way to escape from the library without being seen. For the first time, Sunny realized Sam's reputation went far beyond the four walls of their home. She was beginning to understand why the white folks detested Sam the Dog Man and his dirty Indian kids. She sneaked down a deserted aisle and left by the side door.

Home! School! Indian! And now the library! There was no safe place! Her eyes blinded by tears, she put one leaden foot in front of the other as she headed home. She was Indian, and in the white man's way of thinking Indians were stupid, dirty and unlovable. Realizing this, would she be forced to endure prejudice and rejection for the rest of her life? Was there no place for her in the white world?

Just as Sunny arrived home, she noticed Sam was leaving with another *Wasichu*, white woman. She rushed past his truck and into the house to find Hazel had been beaten again. Not only had Sam left with another woman, he had left the cupboards bare.

Winter was upon them and necessity demanded survival. Sunny felt helpless and overburdened with a responsibility greater than her years. She was left with no other choice but to go to Auntie Rose for help.

Auntie Rose refused to help out, saying, "I wish I could, Sunny, but I cannot interfere with my brother's family. If Hazel would leave him, it would be different, but as long as she's with him I will not get involved."

"To hell with Sam! We need food now, Auntie Rose!"

"I know, but there's nothing I can do. Someday you will understand."

"No, I won't! Grandmother would never have let us go hungry."

With those words Auntie Rose gave in and filled her arms with bags of flour, coffee, sugar, beans and potatoes with a stern warning that she would never do this again.

Sunny stormed out of Auntie Rose's house in anger, saying, "Well, maybe you won't help the family again, but I will!"

She was tired of begging for food and listening to the children cry themselves to sleep every night because of their empty stomachs. She knew this was wrong and something must be done.

After chopping the firewood and doing the rest of the chores, Sunny sat at the table and said, "Hazel, we're not going hungry! I've had enough of Sam!"

Taking a burlap bag, she stepped out of the house and into a moonless night, not as an eleven-year-old girl, but as Wolf, ready to hunt and feed her family.

Cutting across a neighboring farmer's field, she sneaked into his henhouse closing the door behind her. She waited for her eyes to adjust to the darkness, then moved toward the roosting chickens. One by one she grabbed each chicken, pressing it down against the perch until its body went limp. Satisfied, she stuffed the chickens into her bag and slung it over her shoulder, then stepped back into the darkness of night.

When she arrived home, Hazel and the children were waiting. Although they knew how Sunny had gotten the chickens, no one said a word as they helped dress them. Hazel fired up the kitchen stove, then taking an iron pot, she filled it with water and placed three plump chickens in to boil. For the first time since Sam left everyone went to bed with a full belly.

Sunny was proud of her cleverness and every night thereafter she continued her raids. Each night was a challenging new adventure, and each time she came home with her bag filled, she felt invigorated. Her pride soon turned to arrogance as she continued to raid neighboring farms, soon branching out to stealing corn, grain and clothing.

In time Sunny realized her situation was becoming dangerous. She could not afford to get caught and so she decided to change the scope of her operations to allay suspicions. She fashioned herself a frogging spear and traveled to the nearby lakes. Her grandmother had taught her that a bullfrog gets excited when it sees a red cloth and will jump for it. Sunny spent two nights waving a red flag at every frog she saw, but came home empty-handed.

She turned to her Rope of Hope and was soon successful in hunting rabbits and squirrels. She gathered hickory nuts, black walnuts and dug some wild onions to give to Hazel to make a delicious stew. Sunny wasted nothing. After she had tanned the hides, she sold them to the local feed store.

Time went by and still Sam had not returned. Consumed by her hatred for Sam and guilt over stealing, Sunny took her pipe and headed for her private sanctuary. As she worked her way through the densely covered woods, her eyes beheld the majestic beauty around, but her heart felt nothing. Winding her way through the dense vine-covered trees she looked up, trying to find the sun. She listened to the wind gently caress the plant and animal life around her, but still felt nothing. Her alienation from all things beautiful created a fog within that blended with the low-hanging haze surrounding her, and Sunny realized her spirit was no longer connected to Creator.

She began to repair her Medicine Wheel, placing each stone carefully in its original place. Once she completed the circle, she sat in its center and prayed with her pipe:

"Oh, Creator. I have lost touch with what I know to be true. I know what I do is wrong, *Tunka'shila*. Why doesn't Auntie Rose understand the family needs help? These bad feelings I hold inside hurt me, but what else can I to do? I must feed the family. *Hau, Wakan Tanka*, have mercy on me. I have done wrong. Forgive me for what I've done. I come to ask the spirits to teach me to become a good hunter so I can take care of my family. Please help fulfill my needs, Great Spirit."

After Sunny had smoked her pipe she still felt nothing and began to cry:

"Oh, Grandmother, hear me. I beg you to help the family. I've become a thief and a liar. Help me! I fear I'm being captured like Sam. Oh, please, please don't let this happen to me, Grandmother. I beg you to show me another way. I cannot reach *Wakan Tanka*, the Great Spirit. My heart is filled with hatred. I must have your help, or I will never be strong enough to return to my spiritual pathway."

A loving voice whispered, "It is good to be a seeker of knowledge, no matter the method, Grandchild. Sooner or later you will find the good way. Remember, the softest things in life will always overcome the hardest substances. Be patient, my child! You will find your way. These mortal experiences are merely lessons for your soul to learn. Accept them as the beautiful gift they are, and know Creator is always with you, even when he feels far away."

Sunny was filled with joy as she listened to her grandmother's loving voice. Again she cried out: *"Hau, Tunka'shila!* I know I'm wrong to fight with Sam, but his hateful words are burned into my mind. I'm filled with rage and I fear becoming as cruel and heartless as him. Please help me end this hatred that is eating my soul, *Tunka'shila*. I know I am nothing without you. Please help me become one with my pipe."

When Sunny had finished her prayers, she offered the ashes to the winds and cleaned her pipe, knowing her prayers had been answered. Filled with joy, she sat in the Medicine Wheel offering prayers of thankfulness, then walked home in the gentle moonlight.

Daylight was just breaking when Sam pulled into the yard and walked into the house. After he and Hazel had breakfast, he called to Sunny. "C'mon, you're gonna help me in the pasture this morning." Sam, in a good mood, walked briskly toward the barn with Sunny close behind. He grabbed two bales of hay, telling Sunny to get two buckets of water. As they walked side-by-side heading across the frosty field, Sam broke open the bales and spread them around for the cows. Sunny cracked the ice in the troughs, making several trips to the barn to fill them with fresh water.

"I'm moving Auntie's herd this morning. Looks like bad weather coming our way."

"I know! I saw a ring around the moon last night."

"Goddamnit, girl! How many times do I have to tell you to stop that Indian shit around me? Look, you left the fucking gate open. Get over there and close the goddamn thing!"

Filled with rage, Sunny quietly set the bucket down and started to walk across the field. Just before she arrived at the gate, something spooked the herd and Sam's prize bull began to charge toward the gate.

"Close the gate! Close the fucking goddamn gate!"

Sunny tugged with all of her might, but the gate was stuck fast. Thundering hoofs charged past her, swiping the gate, ripping it from its hinges as it fell to the ground. Sam exploded into insane anger as his bull headed toward the main road. "Girl, why in the fuck didn't you stop that goddamn bull? You dumb sonuvabitch! You're good for nothing!" he raved. He proceeded to uproot a dried cornstalk from the ground and beat Sunny with it until it was in shreds. Grabbing a two-by-four from the broken gate, he continued beating her until she lay bleeding and unconscious. Not giving a fuck whether she lived or died, he threw the board aside, got into the truck and drove off to find his bull.

Hazel heard the commotion and ran outside to see what was happening. She saw Sam's truck roaring down the road, and ran to the pasture where Sunny lay. Terror struck Hazel's heart as she saw the small, lifeless body covered with blood lying beside the broken gate. Thinking she might be dead, Hazel screamed, "Oh my God! He's killed her for sure this time!"

Wailing, she struggled with the body, trying to pull Sunny to the house. Afraid of hurting Sunny any more, she called out for the boys to help her. When they finally got her inside, she cradled Sunny in her arms and instructed her oldest son to go to Auntie Rose's for help. "Tell her to hurry and to bring her medicine kit! Sam has hurt Sunny bad!"

Sunny moaned softly and tried to open her eyes. Hazel's eyes filled with tears as she gave thanks to Creator that Sunny was still alive. She sighed with relief when she heard Auntie Rose's car pull up next to the house. Auntie Rose was a nurse and she would take care of everything.

Auntie Rose stared in horror at Sunny's lacerated, bloody body. "This is not a beating! This is attempted murder! My God, Hazel, look at what he's done!" Taking a wet cloth, she began to wipe the blood from Sunny's body. "Geezus H. Christ, Hazel, she's cut to ribbons! These cuts are too deep for me to treat. We've got to get her to the hospital immediately!"

"Oh, please, no, my sister! We can't take her anywhere! If anyone finds out, Sam will go to jail and there's no telling what he'd do when he got out. Just treat her here the best you can."

Knowing Hazel spoke the truth, Auntie Rose slowly began to dress the wounds on Sunny's face. She then stitched her body, and with Hazel's help, rolled her in cotton batting, tying it around her with a bedsheet. Gently, Auntie Rose placed Sunny's medicine bag back around her neck, saying, "I've done all I can. All we can do now is wait and see. Hazel, make us some coffee."

Auntie Rose lit a cigarette and began to pace back and forth across the room. She glanced at her watch and said through gritted teeth, "He should be horsewhipped! I've tried not to interfere in family matters, but Sam's gone too far this time! He's not getting away with this. I promised Mother that I would take care of Sunny and that's what I'm going to do!"

She took the coffee from Hazel and sat down at the table. "I've called the others. They should be here very soon. I'm taking Sunny with me so she can get the rest and care she needs. You tell Sam she won't be coming back."

"Sam won't like that. He needs the help around here. If you make him mad he'll take it out on us."

Auntie Rose glared at her in disgust. "Hazel, that's enough! I know you're afraid of him, but this time he's gone too far. I swear on my mother's grave that he will get a taste of his own medicine, even if I have to beat his ass myself! You tell him he can expect visitors, and they aren't coming for a social call. It's time for him to know firsthand what it's like to have the shit beat out of him!"

"Someday he'll kill us all. I know he will." Hazel wrung her hands and walked the floor.

"You tell Sam if anything happens to you or the boys, I'll kick him off my property and make sure he'll never get another job around here. Now call the boys and let's get Sunny into the car before he returns."

As they drove down the road Auntie Rose passed Sam, followed closely by another truck. When Auntie Rose saw an older cousin and three other men in the bed of the truck, she signaled them to pull to the side of the road and showed them what Sam had done to Sunny. They looked at her badly beaten body and agreed that Sam needed to be taught the lesson of his life.

"Don't worry about this. Uncle is going to find out what it feels like to be hog-tied and horsewhipped. Seeing Sunny's Rope of Hope tied around her suitcase, Paul smiled and asked to borrow it. Auntie Rose handed it out to him. As both vehicles headed in separate directions, everyone understood that this incident would never be mentioned again. The four men sped off down the road, pulling into Sam's yard just as he was getting out of his truck.

"What brings you over here?" asked Sam suspiciously as the group slowly surrounded him.

"Oh, we just wondered if you'd seen Sunny lately," said Paul.

"Not since she let my goddamn bull get away," answered Sam, wondering why they would be interested in his business.

"Well we have, motherfucker, and she's not a pretty sight." The words came from behind him just as a two-by-four broke over his shoulders.

"What the fuck..." Sam was stopped in mid-sentence as a size ten boot caught him in the solar plexus. He doubled up and fell to the ground. "What's going on here? Have you lost your fucking minds? She disobeyed me, so she got what she had coming to her."

"Well now, you're going to get what's coming to you! In spades, gambler," said another member of the foursome, emphasizing his words with a kick to the groin. A helpless and bewildered Sam was hauled off to the barn. They tied his wrists with a long rope and hoisted him off his feet, exposing him to whatever punishment they might think of. They whipped him unmercifully as they shouted obscenities about his cowardice, his heritage and his life coming to an abrupt halt. When red was the only color visible on his body, they tired of the game and left the barn laughing among themselves, leaving Sam hanging there to think about his actions.

When Auntie Rose arrived home, she put Sunny in bed then checked her temperature. She was alarmed to find Sunny was ravaged with fever indicating possible infection. Auntie Rose went immediately to the phone and called a trusted doctor friend. When he arrived and saw the results of the barbaric beating, he was speechless, astonished that she had survived. Gently continuing with his examination, he found internal injuries and informed Auntie Rose that Sunny's recovery was going to be slow, but his greater concern was over the emotional scars that might never heal.

"I suggest you keep Sam away from her, or I'll file a report on him," he threatened, and left with the promise that he would stop by from time to time to see how she was doing.

For weeks Auntie Rose stayed by Sunny's side as she drifted in and out of consciousness. Most of the time Sunny spoke as though she was back on the reservation with her grandmother. Auntie Rose frequently heard her speaking to spirits, but when she looked in on her, no one was there.

Late one night Auntie Rose heard her singing an old medicine song. Getting up to see who her niece was speaking with, she paused at the doorway to listen.

"Grandmother, I need to sit upon your blanket again. I no longer want to be here on this earth. I know you are here with me, but I need you to hold me. Please touch me and let me know you are here."

Auntie Rose opened the door a small crack and peeked in to see Sunny lying on the bed, smiling peacefully. Her face was filled with pleasure and she was surrounded by a soft, glowing, bluish light that seemed to be cradling her in its arms. When she heard her dead mother's voice, chills ran through her body.

"My sweet Grandchild, your short life has already been a hard journey. Do not attach to this suffering, and stop denying your power. Go inside and change your thinking. We both know that you can dream beyond Sam. You have much to accomplish and it is time to claim your power. Time is shifting, and now you must widen your circle of growth. Very soon you will return to the reservation and renew yourself with strong medicines that will be with you forever. Your life's journey is not complete. When it is time to join me, I will come to take you to the Other Side just as I have always promised."

As the glow around Sunny's body faded, Auntie Rose smiled through tears of joy and walked to the foot of Sunny's bed. These were not the ramblings of a child's feverish delirium, she knew her mother had visited Sunny from the Other Side. From that moment Auntie Rose became Sunny's protector and benefactor.

Two weeks passed and Sunny was eating her lunch while Auntie Rose was sitting alongside the bed, telling her of the many beautiful plans that Cheering Woman had made for her future. When Sunny fully understood, Auntie Rose promised that she would help in every way possible to see that these dreams were fulfilled.

Suddenly they heard footsteps in the hallway, and before Auntie Rose could get up to see who it was, Sam walked arrogantly into the room. Without a word, he tossed

Sunny's Rope of Hope, covered with dried blood, on the bed, saying, "You see this? This is my fucking blood!"

Terrorized, Sunny clutched her bedcovers, her body trembling in fear.

"I had good reason to beat you. You're a coward as well as a liar! Cross me again and I'll kill you," he said calmly, then walked out of the room.

"Oh, no you won't, Sam!" Auntie Rose jumped up and raced down the hallway after him. Sunny cowered beneath the covers, crying and hoping that her auntie would not let him come back and take her away.

"Don't you ever walk into my house again without knocking. You deserved your beating and more. You're lucky they didn't kill you and bury your ass in the woods. Sunny will stay with me as Mother wanted, and I promise you that you'll never touch that child again."

Sunny heard their loud voices and was relieved when she heard the back door slam shut. When Auntie Rose returned, Sunny could see her anger was still flaring. "Never mind your father! He will never hit you again! Now finish your lunch and let's speak of happier times. First, we're going to remove your bandages and see that pretty face again," she said, handing Sunny a mirror.

Taking her scissors, she snipped off the bandages and carefully unwrapped Sunny's face. Auntie Rose stared in horror at the sight that met her eyes.

Sunny looked into the mirror and stared at her reflection. A long, ugly scar ran from the left side of her forehead and down her cheek. Stunned by her ugliness, she flung the mirror across the room and covered her face with her hands, crying as though her heart would break. "I'm ugly! Oh, Auntie, Sam has scarred me for life. I'll never be pretty again!"

Auntie Rose held Sunny in her arms, comforting her until the tears subsided. "Now, now, Child. Dry your eyes, you're going to be pretty again. Why would I allow my beautiful niece to be less than she is? I know how to get rid of those scars. After all, our teachings came from the same medicine woman. I'm a nurse, and I've still got a few tricks of my own up my sleeve." Auntie Rose brought in a creamy herbal mixture and applied it to Sunny's face. "I promise this will take away that ugly scar in time."

Sunny's physical health improved, but filled with contempt and self-loathing, she always kept her face covered with either her hair or a scarf. Her ugliness consumed her thoughts until she slowly became a recluse. She felt alone in the world and angry over how she had been treated since she had left the reservation. Every time she thought of Sam, she was again filled with rage and hatred and would refuse to leave her darkened room.

Weeks passed before Auntie Rose was able to coax her out of the house to sit on the front porch swing in the warm sun. Each time she saw Sam in the distance, she would withdraw into the dark recesses of her mind like a wounded animal crawling into its den to lick its wounds. Sunny would cradle her body in her own arms, rocking to and fro, filled with grief and despair. One day when she sat on the porch Sunny heard her own voice cry out from somewhere deep within her heart. "Sam will never break my spirit or beat me again. I'll kill him first." She spent the rest of the day planning his murder in great detail.

Fall, winter and spring passed with little change in Sunny's emotional state. Auntie Rose made arrangements to pick up her books and homework from her teachers so she could study at home.

Sunny dreaded the nights when she would have to close her eyes and see the demon that seemed to lie in wait behind her eyelids, hoping to drive her insane. Driven by fear as the sun went down each day, Sunny began to leave the house and roam the farm in raging anger, her mind exploding with tormented nightmares.

Desperate for inner peace, she began to venture deeper into the stillness of the woods. One moonlit night as she was sitting under a tree, she heard the cry of an owl. She felt its gentle voice slowly blend with the other night sounds, its rhythmic melody melting into the heartbeat of Mother Earth becoming a symphony created by Mother Universe.

At that moment Sunny was liberated from the bonds of earth and an unknown force compelled her to rise to her feet. Embraced by a soft wind, she wiped the tears from her eyes and slowly let go of her pain. As peace entered her soul, Sunny ran from tree to tree in sheer exhilaration, letting the celestial spirits guide her dancing feet. Lost in a world of time and space she danced for hours, filling her hungry soul with a newfound freedom until she fell to her knees in joyous exhaustion.

Sunny continued to dance in the woods night after night, always leaving before dawn touched the horizon. Safe with her secret, she would slip quietly into the house, filled once again with serenity.

As she entered the house one morning Sunny was surprised to find Auntie Rose was already up and busy in the kitchen. Without a word she served Sunny a bowl of hot oatmeal and sat down across the table.

"Sunny, I understand your anger and fears, but you can't continue escaping life's responsibilities. On several occasions I've followed you, and I know you dance beautifully. I've spoken to Madame and she tells me that you need to spend at least two years in study before she can submit your name for a scholarship to the academy in New York."

Sunny frowned with the self-consciousness of being exposed. She feared the ridicule of others if they ever saw her scarred face. What if the horrible scar never faded and she was too ugly to fulfill the dreams that Madame and Cheering Woman had for her?

"Tomorrow you will be returning to school and if you do it without putting up a fight, I will enroll you in the local dance classes. It's up to you, Sunny. It could be the beginning of your future."

Sunny scowled, angry at the thought of being caged up in a classroom again. But more than anything she wanted to dance and going to school seemed a small price to pay to obtain this cherished dream. And so she began to plan for the moment she had dreaded.

Fearing that people would stare at her, Sunny kept her hair pulled over the left side of her face. As she walked cautiously toward her first period class, she recognized many old friends and was amazed when they all ignored the scar and greeted her warmly. Whenever anyone looked at her, she would move her hand up to her face to make sure the scar was hidden, and when the white students snickered and poked fun, Sunny filled her mind with Auntie Rose's promise of dance lessons.

The day passed slowly and it seemed forever before the school bell rang. Sunny rushed from the building, thrilled to find Auntie Rose's car parked at the curb. Breathlessly she hopped in next to Auntie, but as they neared their destination her enthusiasm was replaced by apprehension and fear of failure.

Auntie Rose, feeling her fears, reached over and gently patted her hand as if to reassure her that everything would be all right.

Upon entering the dance school, terror gripped her heart when she saw a group of pretty little girls gathered around the instructor, Master Dana. What if he hated Indians or ugly little girls and would not accept her?

When Auntie Rose introduced Sunny to Master Dana, she did not speak, just nodded her head and withdrew deep inside herself. Auntie calmly completed the enrollment form and purchased the required uniform. As they left the building Auntie Rose handed the package to Sunny who hugged it close until they arrived at the car.

It was not until Auntie Rose pulled away from the curb that Sunny displayed her true emotions. Suddenly she could not contain herself any longer and squealed with excitement, "Yes! Yes! Yes!" Auntie Rose understood and chuckled.

"He accepted me! I start tomorrow! Thank you, Auntie! Thank you so very much!" The words seemed to tumble from her lips.

Once home, she could not contain herself and dashed upstairs to try on her new leotard and ballet slippers. She stood before the mirror staring at her reflection and liked what she saw. She paraded downstairs then danced around Auntie Rose in excitement, talking incessantly.

"Look, Auntie. It's a perfect fit, and he didn't say anything about my face."

Sunny continued to chatter through dinner, telling Auntie Rose about her dreams of becoming a professional dancer. When at last it was time to go to bed, Sunny flipped on her bedroom light and went to the closet where she rummaged around until she found an old pink box. She took the box to her bed then carefully removed the lid and gently took out the pink ballet slippers that she had outgrown. Tears rolled down her cheeks as she hugged them close, recalling the day Cheering Woman and Madame had given them to her. Sunny fell asleep holding the slippers close as she relived that long ago memory.

She was up early the next day and off to another long day at school. When at last the dismissal bell rang, she bolted from the building and ran the two blocks to the dance studio for her first formal class.

Master Dana greeted her warmly and directed her to the dressing room where she changed into her leotard, then shyly reappeared in the workout room. She was standing quietly at the bar when Master Dana stood next to her and said, "Step to the center of the room, and when the music begins, I want you to dance for me."

Feeling nauseous, Sunny silently obeyed, not knowing what to expect. Ballet music began to fill the room as she stood in the center staring at her reflection in the mirrored walls. Although she didn't know what Master Dana was looking for, Sunny's mind slipped away from his presence and into nature's teachings. She moved with the music until there was no music, only the wind blowing and the night birds singing. It felt like flowers blooming all around her as her body moved with the ever-flowing rhythm of nature's symphony.

Master Dana stopped the record player, bringing Sunny abruptly back to the center of the room where she stood motionless like a frightened deer. "I'm impressed. You will do well in the intermediate group."

Sunny was elated and humbled by the idea that someone else understood her dreams. At that moment she promised herself she would always work hard to become the best at whatever she did in life.

The magic of the moment slipped away as the other girls entered the room, chattering about things that did not include Sunny. Feeling self-conscious once more, she quickly moved to the back of the room and waited for class to begin.

Master Dana started the music and the count. She could not understand the French words but persisted, determined to fulfill her dream. Day after day she practiced diligently, hardly able to contain herself until her next lesson.

Master Dana often walked from student to student, adjusting their positions as though he was a sculptor, and they were made from clay. Each time he approached Sunny she would stiffen as if readying for an attack, flinching if he touched her. Try as she might she could not overcome her fear of touch and vowed to herself that she would work so hard and become so good that there would be no need for him or anyone else to touch her.

As weeks passed she became familiar with Master Dana's schedule and would stop by the studio after school to watch his other classes. Watching the advanced classes one afternoon, Sunny had an idea. She would ask Master Dana if she could work at the studio for extra lessons. For weeks she worked at building up enough courage to approach him. Then one day she waited until the last pupil had left and followed him into his office.

"Can I clean the studio to pay for extra lessons?" she blurted out, all of her prepared speeches lost in the fear of the moment.

Taken aback by her request, Master Dana looked up from his paperwork, stared at her thoughtfully, then smiled. "I guess I could use some help. The mirrors and floors could use some special cleaning. Yes, Sunny, I think we can work out something that would benefit the both of us. Be here tomorrow right after school."

Overcome with gratitude, Sunny mumbled a sincere yes and ran out of the studio, her thoughts racing in time with her footsteps as she rushed home to tell Auntie Rose the good news.

Auntie was in the kitchen when Sunny burst through the door. "Auntie! Auntie! I've got a job!" she exploded, her voice breathless and filled with enthusiasm. "I'm cleaning the studio to pay for extra lessons."

Anxious to hear the details, Auntie Rose congratulated her and they sat down at the table for a piece of peach pie and a glass of milk. Sunny talked on and on about her dreams as Auntie listened patiently, offering smiles and hmmm's each time she stopped to take a breath. It made Auntie Rose happy to know her niece was getting better, particularly when she spoke of her feelings about the death of Cheering Woman.

It was late when they finally went to bed, and Sunny did not want to get up the following morning. But when she remembered her new job, she bolted from bed and dressed quickly then headed for school. She went through the motions at school, waiting for the day to end. When the last bell rang, she dashed from the room and ran all the way to the studio.

Happy with her new job, Sunny was determined to prove herself. Within two weeks she was comfortable with her new duties and the studio sparkled with the results of her loving care. Master Dana admired her fighting spirit and was pleased with her tenacity. Slowly their relationship evolved into one of mutual trust and respect.

Within six months Sunny had taken every available class and her abilities had surpassed all of Master Dana's expectations. By the end of the first year she had won several awards and was working as a student assistant in the beginner classes, thankful for every opportunity to improve her skills.

At the end of each day she would stick her head into Master Dana's office to thank him and say goodnight before leaving for another nightly raid in the countryside. Sunny was thankful that her own situation had improved, but she could not forget Sam's neglected family. Each time she took food and clothing to Hazel and her brothers, the filth and poverty of their existence was a painful reminder of living with Sam. Most times she left in tears, feeling guilty about the good things that had changed in her life while her family still suffered under Sam's dominance.

Sunny did not want to steal, but felt it was necessary if the family was to survive. She felt duty-bound to accept this lawless way of life as a necessity and qualified her actions by never stealing anything for herself. Each time she stole, she became more and more consumed with the fear of being exposed as a thief. At last unable to handle the guilt and fear that gnawed deep within her soul, she went to her Medicine Wheel to pray. "Oh, Grandmother, I'm tired of Sam's poison devastating my heart. I want to stop doing bad things and end the hatred between us. I must help the family but I don't know how. I promise if you will help me with this, I will become all that you wished my life to be."

When Sunny arrived home she again asked Auntie Rose to help Hazel and the children. Auntie Rose, hating the tradition that forced her not to interfere with her brother's family, declined Sunny's request using the large amount of paperwork required for so many reservation Indians to move onto her property as an excuse.

She understood that Auntie must follow the guidelines of the relocation program if they were to receive money and commodities from the government. Some of the men had left the farm and joined the service to get allotment checks for their families, and Auntie Rose was taking care of their housing and arranging for others to work on the nearby farms.

Sunny also knew there was plenty of money available. The rules were simple among her people. Family members were supposed to pitch in and take care of each other's needs. With this in mind, Sunny went to the barn and opened the storage room, taking what food she needed for her family.

Proud of her niece's stubborn determination to help the family that had given her so little, Auntie Rose made no mention of the missing items.

Although the Indian children hated the predominately white school, it was mandatory that all children between the ages of five and sixteen attend. Prejudice between the two races was strong and the Indians stayed within their own group. The older boys and girls excelled in sports, track and art, and watched over the younger ones to protect them from the white kids. Each day the Indian group would gather on the school grounds for lunch and recess, always looking out for each other's well-being. Sunny became the protector of a shy, crippled girl named Ruth who was in her class.

As the school year was drawing to a close, the Indian group gathered in the schoolyard to talk about the upcoming school musical, *Annie Get Your Gun*. Even though everyone knew that most of the cast would be white, they decided that Sunny should try out for the lead role of Annie.

Watching Sunny audition, all the Indian students agreed that she was by far the best. When the last student had finished, Miss Anderson, the drama teacher, announced the cast list would be posted on the bulletin board the following day and rehearsals would start at three o'clock.

The day of the posting they all gathered around the bulletin board to find that Sunny was excluded from the show. This complete rejection by the white world caused something inside of Sunny to snap, letting the raging animal loose that had lived caged inside of her since her brutal beating. Until now she had been able to keep her demons of hate, anger and fear well hidden from most of the world, but this senseless denial of her dreams just because she was Indian was more than she could bear. She ripped the notice from the board and tore it to shreds. Finding that did not appease her, she yanked the bulletin board from the wall and stomped it to pieces.

"Sunny, don't be mad. Miss Anderson just doesn't like Indians," said Ruth.

"Fuck that shit! I'm tired of being treated like a second-rate citizen. It's time we do something about the way we're treated. Ruth, go tell the others to meet me in the auditorium."

At three o'clock the back of the auditorium began to fill with Indians of all ages, causing quite a stir among the white students. They waited respectfully to be recognized while Miss Anderson briefed the cast and answered questions. When an hour had passed and still they had not been recognized, Sunny stood up and yelled, "Hey, Anderson! Are you blind? You've recognized everyone but us! We came here to speak with you and that's what we're going to do!"

Miss Anderson looked scornfully over the glasses that sat perched on the tip of her nose, saying, "If you want to know why your name is not on the cast list, then I'll tell you. It's school policy that no student can participate in any performance if their family is on welfare, and I believe your family is receiving commodities." She smiled with smug satisfaction.

With these words an uproar started in the back of the auditorium. The Indian students began making loud comments and George, the leader of the older boys, waved a coke bottle menacingly.

"Quick, someone go get the principal. You pack of wild Indians get out of here immediately!" screeched Miss Anderson.

Sunny stepped into the aisle and moved toward the stage.

"We're not going anywhere. You know I live with my Auntie Rose and she's not on welfare. So why wasn't I considered for this fucking play? And what's the real reason for choosing that white cow, Mary Francis, who can't even say her name without blushing? Could it be that she's white and her father's a doctor?"

"It should be obvious. Look at you. How could you play the part of a white person? You can't dance or sing, and have absolutely no understanding of our history or culture. You're just not qualified," Miss Anderson smirked.

"I am too qualified, you stupid bitch! I can dance and sing, and what I know about white history is that it's full of lies! Hell, who said the part had to be played by a white person? So I'll ask you again, what's the real reason for not letting me be in your play?" Sunny boldly moved to the foot of the stage, chin forward and hands on her hips.

"Look at what you're doing right now! You're nothing but a belligerent, arrogant little animal. Your kind is no better than trailer trash. This rehearsal is for cast members only, and I refuse to jeopardize their safety with a rowdy group of uninvited Indians! And you...God forbid that drunk you call your father would show up and cause a riot."

Sunny's anger exploded into full-blown rage. She leapt to the stage, stopping within inches of Miss Anderson's face. "You fucking bitch! No one attacks my father, even if he is the town drunk!" She shoved Miss Anderson backwards then jumped off the stage and headed for the rear of the auditorium, unfazed by the taunts and jeers of the white section.

Sunny grabbed the coke bottle from George and threw it toward the stage where it grazed Miss Anderson's head, then fell to the floor and shattered. "Bingo!" yelled Sunny as blood began to trickle down the drama teacher's face.

Miss Anderson's overbearing arrogance was quickly replaced by fear.

"You're not so powerful now are you, Miss White Woman? Don't you ever tell me again what I can or can't do! You better think very carefully before you try anything like this again. I know all about you. What if your house burned to the ground while you were sleeping? Or your car tires got slashed in the middle of the night? Or maybe your gas tank was filled with a few bags of sugar? As you know, White Woman, accidents do happen!"

By this time the Indians had assembled in groups around the auditorium. They could see Miss Anderson was terrified and victory was theirs. As they rose in unison and began to leave the auditorium, Sunny paused at the door, bent down and pulled her hunting knife from her boot. Staring insolently at Miss Anderson, she began to clean her nails with it, her message very clear, as a hush filled the auditorium.

"Do you know that I can throw a knife better than I threw that fucking coke bottle?" she sneered. "And since we both agree that I will not be in your fucking show, I want an apology to me and my friends to keep this knife in my hand!"

Miss Anderson's face was ashen and she said nothing for a moment. Then with a sigh, she recanted, "I apologize. Now please go!"

The student body applauded as the Indian group began to file out the door. The last to leave, Sunny hesitated, then thrust her fist upward in defiance. "Now that's fucking Indian power, you *Wasichu* bastards." Then smiling sweetly, she took a graceful bow and slammed the door on her last day in public school.

Auntie Rose had already heard about the incident by the time Sunny arrived home and she was furious. Without giving Sunny a chance to tell her version of the story, she grabbed her by the arm and marched her to the car, then drove directly to the studio to speak with Master Dana.

Sunny was terrified, she knew she was in trouble and feared she would lose everything. She stood in front of Master Dana hanging her head in shame as Auntie Rose described what she had done to Miss Anderson. Through lowered eyes she glanced up at Master Dana's grim face and began to fear the worst. When Auntie Rose finished, he addressed Sunny. "Is this true? Did you really do all this?"

"Yes," she mumbled.

"Is that the proper way for a lady to act? Or better yet, is that the behavior of a future star?"

"No. I guess not. But she deserved it."

Master Dana could contain himself no longer and broke into laughter.

"Rose, we both know school is a problem for Sunny. Let's get past the problem so we can concentrate on her future. If she were mine, I wouldn't waste any more time with public school. Home teaching would be more beneficial and would allow her the time to prepare for her scholarship." He patted Sunny on the shoulder. "And given today's episode, I'm sure the school board will be relieved to have this little problem disappear."

Sunny let out a muffled sigh of relief and offered a silent prayer of thanksgiving to *Wakan Tanka*.

Auntie Rose was distraught and could not believe her ears. She had expected Master Dana to support her, and instead he suggested that she let Sunny quit school. Exasperated, Auntie Rose grabbed Sunny by the arm and yanked her out of the studio. Sunny followed meekly, hoping the worst was over. At least she would still be able to dance, and that was what really mattered. When they arrived home, Auntie Rose went to Sam and told him the whole story.

"Sam I have an upstanding reputation in this community and it will not be tarnished. Sunny has shamed me and she will not get away with this!" demanded Rose.

He calmly rolled a cigarette, then asked, "Did she really do these things?"

"Absolutely, Sam! My God, she acted like a wild, raging animal in public today. Her stubborn ways are getting impossible to control and I've had enough of her arrogance and bullheadedness. I won't tolerate being embarrassed in front of the whole town like this. It's your influence that's causing these problems. Your daughter does terrible things just like you! Either you speak to her, or I am through with the both of you!"

"Okay, Rose, just settle down. I'll take care of it. Send her on down and I'll talk to her."

Sam knew Rose was serious and understood why. But at the same time, he couldn't help but feel a little proud of his daughter. He went to the barn and waited until he heard Sunny enter, then walked up to her with a grim look on his face. "God damn it, Sunny! Boy, have you fucked up this time," he said, trying to swallow his laughter. "Your Auntie Rose is so mad she's ready to split her girdle. What in the hell is this shit you're pulling? Rose tells me you started a fucking riot at the goddamn school."

Sunny, seeing he was not all that upset, played her part. She dropped her eyes and shuffled her feet around in the dirt before answering, "Yeah, kinda."

Grabbing her arm as if to shake her, Sam yelled, "Who in the fuck do you think you're talking to, girl? This is me! Sam the Dog Man." He pounded his chest to make his point. "Your Auntie is pissed off! You better fucking tell me what's going on."

"I didn't do anything. It was that asshole teacher, Anderson. She refused to let me be in the show and called you the town drunk. I got mad and hit her in the head with a coke bottle. That's about it."

"I should bust your ass," Sam roared, but Sunny saw the twinkle in his eye. "So, old fat Anderson said that about me, huh? Well, don't worry, I'll talk to Old Bubble Butt and that'll get Auntie off both our backs. Now, about another problem. Auntie says you're acting like your old man, whatever the fuck that means." He shook his finger in her face. "I'm telling you to stop fighting and stay away from that fucking school and remember to act like a lady! Rose wants to hire you some kinda teacher to get you an education. Fuck if I know why, you ain't that smart. Besides, why does a girl need an education?" Sam turned and walked away with a certain hidden pride showing in his squared shoulders and easy gait.

His words stung, but he had defended her poor behavior and she was thankful he hadn't gone into one of his rages. Knowing his temper, she promised never to place herself in this kind of situation again. True to her word, from that day forward Sunny became the hardest working student in the dance school, determined to win every award possible.

Within six months Sunny had been accepted into the local civic ballet company. She was thrilled, knowing she was now qualified to apply for her scholarship in New York. As she hurried home anxious to share the good news with Auntie Rose, Sunny laughed when she thought of how the townspeople would feel when they found out the incorrigible daughter of a whiskey running, dope dealing, gambling Indian was a part of their local ballet company.

Her time filled with home school, dance classes and rehearsals, Sunny soon learned it would take more than hard work to accomplish her dreams. Master Dana expected nothing less than perfection from her, and his lessons were grueling sessions of pain and sweat. Sunny smiled at each new challenge and loving the discipline, she took advantage of every opportunity that Master Dana afforded her.

Finally the day came when Sunny's dream was answered. Master Dana asked Auntie Rose to come to the studio for a conference.

"Please sit down. I have wonderful things to discuss with you regarding our coming season. I want to give the lead in next year's festival to Sunny, but there is a nasty flaw that must be corrected before I do so."

Master Dana assured Auntie Rose it was not an artistic flaw, but Sunny's attitude, that needed to be corrected. "It has been brought to my attention that she displays a certain coldness toward the other students and her fighting in the dressing room must be stopped. She has a strong tendency to violent outbursts which I will not tolerate in this company. I've had calls from several parents who accuse her of threatening their children. This could be dangerous, Rose. I'd hate to lose Sunny, but I will dismiss her if this behavior continues."

Sunny knew that without Master Dana she would never get her scholarship or escape from Sam. She explained her jealousy of the other students and promised that she would never threaten another pupil or lose her temper again. And for the rest of her training with Master Dana, she was as good as her word.

The other students, well aware of Master Dana's ultimatum, renewed their efforts to bring about her dismissal. But Sunny spoke to no one and kept to herself, staying totally focused on her purpose.

One day as everyone was getting dressed for class, Mary Francis called out, "Master Dana, she's back to her old tricks again! Why do you allow her to be in our class? My mother says she's not culturally suited to study with us. Look at her! She's just a dumb Indian. And you know how much our parents donate to the Civic Ballet!"

Sunny bit her tongue until she tasted blood.

"That's enough! What your mommies or daddies say has no bearing on how I run this company. We have one year to learn a completely new ballet. This is my company, and I say Sunny is the lead dancer. There will be no prejudice or gossip unless you want to be dismissed! Is that understood?" yelled Master Dana, leaving the room.

Sunny looked at Mary Francis and smiled with satisfaction. Someone had finally taken her side! Master Dana's display of acceptance renewed Sunny's determination to be the best, no matter the cost.

At that moment, Sam was sitting at the bar with one of his white girlfriends, when she casually informed him that his daughter was known as a thief by everyone in town. Without a word he stood up, pushed back his chair, and left the tavern to find Sunny. He parked his truck in front of the dance studio and strutted inside.

"Hey, Teach," he called out to Master Dana, "I wanna talk to you."

Embarrassed and driven by fear, Sunny raced past the girls into the dressing room. She slipped into her clothes then stepped silently into the night. She walked home, fearfully wondering why Sam had stopped by to talk to Master Dana. She was so caught up in her thoughts that she did not hear Sam pull up alongside of her until he yelled, "Sunny! Get in the fucking truck." As she climbed in beside him he said, "It's time we talk. I spoke with that *winkte*, homosexual, dance instructor and he tells me you're pretty good, except for your bad ass temper." Sunny looked at the floorboard, refusing to respond. "Damn you, girl! I've heard enough about your fucking temper and your stealing! We both know who's doing the midnight shopping in this valley. I know you're the thief, and if you get caught, don't expect me to do a goddamn thing about it."

"You were never there for me before! What makes you think I need you now?" she retorted.

"Watch your fucking mouth before you eat your goddamn teeth! I do what I gotta do, but what's right for me doesn't mean it's right for you. What you're doing is stupid. Stealing makes you a sneak and everybody hates a thief. You know it's wrong! What would your grandmother think if she knew her granddaughter was a thief, huh?"

Sunny felt ashamed, knowing what he was saying was true. "Maybe I do bad things, but like you, I do what I gotta do. Someone's gotta feed the family," she answered defiantly.

"Damn it, girl! I know I'm a mean sonuvabitch, but I never was a thief or a liar. And I won't have a fucking kid that's one either."

"Then feed the family, Sam, and you won't have to fucking worry about me."

Sam bit his lip trying hard to control his anger. He slammed his fist on the steering wheel, saying, "Okay, Okay! Goddamnit! Stop your fucking cursing around me before I knock you on your ass. I'll keep fucking food on the table if you promise to stop stealing."

"Okay, Sam, I'll stop my stealing as long as you keep the fucking food on the table."

"Sonuvabitch! If you want to help the family, then get off your ass and help me train my goddamn hunting dogs so I can make some money," grumbled Sam, and they rode in silence the rest of the way home.

As Sunny got out of the truck Sam asked, "Have I got your word? No more stealing?"

"Sam, you have my word, and I don't lie!"

"Fucking fine, girl! I'll see you in the morning."

Walking toward the house Sunny began to have second thoughts about how she could keep up with her dancing and still spend time with Sam and his stupid dogs.

Feeling depressed, she entered the house and walked to the kitchen. Auntie Rose could see she had something on her mind, and when Sunny sat down at the table she gently asked her what was the matter.

"Auntie, you're going to be very mad. I've done some bad things and Sam has found out that I've been stealing food from the farmers and I've also stolen from you. I know I was wrong, and I promised Sam I would never steal again. I told him I'd help him with the dogs if he'd keep food on the table for Hazel and the kids."

"Sunny, I know you've been taking food and now that you're been honest with me, I'll give you food when the family needs it."

"Auntie, how can I continue to study and go to the mountains with Sam?"

"Sunny, helping Sam won't interfere with your home schooling or your dance training. There's no rehearsal on the weekends. You two need to spend time together and get acquainted. I'm glad that you're going to the mountains with him. You'll see a different man there. That's his world, and finally you'll get to know your father. Don't worry, things will work out between you two, just wait and see."

"Auntie, he wants me to go with him tomorrow morning."

"I think that's good. You'll enjoy yourself and learn his way of life."

Feeling a little better, Sunny went to bed still doubtful that they would be able to spend a weekend together without a problem.

At three o'clock in the morning Sam pulled into the driveway, his dogs loaded in the back of his truck. Opening the back door to his sister's house, he stepped into her kitchen. As Auntie Rose handed him a cup of hot coffee Sam looked at Sunny and grunted, "You ready?"

Sunny rose from the table and picked up her things before heading for the door. She climbed into the truck, apprehensive about sitting so close to Sam, watching him distrustfully out of the corner of one eye.

"Looks like you've packed enough shit to move in. You ready to learn how to work a pack of dogs?" jeered Sam in a feeble attempt to have a conversation with his daughter.

"Yes, Sir."

Sam gave up trying to make conversation with her and remained quiet until they reached the top of the mountain.

"Pretty good view of the valley, huh?"

"Yes, Sir."

When they reached their turnoff, Sam followed a cowtrail down a dirt lane. The dogs knew where they were and grew excited. They traveled inward for about ten miles through a dense forest until they came to a wide clearing. Sam stopped the truck and got out, letting Sunny know they had reached their destination.

She then watched Sam set up a snap line for his snarling, yapping pack of dogs. Happy to be free again, he unpacked the truck and set up camp.

Surprised at Sam's friendly mood, Sunny was amazed at the change in him and wondered who her father really was. The man who drank and beat his wife and children or the confident friendly man who now stood before her? She soon saw that Sam loved training dogs to hunt bear and raccoon and found it fun to listen to him firmly yet gently talk to his old-timers. But when he turned his attention to the barking, snapping young pups, he scolded loudly. Sunny watched the commotion reach a peak of hilarious play as Sam continued to argue with his dogs. She giggled at the way Sam and his dogs seemed to speak the same language.

"You know anything about dogs?"

"A little."

"Then take the green ones for a run and empty them out."

"What do you mean?"

Sam laughed. "Damn, girl! Thought you knew something about dogs. We sure don't want to smell shit around here all day, do we? A green dog is nothing but a potential. Before I put a new dog in my pack, I want him settled down and able to work on an empty stomach. It makes their instincts sharp. We sure as hell don't want one to stop and take a shit if we're clocking them."

Sunny turned red with embarrassment. She could not believe her father would speak of such things to her.

"Well! Don't stand there! Get going," Sam chuckled as he staked out his lead dogs.

Sunny tried to control the green dogs, but they were too fast and she had to run to keep up with them. When an hour had passed and Sunny still had not returned, Sam blew his cow horn and the pups returned immediately to camp. Sunny followed them, the last one to return. She noticed Sam had set up a tieline between two trees and as the pups came in, he grabbed each one and hooked it to the line.

"It's very dangerous to mix the old seasoned dogs with the green ones. A wrong move and one of your dogs is dead. If a fight breaks out, stay back! I've lost many a good dog because it got hurt and I had to put it down. Hunting dogs are a very different animal. They're born killers and their nerves reach a fever pitch before a hunt or a competition. See that old lead dog over there? He's my best, but he's a born killer. If I'm not careful with Old Blue, he could cost me another good dog."

Sunny spent her first day with Sam watching him at home with all nature. She had never seen him as excited as he was with his dogs. He loved them and they loved him. There seemed to be an unspoken bond between them that could not be broken. As evening approached, Sam fed his dogs then gathered fallen timber and stoked the fire. He cooked their meal and as they ate, both sat in awkward silence. For the first time in her life, Sunny saw her father differently. Not knowing what to do with these new feelings, she mumbled good night and crawled into her sleeping bag.

Sam sat by the fire with his cup of coffee, smoking a cigarette. When he began to tell a story about Raccoon, Sunny was surprised to find that Sam was a good storyteller. She listened with interest as he told the story of why he hunted *We Cha*, the Raccoon:

"*We Cha* is a natural Peeping Tom and a damn good thief. He's the one who created the mask for all the bandits of the world. That little devil's got keen, piercing black eyes. The reason he's got such a pointed nose is because he's always going around sticking it into other people's business. You know how you love your Medicine Wheel? Raccoon's bushy tail has many rings on it which reminds me of the many powers in the Sacred Circles.

"When I hunt coon I know he's smart, so I have to think like him. He's a good climber and always hangs around good rich soil. Last year when I was running my dogs with the Algoqui Indians, I heard them call him 'The Scratcher.' I like that name because when I'm looking for Coon, I look for his marks on the trees. When you look at his little paws they look like tiny human hands. I call him 'The Washer' because he don't have any saliva in his mouth and always wets his food before eating it.

"You gotta be careful around Coon. He'll eat anything, dead or alive. He sleeps during the day, curled in a ball with his little hands covering his eyes. Before he'll hunt, he makes a sound kinda like a *Stiginney*, a screech owl. Since Raccoon is a good fisherman, it's real easy to track one. When you go near his fishing hole you can see his five-toe footprint. He's a damn good swimmer too. When you want to find one in the daytime, you look in the branches that hang close to the water or look in the holes of the hollow trees." His story finished Sam crawled into his sleeping bag. Sunny could not believe her ears. She had not heard Sam talk this much since she was born. Intrigued by his story, Sunny decided to check it out the next day.

Shortly after sunrise Sam left Sunny in the camp and took his old-timers to find a live trail. When he had not returned by late afternoon, Sunny became bored and went to look for Raccoon. She discovered some tracks close to the water and hid in the bushes until she noticed a hollow in a nearby tree. Sunny got up and peeked inside. Sure enough there was a sleeping raccoon, his eyes covered by his tiny hands. She went back to the heavy scrub brush and waited. Before long she saw him head for the water. When he stuck his finger in the water and caught a crayfish, her amusement turned to amazement. Curling back his lips, he flipped it into his mouth and chomped down on it with pleasure. Sunny laughed as she headed back to camp, agreeing with Sam that raccoons were very intelligent animals.

During supper on their second day in the woods, Sunny realized she was actually feeling comfortable around Sam and decided to strike up a conversation.

"I like the raccoon."

"Me too. A coon, like anyone else, uses what he knows. I enjoy hunting him. He's smart and not easy to catch. I remember one time when Old Blue was on the prowl. It was long before daybreak when he had a chance meeting with a cranky old coon. Boy, did that teach him a good lesson! Old Blue was a green dog and still dumb. He chased that coon into the river and those four black paws grabbed hold of his ass and pulled him under the water so fast it would make your head spin. They fought and fought until they got into the deep water, then that coon climbed on top of Old Blue's head and held him under. Coons know how to drown a dog. I was sure Old Blue was a goner that day.

"Well, I couldn't let him drown a good dog, even a green one. I took my gun, aimed carefully and popped that old coon right between the eyes! Old Blue surfaced spitting and coughing, but he attended to business and pulled that dead bastard to shore. Boy, was he a big one! I skinned him out, and Old Blue and I shared a damn good dinner. Coon's good eating. Tastes like chicken and lamb. Yep, Old Blue still carries the scars of that battle, and to this day he hunts coons with revenge and hate. Now that's the kind of training that makes a good coon dog."

As Sam ended his story, they said good night and both crawled into their sleeping bags eager for a good night's rest. Early the following morning they cleaned up the camp area and packed up the dogs to return home.

Sunny continued to go to the mountains every weekend with Sam to train the dogs. Her interest in coons increased, leading her to think that a coon would make a good pet. Although she still distrusted Sam, she appreciated his abilities in the mountains and his knowledge of dogs. Sam the Dog Man was a good tracker and hunter. He was also one of the best trainers and breeders in that part of the country.

As time passed Sunny became aware that when Sam was in the mountains with his dogs he didn't drink. The weekend trips continued as they readied the dogs that Sam wanted to sell before coon season. Feeling frustrated with their progress, Sam said, "These young dogs are too damn anxious. It's going to take more work if we're going to make any big money at the meet. Their instincts are sharp, but their inexperience makes them unreliable. They hit a trail fast and cross the line fine, but they lose it when the pack hits the tree. What we need to make these pups worth a damn is a young coon. We could probably find a young one napping in a tree, 'cause an old coon is too smart to get caught in one. Hell, an old coon would just jump out and break his fall by landing on a dog or a person and make his escape.

"Now, look at that dog over there. She's green, but she's smart and got a damn good nose. She establishes her place in the pack quick, but gets confused when the pack gets into a fight. I'm gonna run her with the old-timers today and see if she's got any balls." The dog he referred to was part wolf and Sunny's favorite. She knew that if Sam couldn't make any money off of her, he'd kill her to protect his breeding stock.

"Sunny, take the coon bag and lay me a long trail. Go out about five miles and let's see what we've got in this pup." Sunny left, dragging the coon bag along the ground. Sam watched her vanish into the woods and sat down for another cup of coffee. He was beginning to like his daughter and enjoyed her quick mind.

Sunny picked her way carefully as she criss-crossed her trail and circled wide. When she found rabbit pellets, she deliberately crossed them to create more excitement and confusion in the pack. Just then an old mama possum carrying her babies waddled across her path. She was glad to have another scent cross the trail, knowing this would make it more difficult. She wondered if Old Blue would break the trail and if he did, would Sam kill him, too? Feeling guilty for her bad thought, she changed her thinking to keep Old Blue from having bad luck.

Her grandmother had always said that Sam was a good man when he wasn't drinking and Sunny was beginning to think maybe she was right. With that thought, she was immediately filled with happiness and ran free as the wind through the woods. Coming to a mountain creek, she dragged the bag through the water then cut back into the heavy undergrowth. Changing her course again, she went deeper into the woods where she climbed a tree and hung the coon bag on one of the higher branches. Feeling satisfied with the trail she had laid Sunny headed back to camp, enjoying the peace and beauty of the sacred mountains. The sun shone through the trees making streams of smoky light as it spilled its soft colors over the densely covered forest floor. Sensing the mystic powers of the moment, Sunny was caught up in a spell of selfish delight.

Suddenly she heard Sam blowing on his old cow horn, and jolted back to reality by its impatient sound, she hurried along. She arrived at the camp out of breath and announced, "I laid a hard trail," then plopped down on the ground to rest.

Feeling rather awkward at the sight of her happy face, Sam let the dogs loose and picked up a broken dog harness that needed repair. As he re-strung the leather, Sunny challenged, "I bet that trail is good enough to confuse Old Blue's nose."

"I doubt that!" Sam chuckled. "My old blue tick hound is a very wise dog. Listen, can't you hear him baying? That tells me he's in front of the pack and already on your trail." Sam set the harness aside and stood up, adding, "C'mon, we'll walk over the ridge and watch the pack as they double back. I'll bet you anything that Old Blue is way out in front."

Sunny didn't want to bet, but she was curious to learn how he knew the location of the pack. Listening intently she suddenly heard them barking in unison and could almost feel the rhythm of the run.

"Dogs communicate. If you listen to the inflections in their barks they tell you what's going on," Sam casually remarked. When Sunny saw Old Blue pull to the front of the pack, she joined Sam in his excitement.

"Sam, look at Blue! He's sure pouring on the coal!"

"Yep," bragged Sam, as he stood proudly watching the pack stretch full out as they faded down into a hollow. "Goddamnit!" yelled Sam, throwing his hat on the ground. "That fucking pack has split off and broken the trail. They're after the real thing. Might as well call it a day. They'll be gone all night."

Sam became sullen and remained quiet. An invisible wall separated father and daughter as they cooked, ate supper and cleaned up the campgrounds. Every so often Sam would stop and listen to his dogs in the far-off distance, hoping they would come in before night fell.

Both crawled into their sleeping bags near the open fire. Sam had his back to the fire and was lost in thought, lulled by the peaceful night sounds around him. He thought about the future of this girl he had fathered.

Sunny lay in her sleeping bag thinking about this man who was her father, a man she hated yet admired, a man she still did not know. Sam was a man of steel to whom emotions were useless. Was it possible to love someone she hated? Sunny tossed restlessly, her mind jumbled with questions that had no answers. Suddenly her thoughts were disrupted by Sam's thunderous snoring and Sunny giggled, then slowly drifted off to sleep.

The sun was barely touching the horizon when Sunny opened her eyes to see Sam sitting under a tree, enjoying his morning coffee. The early chill demanded a heavy jacket. Sunny rolled out of her sleeping bag and dressed quickly. Sam looked her way, asking, "Wanna coffee?" then casually poured himself another cup. "You were sleeping pretty sound. You didn't even stir when some of the green dogs came in last night. I guess the others are still running. Come on, we'll walk down to the creek and let the pups swim to exercise their young muscles."

Sunny grabbed up one of Sam's fresh skillet biscuits and stuffed it in her mouth. Zipping up her jacket, she trailed behind him, the dogs close at her heels.

Sam checked his rifle, peered through the sight and said, "I'll teach you a little bit about shooting." Sunny listened carefully as he explained the importance and the dangers of using a gun. "See that tree over there? See that forked branch hanging down to the left?" Sunny nodded. "Well, try and clip it off," he said, placing the rifle into her shoulder. "Now, aim. Keep your hands steady. When you have it in your sight, slowly squeeze the trigger."

Sunny held the rifle against her shoulder, took aim and fired.

"Goddamnit, girl! What the fuck are you doing! You trying to kill somebody? That fucking barrel jumped ten feet in the air! I told you to press the goddamn butt into your shoulder! Now try it again, and this time try to hold onto the damn thing," he said, jamming it hard against her shoulder. "This time see if you can hit what the hell you aim at. Or maybe I should throw a tree in the air and see if that's a big enough target. I swear! Sometimes you act as dumb as a woman."

Sunny's feelings were hurt and Sam's insults made her angry. She jammed the rifle back into her shoulder and took careful aim. Suddenly she heard her grandmother whisper, "Granddaughter, see it happen. Think of your rope! Reach with your mind to another place and time."

She took in a deep breath and relaxed as she placed the target in her sight then slowly squeezed the trigger. As the limb fell gracefully to the ground, Sunny thrust the rifle toward him, asking with a grin, "Good enough for you, Sam?"

"Hmmm, not bad for a girl," he smiled, acting unimpressed.

"Couldn't get any closer," she retorted.

"Well, now, Miss Smart Ass! What would your grandmother think if she heard your big mouth bragging?" asked Sam, amused by the bristle in her attitude. "Since you're such a bigshot, you carry the goddamn gun! Maybe some of my skills will rub off on you."

At that moment they heard the baying of the dogs and moved down the slope for further investigation. Listening intently, Sam observed, "They're circling back toward us. Sounds like we better get back to camp." Sunny placed the rifle over her shoulder and followed Sam back up the trail.

"Learning to handle a gun properly, or hunt with a dog ain't easy, but both are important. It sure beats the hell out of stealing," badgered Sam. "Hell, girl, when you learn to shoot as good as me and hunt for your goddamn food, you won't have to steal anymore." Sunny knew Sam was right but as always his crude manner hurt her feelings. "Sunny, you gotta do what you gotta do! But you gotta always do what's right. If you can't do it right, then don't do it at all. Just remember, a liar or a thief overlooks a few principles of life."

Seeing it was useless to respond to a truth, Sunny remained silent.

"Look at that bush. See how it's bent over? Something's been here. See that clump of grayish hair on the bush? Betcha don't know what kind of animal that is."

Studying it for a moment, Sunny said, "Possum."

"Damn, you're right! Better give you some credit for what little brain you have," laughed Sam. "Wanna find that old possum? Watch your step, possums will live anywhere. Look for a bed filled with dried leaves and grass. Don't worry, when you get a whiff of one you'll never forget it. Did you know they go back to the dinosaur age?"

Just then they spotted a mother possum carrying her babies on her back. She remembered her grandmother showing her how their hind feet made marks in the soil like a star.

"Grandmother once told me they sleep in the day, and hunt at night after they hear the *Stiginney*."

"Yep, that's right."

Suddenly they heard a ruckus among the young dogs and raced down the trail to find them attacking a possum. Sam laughed when he saw the large possum flipped on its back with its eyes closed and its tongue hanging out of its mouth, the dogs were sniffing, smelling and pawing at its limp body. Sam gently kicked the dogs away and motioned for Sunny to follow him. From a nearby clump of bushes, they knelt in silence and watched the possum slowly get up and run for cover. Breaking out in laughter, Sam said, "Now that's what I call playing possum."

As they continued down the trail, Sam warned, "Sunny, watch where you step. The woods are crawling with snakes this time of year." No sooner had Sam spoken than he froze in his tracks, motioning Sunny to halt. A rattler was singing loudly as Sam tried to locate its whereabouts.

Sunny stayed close, easing the rifle into her shoulder. They both spotted it at the same time, coiled and ready to strike. Fast as greased lightning, Sunny pulled the trigger, hit her mark and reached for her kill.

Sam grabbed her arm, yelling, "Goddamnit, girl! You can't be that stupid! Don't you know a dead snake can still bite until the sun goes down?" He took a stick and poked at its lifeless body. When it did not move, he studied it closely, then grabbed the tail and whipped it hard against a rock, smashing its head. "Well, looks like you killed a wise old sonuvabitch," he grinned, holding the dead snake by its tail. "Yep, sure is a big one. Been around a long time. Look at those rattles! I bet there's at least twelve buttons here. Quick thinking on your part. Not bad. Not a bad shot at all. Couldn't have done better myself." Sam took his hunting knife and cut the rattles loose from the body, then slit open the snake's belly, skinned it out and packed the meat in his hat.

"When we get back to camp, I'll make you something out of these rattles. Might remind you what Snake's saying when it's going to strike you," said Sam, putting them in his pocket. "You need to learn more about Snake. This diamondback skin will make you a pretty belt or hat band," he added, tossing it over his shoulder.

"Listen! Hear the dogs? They're over the ridge. Old Blue's in the lead," he said, running toward their sound. "Hurry, damn it. I wanna see who takes the line and first tree. Did you bring the leashes?" he asked, turning to see that she had them tied around her waist. Sam smiled. "Yep, thinking ahead is good. You got a lot of your grandmother's ways. Always prepared. Yep, life can sure throw you some bad curves if you don't think ahead about what you're doing. You gotta take life as it comes. But mostly, you gotta be ready for surprises. It'll sure keep you out of a helluva lot of trouble."

"Grandmother always told me to know who stands in front of you, whether it's a person, place or thing," added Sunny.

"Yeah, but you gotta make good choices and that takes learning from the hard knocks of life. Take your grandmother, for instance. She always knew what was going to happen before it did, and she didn't mind giving you her opinion when you didn't listen to her warnings. Yep, my mama was a very smart lady. When I was young and would make her angry, she would always say, 'Son, something in you is dying and I hope it's your ignorance.' Yep, Sunny, I sure do miss her." Embarrassed at showing his true emotions Sam turned away. "I'm gonna give you that young pup if she comes in second."

Sunny was shocked. This would be the second gift Sam had given her. Saying nothing more, father and daughter stood together watching the dogs grace the hilltop.

"Look, Sam, Old Blue is in the lead and the pup is right on his heels, holding a tight second!"

"Yep, she's looking pretty good. Stretching out with all she's got."

Forgetting herself for a moment, Sunny became excited, jumping up and down, squealing, "C'mon, on baby! Put on the speed! Give it all you got, girl!" As if the pup understood, it tightened the space then crossed the line. Then Old Blue opened up and took line and tree.

Sam and Sunny were already at the tree waiting to catch each dog to prevent any fighting. When Sam grabbed the pup, he turned to Sunny, saying, "Happy? You got your dog. Betcha you're going to call her Wolf," he grinned.

Sunny leashed Wolf while Sam gathered and leashed the others before they headed back to camp. Once they arrived Sam checked each dog carefully for cuts and bites before staking it out. Taking his logbook, he wrote down the times and places of each pup, then fed and watered them before bedding them down for the night.

As the sun set Sam started a fire and put his coffeepot over the flame. He cut up the rattlesnake meat and peeled potatoes then placed them in a frying pan over the fire. After supper Sunny crawled into her sleeping bag, keeping her eyes on Sam as he sat and stared into the fire, sipping his last cup of coffee. He took the rattles from his pocket and tied them with a string, twisting it in an unusual way around his hands. As he moved his hands back and forth, the rattles began to sing and Sunny, startled, jumped from her bedroll. Sam laughed and handed her the rattle he had made. "I see you at least understand the voice of Snake." He spoke about the power of Snake until the fire burned low. Peace seemed to touch the night as he put more logs on the fire before they turned in.

The sun was just breaking over the ridge when the smell of eggs and boiling coffee caused Sunny to stir from her bed. She took her time getting dressed while Sam doctored his older dogs and let the green ones roam about freely.

"Got something to show you," said Sam, walking away with Sunny following close behind.

As they entered a nearby cave, he let her explore its ancient beauty, pointing out the crystals that were growing from the ceiling and the floor. He showed her how to take a few in the sacred manner and explained their powers. On their way back to camp Sam killed a rabbit for supper. Sunny skinned it out then cut it up while Sam made the fire. After their evening meal he said, "If your life isn't in danger, ain't no sense in killing it. Never waste a kill unless you can eat it or wear it. Well, you better get some sleep, girl. We're gonna be up before daybreak in the morning."

Sunny snuggled deep into her sleeping bag to ward off the cold night air. She watched Sam sitting alone by the fire smoking a hand-rolled cigarette and felt his sadness. When he had finished, she was surprised to see him offer the tobacco to the four winds. For the first time Sunny saw the spiritual side of Sam. He walked with loyalty with the four legs and his spirit soared with the magnificence of the sacred mountains. Sunny smiled inwardly, realizing that Sam did love, but in his own way.

Sunny turned away from the fire and stared into the night with tears in her eyes. As the twinkling stars began to blur, she prayed to her grandmother's spirit:

"Oh, Grandmother, I'm so confused. The months that I have spent with Sam sharing nature have become a common bond. It's forming a relationship that teaches me instinct and survival. Sam is a good mountain man and I'm beginning to understand him. He's teaching me to enjoy a new kind of freedom. We are both learning to accept the other's habits. I know that Sam loves me, even though he always tells me I'm just dumb and he wishes I was a boy. Grandmother, I know you're looking down upon both of us. Please help us have happy hearts." Sunny drifted off to sleep under another enchanted sky, curled in the safety of Mother Earth's arms, knowing her grandmother would always watch over them.

Two weeks later Sam began hiring himself out as a hunting guide. He disliked the job but he needed the money. When the hunters arrived, Sam's attitude changed immediately. He became withdrawn and limited in his conversation. He allowed no drinking when hunting and this applied to everyone. The men respected his knowledge and overlooked his rudeness. After they had unloaded their trucks, Sam collected his money, then allowed them to set up camp. Once this was completed, he explained the hunting procedures in detail. He was adamant about the care of the meat and how the hides would be preserved. It was mandatory for Sunny to stay away from the men and not speak or be around any of them.

Sam took over tending to the pack and readying them for their night hunts. Sunny spent her days running new trails with Wolf and the pup began to sleep with her at night. The bond between them grew as girl and dog became inseparable.

It was the hunters' last night and Sam had promised they would use the dogs to hunt Raccoon. As night approached the dogs were anxious and ready. Sam turned them loose and everyone followed excitedly. About ten miles out the dogs picked up a scent and the run began. It was a fast, hard run and the hunters had trouble keeping up with Sam, who led them from ridge to ridge, through creeks and over rough terrain.

Suddenly Sam shined his flashlight into a tree showing everyone the raccoon wedged in the higher branches. Excitement and stupidity took over one of the younger men and he climbed the tree, thinking he could shake the coon out. Sam stood back watching with delight as the young man vigorously shook the branch and the coon jumped on one of the hunters below. He immediately started kicking and screaming, trying to get free from the raccoon's grip. Sam came to the man's rescue beating it off, as the others unable to see the humor of the situation, decided it was time to return to camp. Ah, how Sam enjoyed pouring raw kerosene into the open wounds of the unfortunate hunter. And as much fun as that had been, he was even happier when they left at daybreak. The young man thanked Sam profusely for doctoring him and gave him some extra money for his trouble before they left. By late afternoon he and Sunny had broken camp and loaded up his dogs.

As they headed home, Sunny asked, "Sam, I'm working real hard to get ready for my first show and I was hoping you'd come. All the important townspeople are going to be there, including the mayor."

"The mayor, huh? You think he's an important person? Bet you don't know that old fool is one of my best moonshine customers."

Sam dropped Sunny and Wolf off in Auntie Rose's driveway, saying, "You did a good job and even beat me out of a good coon dog. You're getting almost as good as a boy."

Life with Sam

It had been raining for days when Sunny stepped out into the cold night air leaving the studio after another grueling rehearsal. Her body ached with pain as she walked home feeling it was impossible to please Master Dana, yet thankful she had the weekends off. When she arrived home, she went directly to bed too tired to even eat.

Sunny crawled out of bed late the following morning and slipped into a tub of hot water to relax her aching muscles. Stepping from the tub, she rubbed her body down with a special mixture of wintergreen oil and cayenne pepper to fire up her muscles before leaving for her morning run.

When she returned, Sunny went to the barn where she overheard Sam talking about going on another run. It was common knowledge that he was the local moonshiner, and the townsfolk overlooked his poor behavior since most were his customers. Although far removed from the town's politics, Sam was very comfortable with the good-old-boy system.

Sam turned and said to Sunny. "I gotta make a run tonight. You wanna go?" She nodded her agreement, then went back to the house to rest for the day.

Around three that afternoon Sam knocked on her bedroom door and before she could reply, he marched in and said, "Hurry up, goddamnit! Get up and get dressed if you're going with me. It's been raining steady, and I gotta get this done before daybreak!"

Sunny wrinkled her nose at the smell of alcohol on Sam's breath. She jumped out of bed, dressed quickly and ran to the truck. Wolf jumped into the front seat, then Sunny slid in and slammed the door. They rode in silence broken by the sound of the windshield wipers fighting against the steady downpour.

As they reached the top of the mountain they drove into a heavy ground fog that held them like prisoners. Sam was forced to hang his head out the window to make sure they didn't run off the road. His patience was dwindling by the time they reached their turnoff. It seemed they crawled along at a snail's pace before they reached their destination. Sunny sat back in the seat, feeling somewhat relaxed as Sam continued to maneuver the truck down the cow trail. Everything was fine until the truck slid to one side, catching the driveshaft on a high rut.

"Goddamnit! I told those bastards to crank this frame up to the sky! The stupid sons of bitches never listen to a word I say!" Sam got out, cursing and kicking the tires. He rocked and pushed the truck until it was finally back on level ground. He drove through the underbrush cursing every tree branch that blocked his view which kept him in a raging dispute with every bush and stone. Sam swore that every *wakanpi* in the world was deliberately attacking him. Since this was customary behavior for Sam under these conditions, Sunny watched in silent amusement, knowing he was acting like an old crazy bear. By the time they reached the whiskey still, Sam's patience was paper thin. He pulled alongside his nephew's truck, slammed the door as he got out to let everyone know he was in a mean and contrary mood. Sunny followed quietly behind as they entered the familiar half-hooded cave.

Sam's nephews, Pete and Peck, had already been there for hours firing up the still. Peck was heavy set, dumb and lazy; while Pete was tall, good-looking and smart. Both knew Sam was smoldering and kept very quiet, not wanting to get into a fistfight. From experience they knew to respond quickly to his every demand and hoped he would not go into one of his tyrannical rages. Keeping their distance, they left the cave and began to unload Sam's truck, but as usual they were not fast enough to suit him.

"Hey, you two assholes, don't take all goddamn day doing woman's work. Pete, let that pinhead brother of yours do that! Go get more wood and keep this goddamn fire hotter than hell!" growled Sam.

In less than an hour the lines were pulling and popping. Sam noticed the temperature gauge was getting ready to blow. "Peck, you dumb sonuvabitch, you're gonna blow us to kingdom come. How many times do I have to show you how to control a fucking fire?"

Pete and Sunny kept silent as they continued working under Sam's relentless demands. Peck was doing his best to get the fire under control when, without a word, he stopped abruptly and ran into the woods.

"Where's that fucking pinhead going now? Boy, get your ass back here!" Sam threw his hat on the ground in disgust. Ignoring him, Peck vanished into the woods. "What the hell is wrong with your brother? Is he deaf as well as dumb? Hell, I don't know how in the fuck he stays alive. One of these days somebody's gonna kill him and put him out of his misery."

Peck ambled back toward them, calmly biting into a fresh plug of tobacco. "Sorry, Uncle. I had to take a piss."

"You piss-ant, you don't have one goddamn reason to go to the woods to take a piss. Why didn't you piss right outside the fucking cave? Next time I call you, you better listen! Running away from me will get your fucking ass filled with buckshot, then you won't need to take a piss!"

Letting the fresh tobacco juice run down his chin, Peck calmly answered, "Well, Uncle, Sunny being a girl and all."

Sam got within inches of Peck's face. "As far as Sunny's concerned, she's none of your fucking business. She knows what the fuck to do when a man is around. Geezus, Man! Wipe your fucking mouth. Don't you know you act like a fucking pig! You think like one and you smell like one! Between your fucking pea brain and this fucking weather, I swear we won't get out of here until next Christmas! Now get your head out of your ass and let's get this shit ready to go."

Sam calmly turned around and started helping Pete set up the screens for the run.

"Yep, Uncle, looks pretty good. It's clearer than spring water."

"Yep, I betcha it's hundred and ninety proof or more. "Probably kick like a mule. Wait till those city folks get a taste of this shit." Sam laughed passing around a cup for everyone to take a sip.

It was about mid-morning when the sun finally broke through the clouds. Sunny knew it was time for her to leave and wandered off with Wolf. She spent the rest of the morning throwing sticks from the rocky shelf above the cave for Wolf to retrieve. Without thinking, she threw one too wide and Wolf jumped in the air to catch it, disappearing over the ledge. Driven by fear, Sunny ran to the edge to see her beloved pet thrashing helplessly below in a vat of boiling mash. Screaming, she raced down to the vat to see Wolf's hair was already falling from her body. Sunny shrieked, "Oh, my God! Please do something!"

"It's no fucking use, Sunny! It's too late! What the fuck! Can't you see the goddamn animal is being boiled alive?" Sam picked up his rifle and shoved Sunny aside. "Move out of my fucking way!" He shot into the vat, then all was still.

An eerie silence engulfed the camp; even the trees held their leaves motionless as nature bowed to Wolf's unfortunate demise. The sickening smell of cooked flesh floated upward as the wind spread the news of another sad fatality. Wolf had returned to the freedom of the spirit world.

"Don't just stand there, get the goddamn animal outta the fucking mash!"

Pete and Peck quickly grabbed the dog's body with meat hooks and dragged it to the edge of the woods, leaving it for the scavengers to eat. Sunny watched in anguish, then ran to dig a hole to bury her loving pet. After placing the dog in the grave, Sunny covered it carefully then lay over the mound and sobbed, knowing her conduct would bring deep rage from Sam. But Sunny was beyond caring and continued to wail with uncontrollable tears.

Sam walked over and stared coldly seething with rage. He raised his fist in warning. "You're nothing but a whimpering female! So shut the fuck up before you join that goddamn Wolf. It happened. So what! It was your stupidity that killed her. Look at you. How many times do I have to tell you that emotions are for fools? Do you want to end up like Hazel and spend your life being afraid of some fucking man? If you don't get your shit together you're gonna end up just like her, becoming another fucking baby machine for some asshole! Is that what you want out of life, huh? Now get your ass up a tree and keep your eyes peeled for strangers." Sam walked away and calmly checked on his run. "Should be all right. Let it settle before you strain out the rest of the hair. Probably take about three times."

Sunny picked up the rifle and went to nurse her heartbreak alone. Sam's brutal words had cut too deep into her soul. Feeling her insides boiling with hatred as she whispered soundlessly, "Someday, Sam, the tables will turn and I'll be there! Wait and see, Sam. Someday I'll grow up and make you pay!"

She climbed onto a high branch of the tree and wedged herself up against the trunk for safety. Placing the rifle across her knees, she stared out over the peaceful terrain. She cried openly over Wolf, knowing the tree understood her grief. As night came and the moon appeared, Sunny watched the shadowy clouds play over the land, slowly lifting their veil to let the stars shine from high above, giving the world a soft, nurturing light. She saw the highway in the distance like a shining strip of ribbon looped across the entire top of the mountain.

Suddenly a cold chill ran through her and Sunny knew something was wrong. Moving cautiously up to the next limb, she looked out to see a car parked in the deep shadows by the side of the highway. She wondered if she should tell Sam, but decided to wait since he seemed to think he already knew everything. Sunny kept one eye on the car as she idly played with the rifle, aiming it at Sam and saying, "Click! You're dead."

At that moment Sam looked up and a knowing grin crossed his lips. The realization that he knew her thoughts filled Sunny with terror and she set the rifle down.

"Oh, Grandmother! What am I doing? I want to kill him. What makes me this way? I can't stop what I feel. Please help me get rid of these bad thoughts before I end up as crazy as Sam."

Sunny felt a comforting presence and listened with her heart. "Be patient, Granddaughter. You and Sam will learn much from each other. In time you will understand that *Wakan Tanka* has a bigger plan for both of you, but for now, trust what you already know. Shift your mind and reshape your thinking." At that moment Sunny felt Cheering Woman's magic touch lift her from her body and she was running in warm sunlight through beautiful green fields alongside Wolf and her grandmother. "Thank you, Little One," said Cheering Woman. "Wolf was a wonderful gift. As you can see, we have become good friends."

"Little friend, be happy for the time we had together," said Wolf. "Sam will teach you the pecking order of a true wolf pack. His lessons are hard, but weakness in a warrioress is far more harmful than a strong enemy. Remember, you must know a person before you expose your emotions."

Suddenly Sunny found herself back in the tree with new understanding, freedom means life.

Sunny watched Sam and her cousins load their trucks and warm up the engines. Sam called to her, saying, "Let's go!" Pete and Peck pulled their truck forward as Sam pulled around, letting Sunny in. She felt rather strange without Wolf at her side, but her excitement at being on her first whiskey run quickly claimed all of her attention. Sam's truck moved slowly under its heavy load as they left Whiskey Flats. The sky once again became starless as heavy clouds gathered and another storm threatened. "Goddamn this fucking weather. I hate driving wet roads with a full load." Sunny smiled. "What's so fucking funny, you little shit?"

"The truck is sitting level for a change," she answered timidly.

"Yeah, a full load of shine under us needs a good souped up engine with heavy duty springs and one helluva driver. Think it's time to change out these springs, though. With this goddamn load it feels like I'm sitting on the frame." As they pulled onto the highway, he stared at the road. "Sorry about the pup. Get you another one."

"It's okay. It was my fault. Should have known better. Oh, I saw a car parked over on the highway about ten minutes ago. Thought I'd better mention it."

"So that's the sonuvabitch I see in the sideview mirror. Their headlights are moving up a little too fast, so hang on partner." Sam began to pull levers while pressing the pedal to the metal. Sunny felt a surge of fear coupled with excitement as she watched the trees blur outside the window. "Hey! Trust me, kid! Let's give them a little ride for their money. This engine can take anything on the road, particularly with your old man behind the wheel."

Sam drove at speeds Sunny had never experienced and when the wheels began to lift off the ground, she gripped the edge of her seat until her knuckles turned white. "Easy, girl. You gotta know your pony if you expect to do this kind of driving," he bragged, spinning onto a dirt road and pulling to a dead stop. Killing the headlights, he let the engine idle. When the other car passed and its taillights began to fade, Sam revved up the engine and drove at breakneck speed in total darkness as he closed in on them. Sam passed them, waving as he gave them a big shit-eating grin. "Now we're where we want to be. You always want to know where your enemy is. I'd rather they follow than chase us."

As they neared the one-lane road that cut into the side of the mountain, Sunny held her breath as Sam put the pedal to the metal, banking into a narrow, blind curve. Working the steering wheel around another sharp bend, he banked it into the last hairpin curve. "Hey, relax, kid. We ain't gonna see the bottom of this old mountain." The truck leaned hard into the next curve and groaned under the stress. He hit the lights scraping the edge of a three-foot rock wall as he pulled out of the turn.

Sunny saw a straight vertical drop of thousands of feet and knew there was no room for error. If Sam made a wrong move they would go over the embankment to an instant death. She stared transfixed at Sam.

Suddenly a strange thing began to happen. A powerful spirit took over every fiber of his body and he maneuvered the truck with utmost skill, weaving it from curve to curve as though he had been bestowed the hands of a wizard. "Hang on, baby, hang on for daddy," soothed Sam, talking to the truck.

A blast of light hit the back of the truck and a rifle shot took out the back window. "Hit the floor," yelled Sam as more bullets sprayed from all directions. "Gimme that fucking pistol!" said Sam, motioning to the side pocket. Sunny dug it out and handed it to him as she lay huddled on the floorboard. "I'll slow down on the next curve! When I say jump, you jump…and roll as you hit the ground!" Sam down-shifted the truck, bouncing off the last breaker wall. As Sunny opened the door to jump Sam yelled, "Stay low, girl, and get your ass behind something till I come get you. Now, jump! Go! Go! Go!"

Sunny leapt out of the truck and hit the gravel just as the other car flipped over the breaker wall and rolled out of control down the embankment. Shaking and bleeding, she hid behind the nearest boulder until she saw Sam's truck hit the side of the mountain. As it burst into flames, Sunny raced toward it, screaming, "Sam, please! Please, God! Don't let Sam die!"

"Hey, hey, easy, girl. I'm okay. Are you?" asked Sam, walking toward her with an open canning jar in his hand.

"Uh huh. Little skinned."

"Aw, don't worry about that, you'll live." They walked over to the edge of the cliff and watched the car encased in flames. Suddenly a loud boom echoed throughout the canyon. "Looks like someone had a bad accident. Guess some people just can't drive in these mountains. Oh, well. Some folks gotta learn things the hard way. Don't think anybody's going to live through that one, but if they do, they've sure got a helluva long walk back to the city," Sam chuckled, taking another swig from his fruit jar. "Damn! Sure hated to lose that load. Had to drive her into the mountain, but would've lost her anyway on the next curve. Fuck! I'd rather drive her into a mountain than have a fucking highjacker take it from me. Ain't nobody ever taken anything from Sam the Dog Man and lived to tell their grandkids. Ain't ever gonna happen either. Sure hope Nephew got through so we'll at least make a few bucks. You were pretty brave back there. Kinda proud of that."

"I don't know. I was too scared to think."

"You hungry?"

"Kinda."

"We'll walk in the back way and have breakfast with Auntie Rose. No need to worry her, let's just keep it between us."

"Oh, I would never tell anyone!"

"Why not?"

"Cause you'd never take me with you again." Both laughed as they picked up their pace and began their long walk off the mountain.

Sunny walked on eggshells around Auntie Rose for the next few weeks. Auntie's suspicions grew, but Sunny knew it would not be wise for her to find out. As things settled down and life got back to normal, Sam stopped by one evening after supper and in his most charming way said, "Sister, I'm taking Sunny with me. We'll be back rather late, so don't wait up for us." He winked in Sunny's direction as she picked up her jacket and headed with him to the truck.

Sunny did not know the purpose of their trip and was surprised when they arrived at the local roadhouse. Sam parked a ways down the road and she followed him into the smoky bar where she saw many familiar faces scattered about the room. They were the high rolling movers and shakers in town. When she spotted Slim, Sam's agent and trusted friend, along with a few new faces, Sunny knew a big game was brewing.

Sam slid onto a barstool next to Slim, asking, "What's the action?"

"Big. About ten long. Mostly new and dumb money." Slim slipped Sam a roll of bills that would choke a horse, saying, "Partners?"

"Yep. Same as before, fifty-fifty. Honey, gimme a double shot of Jim Beam with a water back," he said to a waitress, caressing her butt as she walked away to get his drink.

"Sam, push this game to the limit. I'll take all the side action," said Slim as they discussed and set up the signals. "The matchbook cover open, don't make a move. Closed, you're safe on first base." After a couple of drinks, they left the bar and stepped through the curtains to the backroom.

"Something doesn't feel right. Maybe you should pass tonight," whispered Sunny.

"Don't start that Indian shit, girl. You shake that goddamn feeling before you kill my luck," snapped Sam. "Now stay close," he said, gently scruffing up her hair.

"Hey, I'm with you. We're here to play, not to stay. Right?" she asked with a flippant attitude. The men laughed as Sunny went to the corner and they took their places to work the room. Acting a little tipsy, Sam roared into action like a crazy old bear, laying down a fistful of wrinkled bills and yelling, "Hey, can anybody get in this game?"

Sunny forgot her worries and smiled as he began his hustle. Sam ordered a round of drinks for everyone and smooth as silk slipped in a pair of flats. And once again Sunny watched him ride the edge. He loved playing his game balls to the wall. Sam might be wild and crazy, but he was good at what he did and dice was his game. Sunny watched him roll the ivories again and again, busting out each time. Sam made his own dice and he carried them around in a shoebox hidden in his truck, just in case he might find a game that needed a special pair. Sunny thought of the many hours he spent in the barn switching dice while shooting against a mirror. Like Sam always said, "When the hand can trick the eye, it's time to go make money."

Sam the Dog Man was a drinking, gambling Indian with killer instincts. He was a clever coyote who used his skills well, yet still followed his hunches. At times the drunker he was, the better he controlled the dice. Sam loved to perform, and tonight he was playing the role of just another dumb, loudmouth, drunken Indian. Once again she watched her father set the stage for battle using his wits to go for another victory.

He continued drinking heavily then leaned back and studied the pot, judging it to be about five thousand dollars. "That's pretty high stakes for a dumb Indian. I wonder if I got enough money? What the fuck! Easy come, easy go." He shoved more crumpled bills toward the pot with an innocent grin. He grabbed the dice and shook them close to his ear as though they were sharing secrets with him. Then he let out a war whoop over his newfound knowledge. "Yep, they say they're coming out big!"

Sam crapped out and everybody laughed. He fell over on the floor bemoaning his losses and asking lame questions about the rules of the game. This was a typical scam of Sam's, particularly when new blood was in the game. He didn't give a shit what people thought, he gambled from his gut with great skill. The other players, disgusted at Sam's stupidity, hoped the loudmouth drunken Indian would go away, but he dug into his pockets again and lay down more money to feed their greed. Smokers, sniffers, winners and losers, friends and enemies were all participating in this game, and Sam wanted it all.

Hours passed and petty arguments increased as the game intensified. Slim closed the matchbook and gave Sam a warning look as he walked out with the side bets bulging from his pockets. When Sunny realized Sam had no backup, she moved closer. The dice were passed from man to man. Some made their point while others walked away broke. Sam thrived on taking chances and called his point, bragging, "The sweeter the pot, the better for me. Lay your money down, boys." He knew he was hot and believed a good gambler should take all or nothing. He loved feeling the power of the dice in his skillful, magical hands and could switch the shaves and weights like a champ. The game was reaching a pitch of twisted frenzy when Sam dropped a lighted cigarette and spilled his drink, signaling to Sunny that he was moving in for the kill.

Feeling the volatile air of danger, Sunny moved closer and whispered, "Sit up! Watch what you're doing!" Sam looked over his shoulder, winked, then ignored her.

A disgruntled player with blood in his eyes grabbed the dice, saying, "Hey, Indian, let me see those goddamn bones." The room went dead quiet. The dice were passed around and each player examined them, then passed them on to the next player. Finding nothing unusual, the displeased player grabbed a water glass, saying, "I don't know what you're doing, Chief, but as long as I'm in this game, you're coming out of a glass. Now you bump those bones off the wall!" he ordered, slamming down a shank to make his point.

Sam letting spittle ooze from the corner of his mouth, looked him in the eye as a slow smile crossed his face. "Sure, big man. I like shooting out of a glass." He placed the dice in the glass and stared coldly at his opponent. "And you'll do the same, white boy. Coming out!" yelled Sam, embellishing his threat with a big belly laugh and calling his point. The dice left the glass and bounced off the wall like a couple of rubber balls as his point sat smiling at the crowd. Once again Sam had proven the hand was quicker than the eye. As he raked the pot his way, tempers flared and a fight broke out. As Sunny stuffed handfuls of money into her boots a shot rang out, taking out the overhead lights. Without warning the room turned into the Fourth of July as Sam and Sunny scrambled toward the exit, dodging knives, bullets, chairs, bottles and bodies. "Stay down on your belly, girl, and crawl!" As they inched along the floor, Sam let out a deep guttural moan, "I've been stabbed!"

Sunny took the lead, moving quickly for the rear of the room. When she saw the place was surrounded by police, she motioned Sam to the ladies bathroom. Crawling out of the window, they ended up in the isolated parking lot behind the roadhouse. As they jumped into a ditch, Sunny saw Sam was badly hurt and guided him down a narrow stream. They hid under some overgrown weeds while flashlights held by shadowy figured policemen bobbed up and down as the law closed in on them.

"Hold your breath, Sam!" whispered Sunny as they slipped under the water.

"I know that sonuvabitchin' Indian is around here! I want that bastard, bad!" yelled one of the policemen, flashing his light all around. Sunny could see the light from under the water and waited until it faded to darkness before coming up for air. As they both surfaced, Sam gasped, "What the fuck are you doing? Trying to drown me?"

They eased down toward the open river, hugging the embankment. Sam had lost too much blood and was close to passing out. She pulled him along inch by inch, working her way through the undergrowth until they reached the mouth of the river. Seeing the beams of many flashlights on the bank, Sunny had no choice but to turn inward toward the dreaded marshlands that were infested with beds of blood-sucking leeches. Sunny prayed for guidance as they approached the murky waters. As the water turned red, she felt their writhing, slimy bodies moving through the mud and knew they were feasting on Sam's wounds. The swamp had become a carnivorous trap.

Sam was in and out of consciousness as Sunny continued to pull him along, thrashing through the water to high ground. She found a high spot on a mud bank and pulled him up. Sam groaned, then went limp. Ripping off his shirt, Sunny gasped at the sight of the blood gushing out of the open wound now covered with leeches. Frantically, she began to pull them off as best she could, then packed the wound with mud and tied his shirt tightly around it, then got back in the water.

Sam groaned, "I can't make it. Leave me and go get help!"

"Goddamnit, Sam! You've got to make it to the truck!" Sunny knew they had to get out of the swamp if Sam was to live. Forcing him to lean on her, she pulled him along by his belt as they struggled back into the water toward swifter currents. It seemed forever before Sunny pulled him onto another embankment and forced him to crawl to the truck.

"Come on, Sam! It's just a little further." Sunny helped him get in the truck and climbed into the driver's seat. Glancing over at Sam, she saw to her horror that almost every inch of his skin was covered with black, squirming leeches. "Oh, fuck! The sons of bitches are everywhere!" She leaned over and began to pull them off with her hands.

"Just leave them alone and get us the hell out of here." No sooner had he spoken, Sam slumped over in the seat.

"No, Sam, no! Don't pass out on me! I can't drive! You've got to tell me what to do!"

He struggled to sit up. "Easy, girl, easy. You can do this. It's the same as driving the tractor around the farm. Just calm down and listen to me. Leave the lights off. Turn the key and ease off the brake. Let it coast down the hill." Sunny did what Sam instructed as he continued to encourage her. "That's good, girl. Everything's gonna be okay. Now keep your foot on the clutch. When we reach the bottom, let it out and step on the gas."

Sunny was shaking but followed his every word. As they neared the bottom of the hill she took her foot off the clutch, stepped on the gas and the engine kicked over. She turned onto the highway and drove without lights until she came near their farm, then cut across the back field following the cow path to the barn. As soon as the truck came to a stop, she jumped out and ran to get Auntie Rose.

Sizing up the situation, Auntie Rose pulled Sam from the truck as she said, "Get the nephews, then hide the truck in the barn!"

As Auntie Rose pulled Sam along toward the house, Sunny ran to the sleeping quarters and awakened everyone, yelling, "Hurry! Sam's been stabbed. I'm sure the sheriff is close behind! We've got to hide the truck!"

Dressing quickly, Peck said, "Go! Get the hell outta here! I'll take care of everything." Sunny looked around to make sure it was still safe then ran to the house as the others moved the truck into the side barn. Breaking open bales of hay and piling empty crates around, they buried it.

Sunny dashed into the kitchen where she stripped off her clothes, becoming nauseous at the sight of the leeches covering her body. Grabbing a box of salt, she rubbed her body with handfuls at a time until they fell from her flesh, leaving oozing trails of blood. She splashed her wounds with rubbing alcohol to disinfect them. Then, feeling as if her body was on fire, she wrapped herself in a robe and joined Sam and Auntie Rose.

Sam moaned with pain as Auntie Rose methodically cleaned his wounds. "Sam, you've lost too much blood. I've got to stop this bleeding. Sunny, go heat the blade of your knife until it's red hot, then bring it to me." While Sunny ran to get her knife, Auntie Rose handed Sam his fruit jar. He sucked it dry and numbness took over his body.

When Sunny returned she handed her knife to Auntie Rose, telling Sam, "Gonna fix you up, Sam. Just like we do the dogs." Sam laughed weakly and broke into a sweat as Auntie Rose placed the blade onto the open wound and skillfully worked it around the edges. Sunny grew nauseous as she watched his skin turn black and curl around the edges. Sam let out one bloodcurdling scream, then passed out.

The house was filled with the stench of burning flesh as Auntie Rose mopped his brow, telling Sunny to burn cedar, sage and sweetgrass. When Sunny returned she worriedly asked, "He's gonna be all right, isn't he? Grandmother always told me that the devil rides with him and when he leaves this world it will be from old age, not from his crazy shenanigans."

"We'll see, Child. We'll see. What happened?"

"There was a fight. Please, Auntie, don't ask me to tell you anymore, because I don't want to lie to you." Thankful they were both alive, Auntie Rose smiled and did not press the issue.

Headlights flashed in the driveway. "Quick! Turn off the lights," whispered Auntie Rose, running to peek out the window. "It's okay. It's Uncle." Sunny breathed a sigh of relief.

About noon a few of the Indian brothers met around the kitchen table with Auntie Rose. "We all know how Hazel acts under pressure. I'm concerned about her saying too much," said Auntie.

"Don't worry. I've sent a couple of guys over to stay at the place and bring her and the kids to the farm," answered Pete.

Sam lay racked with fever and infection for weeks. It was rare for him to stay so close to home, but necessary for his body to mend. During this time a strong relationship began to develop between him and Sunny. One day while she was changing his bedding, Sunny decided it was the perfect time to discuss her plans. "Sam, you know there's nothing in this town for me. I'm working on this scholarship and if I get it, I want to go to New York."

"There's nothing wrong with this place. And besides, what makes you think a breed can do anything in New York?" he scowled, staring out the window. "You're barely fifteen years old. What the hell do you think you can do in New York? So just get that notion outta your head. You ain't going nowhere! Besides you hate school and you can study that dance crap right here. Now get outta here and don't talk to me again about this bullshit!"

Sunny had worked hard and was determined not to give up her chance to do something with her life. Angrily she fluffed his pillows, then tossed them into place and bolted from the room in a huff, passing Auntie Rose as she left the house.

"What in the world is going on?" asked Auntie Rose as she entered Sam's room.

"Ah, that fucking kid has a notion about going to New York. She's so goddamn stubborn! Can't tell that mule nothing! Hell, what can a kid do in New York except get into trouble?" Auntie Rose remained quiet, knowing this was not the time to discuss the plan with Sam, he needed time to digest the idea a bit more before pursuing the subject any further.

Auntie Rose found Sunny on the porch swing and joined her, saying, "Give him time, Sunny. You'll get your dream. Be patient. I assure you Sam will eventually come around."

Another month had come and gone and Sam was up and around. Early one afternoon, Sunny came home from practice to find Sam weeding the garden. She quietly joined in helping with the garden chores. As Sam dug the weeds from around the plants, she said, "Let me dig out those weeds and loosen the soil for you. You can pick the tomatoes and green onions for dinner."

As Sunny worked, Sam walked over and sat at the edge of the garden. When she was finished, Sunny put down the hoe and joined him. Sam handed her a salt shaker and a fresh tomato.

"Okay, Sunny, you didn't follow me out here for nothing. What the hell do you want now?"

"Sam, please talk to me without arguing. Sam nodded, listening to what she had to say.

Sunny spoke of the prejudice that the townsfolk had toward the family. "Sam, they'll never let me do anything here."

"Why not? Nobody gave you a damn thing. You've worked hard for what you've learned and who in the hell in this town is big enough to stop what you want to do? You're my daughter!"

"That's one of the problems. Everyone's afraid of you. I pay dearly for being your daughter. And that's okay with me! I just want to get something straight. You won't always be able to take care of the family. Someday you'll grow tired and sick and we'll need money to take care of things. It was you and grandmother who taught me that life has a twin called death and that we never know when that circle will close on us.

Someday we'll join Grandmother, but until then I want a career that will give me the money to take care of the family."

Sam sat up straight, bragging, "Hell, I'm as healthy as a horse. I've got a long way to go before I die. And as far as I'm concerned, those fucking people can kiss my ass. Fuck the people! They goddamn better be afraid of me if they know what's good for them!" Tears welled up in Sunny's eyes as she realized it was useless to expect him to understand. Seeing he had hurt her feelings, he changed the subject.

"You really want to have a career rather than a family?"

"Yes," she murmured.

"Auntie says you're real good."

"Sam, I am good. I've worked hard to become a dancer. Dancing with the ballet company will give me my last letter of approval and I can go to New York on a scholarship. But what I want to do first is return to the reservation for my Womanhood Ceremony."

"What the fuck, girl! You want to do what?" Sam threw down the salt shaker.

"I have to go home! I've had my first moon."

"Hell no! How many times do I have to tell you, you're living in the white world now and you don't need that fucking ceremony. So, just forget about the goddamn reservation!"

"Sam, wait! Listen to me! You say I'm like Grandmother in many ways. Well, let me learn more of her ways. You know I need a medicine person before I can have this ceremony. I'm not being disrespectful, but if you don't let me go, I'll run away."

Sam threw the basket of tomatoes to the ground and stood up, shaking his fist in anger. "Get in the fucking house and don't you ever threaten me again. I swear, girl, you were born just to fucking aggravate me. Now is that all you want?"

"Yes and no. I want to go home, then I want to go to New York."

"Goddamnit! You never give up! Let me fucking think about it." Sam was so angry he was stammering.

Several weeks later, Sunny found Sam in the garden leaning on his shovel. Walking toward him, she blurted out, "Sam, I talked with Shung'. She says even if I'm living in the white world I have to come home to have my Womanhood Ceremony.

Stunned, Sam dropped his shovel, saying, "You're nothing but a damn pain in the ass! I haven't made up my mind, so don't bother me with this shit again!"

Sunny was startled by his sudden outburst, but stood her ground. "It's time for my Womanhood Ceremony, and it's time for me to do another *Hanblecheyapi*. I need to go home, Sam. I've also talked to Auntie Rose and she thinks it's a good idea."

"You're crazy! You're fucking crazy! You just forget about the goddamn reservation."

"Please, Sam. Listen to me! I can't do what I need to do here. I need to go to the medicine people. Shung' will help me. I'm not exactly asking you Sam. If you don't let me go, I'll do what I said and run away."

Sam threw the shovel at her. "Get away from me before I kill you, and stop your fucking threats! I swear! All you ever do is want, want, want! Goddamnit, Sunny. I already told you I'd think about it. But don't think I'm driving you all the way back to that damn reservation."

A week later, Sam and Sunny were in the truck heading for the reservation. Bursting with excitement as the landscape grew more familiar, Sunny could hardly contain herself. Looking over at Sam, she saw a new calmness on his face and knew he too was glad to be returning to his old home.

Before they left Sunny had written a long letter to Shung' confirming that they were coming. Shung' and Otis stood waiting on the front porch as the old truck pulled up to the house where Sunny had spent so many happy years. Shung' had prepared everything for her arrival, and there was a steady stream of visitors throughout the afternoon and evening wanting to see them. Sam and Sunny were very pleased to hear Cheering Woman's name being mentioned with great love and respect as the people told stories about her sacred work.

Sunny could feel Cheering Woman's presence in the people and was proud to see her grandmother's medicine work was continuing through Shung' and Otis. It seemed Cheering Woman whispered to her from every life force on the reservation and it felt good to be home. Sunny could even hear her grandmother's words coming from Shung's mouth. She honored Shung', and felt a new respect for this medicine woman who had once been Cheering Woman's apprentice.

Like Cheering Woman would have done, Shung' wasted no time in getting Sunny prepared for her Womanhood Ceremony. Sunny spent a great deal of time sitting under the arbor with different medicine people preparing for another *Hanblecheyapi* and learning her role in the upcoming ceremony.

Sam helped Otis with the chores and admired Sunny from a distance as he watched her gentleness and her respect toward Shung' and the elders. His daughter was turning out to be a lot like his mother. He was glad that Sunny had forced him to return to the reservation and realized that the raw wound of losing his mother was beginning to heal.

Everyone was up before dawn the following morning, excited that Sunny was going to go and lament for her second *Hanblecheyapi*. When Sam joined her in the *Inipi*, Sunny was both surprised and pleased. When the last round was over and everyone had left the sweat lodge, Shung' took Sunny to her private quarters.

"Have you had your first moon?" Sunny nodded as Shung' continued. "The *Ishna Ta Awi Cha Lowan*, the preparing for womanhood, is a ceremony that you must observe each month during your moon time. It's a transitional change, and a very sacred thing for all women. Since you have had your first moon time, you are now the same as your sacred mother, the earth. You too will bear children and train them in the sacred manner of your pipe. Understand this is to make you aware that you are leaving behind your girlhood ways and learning how to become a strong woman. As woman, you will know pain and hardship. You will be as Buffalo and train your children in a sacred manner to follow the old ways. You will nurture and help the needy while sharing your knowledge to help others grow strong and happy.

"Once long ago we had a grandmother lodge for our women. It was there that girls your age learned how to be a good wife and mother. It was there that the grandmothers shared their secrets as they taught the young women to become industrious and beautiful artists. They learned how to make hides soft and sew their tipis and clothing, placing their power in every bead and bone used in decoration. As they worked together they shared their stories of how they had walked in honor as women.

"If you had lived then, you would have been excluded from the tribe during your moon and required to live separately from your husband and family at this powerful, sacred time. As a woman you may have a husband that will bring you heartache. As a mother you will know pain. These many sufferings must be done in silence so that you will grow into a strong, spiritual woman. Since you will be living in the white world for many years before you return to us, you must keep a moon room for yourself during this sacred time. A woman is very powerful during this time and she must be careful around all men, particularly medicine men, as she will take away their power.

"Auntie Rose has been through this ceremony. I've spoken to her and she will become the older woman that will teach you all the virtues and the comfortable beauty in being a woman of power. She will be with you until you understand all the responsibilities of a woman's life. During your *Hanblecheyapi* call upon White Buffalo Calf Woman, the bringer of our pipe, and ask her to guide you to become a powerful woman.

Long ago we knew that *Tatanka* was our closest relative. We call upon Mother Buffalo to ask her to breathe upon our young girls during this transition just as she does for her newborn. When Mother Buffalo gives birth she always blows a red film over her calf. This keeps it warm and safe. Pray for her to come and give you this blessed gift so you may be born as a kind, giving, patient, persevering woman.

"When you were a mere toddler, your grandmother told me that you would leave the reservation, but when you returned you were to do a *Hanblecheyapi* before your Womanhood Ceremony. Smiling, Shung' handed Sunny a beautiful pipe wrapped in buffalo hide. "I was to tell you that she had awakened this medicine pipe for you and that I should present it to you for the completion of these two ceremonies."

Tears of joy stung Sunny's eyes as she took the sacred gift, then headed up the hill to begin her second vision quest. This time it seemed easier to settle down and get to work. She recalled her first *Hanblecheyapi* in great detail and found nothing had changed. It was as though she was beginning from where she had left off the first time, except that this time she felt much wiser.

The soil that she sat upon was rich with new life. The everblowing winds embraced her with the sweet smells of the flowering wild plants that graced the plains. The nights were chilly and the days were hot, but Sunny welcomed everything that appeared to her and was thankful she no longer danced with fear. Her newfound assurance created a certain power within her and it was much easier to leave her body any time she chose. To quench her thirst she would visit Father River; when she was cold she went to Father Sun to feel the warmth. Many spirits came and spoke of her future. Sunny was especially happy when her Wolf came and stayed with her until she stepped out of the pit on the fifth day.

When Shung' came for her, both were proud of her success as they walked down the hill for her final *Inipi*. During the sweat, Sunny spoke in detail about what she had seen and listened intently as the elders explained her visions. These wonderful gifts helped her find a grace in her peace. Sunny felt serene and secure with her future walk on earth. Her *Hanblecheyapi* had given her a direction and the power to walk in a spirit-guided way. Sunny knew she was finally bonded to the Wolf Clan and would always walk as Wolf.

Sam was proud of what she had accomplished. When they left the *Inipi*, he watched her from afar as she loaded his mother's sacred pipe and went to smoke it with the elders who were waiting for her under the arbor.

Sunny's world seemed full of peace, and she felt strong and whole as she entered the lodge to begin her *Ishna Ta Awi Cha Lowan*. She was humbled when she saw Sam and four generations of relatives waiting to help her learn the value of all those yet to come.

Otis sat in the West with an altar of dirt in front of him. Taking a piece of sweetgrass, he lit it from a hot coal and prayed. "We have done as you have asked the people to do so long ago, *Tunka'shila*. May all these things we have done for this young, virgin girl be held in our hearts in a scared manner. May her ancestors help her walk as a strong woman on Mother Earth. We ask for the powers in our universe to come and help her carry a strong pipe as she follows her destiny and births the power of beauty for the children to come."

Otis called in all the powers from the West, North, East, South and the four winds. He walked around the tipi six times as a bull buffalo, chanting an old buffalo song. At the end of each trip around, he blew a red liquid over Sunny until the tipi was engulfed in a red mist. When this was done, Otis dug a buffalo wallow and drew a straight North-South line then an East-West line through its center. Picking up the buffalo skull whose eyes were filled with sage, he painted a red line around its head from horn to horn. After drawing another red line down the center he placed the skull on the altar. Shung' handed Otis a bowl of sacred water and he placed a handful of wild cherries in it before placing it in front of the skull, asking Sunny to stand in front of the altar.

Reaching his hands up to *Wakan Tanka*, Otis prayed, "*Hau, Tunka'shila*. These cherries represent the fruits of life. May their sweetness stretch from this woman's heart to Mother Earth and to Father Sky." Gently holding a cherry branch upward, he continued, "See this buffalo hair that I found on this branch? Buffalo is joining our ceremony and is offering a piece of its hair to this young woman. Oh, Great Spirit, no matter what comes, if anything stands over this woman, it must be sacred because she reaches from the earth to the sky and touches all that is."

Sunny reached her hands upward to Great Spirit so that she might become a branch on the Tree of Life as Otis prayed, "You are as pure as a holy woman and you will always be aware of where you place your steps as you walk upon Mother Earth in a sacred manner." He took a sacred bundle and rubbed it over her head. Shung' smoked off a piece of buffalo meat then handed it to him. He offered it to the four directions, saying to Sunny, "You will be merciful to your children as *Wakan Tanka* has been to you. If a child should come to you hungry, you will take the food from your mouth and feed it." He then placed the buffalo meat into Sunny's mouth. "At the end of this ceremony you will leave your girlhood innocence behind. You will walk as woman," said Otis as Sunny left the tipi with all of her relatives following in a sacred manner.

Sunny, the woman, was taken to the arbor to sit with the elders. Having already loaded Cheering Woman's medicine pipe, she offered it to Shung' then sat at the elders' feet with head lowered in deep respect. After a prayer had been said and the pipe had been smoked, everyone sat in silent reflection, listening to Sunny as she spoke of the experiences of the past four days and nights. Sam listened intently, tears of pride rolling down his cheeks as each elder interpreted her vision.

"You must hold your vision in silence," instructed Otis. "You must follow these spiritual directions if you are to complete your birth purpose. This is a great undertaking, and as Medicine, Shung' and I offer you this special bundle to help build your power. *Sku'ya*, always walk with integrity and honor yourself by keeping a pure heart. Call upon this spirit bundle when you need help. Hold your vision in silence and create its power through thought."

Shung' stood then placed her hands on Sunny's head and prayed: "*Hau, Tunka'shila.* Thank you for my daughter's powerful vision. Cheering Woman prepared her well for this long and hard walk. Keep her safe as she travels the world. Help her find the truth she seeks and let her bring it back when she returns to us. Keep her free and strong on her earthly journey so she may return and help the people save the land. As she leaves us, we will travel with her in our hearts. Help her feel and know our love so that she may rest with the strength of the blood of her long ago ancestors that flows in her veins."

Shung' picked up the bundle that was wrapped in deerhide and handed it to Sunny. "We offer this bundle to assist you in this dignified undertaking. It will protect you as you walk in honor, proud of who you are. Throughout your life you will add to this bundle as you grow in spiritual power." Sunny took the bundle and stood with it while all the people walked forward to give her gifts. Shung' and the grandmothers served the giveaway foods and gave gifts to the poor as Cheering Woman had done long ago. When the last of the people had departed, Otis and Shung' helped pack up Sam's truck, and by daybreak the following morning Sam and Sunny were well on their way home.

They spoke little of the ceremonies, but both enjoyed the food that Shung' had packed for them as they laughed together over some of Cheering Woman's old stories.

It was hard for Sam to accept that Sunny had become a woman, and he feared that he would soon have to let her go. Although he could not bring himself to share the feelings she so longed to hear, he did listen with a more attentive ear about her dreams.

When they pulled into the driveway, a very excited Auntie Rose approached them waving a letter in her hand. As the three sat around the kitchen table sharing stories from the reservation, Sunny waited on pins and needles for Auntie Rose to open the stark, white envelope. At last with trembling hands she ripped it open and unfolded the letter inside. Reading it quickly, she discovered that once Sunny had performed for Master Dana, she would be qualified for her scholarship. "Sam, she's been accepted!" Sunny could hardly believe her ears, and unable to contain herself she danced around the kitchen holding the letter close to her heart, knowing this was the beginning of her future.

The following day after she told Master Dana of her acceptance, she soon found he was harder than ever on her, but this was fine with Sunny because it was going to help her accomplish her dream. His grueling sessions were filled with pain and sweat. Being a lover of discipline, Sunny met the demands of each new challenge with a smile as she remembered how the townspeople had rejected her for being Indian and the daughter of a whiskey running gambler. With these thoughts, her energy and determination soared tenfold.

The news elated Auntie Rose who could hardly contain herself, but she also knew if Sunny was not allowed to perform, her scholarship would be in jeopardy. The rest of the cast was well aware of this requirement and maliciously renewed their efforts to bring about her dismissal.

As the days flew by Sunny was consumed with the idea of getting her scholarship and traveling to New York. Each time she approached Sam on the matter his response was the same, but his no's were growing less intense as he listened more carefully to what she had to say.

A few days before the performance Sunny again found Sam working in the garden. Hoping to take advantage of the situation, she knelt down and began to help. When they had finished, they walked to the edge of the garden. This time Sunny offered Sam a freshly picked tomato and the salt shaker.

"Okay, Sunny. What's on your mind?"

She took a bite of her tomato, then asked, "Are you going to let me go to New York?"

Sam said nothing for several minutes. "I told you before, I'd give it some thought and that's what I'll fucking do!"

"Sam, I'll prove to you I'm good. I want you to come to my performance this Friday night to see for yourself why I must go to New York. Here's your ticket."

He studied her for a moment, then smiled as he picked up the basket of tomatoes and headed toward the house. "I can't go, but you can tell me about it after you get home."

Early the next morning Sunny spoke with Auntie Rose, begging her to talk Sam into coming to her performance. "Please, Auntie, I really want him to come and see me perform, but he says no."

"I'll try, but I doubt that it'll do any good. You should know by now that Sam doesn't put himself in any uncomfortable situation. Right now, young lady, you need to get to rehearsal."

Sunny arrived early and by the end of the day she had completed another grueling session filled with fiery tempers, jealousy and heavy competitiveness. During the next two days her life was a whirlwind of costume fittings, lessons in stage makeup and discovering the intricacies of light and sound. Each crew had its own jargon, and all the words were foreign to her. The closer she came to the night's performance the more tense she grew. She slept restlessly, rehearsing even in her sleep.

On opening night Sunny once again begged Sam to come to the show. She left the house with Auntie Rose, hoping he would surprise her and show up at the last minute to see the performance. As she sat in her dressing room with Auntie Rose, it seemed as if Creator had released thousands of butterflies in her stomach. Her hands trembled as she pulled her hair back into a tight knot and carefully applied her makeup. When she was finished she could hardly believe her eyes. The makeup had completely covered her scar and the face that looked back at her from the mirror was beautiful.

Auntie Rose checked her over to make sure everything was perfect, then declared, "You look lovely. I know you'll do fine. Now stop being so nervous."

"I can't help it, Auntie. I'm really scared. What if I'm not good enough? What if I forget the steps? Or worse yet, what if I lose my balance and fall?" Sunny neurotically untied and retied the ribbons on her shoes.

"Oh, pooh! Will you please stop this? You know you're the best. I won't hear another word of this silly nonsense. I'm going now. You'll do fine."

Sunny felt nauseous as the house lights dimmed and the music began. She paced back and forth in the dressing room and finding nothing to relieve her stress, she picked up a pen and notepad and began to write:

> Blue tick hounds, mountain high
> Quit school, scary time, oh my.
> Church mouse poor, privies outdoor
> broken fences, shanties galore
> Dirt yards, swamps and snakes for play
> This was her entertainment of the day
> Sawmill running long into the night,
> Buzzards hovering to make another strike.
> Mountains, dogs and whiskey stills,
> Oh Grandmother,
> How can I ever climb this impossible hill?

Just as she finished writing, Sunny heard her cue. She put down the poem and ran from the dressing room. Trying her best to remain calm, she stepped onto the wings of the stage and peeked through the curtains to see Auntie Rose sitting in the front row. The audience waited with baited breath as the curtain slowly rose. Sunny watched the Corp de Ballet dance onto the softly lit stage, then heard her cue as Master Dana smiled and said, "Good Luck."

Sunny floated onto the stage as if she had wings and it felt like she had been dancing all her life. The warmth of the lights embraced her like the noonday sun as she drifted into her world of magical fantasy. Sunny heard Cheering Woman's voice humming the music in her ear. Feeling her grandmother's support, she danced without a flaw, her body flowing as a wave carried by Father River. Sunny became one with the music and was barely aware that the curtain had closed on the last act until she realized that she and the cast were bowing to a standing ovation. When she stepped forward for her principal bow, the crowd stayed on its feet, smiling and applauding loudly. Overwhelmed with the tribute, Sunny took her final bow with graceful humility as Master Dana handed her a bouquet of twelve long-stemmed red roses. Her eyes filled with tears, she hugged them close, praying that she would never awaken from this dream. Glancing over toward Auntie Rose, Sunny saw that she too was crying and knew her Auntie also fervently believed in her dream.

Tears of joy running down her face, Sunny returned to her dressing room to find Master Dana strutting around like a proud peacock. "Just who do you think you are, young lady? And what did you think you were doing? This is classical ballet, not the 'goulash circuit,' my dear. A novice just doesn't make changes in classical works. I watched you add your own interpretation in the second act," he scolded sweetly as he flicked his wrist and daintily tossed his head.

Sunny recognized Master Dana's left-handed compliment beneath his gentle criticism and with head bowed, she apologized. "I'm sorry, I guess I was swept away by the music."

Ostentatiously, Master Dana hugged her, saying, "Darling, you were still great! But remember, I expect my pupils to always show the greatest respect for the theater. Now enough. The press and well-wishers are waiting, so please conduct yourself as a lady."

A knock sounded on the door, as Master Dana called out, "Entré, entré, my darlings." Sunny smiled at the affectation in his voice as the press and city council members, along with the mayor, walked in to express their appreciation of her performance.

"I want to meet this young lady," said the mayor, taking Sunny's hand.

A shy smile crossed her face. Grateful that she was dressed in costume and hidden behind stage makeup, Sunny giggled when she remembered that this man was Sam's best customer. Suddenly a brilliant light flashed from a camera, momentarily blinding Sunny. What would the mayor think if he knew his picture was going to be on the front page of tomorrow's newspaper with the daughter of Sam, the gambling, womanizing, hell-raising, drug dealing, bootlegging Dog Man?

After everyone departed, Sunny reluctantly removed her costume and handed it to Auntie Rose. The whole evening had been a fairy tale. Regretfully, she climbed into her jeans and sweatshirt and slipped into her loafers still savoring the night, knowing she had fulfilled the first of her many dreams.

Lost in thought, Sunny and Auntie Rose drove home in silence. Sunny knew her grandmother would be proud. She could almost hear her familiar voice saying, "Careful, Grandchild. This is merely a beginning, so don't become too impressed with yourself. Watch the sweet words of flattery as praises can spoil the dream. Tomorrow that picture of you in the newspaper will become a liner in the bottom of someone's bird cage. And I assure you, the bird will probably shit right on your face."

Sunny straightened up in her seat with a start, knowing what her grandmother said was true. "Oh, Grandmother. You say the nicest things," she said half aloud.

"Who on earth are you talking to?" asked Auntie Rose, startled out of her reverie by Sunny's voice.

Sunny burst out laughing and told Auntie Rose the story.

"Yes, that's exactly what your grandmother would say," chuckled Auntie Rose.

"Oh, Auntie Rose! She was there earlier, too. She was with me while I danced."

"I know, Sunny. I really do know she was with you."

As soon as the car came to a stop in front of the dark house, Sunny jumped out and ran into the kitchen. Grabbing a glass of milk and a big piece of chocolate cake, she headed for her bedroom. After her shower, she sat in the middle of the bed devouring her cake, knowing she was going to fulfill her deepest aspirations.

It was late morning when Sunny awakened and joined Sam and Auntie Rose at the kitchen table. "I did good last night. The people really liked me," she gloated as Sam laughed and handed her a copy of the morning newspaper.

When she saw her picture with the mayor on the front page, she blushed as Sam grumbled, "Don't know what you're going to do with it, but it's nice that people like you."

Sunny was disappointed that he had not mentioned New York, and decided she would bring up the subject at a later date. Auntie Rose saw her reaction, and hugging Sunny she whispered, "Leave me alone with Sam so I can talk to him." Thankful, Sunny hugged her back and sat on the nearby stairs to listen.

Auntie Rose poured Sam a second cup of coffee. "Brother, you've always known Sunny is different and that she would leave us someday. You know this is what our mother wanted for her. It's time to let her go to New York and study. Sunny is much like you, and you know that if you don't let her go with your blessings, she'll run away. Sam, she's strong like you and has a loving soul. I'll go with her and stay until she gets settled, so there's nothing for you to worry about."

Sam hung his head and remained silent for a moment before asking, "When are you planning to leave?"

"A week from Monday."

"Rose, I've got no money. I've got Hazel and the boys to look after, and we're barely making ends meet. I can't afford to send her to New York," he said, making one last feeble attempt to postpone the inevitable.

"I know, Sam, but Mother made all the arrangements and has provided her with enough money for at least a year's training. It would mean a lot to her if you gave your permission."

"Goddamnit, Rose. You always win," he answered attempting to disguise his pleasure and pride that his daughter had been accepted at such a fine school.

"Only when I'm right, Brother. Only when I'm right."

"Of course she's good, she's my daughter. Why shouldn't she go? Hell, she'll be the best."

When Sunny heard this, she raced into the kitchen, squealing with excitement as she grabbed Sam in a big hug. Feeling embarrassed, he huffed out of the kitchen, grumbling that she had lost her mind.

Sam agreed to live at the farm while Auntie Rose was in New York. Happy with this decision, Sunny and Auntie Rose packed and made arrangements for their trip. Sam felt awkward with all the woman talk going on around him and searched for a way to say his own goodbye to Sunny. "Let's go for a ride in the mountains. I don't want you to get any high ideas and forget where you come from."

Thrilled to be alone with her father, Sunny agreed wholeheartedly and they left the following morning for the mountains. It was a beautiful day and during their drive Sunny felt a special closeness to Sam as they talked over old times. He parked the old truck and turned the dogs loose to run while they walked together toward the creek. Sunny took off her shoes, rolled up her jeans and waded out to sit on a fallen log, letting her feet dangle in the water.

"Sam," she said, "I'm gonna be so big they'll have to tie a rock to my tail to keep me from flying through the sun."

"Right. And if a frog wasn't built so close to the ground, he wouldn't bump his ass every time he jumped."

"You watch me, Sam. Someday I'm gonna be a star."

"Well, fuck, listen to you. Why do we need another fucking star in the sky when it's full of them? Hell, stars have been around since the beginning of time. I don't need you to remind me that they exist!"

"I know, Sam, but just you wait and see," she answered, playfully splashing water at him.

Sam dodged the water with a guarded grin. "Well, don't get too big for your britches. There's a helluva lot better talent out there than you."

"What Grandmother said is gonna come true. I'm gonna do it, Sam. I want the people, the applause and the world travel. It's all there, just waiting for me to make it happen."

"I've heard most show people change their names. What'll you call yourself when you're a star?" he teased.

"Well, I've been thinking. You drink Jim Beam and you call me Sunny. I'm gonna keep my boy name, but say it a little different. Kinda split it up, you know. How do you like Sunny Beam?"

"That's fucking stupid!"

"I don't think so. I've really thought about it. I want you to have pride in what I do. After all, everyone says I'm just like you. I heard you were drunk for a week just because I was a girl. Why not let me fulfill your dreams of a firstborn? This name will be our secret, no matter where I go." Suddenly Sunny stood up on the log and ran to the center, throwing her arms in the air as she shouted, "Hello, New York! Get ready to meet Miss Sunny Beam!"

"Yeah, right! I'm glad you're going, it's just one less mouth to feed."

"I'm gonna miss you too, Sam," said Sunny, gazing off in the distance.

"Bullshit! You'll be too busy with those high falootin' big shots. You'll forget all about me."

"Not me, Sam. You wait and see. Grandmother always taught me that I was nothing unless I kept close to my family."

"Well, we'll see," said Sam, glancing at his watch. "It's getting late. Tomorrow's your big day, so we'd better head back or Auntie Rose will have my head on a platter."

Early the next morning Sam took them to the airport. He handed Sunny her suitcase and said, "Well, Miss Sunny Beam, I'm gonna miss you, but you do what you gotta do!" Turning to Auntie Rose, he said, "Take good care of her, Sister," then quickly walked away.

Sunny watched him climb into his old truck and felt a great sadness at parting from the father she had so recently discovered and had come to love.

Sunny Travels

Sunny was filled with apprehension as she and Auntie Rose boarded the airplane. This was their first flight, and she wasn't sure who was more nervous. The stewardess directed them to their assigned seats where they placed their luggage in the overhead storage bins and sat down in thoughtful silence.

Auntie Rose reached over and gripped Sunny's hand as the powerful engines roared and the plane raced down the runway, lifting into flight. They huddled together, seeking comfort in each other until Sunny's hand began to tingle from numbness. Seeing that other passengers were already moving around the cabin, Sunny felt a little braver and slowly released Auntie's grip. She moved closer to the window to look out and could hardly believe the sight before her. The sky was a brilliant blue, spattered with clouds so soft and billowy she wanted to reach out and touch them.

I'm flying like an eagle, she thought proudly. There below, was Mother Earth, stretching further than she could possibly imagine. She could feel the energy of Mother Earth holding her children close to her bosom for protection. Suddenly the panorama changed, and Sunny gasped in amazement. A river appeared from nowhere. She could see it from beginning to end. It was a miracle!

Just as quickly a whole range of snowcapped mountains seemed to birth themselves from the earth's floor! When the reality of their altitude registered, Sunny held her breath in wonderment. She sensed the powerful wings of the golden eagle hovering near, and into her mind sprang the realization that it was the eagle who taught mankind to fly. She turned to Auntie Rose, anxious to share the magic of the moment.

"Auntie! Auntie!" She bounced in her seat with excitement.

"Please sit still. You will make the whole plane rock," grumbled Auntie Rose. Sunny could see that she was gripping the arms of her seat as if her life depended on it.

"Okay." Sunny turned back to the window, hoping Auntie Rose would never realize how high they truly were. Before long, she was once again overcome with the magnificence of the view and tried again. "Just look, Auntie," she pleaded with a smile. "You've never seen anything like it."

Auntie Rose responded with a stern look and a curt "No," then continued to stare straight ahead.

"Oh Auntie," Sunny giggled, "don't let your fears swallow up all this beauty. Please, just look, so we can share this moment." Auntie Rose ignored her and held on tighter.

"Please fasten your seatbelts and return your seats to their upright position. We'll be landing in approximately fifteen minutes," the stewardess announced. The plane banked, and Sunny could see Ellis Island and the Statue of Liberty in the distance. Unable to believe the flight was almost over, she buckled her seatbelt and reached over to help Auntie Rose fasten hers, to find that it was still buckled.

Auntie Rose smacked Sunny's hands. "Stop it! Do you want to get us killed?" She grabbed the arms of her seat and did not let go until the plane was once again on the ground. As it taxied to a stop and the doors opened, Auntie Rose was the first passenger out of her seat.

Auntie Rose relaxed once they were inside the terminal. Kate Cohen a friend of Madame's was supposed to meet them. Auntie Rose, seeing no one who appeared to be looking for them, started to fret. "Oh, Sunny. There's no one here to meet us. What are we going to do? This place is too big. I know we're going to get lost. Sam will never forgive me for bringing you here."

Feeling uncertain herself, Sunny scanned the terminal, then pointed toward the baggage claim sign. "See, we're not lost. We'll just follow the signs. That's probably where she's supposed to meet us." It was a long walk that seemed to take forever and more than once she had to reassure Auntie Rose that they were going in the right direction. Sunny breathed a deep sigh of relief when at last they arrived at the baggage claim. They retrieved their bags and stood waiting at the exit door, like two forlorn children waiting to be rescued. But time passed, and still no Kate.

When they had almost given up hope of being found, a young man walked up to them. "Are you Miss Rose Hoffman?" Auntie Rose nodded, her face brightening. "Sorry I'm late. Heavy traffic. Miss Kate had a business meeting. I'm Ted." He grabbed their bags and strode briskly through the exit with Sunny and Auntie Rose close behind.

Ted hailed a cab, put them in the backseat along with their luggage, then crawled in the front and gave the cab driver directions. Auntie Rose and Sunny sat quietly as they inched their way through rush hour traffic, amid a cacophony of horns and screaming drivers. The cab pulled to a halt in front of a high-rise brownstone building. Ted jumped out, opened the door for Sunny and Auntie Rose and set their bags on the curb. "There you are, ladies," he said, then climbed back in the cab and motioned for the driver to move on.

They just stood there, bewildered and in a state of shock, not knowing what to do next. A tall man dressed in a red and black uniform walked out of the building, grabbed their bags and ushered them across the lobby and into a small box with the word 'Elevator' written above the door. Lifting them skyward, the elevator stopped on the fifteenth floor. The man took their bags and motioned for Auntie Rose and Sunny to follow him down a well-lit hall. He unlocked a door, set the bags inside and handed Auntie Rose the key. "Miss Kate will be arriving soon. You ladies enjoy your stay in

New York," he called as he closed the door behind him. Sunny and Auntie Rose stared at one another in disbelief. Then suddenly they burst into hysterical laughter.

Auntie Rose managed to say, "These people sure are in a big hurry to go someplace. Everyone moves and talks too fast. I can't understand a word they're saying."

"Me either. This place is going to take a lot of getting used to," Sunny replied. "C'mon, Auntie, let's take a look around."

They found they were in a small furnished apartment with two bedrooms, a bath, a small kitchen, living room and dining room. Through a glass door in the dining room, Sunny could see some plants and potted trees. Sliding the door open, she stepped onto the balcony to get a closer look. Gathering her courage, she ventured closer to the edge and looked down. The height made her dizzy, but the view of the city took her breath away.

"Come Auntie, look at the view. It's beautiful," yelled Sunny.

"No! You know I'm afraid of heights. I'll never stand on that little platform, so don't ask me again. You come in here right now, before you fall and kill yourself. God forbid if I ever had to tell Sam you fell off a building." Sunny giggled at Auntie's reasoning and started back toward the apartment, dreaming about the little garden she would plant.

Someone knocked harshly on the door and Auntie Rose, overwhelmed with the day's experiences, sent Sunny to answer it. She opened the door hesitantly, to find a small-framed woman standing there with her arms filled with bags of groceries. The woman smiled, brushed by her and headed to the kitchen. A second more familiar face followed and Sunny, searching her memory, recognized Madame Bianchoff. Madame closed the door and stretched out her arms to embrace Sunny. Then, pushing her away to arm's length, she studied her closely. "I'm so glad you are finally here, my dear. You have developed into a beautiful young lady with a strong dancer's body. You've turned out just as wonderful as your grandmother predicted. Now, let's go meet my good friend, Kate Cohen. She's an agent for some of the best talent in New York, and has kindly agreed to show you the ropes to help you get started as a professional dancer."

They joined Kate in the kitchen and introductions were offered all around. Sunny and Auntie Rose put their things away while Kate and Madame made sandwiches and iced tea. Soon they were all gathered around the table, talking and eating like old friends. Madame and Kate broke into laughter as Sunny and Auntie Rose shared the experience of their first airplane trip and elevator ride.

As Auntie Rose cleared the dishes from the table, Kate opened her briefcase and removed several stacks of papers which she placed on the table in front of Sunny. "I will need you and your aunt to sign these contracts so that I can help you make the best possible career decisions while you are here." Sunny nodded and smiled, not sure if she should ask what a contract was. When Auntie Rose returned, Kate took the contracts one by one, and explained them in detail. She talked rapidly, with a thick New York Jewish accent. Sunny's head began to spin with the pressure of trying to understand what she was saying. The look on Auntie Rose's face told Sunny that she too was overwhelmed. There were contracts for management, disbursement of monies and a lease for the apartment. Each was scrutinized carefully by Madame and Auntie Rose, then explained in detail to Sunny. When these had been signed, Kate produced a list of required behavior guidelines, and a list of suggested classes at the dance academy. She then asked Auntie Rose to sign a document giving her temporary guardianship of Sunny until she became of age. This contract specified that if Sunny broke any of the agreements, she would immediately be returned to her father.

Madame spoke at great length, explaining how the money left by Cheering Woman was to be spent, and presented the check to Kate. Kate saw that it was enough to support Sunny for two years if she was very frugal and got a job to subsidize the small monthly allowance she would be receiving.

The hour was growing late, and Kate, seeing that Sunny and Auntie Rose were exhausted, decided to call it a night. At the door, Kate put her hands on Sunny's shoulders and looked straight into her eyes. "Madame would never have asked me to help you if she didn't believe in you. Don't disappoint me. If you are good, and do what I ask, I'll see that you get your shot at stardom. We will pick you up at ten tomorrow to take you to some prearranged appointments. So, be ready and don't forget to bring your workout clothes."

Sunny hugged Madame goodnight, and thanked her graciously for all her help, knowing that without her and Kate, she would not have made it through a single day in this madcap city. After closing and locking the door, she and Auntie Rose stayed up awhile longer, discussing the day's events. They both agreed that Sunny must do everything Kate asked if she was to get the training needed to begin her career in show business. Kate's aggressive, hard-nosed attitude was intimidating, but they trusted Madame's judgment. It was after midnight when Sunny at last crawled into bed. She prayed to *Wakan Tanka*, asking for protection and guidance, and thanked her grandmother for giving her this dream, then closed her eyes. Thoughts of Madame, New York and Kate filled her head, until at last she drifted off to sleep.

The following morning Sunny and Auntie Rose were up early. Sunny was dressed and waiting long before ten o'clock. The phone rang promptly at ten, and Kate told Sunny that she and Madame were waiting for them in the lobby. "Today you will learn to use the subway," Kate said, businesslike just as before. They stepped out onto the street, Kate walking briskly ahead; Madame, Sunny and Auntie, clutching her handbag, taking up the rear. We look like ducklings following our mother, Sunny thought with a smile. Auntie Rose kept falling behind and Sunny, seeing that she was upset about something, fell back to see what was the matter.

"Why can't they have their trains above ground, like everyone else," grumbled Auntie. "This subway sounds just as dangerous as an airplane."

"Don't be afraid, Auntie. It's like living with the mole people. Grandmother always said you never know when or where they'll come up out of the ground."

Auntie Rose took her free hand and pinched Sunny, whispering, "You be quiet." Once on the train, they giggled and held on tight, swaying back and forth as they hurtled to their stop. As they climbed the stairs back to the light of day, Auntie Rose smiled, thankful that she was still alive.

The four ladies walked up a narrow flight of stairs into a large airy room that was obviously a dance studio. "I'd like you to meet my old friend, Master Ivan Nikolai, director of the Academy," said Madame, introducing Sunny and Auntie to a tall, middle-aged gentleman with deep set brown eyes that rested in a strong, gentle face. "Now go get dressed while I speak with Ivan."

Sunny slipped into her workout clothes while Madame and Master Ivan spoke together in a combination of Russian and English. Sunny couldn't understand most of what they were saying, but it was obvious they were talking about her.

Master Ivan demonstrated a combination of dance steps, then motioned for the piano player to begin. The women sat in folding chairs and watched as Master Ivan led Sunny through some extremely difficult combinations. "That's enough. You may go and get dressed," he said. Sunny tried to read his face, but his expression told her nothing. She could hear him talking in low tones to Madame and Kate as she changed back into her street clothes.

They were all smiling as Sunny stepped out of the dressing room. "You've been accepted," smiled Kate. "Your classes start tomorrow." Madame handed her a signed two-year tuition free contract and gave her a hug. Auntie Rose, bursting with pride, hugged her too. "Now," said Kate, "let's go celebrate over lunch at Stefano's. They have good food and a great view."

When they had finished eating, Kate took them to their next appointment. After another brisk walk, they entered a smaller building, filled with private offices. Noticing that most of them were being used for drama, modeling and voice training, Sunny wondered why Kate had brought them there. As though reading her mind, Kate looked at Sunny over her bifocals and said, "There are many things that you need to become a star. You must learn how to speak properly, dress correctly, walk, sit and stand in a manner befitting a lady. And you must know how to eat properly at formal dinners." Sunny cringed at the implied criticism and bit her tongue to keep from saying something she would later regret.

They entered a door with the name 'K. Stearns, Inc.' on an engraved plate above the number 701. The receptionist greeted Kate warmly and took them directly to the back office, where a tall well-dressed gentleman sat at his desk.

"Kevin, this is the young lady I called you about," said Kate.

He got up and walked around Sunny, studying her from all angles, as if she were packaged meat. "Walk across the room, then turn and come back to me," Kevin commanded. Sunny, her legs shaking, did as she was told. "The rest of you ladies may wait in the front office. We will join you in about an hour," he said.

Kevin walked into a room adjoining his office and motioned for Sunny to follow. He led her to a dinner table set with silver, crystal and china, the likes of which Sunny had only seen in the movies, and motioned for her to sit across from him. Sunny sat down, unable to believe her eyes. Did people really eat like this? She gazed at the beautifully folded napkins and saw that there were three forks, three spoons and two knives at her place. In the center of the table were dishes of all shapes and sizes.

As soon as she was seated, Kevin began to lecture her on what each piece was for, rattling on and on, so that by the time he was finished, Sunny was totally confused and couldn't remember any of what he had said. Then he ushered her back into his office, handed her a book and said, "Read this aloud." When she had barely finished the first page, he took the book and closed it with disgust, saying, "That's enough."

Kevin left Sunny nearly in tears and went to get the women waiting outside. When they had been seated, he completely ignored Sunny and addressed Kate in the soft, cultured voice Sunny had already begun to hate. "She has great hair and bones, and she will be exquisite with the proper makeup. Leave her hair long and natural. We'll need to start at entry level as far as etiquette and protocol are concerned, but you already knew that. The big problem is her accent, and that has to go. She talks as if her mouth is filled with mush, and I can't understand a word she says. She speaks too softly and doesn't know how to project her voice. In fact, I can't even tell if she speaks English."

Sunny was humiliated and angry. Everyone had always complained about her loud, boisterous mouth. Now this Kevin person was saying she spoke too softly. Why couldn't the world make up its mind so she could get it right once and for all?

Kate, nodding her agreement, thanked Kevin then turned to Sunny. "You will study with Kevin on a weekly basis until he feels you are able to handle any employment situation that the entertainment world may require. He's the best there is, and he's done wonders with most of my other clients."

Sunny was angry, but said nothing. Try as she might, she just couldn't comprehend why Kate wanted her to learn all these foolish things, when she had come to New York for one reason only, to dance. Madame seemed thrilled with Kate's decision. Softening a little, Sunny decided to give it her best effort.

Since Madame Bianchoff was returning to Los Angeles the following morning, Auntie Rose prepared a special dinner for everyone. Much of the dinner conversation revolved around Cheering Woman, and how thankful Sunny should be for this wonderful opportunity to create a good life. It was getting late when Madame said her goodbyes, promising to stay in touch through Kate. As the door closed behind them, Sunny's lips began to quiver and soon she was sobbing.

"I was so ashamed, Auntie, the way Kevin spoke about me. It's true that I didn't know what to do, but he scares me, and I'm afraid I'll never fit in with these people."

Auntie Rose hugged Sunny close. "I understand. It was the same way for me when I first started nursing school. But I just reminded myself that I was there to learn, and friends were time-consumers who took away from my study time. It hurt when I wasn't invited to parties with the other students, but in time I found a few good friends who liked me for who I was. When I graduated, I was at the top of my class. I went to work at a hospital and worked there fifteen years, until I met and married a wonderful doctor. My home and all the properties I own came from that marriage. When he became ill, I quit my job to take care of him. He died soon after of heart failure, and I decided to give up nursing to build the farm which was our shared dream. Sunny, I know you have many difficult decisions to make, but I feel that this is your big chance, and you must take advantage of every opportunity that is offered to you."

"Auntie, when I was home, I knew exactly what I wanted. But here, I feel so confused. What does speech and modeling and all that other stuff have to do with dancing? Why can't I just dance?"

"Sunny, the world of dance is much more than dancing. In reality, you have no choice if you want to stay in New York. The papers we signed give Kate the right to guide your career as she sees fit. I never thought your speech was a problem, but we're not city folk and neither of us really know what you need for your career. If you feel you just can't do it, then you can come back home with me."

"No Auntie. I can't. I want to dance more than anything else. Some way or another, I'll manage."

"Then you'll have to trust Kate's judgment and do as she says, and that includes studying with Kevin."

Sunny nodded, knowing Auntie was right.

"Well, it's been a long day for both of us, and it's time to get some sleep. Maybe things will look better in the morning."

And so Sunny went to bed, feeling that rather than capturing her dream, her dream had captured her. She slept fitfully, her mind wrestling with her doubts and fears until at last she accepted what she must do.

She awakened before sunrise, and taking her pipe, went directly to the balcony for morning prayers. By the time Kate arrived, Sunny was dressed and waiting. Auntie Rose, feeling Kate and Sunny should spend some time alone together, declined Kate's invitation to join them.

As they walked out of the building, Kate handed Sunny a subway schedule and a map of the city on which she had marked off the station numbers of home, the dance studio, Kate's office, Kevin's studio and Central Park. "You can't get around in New York without using the subway," she said matter-of-factly. "You will need to commit these trains and stops to memory. Central Park is close to the apartment. I jog there every morning, and I'll be expecting you to join me. That's where we're going right now." Sunny, not knowing what the word 'jog' meant, and too afraid to ask, followed Kate.

When they entered the park, Sunny was thrilled to see the green of the trees and grass. As Kate broke into a slow run, Sunny realized that 'jog' was simply another word for run, and was glad she had not shown her ignorance by asking. At first, she matched Kate's pace, but it was too slow for her long legs. She desperately wanted to run, wild and alone, feeling the wind in her hair. She finally mustered up enough nerve to ask Kate if she could possibly run ahead. Kate laughed. "I'm too slow, huh?" she said, motioning for Sunny to go on. Sunny took off running, and for the first time since her arrival in New York, she felt totally free.

Not wanting to get too far ahead, Sunny would return to Kate, then sprint off again. They jogged this way for an hour until Kate panted, "Okay, race horse, you've worn me out. Let's go home and get dressed." She covered her damp head with a towel and turned to leave the park. "Sunny," Kate said, as they headed for home, "you are going to have to learn to button up your feelings and keep them tucked inside where no one can see them. You're too sensitive to handle criticism, and if show business is going to be your life, you had better get used to both ridicule and compliments. That is, if you expect to be a star. So young lady, it's time to learn to listen, follow directions without an attitude, and smile whether you like it or not. And until you know something I don't, never question anything I say. Remember, I'm responsible for you. Use your common sense. Why would I invest my time and hard work if I didn't think you were going to make me a lot of money? Do you understand?"

Sunny nodded. This was good advice, and she found herself beginning to like and respect Kate.

As they entered the building, Kate said, "Look around. You like this place?" Sunny nodded with enthusiasm. "Well, I own this building. Some of these flats I sell, some I rent."

Sunny was astounded. "You own this building?"

"Yes. And I expect another one, paid for by you, when you become famous," Kate grinned.

When the elevator stopped at the fifteenth floor, Sunny stepped out, followed by Kate. As Sunny put her key in the door, Kate unlocked an apartment across the hall and Sunny realized for the first time that they were neighbors. "Don't just stand there with your mouth open!" Kate said. "Hurry up and take a shower. I'll drop you off on my way to the office, but you'll need to find your way to the other appointments by yourself."

After her dance classes were over, she opened the map Kate had given her and located Kevin's studio. Suddenly she could not remember how to use the subway, but her fear of Kate's wrath moved her to get a grip on herself, and her jitters began to subside. She breathed a sigh of relief when she arrived safely at Kevin's studio.

Kevin took her to the table and taught her to use the proper utensils to manipulate the fake food that had been placed on the dishes. He was more patient this time, and Sunny felt proud of herself as they finished the lesson.

She was almost two blocks away from Kevin's studio when she reached in her bag for her map and found it wasn't there. Filled with panic, she ran back to Kevin's private office. Kevin held up a piece of paper. "Is this what you're looking for?"

"Yes, thank you. I'm sorry to bother you," Sunny blurted out, then dashed for the subway. Getting off at the station Kate had marked, she headed up the steps, hoping she'd done everything right. The street looked familiar, and she was elated to see her brownstone building right where it should have been. After walking across the lobby and into the elevator, she pushed the button for her floor. She unlocked the door and flew into the apartment. "I did it, Auntie! I did it," she called out joyfully. "I made it there and back on the subway, all alone!"

In time, Sunny learned to get in and out of a chair properly and to sit with crossed ankles like a lady, but her speech and projection were a constant battle. She found herself beginning to like Kevin, and with each accomplishment realized clearly the value of his instruction.

Sunny also began to realize and appreciate the wealth of information she gleaned from Kate's business lectures during their early morning runs through Central Park. "Sunny," Kate said on one of those daily outings, "there is show, and then there is business. There's much more to being a headliner than talent and classes. In this business you must possess a strong body, good looks and knowledge. The training never ends. You must be prepared for anything, at any given moment. For the rest of your show business life, it's learn, learn, learn and please, please, please."

Soon Sunny's training intensified, and although ballet remained her favorite, other styles of dance were added to her schedule. There was modern, primitive, tap, jazz and acrobatics dance, in addition to the supplemental classes in grooming with Kevin. Her class schedule increased to eight hours, followed by several hours of intensive practice, leaving her little time for anything but work and sleep.

Kate was delighted with Sunny's enthusiasm and continued to advise her carefully in every area of life. Sunny accepted Kate's decisions without question, but when Kate hired a vocal and drama coach she rebelled. "Kate I can't sing. I can't act. And I don't like using my voice. Please don't make me do this," she begged. Nevertheless, a piano was delivered the following day and Sunny started her voice and drama lessons the day after.

Three months had passed, and Sunny was beginning to like the fast-paced style of New York. Seeing that Sunny was well settled, Auntie Rose made arrangements to return to her farm. Sunny hated the idea of her leaving, but knew the time had come for their parting. Auntie Rose, remembering the trauma of her first flight, made train reservations for the following Monday. Kate and Sunny accompanied her to the station, and Sunny's eyes filled with tears as she hugged Auntie Rose goodbye. Auntie Rose hugged her tight, saying, "I'll miss you, Sunny, but I'll be glad to get back to the farm. I'm just not a city person. Sam's going to meet me, and I can't wait to see his expression when I tell him about all of our experiences."

"Yes. Sam will get a kick out of your stories. Tell him I'm behaving myself and love what I'm doing." With tears in her eyes, she watched Auntie Rose go to the check-in counter, then turned and hopped back into the waiting cab, next to Kate.

Sunny was overcome with loneliness when she returned to the empty apartment. She was going to miss Auntie Rose's cheery presence. Even though she really was on her own now, it was going to be a difficult adjustment. With Auntie Rose's departure, she and Kate began spending more time together. As they grew closer, Sunny gave her a key to the apartment, and Kate kept a close check on her comings and goings.

At those times when Sunny seemed especially lonely, Kate would suggest she call home. She especially enjoyed it when she could speak with Sam. He enjoyed her tales of city life, and his advice always seemed to go right to the core of her problems. "Sunny," he would say, "when you're confused and feel the walls moving in on you, it's time to make a decision. If those walls get too high to climb, too wide to cross, too far to go around or too low to crawl under, then blow the damn things up and wait till the dust settles so you can see what you have to do. Now, keep those knees together and use that space between your ears. Just do whatcha gotta do." She would hang up the phone, her troubles gone, trying to picture Kevin teaching Sam manners and proper social behavior.

By the end of her first year in New York, Sunny's reality had become nothing but long grueling hours of study and practice. "It's time for you to learn how to audition," said Kate on one of their morning jogs. "If you're going to be in show business, you've got to be more than a good dancer. You've got to learn to sell yourself to the public. And more important, you've got to be able to handle rejection."

Kate began taking her to auditions, but she was never chosen for any of the shows. "Don't be discouraged, my dear," Kate would say, after yet another unsuccessful audition. "You're not ready, but the experience you're getting is invaluable." Despite Kate's reassurance that this was merely practice, Sunny couldn't help feeling discouraged when she was met with rejection after rejection and her insecurity began to affect her performance and personality.

Kate, noting that Sunny was becoming quiet and withdrawn, decided to change the course of action. "It's time for me to take you to the garment district to meet my friend, Bernie Lampl," said Kate. "We've known each other since high school, and he may be able to give you some experience in modeling."

The following afternoon, she and Sunny took a cab to the garment district to meet Mr. Lampl. Kate introduced them, and Sunny felt a surge of confidence when he suggested that she model something for him. Sunny and Kate followed him to the designer's studio where he told the head designer to pick out a few of her best designs. Handing them to Sunny, he directed her to a dressing room where she was to change and model them so he could see how she wore the garments.

Sunny changed quickly and located the runway. As she stepped onto the runway, she thought of how Kevin had taught her to walk head high, shoulders straight. Suddenly overcome with stage fright, she paused and took a deep breath to calm herself. Then, imagining herself as a graceful white swan, she began to glide effortlessly down the ramp, turning now and then to display the best qualities of the garment before making a confident stroll back to the dressing room where she made a quick change and repeated the performance.

After she had modeled four outfits, Mr. Lampl offered Sunny a part-time modeling job that would not interfere with her studies. The pay was minimal, but Sunny was overjoyed at the prospect of getting paid to wear beautiful clothes.

"He liked me, Kate, he liked me!" she bubbled when they were back in the cab. "My first job! Wait until Sam and Auntie Rose hear about this! How can I ever thank you?" Sunny looked at her watch and saw that it was almost dinner time. "Let's go out to dinner to celebrate. It'll be my treat," she said proudly.

Sunny, recalling her first meal with Kate, had decided to go to Stefano's to show Kate how much she had learned in one short year. Confidently, she sailed through the meal, the perfect lady, ordering for both of them and using all the right utensils at the right times.

"Our first meal here was quite an experience," said Kate as they waited for dessert. "Tonight was flawless. You have come a long way, my dear." Sunny beamed with pride at the hard earned praise.

Kate allowed her to work some of Bernie's shows, but she demanded that Sunny come directly home afterward. She was not allowed to model if it interfered with her training schedule. Kate's strict rules gave Sunny an excuse to decline when she was invited to dinner or drinks by a client. This allowed her to develop her skills as a model without the outside pressure the other girls faced.

When Sunny had been modeling a little over two months, Kate called her to the balcony for a chat. "What has happened to the money you've earned from your modeling job?"

Looking somewhat puzzled by the question, Sunny went to her bedroom and pulled several checks out of her top drawer. "Is this what you mean?" she asked, handing them to Kate.

Kate stared, dumbfounded. "Sunny, why haven't you cashed these paychecks?"

"I don't know how," answered Sunny matter-of-factly. "Besides, I don't really need anything. I thought I was supposed to keep them until I needed something."

"Are you telling me you don't have a bank account?"

"I thought only rich people kept money in the bank. Grandmother used to bury her money under the apple tree in the back yard, and Auntie Rose keeps hers in an old coffee tin in her closet. I didn't have a coffee tin, so I just tucked it beneath my underwear."

Kate roared with laughter. "Sunny, Sunny, Sunny," she said. "Get dressed. We're going to open your first bank account."

As they left the bank, Kate handed Sunny a checkbook and patiently explained how to enter transactions into the ledger at the front. She cautioned her to always record purchases immediately and keep all deposit slips until the deposits showed up on her monthly statement.

Another year had come and gone when Sunny stepped onto the stage to audition for the lead in an off Broadway production that would travel as a road show until it was seasoned enough to open in New York. Kate sat with Sunny, giving her last minute instructions, as they waited for the choreographer to call the dancers. "Remember, Sunny, this is a musical comedy, and there will be several auditions for the lead part. Be free with your expression and stay in the limelight. I want you to own that stage and that means all eyes are on you, and only you." She adjusted a strand of Sunny's hair and smiled with satisfaction. "You look marvelous! Now go do your warm-ups. Make sure those muscles are ready to reach any place that's needed in the dance combinations. When he asks you to sing, sing with feeling. Watch your facial expression and timing. When he asks you to read, become the words. This time, when you come back I want you to tell me you have the lead in the show."

"Kate, I know you want me to be a winner, but not as much as I want to be one," Sunny replied. "Let's keep our fingers crossed."

When her name was called, Sunny smiled confidently and stepped up on the stage. When the choreographer called for line and marked three combinations, Sunny was ready. As the music began, she was carried back home to the woods where she had once danced so freely in the moonlight. The difficult steps became effortless and the stage belonged to her. It was the same when she sang and read, and as she finished the last audition, she knew she had the lead. Dripping with sweat, she stepped from the stage and toweled herself off, then sat down to catch her breath.

Kate handed her a glass of room temperature water, saying, "Well, we did it! You're on your way, kid!"

"And what about me? She wouldn't have accomplished this without me." Sunny was pleased and surprised to see Kevin had taken time from his demanding schedule to watch her audition. He gave her a big hug, saying, "Even when you become famous, you will always be my little ragamuffin."

"Oh, Kevin," Sunny laughed, "I'll always be a little ragamuffin inside. It'll be our little secret. Seriously, though, thank you. Thank you both."

Rehearsals were at six o'clock in the evening, Monday through Friday. Sunny drove herself hard, striving for perfection. Each Friday, she picked up her rehearsal pay and deposited it in the bank. Kate usually demanded she rest on the weekends, but occasionally allowed her to attend parties which would further her connections in the business. As the opening of the show drew closer, there were additional sessions scheduled for costume fittings, props, sound and lighting. Sunny worried about the scantiness of her costumes, but Kate just laughed and said, "When you got 'em you flaunt 'em, baby. Your looks are what's going to make you the money."

The tour was postponed twice for changes before everything was finally ready. A select group of show business VIP's were invited to the final dress rehearsal, and their input solicited. It was the opinion of most that the cast was excellent but inexperienced, and the four month road tour would allow them to become seasoned enough to survive off Broadway. Sunny and the other cast members were elated and lavished in the critics' praise until it was time to begin their tour.

The cast was on the road four long months, traveling from town to town. Sunny loved the traveling. Determined to be the best, she maintained a tight practice schedule and made it a point to stay late after each show to meet with the director and discuss ways to tighten up her performance. By the time she got back to the hotel, she was usually exhausted. She would take a long, hot shower and sit in the middle of her bed, picking at her room service meal. When she was no longer able to keep her eyes open, Sunny would fall asleep.

When they were informed they were going home and would have a week off before beginning their off Broadway run, they went their separate ways, taking advantage of the time off to visit friends and family. Arriving in New York very late at night, Sunny caught a cab home. Glad to find the apartment just as she had left it, she spent her first hours sitting on the balcony under the stars, enjoying the pleasure of once again being in the sanctuary of home.

The first two days she did nothing but sleep. In the evenings, Kate would come over and they would talk about the tour and Sunny's plans for the future. By the third day she felt rested enough to go to the studio to brush up on her technique and get ready for the upcoming rehearsals.

On opening night Sunny sat backstage, nerves raw and jittery. This show could make or break her career. The audience was filled with critics, writers and agents, and their opinions would determine the show's success or failure. She heard the orchestra warming up, followed by the first notes of the opening number. Quietly she walked to the edge of the stage to wait for her cue. The moment she stepped on stage, her jitters disappeared. She floated through the show, realizing it was over only when she had completed her last curtain call and the theater lights dimmed.

She and Kate scanned the morning newspapers over coffee, and from the reviews they could tell the show was a hit. The next months passed quickly in a flurry of rehearsals, performances and promotional activities.

After a six month run, the show was still going strong, but for Sunny, the glamour was beginning to wear off. Sitting alone in her dressing room one evening as she waited for her stage call, Sunny began to recall the simple, peaceful childhood days she had spent on the reservation with Cheering Woman. It was all so far away now, she mused, wondering for just a moment if her past was real, or merely a dream.

This night after the show, she dressed quickly and hurried off to another party with Kate and Kevin. The parties had been exciting at first, but she soon realized it was the same old faces repeating the same old conversations. Tonight she would stay just long enough to be socially acceptable, then excuse herself and go home, the one place where she could be herself.

Back home, she went to the kitchen to fix a plate of snacks. Taking them with her to the bathroom, Sunny turned on her favorite radio station and began to run her bath. She sprinkled a handful of aromatic herbs in the water, lit several candles and placed them around the tub. When everything was ready, she stepped into the warm water and leaned back to relax and enjoy her midnight meal. As the hot water cooled, she got out of the tub and dressed for bed in her best nightshirt. Crawling in between the smooth satin sheets, she snuggled into the warmth of her down comforter and fell into a deep, restful sleep.

The next thing she knew, a key turned in the front door, followed by footsteps and a familiar voice, saying, "This is your wakeup call."

Seeing it was Kate, Sunny groaned and rolled over. "What time is it?" she managed to mumble.

"Three o'clock in the afternoon, and my accountant will be here in an hour to go over your books. I brought you some hot coffee and breakfast." She set a tray down on the bed and began to pour Sunny a cup of steaming coffee.

"Oh God, Kate, not today! Please. Every muscle in my body is screaming."

"You'll feel better if you get up and take a shower. You don't have to dress. You can lounge around in your robe and pajamas if you wish, but I need to know what's going on with your finances so I can have everything ready before Harry gets here. Where is your checkbook and your ledger?"

Knowing it was useless to argue, Sunny went to take a shower while Kate gathered the necessary materials for the accountant. She dressed in soft pajamas and rolled her wet hair up in a towel, then went out to the living room to join Kate and Harry Newton. "Good afternoon," she said, plopping herself down on the sofa.

"Sunny," Kate said, "I couldn't find your checkbook or your canceled checks. Will you get them for me?"

Sunny went to her purse, took out her checkbook and deposit slips, handed them to Kate, and sat down again.

"Where are your canceled checks?" Kate inquired.

"I don't have any."

"My God, Sunny! What have you done with them? Harry can't do your taxes without them."

"Kate, I never wrote a check because I didn't know how."

Kate opened the check book and saw that what she said was true. "If you haven't been writing checks, what have you been living on?"

"The allowance you give me."

"Oh, dear God! You've saved all of your earnings?" She handed the deposit slips and a bag of receipts to Harry. When his calculator stopped, he informed Sunny that she must invest quickly unless she wanted to give the bulk of her money to the Internal Revenue Service.

"This is madness! I can't fucking believe it!" raged Kate, lighting a cigarette. "What should we do about this, Harry?"

Peering at Sunny over his thick glasses, the accountant suggested some possible solutions. "I'd suggest she invest in stocks, bonds, or a piece of real estate."

"My God, Harry! We only have three weeks. I can't find a good investment that quick."

"Kate, do I have enough money to buy my apartment?" asked Sunny.

"More than enough, but that doesn't really solve the problem."

"Kate, you can't possibly understand what it would mean to me to own my home. I've never had a home. I love this flat, and want to buy it from you." Kate agreed to the sale for a nominal figure, saying, "That will solve part of the problem, but there is still more that needs to be invested immediately."

"I have an idea Kate," said Harry. "What about that small motel that you're selling in upstate New York?"

That thing is a white elephant. I would never saddle her with that crap."

"What's wrong with it?" asked Sunny, suddenly interested.

"It was a bad investment I made years ago. It's out in the country and I can't be there to take care of it. You don't want it, Sunny. It needs too much work, and besides, it's a summer business."

"Do you have any pictures of it?"

Kate nodded and went across the hall to get them. Flipping through the pictures, Sunny was shocked to see that New York actually had forested lands and snow covered mountains. She got out her atlas and asked Kate to show her the location.

"It's about six miles from Cooperstown," said Kate, pointing to a spot on the map. "It has twelve cabins, a house, an old barn, a restaurant, an apple orchard and a cistern. It's set on thirty-six acres on Wyanthia Mountain. In late fall the area is covered with deer that come to feed off the apples. I thought I could make some money during hunting season, but the hunters trashed the place, so I keep it shut down in the winter. It's hard to keep help, and because I'm an absentee owner, they think it's okay to steal me blind."

"I have an idea," Sunny said. "Do I have enough money to buy both properties?"

Harry looked at the calculations again and smiled. "Yes, and a comfortable amount left over." He handed the figures to Kate.

"How would you run it?" asked Kate. "Your show keeps you tied up here in the city year 'round."

"I have ways, Kate. I'll call the reservation and have my grandmother's sister, Shung', and her husband, Eddie, move out here and run it. They've always lived in the country, and Eddie is a great handyman. This would be a perfect place to fix up and sell, and it would give me a place where I could get back in touch with nature. I've been feeling burned out, and this may be just what I need to rekindle my fire."

After a lengthy discussion on the pros and cons of Sunny's plan, Kate finally agreed to the sale, and Harry assured Sunny that the Internal Revenue Service would leave her alone at least another year.

When Harry had gone, Sunny went directly to the phone and called the reservation pay phone, asking the person who answered to send someone to find Shung'. Kate sent for takeout while they waited for the return call.

Two hours later the phone rang, and Sunny jumped up to get it, knowing it was Shung'. They talked for some time, catching up on each others' lives, before Sunny mentioned her plan. Shung' agreed to come if Eddie would come with her. Sunny handed the phone to Kate, who introduced herself and worked out the finances for their move.

Kate smiled as she hung up the phone. "I never realized how much you missed being with your people, Sunny. I think your idea just might work. Let's have a glass of wine to celebrate." As Kate poured two glasses of wine, she said, "Sunny, I can't believe you're such a tightwad, saving all your money like that. Most of my clients seem to spend it as fast as they get it."

Sunny chuckled. "If you knew how I was raised, you wouldn't think so. This flat is elegant compared to the other places I've lived. Seriously, Kate, you've become my family. You can't begin to realize what you've done for me, and I thank you for giving me the tools to achieve a bountiful life. I've learned so much from you, and with my new properties, I too can become an independent woman. I hope someday I can become as good a businesswoman as you."

"Well, you can start by learning to write checks and to manage your money, rather than hoarding it," replied Kate fondly.

Two weeks passed before the properties were transferred into Sunny's name. Sunny bought frames for the title papers and hung them on the wall of her bedroom to remind herself how far she had come and where she was going. That evening she and Kate had dinner to celebrate as business partners and good friends.

As they stepped out of the elevator, Kate invited Sunny into her apartment for a nightcap. "Sunny," she said once they were comfortably seated in front of the fireplace, "since I've known you, you have never had a date. You're almost twenty-one, and I think it's time for you to take an interest in the opposite sex."

"Kate, I'm not comfortable with men. I get asked out all the time, but I know what they want, and I'm not interested."

"No one is an island unto themselves, Sunny. We all need people. It's time to expand your horizons. You can't continue to live through books and work."

"Why not? I'm happy. I have a goal, and I love what I do. I see too many people wasting their lives on nothing but trivia, and anyway, most people my age are dumb and boring. I have no time for such foolishness. I have a vision of what my life should be, and I must follow my vision."

The following morning Sunny stood in front of the brownstone and hailed a cab to take her to another of her many dance classes. Her rigid schedule was tiring and it took all of her energy to keep the pace. She was becoming well-known in the business, and jobs often came by word of mouth, without the hated auditions. Her needs were few, and although she spent some of her earnings, she continued to put most of it aside to invest in her properties. Her apartment was becoming a showplace and with Kate's sound advice, the motel was running well and showing a small profit. Sunny visited Shung' and Eddie as often as she could. She loved these visits because they allowed her to spend time with family and renew her medicine training.

She purchased three horses, and enjoyed riding with Shung' and Eddie. The slow paced simplicity of country life reminded her of the reservation. After each visit, she would return to the city refreshed and full of energy.

One warm spring day, Sunny sat on a park bench cooling down from a long run surrounded by people who swarmed past her like angry hornets searching for their nests. She thought it comical the way people were pulled along by leashes connected to dogs wearing people-type outfits. She nearly collapsed with laughter as she imagined Sam training one of these spoiled, ribboned canines. Glancing at her watch and seeing that it was getting late, Sunny got up, stretched and headed for home. She took a quick shower and dressed for work.

As usual, she was the first cast member to arrive. She went to her dressing room, sat down in front of her makeup table and idly began to create her stage image. The transformation never ceased to amaze her. With a little bit of greasepaint 'plain little Sunbeam' became the glamorous 'Miss Sunny Beam' who looked like she was born to the part. But only she knew how much hard work, sweat and tears had gone into creating the image before her. Had all those layers of greasepaint crept into her body and darkened her soul? Or was it the lack of love during her childhood years that forced her to look for love in the applause of her audiences? Were her demands upon herself a need for perfection or an addiction? Was she a workaholic? These and many other questions coursed through her mind as she put the finishing touches on Miss Sunny Beam.

She glanced into the mirror for a final check, slipped into her gown and walked to the wings of the stage. Once again, Miss Sunny Beam walked gracefully onto the stage to face yet another sea of unknown faces and bask in the sound of the audience's welcoming applause. As the lights dimmed and a spotlight lit her face, she picked up the microphone and began to weave the spell of another glamorous night of illusion, hearing her own words of long ago echoing from somewhere deep within, "I'm gonna be a star someday, Sam, I'm gonna be..."

Meeko's Birth

It was earth year 1943 when a powerful force hurled a spiritual being forward with great urgency to another life on Mother Earth. This male soul agonized over the possibility that without this birth it could be lost forever in time and space. Consumed with despair, he cried out to *Wakan Tanka* to have mercy.

A grave cloudiness loomed over another Montana reservation as the spirit neared its destination. The mortal energy was very dense and held deep sadness, overwhelming the soul who recognized it as remorse exuding from the people. Defenseless against such intense negativity, the spirit succumbed to the stabbing pains of terror that ran rampant over Mother Earth. "I will not be cheated out of this mortal life. I must find the appointed vehicle if I am to have a physical birth," raged the soul.

The local bartender who knew nothing of these happenings was thankful to be closing another pseudo-glamorous night in his Indian bar. With haughty arrogance he observed his customers, knowing he had taken the lion's share of their monthly checks. He smiled coldly as he opened the cash register to check his revenue, then hit the overhead lights. "Okay, people, let's go. It's been a long night. Last call! Motel time! Come back tomorrow and we'll do it again," he announced, his nose curling at the smell of missed urinals and stale vomit drying on the floor.

One by one his customers reluctantly drained their glasses and staggered toward the door, carrying many a bottle hidden under their jackets for the early morning hours to provide the hair of the dog that bit them the night before. As the bartender locked the door behind the last one, he chuckled, knowing they would be sitting on the curb before six o'clock waiting for him to open. He wasn't surprised when he saw a young Indian girl lying face down at the end of the bar. "Goddamnit, Renna! C'mon, get the hell outta here. I'm closed," he barked, shaking her by the shoulder. Renna raised her head and stood with the help of the nearest barstool.

"C'mon! Get your shit together, goddamnit! This pisses me off!" he yelled, grabbing her by the jacket. Renna downed her drink and vomited before she reached the front door. "Sonuvabitch! Get the fuck outta here. You goddamn fucking Indians are all alike!" he yelled, pushing her onto the street. "What the fuck are you doing out anyway? You should be home! Don't you fucking know you're ready to drop that baby any time?"

"Don't tell me nothing, you *Wasichu* bastard. I do what I wanna do," growled Renna.

"Fucking right, bitch! You're all alike! Drunk, broke or begging," he mumbled, slamming the door.

As the sidewalk spun up to meet her face, Renna leaned against the building then fell down in a drunken stupor. The winds joined her in a mournful cry as they whipped the freshly falling snow over her body. As she lay staring at the bluish haze reflecting from the street light, she saw the town through mystic eyes and enjoyed this moment of strange beauty. The cold night had a sobering effect and made her realize that she could not go home in her present state. She dragged herself to her feet, knowing she must make it to the truck stop if she was to have a free meal and a bed for the night.

The seventeen-year-old Renna struggled as she staggered slowly along, fighting against the unrelenting winds that punctured the shadowed futility of her pitiful life. Crossing the railroad tracks, she felt the impact of yet another invisible wall, the wall which separated the white people from the dirty Indian. "Damn this fucking place and all that's connected to reservation life!" She screamed as she tried to cover her protruding belly with her coat for protection against the unyielding winds that fought hard against her. "Fuck it! I'll take my peace from the bottle," she wailed into the silent hours of the early morning. Desperately she searched for her brown paper bag and with unsteady hands unscrewed the cap then sucked the bottle dry to rid herself of the excruciating pain. She flung the bottle onto the pavement in defiance, laughing in triumph as she watched it shatter into a thousand pieces.

At that moment, Renna's water broke, causing her to catch her breath as she went into labor. Crying out for help into the darkened and deserted street, she slowly staggered back toward the bar. As the pains intensified, she managed to crawl down the alley behind the bar until the pain finally forced her flat on the ground. And there she lay, helpless among the overflowing garbage cans, wailing, praying and screaming in pitiful agony.

"*Hau, Wakan Tanka,*" she screamed, bearing down hard against the torrent of pain, feeling as if her body was going to explode. "Somebody! Please send me help!" she begged. Placing her hands between her legs, she felt the baby's head protruding from her body and clawed at it until the infant slowly emerged into the world, still connected to the cord of life that had sustained it for the last nine months. Renna's pain was replaced by a dull, throbbing ache as she lay in silent helplessness, unaware that the child had not yet filled its lungs.

The snow continued to fall, covering her unwanted child with its first blanket. Renna was oblivious to the soul encased in a sphere of soft blue light that hovered above the infant. Feeling the loveless moment, it accepted with great sorrow the reality of never knowing a mother's love. Attempting to protect this fragile new life and hoping to generate a life force, the soul tried again and again to enter the motionless, wet body. I must protect this vehicle if I am to experience this birth, the soul thought and called upon the powers of life. "Oh, *Wi*, touch this newborn with warmth and ignite its life fire." But Father Sun did not hear, and the child's body remained cold and lifeless, its lungs not yet filled with their *Niya*, the breath of life, given by *Taté*, the Wind.

The silence of the night was shattered when hoards of hungry rats, the four legged vultures of death and disease, started searching among the garbage for their dinner. Finding meager pickings in the trash cans, they approached the newborn and began to eat from its bloody body. A little field mouse, surveying its surroundings from the top of an overturned garbage can, twitched his whiskers in great puzzlement, unable to recollect ever having seen a hairless two legged lying in his dinner. He watched the two legged's soul light moving in and out of the wee body as more rats began to nibble at its arms then its legs. Filled with heartache, the soul cried out in desperation to *Wakan Tanka*, begging Great Spirit to save the child that was to house him.

At that moment in a small house across town, an old white-haired medicine man awakened with a start at the sound of a baby's cry. He sat up to see a large bluish ball of light hovering over his head and heard the heart-rending cries from within its core. Renna! He jumped up and raced to the other room to find her cot empty. Dressing quickly, he jumped into his truck, allowing the blue light to guide him toward Wolf Point where he knew Renna was likely to be found.

"Where is that girl?" he asked himself as he approached the south side of town. The streets were deserted, yet he still felt her presence. As he neared the alley he saw the ball of light hovering behind the bar. He pulled to a stop and got out, rushing as fast as his legs would carry him. He stopped abruptly when he saw Renna lying on the ground with a small form between her legs. "Oh, *Tunka'shila*," Granbear said, tears of gratitude filling his eyes. "Thank you. You have guided me well."

Opening her eyes, Renna saw her grandfather and cried out, "Oh, Granbear. Over here! Hurry! Thank you for coming. Please help me."

Granbear squinted his eyes for a better look. "Oh, *Tunka'shila*, are my eyes deceiving me? Has my great-grandson been born?" Bending down to look closer at the small shape between Renna's legs, he saw the rats chewing on the baby's blood-covered body. Immediately his joy turned to fury as he stood up and began swinging his walking cane over the child until the last of the heartless intruders had scurried away. Looking more closely, he saw a round silver-blue light enter and re-enter the baby again and again. "What miracle is this?" asked Granbear, knowing he had been guided by the Great Spirit to save this child.

Filled with amazement, Granbear humbly witnessed the miracle of a spirit entering a body to give it life. "*Hau, Wakan Tanka*, thank you for allowing me to be part of my great-grandson's birth," he prayed as he knelt down, joyful tears flowing down his wrinkled cheeks. Using his pocket knife, he severed the umbilical cord and stuffed it into his pocket. Taking his fingers, he cleaned out the baby's mouth and offered it his breath, then smacked its tiny butt. As a lusty cry burst forth breaking the silence of the night, Granbear echoed this moment of happiness with joyful laughter, offering the baby up to *Wakan Tanka*. "Oh, thank you, Great Spirit, for allowing my great-grandson to live. How can I ever repay you for such a wonderful gift? *Tunka'shila*, I am honored to witness such a miracle. *Hau, Mitakuye Oyasin.*" With trembling hands Granbear tightly wrapped the baby in his jacket and held it close to his body for warmth, saying, "Come, Renna, the baby is badly hurt. We must get home."

With Granbear's help Renna struggled to her feet, and three generations of Bear Clan headed for home. Gently the old medicine man placed the infant on the seat between them. They drove in silence until without warning Granbear burst into a special birthing song. He knew *Wakan Tanka* had extended his ninety-two years of earth time to train this baby in the old ways and the mere thought made him feel young again. After he pulled into the front yard, Granbear shut off the engine and got out of the truck. Holding the baby lovingly in his arms, he carried it into the house where he proceeded to take total ownership of Renna's child.

Auntie Lizzie, a heavy set woman with a worry-creased brow, was standing in the doorway and smiled when she saw they were all safe. Wringing her hands in her apron, she said, "Oh, Grandfather, I was so worried. I'm glad you found her and that everyone is safe."

"No need to worry, Lizzie. Renna's had a boy child. You help her, and I'll take care of the baby."

Auntie Lizzie guided Renna toward her cot behind the cookstove. "Whatever are we going to do with you, Daughter?" she scolded, covering her with a star quilt. Renna, still dazed from alcohol and giving birth, rolled over and faced the wall to escape another lecture from her mother. Lizzie quickly boiled some bitterroot tea and forced Renna to drink it, saying, "This will help you get well."

"Let her be, Lizzie. Heat a kettle of water and let's get this baby cleaned up and into some warm clothes."

Auntie Lizzie stoked the fire and placed another kettle on to boil, thinking it had been a long time since a baby had blessed their home. Filling a pan with warm water, she took the baby from Granbear, and as she started to bathe it, she burst into tears. "Oh, Granbear, this child is so weak and what are these awful bites? It looks as if a demon has tried to take its life. I think these wounds are going to leave bad scars." Raising her voice to *Tunka'shila*, she prayed, "Have mercy on this family. Do not let this child become another cursed soul."

"Easy, Daughter, the baby will live. The rats may have taken some flesh, but don't worry, no demon will ever take a soul away from this medicine man," declared Granbear as he busied himself preparing a medicine salve. Lizzie handed the baby to Granbear and stood watching him as he applied it to the infant's wounds while chanting an old medicine healing song.

He then handed the baby to Lizzie who wrapped it tightly in a soft blanket, saying, "Grandfather, I know this soul will be safe with your medicine. Did you notice the big bones of this child?"

Granbear took the baby in his arms and sat down in his rocker next to the stove. "Good Sioux blood, Daughter. Someday he will be very big in many ways," chuckled Granbear.

"Is that so, Grandfather?" responded Lizzie, smiling fondly as she got up and put another pot of coffee on the stove.

As the wonderful aroma of boiling coffee filled the house, a gentle smile crossed Granbear's face and he gathered his thoughts before speaking. "Lizzie, I witnessed my great-grandson's soul enter his body. Ah yes, *Wakan Tanka* works in strange ways. Who would ever think I would be given such a beautiful gift from the Great Spirit? This soul and I have shared many lifetimes and *Wakan Tanka* has seen fit for us to share in another mortal destiny. Yes, Daughter, this soul has a profound destiny and is a gift to the people. This is why he has been given to us. I will help direct his birth purpose and prepare him to someday become medicine and serve the people. This child will help bond all the Indian nations as one people. If this is not so, then who is this I hold in my arms?"

Upon hearing Granbear's words, Auntie Lizzie recalled when long ago he had spoken of a special one that would be born to the Bear Clan. As she fussed with the baby's blanket, she had no doubts about his predictions of the future. They waited for the coffee to finish brewing, soothed by the pot's steady rhythm as its fresh aroma joined their thoughts.

"Pour me a cup of that coffee, Daughter," said Granbear, looking deep into the bright face of his great-grandson. As if in answer to his unspoken words, the baby opened its eyes and stared back. Granbear felt an intense inner knowing between him and his great-grandson and he embraced the moment in silence as he sipped his coffee. This connection between them seemed to come from the understanding of their many shared dreams from another time and place. "Lizzie, I want you to always remember what I'm about to say. I know this soul. This child belongs to me, not to Renna. We will raise him until he is ready for his boy training, then I'll take him to my apprentice, Shadowhawk."

"Well, Grandfather, that's a wonderful plan." Lizzie smiled thinking fondly of Shadowhawk, her ex-husband. They were very young when they had first met, what a pity they were no longer together. But still, Shadowhawk was a fine man, a great warrior and a very good medicine man.

"Ah, Granbear, it seems the past has met with the future. Don't you think you and the new baby have many things to discuss. But first Grandfather, don't you think you should give him a name before he starts on this long journey with you?"

Noticing the projected indifference of the baby's eyes, Granbear said, "Lizzie, this child carries two souls, yet they are one. This is very unusual. I think the younger soul was Creek in its last life, but the older one is, and always was, Sioux. We must choose the name carefully so as not to offend either spirit. A Creek friend once told me that such a child as this was called a Meeko, a special born one. If what I suspect is true, I must train him in a special way so he will surrender his soul to deeper awareness. Hmmm, this is definitely a Meeko. That's what we will call him. Meeko, the special born one."

Lizzie did not reply. Seeing the tightness of her lips, Granbear laughed and said, "I did not know you were so prejudiced. Isn't a Creek name good enough for your grandson, or did you want him to have a good Sioux name?"

"Yes, Grandfather, I did. This child is Sioux, and a Sioux name is more fitting. But I know what you say is true, therefore I have no doubt about your decision. I know nothing of this other soul, but you are strong medicine and the name is up to you."

"Well, Daughter, if my decision is bothering you, then bring my pipe and we shall ask this soul for its name."

Lizzie handed him the pipe and as Granbear filled and lit it, he prayed, *"Hau, Wakan Tanka*. I am no longer a tired old man. Once again you have given me the opportunity to become a useful tool and be your faithful servant. Help us understand this soul's mission and give us a sign to guide us to his rightful name." Granbear passed the pipe to Lizzie. As the winds came down the stovepipe it suddenly popped loudly and shot bright red flames across the room.

A strong voice echoed, "This soul is a true Meeko. Teach him the ways, and as spirit I will guide him until his mission on earth is completed."

Terror struck Lizzie's heart and she quickly handed the pipe back to Granbear. As he smoked the last of the tobacco, he prayed, "Oh, *Tunka'shila*, thank you for the sign. I am humbled. I will do as you ask and train him to walk in honor just as his forefathers, so he too can learn the joy of sharing in a good way. *Hau, Wakan Tanka*, let it be so. *Hau, Mitakuye Oyasin.*"

Granbear and Lizzie wept with happiness at the completion of the spirit's visit. Lizzie wiped her eyes and apologized profusely for having doubted Granbear's knowledge. "Oh, *Até*, if this is what *Tunka'shila* wants, I will support your every endeavor in raising this child." Picking up the baby, Lizzie held it close to her breast and beseeched the spirit helpers to give Granbear no more responsibility than he could handle at such an advanced age. Yet, underlying her thoughts, remained the fear that this baby would become just another damned soul, born to have its life choked off by the government's steel grip on reservation life. Fervently hoping otherwise, she readied for bed and as Granbear blew out the light, all was silent and peaceful in the Bear Clan home.

The old medicine man got up as first light appeared on the horizon and went to inform the relatives of this miracle birth. It was around ten that morning when the family members began to gather at the house to celebrate the new arrival. Proud and happy, each one arrived with boisterous greetings. Renna awakened with a terrible hangover. Annoyed with the noise around her, she searched under her cot for a hidden bottle. Auntie Lizzie was watching and went immediately to make sure there was not one, scolding, "You better not have a bottle in this house! Stay where you are and get well."

Granbear heard the angry words and seeing Renna's sullen face, he said, "Lizzie, don't argue with her." Handing Lizzie the baby, he added, "Never you mind! I'll speak with her!" Granbear took his medicine pouch and made a woman's tea, then walked over and handed it to his granddaughter. Sitting down on a corner of the cot, he gently encouraged, "Renna, drink this medicine tea. It will clean out your body and help you rest. I'm an old man and I have seen many winters. What I'm about to say to you is true. You have given birth to a special child who must be protected and trained in the old ways. Many times while you were carrying this child you said that you did not want it, so your mother and I will raise him and see to his welfare. He will be taught the old ways, and before I return to the Other Side I will reveal many secrets about this child to you."

Renna felt great relief knowing that she would not be stuck with a baby at her young age. She sighed then nodded in agreement before she rolled away from Granbear and fell asleep.

By late afternoon the house was filled with family and friends that had come to see the newborn. Granbear proudly walked around among the guests showing off his great-grandson. When the light of day began to dim, he picked up his jacket and placed his old Billy Jack hat on his head, saying, "Lizzie, make sure everyone is well fed. There's something I must do. I'll be back soon."

Granbear walked to his truck and after coaxing it to life, he headed to the old abandoned homestead. When he arrived he took great pride in walking over the land as he offered tobacco to the spirit of Mother Earth. He thought of the many prosperous years long ago when the Bear Clan family ran the reservation. He did not see the weather-beaten, rock-framed shack that no longer had any doors or windows, instead he saw the future blending with the old, knowing that Meeko would someday rebuild the old homestead. But for now, he must do what he came to accomplish. Humming an old Indian song, he climbed upon a rickety bench next to what had once been the front door. Taking the umbilical cord from his pocket, he nailed it above the door frame. Once finished, he climbed down and chuckled with satisfaction, saying, "Grandson, now I have you forever."

The sun was setting as Granbear walked down by the river and sat among the cottonwood groves, then lit his pipe to speak to the Great Spirit. "*Hau, Wakan Tanka.* I do these things, *Tunka'shila,* because your ways have never failed me. I place the lifeline cord of my great-grandchild, Meeko, above the sacred door of the Bear Clan people to keep the little one tied to us. Now, no matter where life may take him, I know he will always find his way home. *Tunka'shila,* I ask you to guide him and keep him connected to our ways, but also give him a strong desire to learn the white man's system. Someday let him walk with awareness on Mother Earth to all the sacred places of his forefathers. Let him follow the above calendars and understand the teaching of the sky maps. Give this soul the power to walk between two raindrops so he may bathe in the clean, singing rivers and carry their power as a great life giver. Help him become one with all, so he may walk with peace within the great mystery of time.

"From this day forward, I give my great-grandson to serve future generations of the Sioux nation. Let him be the one to show them how to keep to the old ways so they may rebuild the old ways of our ancestors upon this sacred land. Take him far, *Tunka'shila,* so I may return home with peace in my heart, knowing the people will live in a good way. It is said, therefore it is so. *Hau, Mitakuye Oyasin*." Granbear cleaned his pipe and gave the ashes to the four directions. His heart humbled as the wind lifted the ashes from his hand, embracing and carrying them across his beloved land. With joy in his heart, he turned toward home.

Life soon returned to normal and Meeko thrived under the loving guidance of Granbear and Auntie Lizzie. Even Auntie Lizzie had to admit that her fears for the child had been unfounded. Renna continued to drift through life in a drunken stupor, coming to see Meeko only sporadically during his first three years of life, then, not at all. As time passed Auntie Lizzie heard Renna had left the reservation with a trucker.

It was almost time for Meeko to start school when Renna once again began to visit her son. She would stay for a day or so, then take off again. Granbear, concerned about Renna's drinking problem, always stayed close by to make sure she did not harm the child, and her visits were always punctuated by vicious arguments about her drinking and lifestyle. Normally the visits would end up with Renna cursing and taking off in a huff, not to be heard from until she needed a bed or a hot meal. Just before Meeko turned six years old, Granbear angrily informed Renna that he would no longer allow her to visit the boy if she had the smell of alcohol on her breath. She stormed out, cursing and screaming that she would never return.

Granbear walked Meeko to school each day, always reminding him of the importance of the white man's education. At the end of each day Granbear would be waiting, and as they walked home he would question his great-grandson about what he had learned, comparing it to the ways and beliefs of their people. In this way Granbear hoped to arm his great-grandson for his future as an Indian living in the white world.

When the summer winds came and school was out, Meeko and his friends gathered their ponies and rode bareback across the open plains, staging mock battles under the watchful eyes of Granbear. Many a night Meeko and Granbear bedded down by an open fire and watched the stars move across the sky. One especially warm night Granbear and Meeko were camped out under a canopy of brilliant stars, not far from the old homestead. Meeko looked up and found the Great Bear in the sky. As he watched the heavenly stars inch their way from East to West, he asked, "Where are the stars going, Granbear?"

Granbear smiled fondly, answering, "The stars travel across the heavens bringing the sacred messages of *Wakan Tanka* to the people. Tomorrow I will draw you a star map and show you how the stars line up with the sacred places on Mother Earth. It's the placement of the stars that tells us when it is time to do our sacred ceremonies. Grandson, the stars also hold all of our history. Someday I'll teach you how we were seeded by the star people."

Another summer had come and gone and as Meeko watched the geese flying South for the warmer weather, he knew that winter was fast approaching. Many of his uncles came by and he helped them chop and stack firewood in readiness for the harsh winter to come. When the plains slowly turned white with silent snow, Meeko loved the trek home from school with his friends. Each day they would rush from school to build caves in the cold snowbanks. At the end of the day when his studies were completed, Meeko would wrap himself in a heavy blanket and sit at the foot of Granbear's makeshift bed, listening to his deep, soothing voice breathe new life into ancient battles that came alive through his words. Granbear was making sure Sioux history was steeped in each story until it took solid form in his great-grandson's mind. Meeko treasured Granbear's stories and loved knowing that his people always made sure their oral history was passed down intact from generation to generation.

"I was only six winters when I watched the great, victorious battle at the Little Big Horn," said Granbear. "For months I had listened to the leaders plan how best to win the upcoming battle with the Long Knives. All the medicine people had foretold we would win this battle against the whites, long before Yellow Hair was known to us. Our people knew it would become a battle of great honor for the Sioux and an everlasting embarrassment to the white nation. Even the women knew of this battle with Yellow Hair and they too spoke of our victory at Greasy Grass.

"Ah, Grandson, I will never forget my first glimpse of General Custer," smiled Granbear, leaning back on his pillows. "He was a man that fought by the book and hated the Sioux because we abided by our own rules. Our warriors were trained to organize, scatter and regroup during a battle. Ah yes, those were the days, Grandson. We were a proud nation of fierce Dog Soldiers. Back in those days honor was everything, and a man had to uphold his beliefs. That's why our warriors always painted their power signs on their tipis, fighting horses and clothing. A warrior lived, fought, and died with great honor. We Dog Soldiers were different than the white man. We planned our strategies for battle, but we also prepared our spirits, minds and bodies to win," said Granbear from under penetrating, hooded eyes.

"It was early morning long before dawn, when a great commotion started in the camp. I jumped out of bed and ran outside to find many painted warriors dressed in their finest garments, ready to ride into battle on their fierce fighting ponies. They whooped and hollered as they rode them back and forth through camp, letting the people know their fighting spirits were alive and victory was in the air. In great excitement I ran to my father, pleading with him to allow me to fight alongside my brothers against the Blue Coats. My father, one of our bravest and most revered Dog Soldiers, answered, 'No, Son. You are much too young. Wait until you are older and as strong as your brothers.'

"I longed to fight in this battle, so I went to my oldest brother and begged him to take me with him. 'Run along, Little Brother,' he said. 'I know you are very brave. When you are older I will be proud for you to ride by my side, but not today.' I knew my big brother loved me and wanted to keep me safe, but I continued to plead with him to let me do battle with Yellow Hair. I told him I must fight so that I could tell my children's children that I was one of the warriors who had defeated the Long Knives. My brother smiled, then reaching down he pulled me onto his horse, saying, 'All right, Little Brother. You can ride with me for awhile, but then you must go back to the safety of the camp.' My heart burst with pride as I imagined that I was riding off to meet the enemy. As I rode out of camp, my body pressed into my brother's, I felt like a real warrior going off to battle to earn his warrior feathers. Suddenly we heard a group of Long Knives approaching from behind. Silently my brother took me from the saddle and placed me on the ground, motioning for me to quickly return to the safety of the camp.

"Filled with disappointment, I watched him ride off to join the others. I crouched low behind some rocks until the enemy had passed. At once I knew that I could hide no longer. I was not a child, I was a proud young warrior, ready to fight with honor by the side of my brother! Using my tracking skills, I stayed out of sight, following my brother's trail until I found him. When he saw me, he was angry that I disobeyed him. He grabbed my arm and slammed me down to the ground, saying harshly, 'Stay there! We will talk to our father about this when the battle is over!' I scrambled to safety and crouched under some scrub brush where I could crawl on my belly to the very edge of the ridge and see the entire valley.

"Suddenly I heard the sound of a bugle and spotted Yellow Hair leading his regiment fast across the open valley. It was a suspenseful moment as they moved forward, and filled with the excitement of victory, I hugged Mother Earth. The Dog Soldiers had already established their boundaries and we had the enemy surrounded on three sides of the valley. Our warriors crested the hills in massive numbers, dressed in their finest to intimidate the enemy, then all at once they disappeared. Suddenly I saw our fearless, half-naked warriors swooping down from the hills with only one thought. Destroy old Yellow Hair! Destroy the enemy! Ah yes, history was in the making.

"They say we were seven thousand in number. Oh, we were many, but in number we were maybe three hundred," chuckled Granbear. "Without any words being spoken each man knew when to alternate his position as he rode back and forth into battle while others waited anxiously to take his place. This was how we kept all of our warriors fresh and hungry for blood.

"When I saw my father riding hard and fast back to where we were hidden, my heart filled with pride. He quickly dismounted and called out to me, saying, 'Son, take care of the horses and the wounded. Keep close to the ground like a mouse.' I was happy he showed me no anger and I did exactly as he asked, thrilled with the responsibility he had given me.

"Ah, Grandson, our Dog Soldiers had power that day. Each one had committed to do battle, and if necessary, give his life for the people. The valley floor was covered with Dog Soldiers staked to the ground by their sashes. Ah yes, the Dog Society was at its best. The loyalty between them was unequaled, these brothers would risk it all for each other. I saw many a Dog Soldier ride low and cut another free; others would stake themselves next to a brother warrior and fight to win or die.

"Ah, Grandson, all the Blue Coats fell that day. A Dog Soldier takes no prisoners. We had lost too many of our people at Sand Creek to show any compassion. The white soldiers had ridden in while the men were gone and slaughtered our old people, our women and our children. The day Custer died everyone was taking their revenge for that blood bath twelve years earlier. Remember, a Sioux never forgets.

"We went to the battlefield to make sure all the white soldiers were dead. We slashed their arms and legs and cut their tongues from their heads so they could not lie or fight against the Sioux in another life. Why, even our women stripped the valuables from all the dead bodies, then went to Custer's body and made sure he would never father a child in another life. Ah, yes! This was a great victory for us, and believe me, Grandson, it was truly Custer's last stand against the Sioux nation. The battlefield lay quiet as I sat proud, riding with my father back to camp in high spirits. I can still smell the sweetness of that victory, knowing we killed them all."

"Granbear, I want to become a Dog Soldier."

"Grandson, we'll not talk about that now. When you're older, you'll learn about these things from Shadowhawk during your boy training. A Dog Soldier never kills senselessly. Life is too precious and death is never taken lightly by a Sioux, otherwise his soul will mourn for those he kills in battle. But there are times when a warrior is forced to kill another and he must be forgiven by *Wakan Tanka*. That's why a warrior paints his face. It's to hide his identity and let Creator know it was not he, but the warrior who lives within, that did the killing. When a warrior returns from battle, he must remove his war paint and go immediately to the *Inipi* to speak with *Wakan Tanka* about this bad deed. Once he has cleansed his mind, body and spirit, he dresses in his finest, then goes to the people to receive his just honors in celebration.

"I did all these things with my father and brother. I too was honored by the people for my bravery since I was the youngest warrior ever to ride in such a great battle. They gave me my first eagle feather that day," said Granbear, letting his face take on the fierceness of a true warrior. "Ah, there was never a doubt of who stood in front of you in those days. A good warrior always rests upon the power of Great Spirit."

Meeko lay curled under his blankets at the foot of Granbear's bed, yearning for the old days to return. He could see himself dressed as a Dog Soldier, riding his painted pony off into battle. His soul hungered to be a Sioux warrior, protecting his nomadic people as they roamed across the land. He remembered when Granbear had told him about the useless killings at Wounded Knee and how the people still mourned that sad day. It had happened in December on a cold, wintry day as Chief Bigfoot was leading his people to safety at the Pine Ridge agency. The white soldiers opened fire on them and killed everyone, then buried them in one large grave. Saddened by thoughts of this massacre, he stared at the moonbeams crossing Granbear's bed and wondered what he could do to keep things like that from ever happening again.

The following morning Meeko got up late for school, rushing off with only a piece of buttered fry bread to eat. The day was long for him and when the bell rang he ran all the way home. Auntie Lizzie knew he would be starving and had a plate of food waiting as he entered the door. After his studies were completed, Granbear called him to his side, saying, "Grandson, I've thought about your desire to become a warrior. Always remember there are many ways to be a warrior. Think over the old battles and see if you can find a way that would have changed those bad things. Remember to win a battle you must be well prepared. Our future warriors will need strong medicine and their new weapons must come from the educational system of the white man. Knowledge will become our most powerful tool for future battles with the white nation. You must learn to walk in both cultures when you fight the white man's council. Only then can you speak a truth without offending either race. By joining these two cultures you will complete your destiny before you leave this earth. Grandson, you've already begun building your weapons. Eat the knowledge and know an honorable person always acts upon his instincts. It would sadden me if you ever became one of those lost-spirited reservation Indians.

"I would like for you to think of the world joined together as one nation where all the races fight side by side to defeat the injustices which enslave the people who are without knowledge. World conflicts will cease when spiritual warriors of all kinds walk the Red Road, bringing all the people back to the blanket. There will be no lies when the world tribe sits around a campfire in peace. Ah, Grandson, what a sight to see when their children's children join hands as Sundancers, blooming from the sacredness of the cottonwood tree."

Granbear blew out the kerosene lamp and as darkness encompassed them, Meeko lay quietly with his thoughts. Granbear smiled, knowing his never-ending stories were awakening something very deep within his grandson's soul.

It was late spring and Meeko was out of school when Granbear decided the family should spend the summer at the old homestead. The Bear Clan began to spend every spare moment helping bring the place back to a livable condition. Auntie Lizzie spent her days cooking and delivering meals to the workers during this time. Once the homestead had been made comfortable, the family moved in so Granbear could continue to strengthen Meeko's understanding of his life journey. Granbear always used the oldest of history plus everything around him to weave each lesson into the present. One day he decided to take Meeko directly to the old battlegrounds so he could feel the blood of his people in the soil.

It was early morning when Granbear called to Meeko, telling him they were going to visit another battleground. Driving until they reached the bottom of the mountain, Granbear parked his truck then he and his Grandson followed an old dirt trail to the top. Granbear hoped when they finally reached their destination his grandson would be able to feel the depth of those who had died here for their cause. He sat down to rest as Meeko wandered about, feeling the history that was written in the land. Granbear made a fire and brewed some coffee as he set up camp. When this was finished he poured himself a cup and went to sit on the highest peak with Meeko. They sat in silence letting their eyes embrace the beauty of all that lay before them.

"I remember as a young boy I ran and played in these mountains. From this point I once watched thousands of buffalo roam the range. The smell of sweetgrass was everywhere and the water and air were pure and clean. The medicine people would come here each season to gather the sacred medicines. Ah, there was a great power among the people in those days." Granbear sighed and got up, saying, "Come, Grandson, let's walk the land together."

They had been traveling for several miles discussing Mother Earth when Granbear stooped down and picked up an unusual stone. Handing it to Meeko, he said, "The Stone People carry the oldest of history. It's a shape that Creator likes to become, so we must be careful what we do to a stone."

Intrigued by this bit of information, Meeko filled his pockets with stones, hoping that Granbear would teach him how to read their messages when they arrived back at camp. When they returned Meeko gathered a bundle of dead wood to stoke the fire as Granbear prepared and cooked their evening meal. Once they were finished eating, Granbear poured himself another cup of coffee and lit his happy pipe. As they sat under a blanket of stars, Meeko asked, "Grandfather, if the reservation is so bad, why don't the people just move away?"

"Well Grandson, I really don't know, but possibly we should consider that many of us learn best from hardships. Maybe this is what the Great Spirit demands from us as a race." Seeing the confusion in his grandson's mind, Granbear chuckled, saying, "Grandson, where is your sense of humor? Why even Creator has a sense of humor. He created me, didn't he?

"Grandson, we live on a prize piece of real estate. All races fight to own the land. The reservations are all the Indian has left. This land is our home and we must keep it because it holds the bones of our ancestors. We must never desert the bones of our people cradled in the bosom of Mother Earth. Where else can we live and stay close to our ancestors if we're not on the reservation? You might say we are a country within a country, and we are very rich with land."

"Then why do the white people hate us and make us suffer?"

"We suffer because we are not free to live as our forefathers taught us to live, Grandson. You must remember we have won a few battles, but we have not yet won the war. That battle is going to be fought by our young people, like you. Ah, Grandson, look all around at all this rich beauty. When we speak of a Dog Soldier fighting a battle in the future, it will be to save the land." Granbear spread his arms wide, emphasizing his point.

"It was the land and all its creations that gave us everything we needed. It is written in the sacred records of *Inyan*, the Stone People. If you listen, you can hear *Inyan* whisper the history of all peoples including the two legs, the four legs and the no legs. The motherland is alive and gives to her children the sacred waters, the minerals, the gas and the oil. Someday the white man will come with his drills and dig holes in her body for mere stacks of money. Some of our people will sell the land and destroy the bones of our relatives. Meeko, always look for the true riches in the land and she will take care of you forever.

"When the white man came to conquer our people, he wanted the land and its riches. He offered us a mere pittance for what was already ours. Now I question the white man's reasoning. How can you buy and sell your Mother? The government assigned us pieces of our own land and placed them in an undivided interest to be shared with our future relatives. But as individuals, we can do nothing with our own land, unless it is approved by all who share ownership. Then it must be approved by the same United States government that stole it away.

"Grandson, in time you will know these things to be true. You must never forget we Sioux are, and always will be, at war with the United States of America. We are a race of people that want to live as our forefathers lived. The fact that the government does not understand our relationship with *Wakan Tanka* does not matter. There will never be a government system big enough to prevent us from worshipping the Great Spirit in the proper manner. The United States government may think of us as a conquered people, but this is not true.

"Meeko, by law we are controlled by the Bureau of Indian Affairs, which is controlled by the Department of the Interior. And since we are wards of the government, and the bureau is only number ten in importance to them, they feel they can tell us what we can and cannot do. The old people say that BIA stands for 'Boss Indians Around'. They also say it is run by the 'I don't know people'. Why, they have even placed the standing ones on a reservation that they call a park and I've heard they squeeze wild animals into a reservation they call a zoo," chuckled Granbear mischievously.

"Oh, Granbear," smiled Meeko.

"Oh, Grandson, in time you will learn what I say is true. Know we are not a beaten race. We are still at war with the United States government. It is sometimes very difficult to keep our traditional ways when the laws and the white churches try to prevent us from worshipping *Wakan Tanka*. They do not understand our relationship with Creator and find us unacceptable as a people. To them 'Indian' is a dirty word and they consider us savages. But someday your kind will boot out that narrow thinking. Learn our ways well, Grandson, and someday you may lead the big battle to merge all people so that they worship one God without prejudice in how they do so."

Meeko quietly reflected upon Granbear's words and knew what he said was true. Many times he had heard white people say insulting things about Indians, and he hated being called a dumb or dirty Indian. "Granbear, why do all the ranchers' children say that all Indians should be gassed by the time they're five years old?"

"Because they've heard their parents say those cruel things. Never blame the children for these hurtful remarks, Grandson. Blame their parents. Prejudice could not exist if we respected and understood each other's ways. Someday others will learn our ways and a bridge of unrestricted love will span those hateful racial beliefs. Many will come to believe as the Indian and will accept their responsibility and relationship with the earth and all her children. The people, animals, stones and trees are all the same in the eyes of *Wakan Tanka*. Until the time comes for others to consider these things, the Indian will remain on reservations. The Indian as well as the animals, serve to teach humans to find the real purpose in their life. I have never seen a bear trying to become a cougar. As long as an Indian is an Indian, instead of trying to be something else, we just might rebuild our nation that is located within the United States of America. We must pay attention to these things, or our blood will become so watered down from intermarriage that our future children will just be a dark-skinned people with long hair."

"Granbear! How can this be? Why can't we just follow our own ways? And why do they keep tearing up Mother Earth and moving everything around?"

"Well, Grandson, maybe they think everything is out of place and needs to be rearranged," chuckled Granbear. "Don't worry, sometimes I think the world is going to hell in a handbasket. When people weaken their beliefs in *Wakan Tanka*, they have no truth in themselves. Chaos and confusion kills their dreams before they are ever born. As individuals, and as a nation of people, we must hold onto our dreams. Mother Earth tells us to reproduce our own kind, yet there are many mixed bloods being born. If we don't start producing more full-bloods, we are going to become an endangered species like so many of the animals. Now wouldn't that be sad to have a full-blooded Indian placed on display in a zoo to entertain an afternoon crowd every Sunday?" chortled Granbear. "Come, Grandson, my old body is too stiff and tired to camp out another night. I'm hungry for some home cooking and if we leave now we can be home by supper."

Meeko packed up the camping gear and as they walked off the mountain, the last rays of the sun could be seen bouncing off the back window of the truck. They drove directly to Auntie Lizzie's house where their bellies were filled, followed by a good night's sleep.

Early the following morning everyone packed up and drove to the old homestead. Granbear gathered his leathering tools and sat at the old picnic bench under a cottonwood tree. Meeko watched with curiosity as Granbear spread his things out on the bench. "Granbear, why don't our people make the ritual things anymore?"

"Oh, Meeko," Granbear replied, "That's not necessarily true. There are a few of us who will always follow the old ways. What makes me sad is that there are many who no longer feel they have to earn a place of honor among the people. Someday I hope you will grow up to be one of those people that stick to the old ways. Now instead of asking so many questions, go to the river and get Auntie Lizzie some fresh water."

Meeko got the water then returned to the river for a swim and spent the rest of his day looking for something to do. When Auntie Lizzie finally called them to supper, Meeko ran to tell Granbear. After dinner everyone seemed quiet and tired as one by one they drifted off to bed.

Long before sunrise Granbear walked to Meeko's bed, yelling, "Get up! Today we begin searching for your powers." Meeko struggled with heavy eyelids and rolled out of bed in a foul mood. Auntie Lizzie had a roaring fire going in the stove and breakfast was sitting on the table. When Meeko saw she had made his favorite raisin fry bread, his mood lightened. Auntie Lizzie poured herself and Granbear a second cup of coffee and when Meeko had finished eating, he announced he was going to the river to bathe. When he came out of the river, he shook his hair free of water then returned home.

Granbear was sitting under the cottonwood tree tooling a piece of leather and as Meeko sat down to watch him, he said, "Well, Grandson, the sweat was good this morning. Everything is good," he added, touching himself and then the earth. "Yes, everything is in balance. Today is a good day." He smiled and handed Meeko a round piece of leather with a circle drawn in the center. Meeko studied the leather circle and wondered about its meaning.

"I made this for you and I want you to always wear it. It will teach you many things. Everything is birthed from a circle and reminds us we are related and connected to all things in the universe which is the home of *Wakan Tanka*. This circle will teach you how to find your true strengths through silence. Gather these seeds of knowledge and plant them deep in your soul so you can harvest the sweetness of their fruits to use someday in your future."

As Meeko fondled the leather between his fingers, Granbear added, "Do you see that a circle has no beginning or no end? It teaches you to always complete what you start. The paints I used are from Mother Earth. The red says you are one with the Red race and you are walking toward the West Door on the Medicine Wheel. The small green circle in the center says you are a child of Mother Earth and you understand all of her medicines. The blue color speaks of *Até*, Father Sky, who gives motion to all life. The star to the right tells where you come from and this is your guide to the truth of all the above powers." Granbear took it from Meeko's hand and tied it around his neck, saying, "Grandson, wear this so it can help you build your power and teach you to walk a strong pathway."

As both sat in silence, Granbear opened his pipe bag and removed his carved bear head pipe. "Grandson, this pipe is *Lela Wakan*, very sacred. It has been carried by our people for many generations and has always belonged to the Bear Clan. It was a gift from my father, who received it from his father. Someday I hope you too will carry this pipe. It has always made a strong pathway for Bear Clan Sundancers. Someday you will become a Sundancer, and when you have a son, you will prepare him to carry this sacred Bear Clan pipe as your forefathers did before you."

Meeko grasped the magnitude of this gift and held it close to his heart, saying, "Granbear, I promise that someday I will earn the right to carry this pipe."

"Grandson, it will take many years to fulfill that dream. One must have a pure heart to carry such a gift. I will let you join me in a smoke so you can feel its power. We load the pipe in a certain way. We must always offer the sacred tobacco to Father Sky, Mother Earth and the four directions." After Granbear had done these things in a sacred manner, he prayed, then lit the pipe and offered it to *Tunka'shila*. When the ceremony was completed, Meeko told Granbear he hoped to someday understand all the responsibilities of a pipe carrier. His mind drifted to White Buffalo Calf Woman who had brought the pipe to the people, and he could almost see her stepping from the brightness of a cloud as the beautiful and loving woman who came to fulfill *Wakan Tanka*'s wishes.

"Grandson, you have done well with the handling of the pipe, but I must ask you to never allow anyone or anything to capture or dampen your spirit. The white society sees the Indian as just a character in a history book and know that is not so. You have done well, but I think it's time you spend the day alone thinking about the pipe."

It was late afternoon when Granbear called Meeko to supper. As they walked into the house, Auntie Lizzie greeted them, saying, "Hurry and get washed up, you two. Your supper is ready."

Meeko took Granbear's medicine bundle, went to his room and placed it on his altar. As they were washing up for supper, Granbear heard a car pull into the yard and went to the door where he saw Renna staggering toward the house with a white man. With a grim look on his face he stopped her from entering, saying, "Granddaughter, it's been some time since we've seen you and you're drunk again. I've told you to never come here when you're doing these bad things. Now get in the car and go back where you came from."

"I didn't come here to get another lecture from you. I came to see my son," Renna argued.

"Come back when you're sober, then I'll talk to you about seeing your son," Granbear answered, closing the door.

As she stumbled toward the car Renna turned around and headed back to the house in a drunken rage. "You can't stop me from seeing my son!" she screamed at the top of her lungs, pounding on the door. The driver got out of the car and grabbed Renna by her arms as she kicked and screamed obscenities. He managed to get her into the car and as they pulled out of the yard, Renna rolled down the window and shouted viciously, "You can't tell me what to do, old man! I'll be back! You'll see!"

Wearily, Granbear sat down at the dinner table, his eyes filled with sadness. Although no one spoke of the incident during dinner, it rested heavily on everyone's mind. Renna's raging infuriated Meeko, and Auntie Lizzie grieved for the beautiful child Renna once had been. Granbear picked at his food then pushed his plate aside and broke the silence, saying, "Renna will not bring anymore heartache into this house! I'm an old man and I've seen many things in my life. What she does with her life is none of my business, but what she does around my home is my business. If she comes back, neither of you will let her in!" Without a word he rose from the table and retired for the night.

When twilight gave way to another sunrise, Meeko found Granbear and Auntie Lizzie sitting at the table speaking in low tones. Feeling as if he was infringing, Meeko quickly ate a bowl of hot cereal, grabbed his basketball and headed off to school, anxious to shoot a few baskets before class. He took his usual shortcut down the railroad tracks, jumping a back ditch then climbing a fence into the school yard. Joining his friend in a game, he missed a difficult catch and ran toward the fence to get the ball. As he bent down to pick it up, he noticed Renna was parked in a car across the street. She opened the door nearest him, and yelled, "Come here! I'm sober. I need to talk with you!"

Meeko threw the ball to the others, climbed the fence and approached her cautiously, asking, "What are you doing here? Granbear will be angry when he finds out you came to the school."

Renna smiled enticingly at Meeko and said in a sugary sweet voice, "Please, Meeko, get in the car, I have a surprise for you. It'll only take a minute." Hesitantly, he got in the car and before he had time to react, Renna reached over, slammed the door and sped off down the road.

Frantically, Meeko tried to open the door. Finding it jammed tight, he yelled, "What are you doing? Wait! Stop! Let me out! I can't go anyplace with you! Granbear will be mad! You know I can't be around you!" Meeko soon realized she was trying to leave the reservation to escape being caught by its police, and as they passed the border he knew he no longer had the protection that the reservation offered.

Renna ignored him as he sat sullenly pressed against the door. She drove onward for another twenty miles, but as they neared a truck stop she pulled in and casually asked, "Hungry?" Meeko followed at a distance as they entered the restaurant. Taking a booth near the door she motioned for Meeko to sit down. She ordered two breakfast specials and waited for the waitress to leave the table before speaking. "Meeko, don't be upset. Granbear won't let me see you. We need to spend some time together and that's why I'm taking us on a fun vacation."

Meeko knew she was lying. Somehow he had to get back to the confines of the reservation. "Renna, I'm not going anywhere with you! I'm going back to Granbear's!" he shouted and bolted out the door, running down the highway.

Renna threw some money on the table and chased after him. She caught him by the jacket and violently wrestled him to the ground. Meeko fought to get free, but she slapped him hard across the face, yelling, "Goddamnit, you little bastard! I'm your mother and your going with me, so stop fighting!" She dragged him kicking and screaming back to the car and threw him into the front seat. Grabbing his jowls, she pulled his face close to hers until he was forced to look at her as she bluntly stated, "You're going with me, whether you like it or not!"

When she let go, Meeko scooted across the seat, again fighting with the broken door handle to find he was captured. Frantic, he boldly retaliated, "You're not my mother and I won't listen to you! I'm going home!" Renna laughed at his efforts, poking fun at him as she continued her drive down the highway. Meeko sat nursing a bleeding mouth, glaring at her contemptuously. She glanced over at him from time to time, until eventually his silence and dead stare became unnerving and she knew his hatred for her was growing by the minute. With her nerves on edge, she began to drive erratically. Feeling his hatred piercing her mind, she lit a cigarette and turned the radio on full blast to distract her thoughts.

"I know why you hate me!" she blurted out. "It's that sonuvabitchin' Granbear's influence. You don't know him like I do! That stubborn old coot stole my mother and father from me. He's ruled my life since the day I was born. I'll be goddamned if he takes my son from me too! I know that old fool is brainwashing you with that old Indian shit. Humph! I bet he's even told you that you're the one that will bring back the buffalo herds. Well, Kid, I've got news for you. The only way those fucking buffalo are going to return to the reservation is when someone buys the goddamn things.

Every day I pray that the old bastard dies so I can move back home, but with my luck he'll probably outlive me!"

Her words cut deep into Meeko's heart, creating such penetrating pain that his feelings registered immediately on his fine, chisel-boned face. He clenched his jaw, wondering how she could speak so disrespectfully of Granbear. She seemed to prefer expressing rage rather than sorrow, and she kept this tirade up for the next fifty miles. All of a sudden the car started to sputter and shimmy as steam poured out from under the hood. As she pulled to the side of the road the engine sputtered one more time then died. Holding on to Meeko, she dragged him to the front of the car, then struggled to remove the baling wire from the hood, cursing and screaming all the while.

"Don't even think of running!" she yelled as she kicked the car in frustration. "It seems no matter what I do, something always fucks it up," she added as they walked in silence down the desolate highway, leaving the car behind. Renna stuck out her thumb to every car that passed, but not one stopped.

This had gone on for hours when suddenly she heard a truck's air brakes. Renna knew it was a good sign that an eighteen wheeler was stopping to give them a ride and Meeko saw his freedom fading fast. The driver turned out to be an old boyfriend who had recognized Renna and stopped. Jim, a burly, balding man with a big smile, opened the door and drawled, "Hey, Girl. What are you doing so far from home? Ain't seen you around lately. Where've you been?"

Not wanting to miss this golden opportunity, Renna smiled brightly and climbed aboard, kissing Jim full on the lips. "Hey, Baby, me and my son were going on a vacation to see the country, but the car broke down."

"Well, let's party," Jim grinned, shifting gears and pulling back onto the highway.

"I'm for that," she answered, pushing Meeko up into the sleeper and drawing the curtain. Meeko peeked through the curtains and listened to Renna and Jim talk about old times. It sickened him when she snuggled close and giggled while Jim ran his hand up her thigh. He resented Renna. She had abandoned him just as she had the car.

Meeko's hope of escape faded as the semi roared down the highway, taking him further away from Granbear and the reservation. As night came he wondered what would happen to him. Granbear and Auntie Lizzie must have been worried sick when he had not come home from school. Filled with worry, he fell asleep to the sound of the truck's tires rolling over the pavement.

For the next eight months Meeko, a virtual prisoner of the semi, traveled across the country with Renna and Jim as they slept, ate, bathed and fought from truck stop to truck stop. Each day began with whiskey-spiked coffee and pills, ending with another drunken fight before bedtime. Jim would sometimes rent a room for himself and Renna, and on those nights Meeko was left to his own resources. When he was sure Jim and Renna were fully occupied, he would sneak to a pay phone and dial the reservation police station, leaving a message for Granbear. But alas, when he called back there were never any messages for him. Meeko became saddened and disillusioned, believing he would never see Granbear again.

They had traveled for weeks in bad weather. On this particular dark rainy morning, Meeko awakened somewhere in Kansas. Getting out of the truck, he saw Renna and Jim fighting in the parking lot like two crazed animals. A crowd of onlookers watched as the police surrounded the arguing couple, trying to break up the fight. Meeko overheard one of the officers threatening to take them to jail. Jim took the officer aside, and as they talked in low tones, he shook the patrolman's hand, slipping him a twenty dollar bill. Then, without a backward glance at Renna, he jumped into his eighteen wheeler and drove away.

Meeko watched in disgust as his mother ran after the truck, screaming and hurling rocks as it headed down the highway. When she realized they were stranded, she lay down on the side of the road and began to sob. For a moment Meeko felt compassion toward this beaten, raging woman that he knew as his mother. This pity helped curb his anger toward her, but in reality he knew she had become just another drunken Indian, half out of her mind from alcohol and drug abuse.

When Renna's rage was finally spent, she wiped her eyes, tied her hair back and brazenly hiked her dress waist-high, walking from truck to truck asking for a ride. Meeko followed at a distance hoping this would save them from another dismally cold and hungry night. He no longer hated Renna, but he didn't like her either.

They heard another eighteen wheeler revving up and Renna took off running. The driver leaned out the cab window and motioned them aboard. Renna and Meeko climbed in, bound for another unknown destination. Meeko noticed the driver was Indian, and he seldom spoke except to inform them he was headed for Sioux country. Renna knew she could not use her flirting ways to get his attention and awkwardly asked if she could climb into the back to get some sleep. Meeko smiled with sadistic pleasure knowing his mother's coyote ways would not work this time. As he sat up front with the driver, he stared at the headlights, fascinated by how the light bounced off the wet roads at them. Meeko listened to the windshield wipers slapping out a rhythm that almost matched the big rig's droning tires.

A few hours later Renna suddenly raised herself up to tell the driver she was feeling motion sickness and needed some water. He motioned for Meeko to hand her the thermos. Slipping two pills into her mouth, she drank a cup of water, then lay back down.

It was snowing and the roads were getting very slippery. The driver kept his eyes fixed on the highway while Meeko listened, fascinated, as the CB kept blaring out road conditions ahead. It was around midnight when they entered the city limits of Yankton, South Dakota. The driver opened the door and quietly said, "This is as far as I go."

Still half asleep, Renna and Meeko climbed out of the truck into a snowstorm on a lonely, deserted street. Cursing under her breath, she stood there watching the truck's taillights fade from view, then they walked into town to find a pay phone.

"I'm glad we're back in Sioux country," said Meeko.

Renna, shaking from the cold, gave him a dirty look then dug in her pockets for a smoke. Pulling out a few crumbled bills and a bent cigarette, she picked up her pace, yelling, "Damn, I'm tired of this fucking running! If that sonuvabitchin' Granbear would die, we could live at home and not have to put up with this bullshit! But hell no, that old man will probably live forever!" Spotting a phone, Renna handed Meeko a handful of change, saying, "Oh, fuck him! We'll call Mom! Yeah, that's what we'll do! We'll call the police station and have them bring Mom to the phone. Then we'll tell her we need to come home."

Meeko snickered at the craziness of her thinking. Ignoring him, she grabbed the phone and dialed. After several rings with no answer, she slammed the receiver down. Meeko dialed again and as he was asking the officer to get a message to Granbear, Renna interrupted, "I said forget Granbear. Tell him to have Mom wire us money at the Western Union in Yankton." Meeko began to stammer his request into the receiver, but Renna was impatient and jerked the phone from his hand to find the line was already dead. Frustrated, she yanked on the receiver until she broke the cord, then calmly placed it back onto the cradle. Shaking his head, Meeko threw his hands up at another one of her absurd tantrums, then watched her drink the last of her booze.

As they started to walk, Renna said, "Meeko, if I get off the booze and pills, maybe I could get a job and you could go back to school. So come on, Kid, what do you say? Wanna help me get this on? When you get him on the phone, tell Granbear you're really sick and you can't make it home without me. If you do that, we could be home by tomorrow."

Meeko desperately wanted to go home, but considering the many consequences, he answered, "Renna, I want to go home, but how can you ask for money when you know all they want is for you to stop drinking? No, I won't let you hurt them anymore and I won't lie to Granbear!"

Furious at his words, Renna reached out and struck him across the mouth. "You little sonuvabitch, don't you realize I'm broke? Don't you know we're either going to freeze or starve to death in this goddamn weather? Oh, fuck it! I don't give a shit anymore!" They walked in an angered silence down the railroad tracks heading out of town. A harsh wind was blowing and both shivered from the bitter cold while they trudged onward through the snow. "Goddamnit! I hate this part of the country. It's almost spring and it's fucking snowing again!" Suddenly Renna spotted an abandoned railroad house, saying, "Come on," then ran toward the shack. "We've got to get out of this weather. I'm frozen to the bone." Finding a broken window, she removed the loose pieces of glass and they crawled inside the abandoned shed.

Feeling safe and too cold to fight, they huddled together for body warmth until they fell asleep. The winds howled throughout the night as fresh fallen snow covered the ground. By morning the snow had filtered through the open cracks in the walls and ceiling, covering most of the floor. Meeko stepped outside into warm sunlight and found everything was covered with a powdery snow. Thinking it was beautiful, he smiled knowing it would be melted by afternoon.

They explored their surroundings and discovered they were only a few blocks from town. Both agreed that with a little work they could stay in the railroad shack until they decided what to do. They were feeling hungry so Renna checked her pockets and found a few dollars. They went into town to buy some staples and on their way home, Meeko spotted a garbage dump. Setting the groceries aside, they rummaged through the debris looking for things to keep them warm. Meeko found an old kerosene lamp which inspired them to search for other things that they could use in their new house.

By early afternoon Renna was back in an optimistic mood. Happy to see the turnaround in her attitude, Meeko gathered wood then went to the river for water. When he returned with the last two buckets, he saw that Renna had built a fire in the old pot-bellied stove and was cooking a pot of beans. As they boiled rapidly, she heated some grease to make fry bread and potatoes. Once they had eaten, they decided to tackle the outhouse behind the railroad shack. Meeko took his knife and cut a pathway through the weeds to the door that was hanging from its last broken hinge. They struggled until they had the door in an upright position, and Meeko laughed when he saw the lavishly carved crescent moon in its center.

"Even though it's tilted slightly, don't you think it looks rather proud?" asked Renna, breaking into laughter.

"I think it looks very proud," giggled Meeko.

"Oh, fuck it. Leave it hanging. At least it covers the entrance," she laughed.

They walked back to the shack, where Renna built a fire as Meeko took old newspapers and stuffed them into the cracks to keep the shack warm. Making a rag wick, he lit the oil lamp they had found in the garbage dump and for the first time Renna and Meeko shared a moment of cooperative silence. Mesmerized by the soft red glow coming from the cracked cookstove, Meeko felt a camaraderie developing between him and his mother in their struggle to survive.

Early the next morning Renna agreed to stop drinking and drugging and to look for a job. She went to town, and when she returned late that afternoon she proudly announced that she had been hired as a dishwasher in a local bar.

Within two weeks Meeko had a job cleaning stalls at the stockyards. This gave him hope that their life was going to be okay, and if they continued to save their money, they could finally go home.

Renna stayed sober and came directly home from work everyday with food from the bar. With all this consideration and kindness, Meeko decided to give her a surprise. He remembered seeing an old galvanized tub at the dump and went to get it. After dragging it home, he scrubbed it shiny clean then took it into the house and placed it behind the cookstove. After many trips to the river, he built a fire to heat the water, then filled the tub. As he sat waiting for Renna to come home, she strolled through the door, her arms filled with groceries and a smile of greeting on her face. Meeko pointed to the tub as she set down the groceries. Seeing it was filled with warm water, she squealed in delight. "Oh, my God, no more PTA's for me. I can take a bath." Oblivious to Meeko's presence, she stripped naked, stepped into the tub and slid into the water.

Embarrassed by her brazenness, he turned his head away, asking, "What's a PTA?"

Renna howled with laughter, then seeing his shyness calmly answered, "Pits, tits and ass." When she had finished her bath she wrapped herself in an old blanket and made dinner. After they had eaten their evening meal and Renna had fallen asleep, Meeko took his bath, then stretched out on the floor, falling into a peaceful slumber.

As spring turned to summer Meeko continued to gather treasures from the local dump, and with his imagination their makeshift little home was becoming rather comfortable. He bound orange crates together and made a table. An old car seat became a couch until the steel springs broke through the upholstery, making it impossible to sit on. Both agreed it must stay since it kept them amused when it rocked precariously as the trains passed by. During the day the place was a hopeless shambles, but at night it held a certain charm as the glowing cookstove caused shadowy figures to dance across the newspaper covered walls.

Every day Meeko counted their money and was pleased to see they could go home after their next paychecks. Thrilled, he walked down the railroad tracks to meet Renna and tell her the good news. His happiness soon faded as the smell of alcohol reached his nostrils, and they walked home in silence. As they entered the shack, Renna tossed him a pair of pants. "Sorry about the drinking. Got fired! Don't worry, I'll have another job by tomorrow afternoon," she promised, then lay down on the floor and immediately passed out. Fearing she might awaken in the night and steal the money, he hid it before going to sleep.

When Renna left the following morning everything appeared to be okay. As the darkness of night arrived, Meeko built a fire and ate his dinner, then sat in the doorway waiting for her to return. The night grew cold and many dark storm clouds gathered overhead until the rains came down hard and the shack leaked like a sieve, compounding Meeko's fears. He huddled behind the stove and sadly watched the last of the flickering embers slowly die. Awakening early the next morning wet and cold, Meeko decided to check their money and found it was gone.

Shivering in raw naked anger and filled with a boundless hate for Renna, Meeko splashed water over his face, then headed into town. His first stop was the Indian bar. There he found Renna dancing with a white man as the jukebox cried out another tearful country-western ballad. Disgusted, he left without a word, knowing it was merely a matter of time until she ended up in jail.

Three days passed before Meeko made another trip to town, this time going directly to the local jail. As he entered he heard an electric coffeepot perking on the windowsill and saw a box of stale doughnuts sitting on a desk. Having had little to eat since Renna left, his mouth watered as he waited for the sheriff to get off of the phone.

"I'm looking for an Indian woman named Renna Louise Long Bear," he said hesitantly.

The sheriff leaned back in his squeaky chair and placed his feet on the desk to observe Meeko. "Yeah, I arrested that squaw two nights ago. Why are you looking for her?"

"She's not a squaw, she's my mother."

The sheriff ignored his remark. "Your mom, huh? Hell, Boy! I found her drunk as a skunk. Arrested her for prostitution and fighting. A white man pressed charges for theft. Says she tried to roll him. You can bet your sweet ass she's gonna sit here for sixty days waiting on her trial date." Seeing the look of distress on Meeko's face, he went on, "I'll let you visit for a few minutes." He took the keys from the backboard and led Meeko down the dark hallway to Renna's cell. "Get up, Renna. Your kid's here to see you," he said, then walked away to give them some privacy.

Meeko stared in shock as the sun filtered through the barred window. She was sitting on an iron cot, and when she turned to look at him with two blackened eyes and a shamed face, a feeling of sadness tugged at his heart. Her clothes were half ripped from her body, and her face was swollen almost beyond recognition. Even her long, beautiful black hair was fused in massive tangles by her dried blood. She got up slowly and hobbled toward him with a gentle smile on her face, exposing a toothless mouth. Grabbing the bars for support, she mumbled through a split lip, "Go get me a bottle and some cigarettes." With trembling hands she dug into the toe of her shoe and handed Meeko a ten dollar bill.

A disgusted Meeko went directly to the closest Indian bar where he spotted a Blood sitting on the sidewalk and said, "My mom's in jail. She needs a drink and some cigarettes." The man got up and staggered behind Meeko to the liquor store. Meeko waited outside until he returned and handed him the cigarettes. Cracking the seal on the bottle, the Blood took a long drink and without a word reluctantly handed it to Meeko, who placed the bottle under his shirt and returned to the jail. When he saw the sheriff was again on the phone, Meeko held up the cigarettes and pointed toward Renna's cell as the sheriff nodded his approval and returned to his conversation. Renna stood pressed against the bars as Meeko took the bottle from underneath his coat and handed it and the cigarettes through the bars. Then without saying a word, he left.

Meeko continued to live in the railroad shack and work at the stockyards for his food and Renna's cigarettes and booze. Two months and ten days later she went to trial and was sentenced to time served. Meeko was waiting when she was released.

"You've got a good kid here!" said the sheriff. "You better start taking care of him. If I catch you drinking or selling your ass again, I'll lock you up and throw away the key! Do you fucking understand me, Squaw?"

"Yeah, sure!" Renna answered nervously. "Just like I promised, we're on our way to the bus station. We're leaving for the rez today."

"You better do that," he answered, spitting out his words in an implied threat. "Now get out of here and don't let me see you around this town again!"

As they left, Renna kept her eyes focused downward on the sidewalk while Meeko trailed close behind. She stopped when they reached the first Indian bar. "Hey, what are you doing?" questioned Meeko. "You told the sheriff we'd be on the next bus out of town."

"Shut the fuck up," Renna snarled. "I've got something to do. Now beat it! Go on, get the hell outta here," she growled as she entered the bar. Stunned by her actions, Meeko stood in shocked silence, not understanding anything about this woman. Turning away, he kicked a beer can off the sidewalk in total frustration. Not knowing what else to do, he roamed the streets for hours, then as it grew dark he headed home, wondering what his future would hold.

It was very late when Renna staggered through the door with a white farmer on her arm. Meeko pretended to be asleep, but this was a night he would never forget. Without a care for her son, she let the white man fondle her as they undressed each other. And for the first time, Meeko was forced to watch and listen to his mother having sex. Feeling great shame, he watched the man give her a twenty dollar bill then walk out the door. Furious at her lack of shame and honor, Meeko jumped up from his bedroll, glaring at her in hatred.

"How dare you look at me like that? Don't you say a fucking word! We need this money to eat! Don't you get it kid? I'm a fucking whore and it's my job!" Renna shrieked in a defensive voice.

Filled with disillusionment and anger, Meeko ran from the house and walked for hours with his tortured thoughts, knowing he could not return to Granbear and the reservation. The mere thought of the pain that this would bring Granbear and Auntie Lizzie caused him to sob in anger. On the other hand if he did not return he would be captured by a world he did not understand. He couldn't go back to the railroad shack, knowing Renna would be there with another man.

Meeko turned to sleeping at the stockyards where he worked, making his bed from the same hay he would later feed to the cows. When he was hungry he turned to the streets, where he often followed the town drunks around like a stray dog begging for food and drink. As an absolute last resort, he would go find Renna who occasionally took pity on him and gave him hard-boiled eggs, pickled pig's feet or the leftovers from a stranger's plate. Sometimes she would toss him a blanket and let him occupy a corner of some stranger's room for the night while she was working. When daybreak came she would turn him back onto the streets and hand him a couple of dollars.

For the first time, Meeko knew he was stuck between two cultures. His world had become filled with severe pain that soon turned into a hateful rage against all people. Nothing mattered and he eventually learned to join in Renna's drunken parties to escape his misery. He took a liking to the soothing, golden liquid that warmed his stomach and seemed to appease his disillusionment.

Meeko had to become street smart and learn to react quickly to his gut feelings. He played a heartless game to meet his needs and could spot a bleeding heart in a second. Using the weakness of others became his personal challenge. Gentleness and kindness were foreign emotions to him, and he soon learned that a smile merely represented usability. Yes, Meeko had become an expert in the game of manipulation and deception. Life slowly became easier as this ten-year-old improved his abilities as a clever, fast thinking, hard-core street urchin. He used his little boy charm and innocence to touch every frailty of another human being. His vengeance grew into a sadistic pleasure and women became his favorite prey. Beneath the surface of all this hate, Meeko fought to keep from despising what he was becoming.

Every morning he awakened with a plan to escape his hell, but as each day of trying to cope ended, his life remained the same. Weeks passed and he had not seen Renna. He heard she had left town and thought about calling Granbear, but was too ashamed. Sometimes his hunger drove him to fight the rats for leftovers in the garbage cans behind the bars and restaurants. Other times he picked up discarded whisky bottles and drained the last few drops to kill off his hunger.

One day as he sat on the curb with all the other drunken Indians, he found his hatred directed toward the clean, well-fed white kids who passed by him on their way to school. He remembered Granbear telling him education was the future weapon against whitey, and his strong desire to retaliate against the white man's brutality took him to the school yard in search of another victim. He hung around until he caught the attention of Miss Johnson, a middle-aged school teacher with a kindly face who looked like she might feel sorry for him.

Miss Johnson soon invited him to join her classes, but Meeko demurred, saying his mother was sick and couldn't come to school to fill out the papers. He was most appreciative when she took him to the office and filled them out for him using the lies that he provided her. Once enrolled, he attended class everyday, expressing appreciation for her gifts of free lunches. When she gave him study books, her kindness touched Meeko's heart. He returned to his job at the stockyards, and within a month, he had become an astute pupil, no longer hanging out on the streets.

One day as he entered the school building, Meeko saw a little blonde girl who was the prettiest creature he had ever seen. His interest in her developed quickly when he found that she was the only child of a white family that had just moved into the area to work for the BIA. Knowing the friendship would end once she had been exposed to the local prejudice against the Indians, he decided to enjoy her innocence and friendship as long as possible. He hoped it would build into something good before she became brainwashed like all the other white kids.

He manipulated a seat next to her in class and gave all of his attention to her during lunch and recess breaks. His plan seemed to be working well, and when he thought the moment was right, he asked her if he could carry her books home from school. He began walking her home everyday, often explaining to her what it was like to be an Indian on a reservation. She was very interested in what he had to say and he felt good being with her.

One day as they turned into her yard, Meeko saw a heavyset white woman with a scowl on her face standing on the front porch. "What are you doing?" she screamed, shaking her finger at her daughter as she scrambled off the porch to where they stood. Her face turned bright pink and wrinkled up like a dried prune. She grabbed her daughter by the arm, and whacked her hard across the head, ordering her into the house. Then turning to Meeko she said in no uncertain terms, "You dirty little Indian. You stay away from my daughter!"

Meeko handed her the girl's books, then silently walked away.

A light snow was falling as he hurried along the road heading back into town. He knew Indians were hated, but that no longer mattered compared to the sadness he felt at having lost a good friend. Suddenly a speeding car filled with white boys deliberately drove close and splashed him with the new, wet slush. Angry and hurt over his constant rejection, Meeko cried out to the wind, as each emotional pain cut a little deeper into his soul.

When he arrived in town, he saw more cars than usual at the local car lot and stopped to look at them. Noticing there were more cars parked in the back, he walked over to take a look, thinking how nice it would be to someday ride in one. He tried several of the door handles until he found one that was unlocked and climbed inside. Leaning back in the seat, Meeko pretended to be driving away from his misery until he spotted the night watchman approaching. His fear sent him over the front seat and under a folded tarpaulin lying on the floor in the back. His heart pounded as the man opened the door, pushed down the lock and slammed it shut. Meeko waited until all the lights were turned off for the night, then carefully peeked over the seat and let out a sigh of relief when he saw the man had gone. Feeling safe and having no other place to go, he covered himself with the tarp and fell asleep with his nose buried in the wonderful smell of new leather. At sunrise he stepped quietly from the car, crouching low until he reached the street.

From then on, the car lot became one of his regular places to sleep, except for the night he found all the cars locked and was forced to roam the streets. He noticed white, billowy clouds of steam coming from the top of the laundromat, and remembered the time when he had sneaked up on the roof to get a better view of the little city. Once again he climbed up and squeezed himself between the air vents to stay warm and get a night's rest.

The following morning he awakened to find himself completely covered with white lint. He climbed down from the building and headed to the gas station to clean up for school, but no matter how much he pulled and wiped, he could not get all the lint off his clothes. At first he laughed at his reflection in the mirror, but it was no longer humorous when he thought of the embarrassment it would create for him and Miss Johnson if he went to school that way. He could just imagine her very proper nose wrinkling as she would politely say, "Meeko, today I feel it best that you sit in the back of the room."

Meeko laughed at his situation and decided to go back to the laundromat to visit the Indian ladies who usually arrived early to get their laundry done. He walked in and smiled brazenly, proceeding to help fold their clothes without asking their permission. The ladies giggled behind their hands at this strange looking child.

"Can I throw my clothes in with yours? I think there is a new kind of bird in our area," said Meeko as he removed his clothes, then wrapped a woman's towel around himself and paraded around shamelessly, shouting war whoops as they hid their faces in amusement.

Entertained by his antics, an old grandmother put his clothes in the washer with hers. When she took them from the dryer, he dressed quickly then grabbed her basket. After helping fold her laundry he carried it home for her. Her house was small and had good smells coming from the kitchen. Looking around for a way to pay back her kindness, Meeko chopped her wood, brought it in and stacked it next to her stove. And as custom demands, she invited him to stay for dinner. After eating his fill, she invited him to watch some television with her. An hour later, Meeko pretended to fall asleep and was grateful when the old woman covered him with a blanket, aware that when morning came he would get a hot bath and could attend school properly dressed.

Meeko felt good as he walked to school the following day, knowing that he had established his third possible home. Between the car lot, the top of the laundromat and his new friend, he felt better about his life. When school was over, Meeko walked the streets until he decided to go visit the car lot. He walked around, imagining he was going to buy a car when Bob, the car dealer, called to him. "Hey, Meeko! Haven't seen you around lately. How's things going?"

Meeko dropped his head in fear, realizing if the owner knew his name, he probably also knew that he had slept in the cars at night. He mumbled, "Pretty good."

"How would you like to wash a few cars for me?" the man asked.

Meeko nodded yes.

It wasn't long before Bob offered him a night watchman's job. When the lot was ready to close, he said, "I want you to stay in the office and keep the doors locked. I think I've got a prowler around here, so you call me if you hear anything," he added as he tossed Meeko the keys. Meeko remained expressionless trying to hide his joy at the thought of sleeping on the soft sofa and using the shower. After that his days would start by making coffee then waiting anxiously for the boss to walk in with fresh doughnuts before he left for school.

It was a dream come true for Meeko until one day when he found the sheriff waiting for him at the school. It seemed Renna was back in town and had been charged with child neglect. This was a bad sign because Meeko had heard the authorities were insisting that he be placed in the local Indian orphanage. As the sheriff escorted him into the courtroom, Meeko could see Renna was angry and a wave of nausea ran though his body. The judge handed her some papers and insisted she sign them.

Furious, Meeko asked, "Why are you doing this? I'm not an orphan! Send me back to Granbear!" But his fate had already been decided, and by ten o'clock he was in the car with Renna on his way to the Catholic Indian orphanage in Sisseston, South Dakota.

As Renna turned into the long driveway and pulled around to the back of the building, she handed Meeko the papers and said, "Get out!"

"Don't do this! I have a family! I'm your son and you're my mother! What kind of woman throws away her son? How can you let them put me in an orphanage? You know I can take care of myself. Let me run! I'll find my way back to Granbear and Auntie Lizzie."

"Hell no! You don't understand. They'll lock my ass up! Meeko, this is a good place for Indian kids. You'll get an education and, besides someone may adopt you. Can't you understand, I want my fucking life back, and I'll be damned if Granbear gets you! Now get out of the fucking car!"

Meeko looked deep into Renna's eyes, then answered, "I promise you this, Mother, we will meet again!"

The look on Meeko's face scared Renna. She saw that he was no longer a child but a man. Feeling the futility of the situation, Meeko stepped out of the car and stood watching her drive away as her words burned a deep hatred for her into his mind.

A short, hooded nun approached with outstretched arms. "Come, My Child. This happens all the time. You will adjust to our ways," she said sweetly, taking the papers from his hand and directing him to the office. "Sister Teresa, come, we have another one this morning. He's assigned to the big boy's quarters. Show him where to put his things."

Sister Teresa looked him over from head to toe, then in a thick Spanish accent said, "Follow me, Son."

Amused and curious, Meeko followed her, smiling as he listened to the swishing sounds coming from underneath her long black skirt. He couldn't help but wonder what she was wearing to make such a funny noise. The good sister led him up the stairs and opened the door into a room filled with six bunk beds and six chests placed neatly around the room. An alarm clock sat on the center of a study table. Meeko's instincts warned him to run, but instead he sat quietly on the edge of his assigned bed contemplating his situation.

"We work for our keep here. Come, I will give you the schedule," snapped Sister Teresa.

Meeko found the orphanage to be very strict, run by the iron hands of the nuns. The rules were enforced by these scowling, hooded sisters and everyone was expected to smile and greet Father Hanby, known by the other students as the 'good father,' feigning their respect. Everything was scheduled. There was a time to eat, a time to play, a time to study and a time to pray to a foreign God. But there was never a time for kindness or consideration, and there was certainly no time to be Indian. Contempt for the Indian was overtly blatant in the orphanage, and if you were caught speaking your native language, a ruler came down hard across your outstretched hands.

"How many times must I tell you to speak English?" demanded Sister Teresa.

Meeko held on to his pride and refused to obey any woman that couldn't speak English herself. He soon found his actions were not taken lightly, and he quickly tired of letting his outstretched hands meet with the ruler. He hated the nun with the funny accent, and since she was in charge of the kitchen, he loved making her life miserable by making nightly raids on the kitchen and distributing his take among the other kids. He taught the older ones how to pick the locks, and the good sisters worked hard trying to capture the unknown thieves.

But soon the older children became too confident and grew careless. One night as they loaded up with handfuls of chicken legs and cookies, Sister Teresa jumped from her hiding place in the pantry and caught everyone red-handed. Her angry screams drove them all back up the stairs, except for Meeko. Sister Teresa searched everywhere trying to find him. When she pounced through the door of the young boy's dormitory, she saw Meeko and grabbed him by the ear, escorting him to the closet under the stairs.

"Stay there, you little thief. God will punish you for stealing our food," she bellowed as she locked the door and swished away.

Meeko spent the night and part of the next day under the darkened staircase. By late the following afternoon he desperately needed to relieve himself and was thankful when an understanding brother quietly picked the lock and opened the door for him, whereupon he dashed to the bathroom. On his way back, his friend handed him some food then locked the door again and quietly stole away. After supper was served, Sister Teresa came and took Meeko to the good father. Meeko dreaded the thought of confronting Father Hanby and cringed as they entered his office.

Sister Teresa spoke harshly about his bad behavior, then left. Father Hanby asked Meeko to sit down then began his long lecture about their God of punishment. When he had finished, Meeko wondered why this man's God would make him burn in hell if he did not stop his thieving and lying ways. He already knew about the beatings that many others had endured and remained stoic through the session. He also knew there were certain little boys who dreaded their nights spent "watching television" with Father. Many had attempted suicide, while others ran away. Some stayed, but no longer talked with the other children and continually wet the bed. It seemed everyone knew what was going on, but were too afraid to say anything.

This evening Meeko had the opportunity to experience Father Hanby firsthand. After the last blow of the leather strap had cut into his naked back, Meeko was handed his shirt by the good father who said with a smile, "Son, you must do penance. I want you to go to the chapel and say fifteen Our Fathers and ten Hail Marys. Wait for me until I come for you."

Meeko left Father's office and went to sit in the quiet of the little chapel, still not understanding the white man's angry God. Why would God punish children with hungry bellies? The smell of burnt candle wax blended with the stench of the raw sewage coming from the open ditch behind the building As he compared these foreign beliefs to the goodness of Granbear's teachings, he cried within as he remembered the smell of sweetgrass and sage and the feeling of freedom that keeps the Indian soul alive. He remembered Granbear's love and kindness and prayed to *Wakan Tanka* to help the other children who could not comprehend this angry white God who punished those who were hungry and had a different color of skin.

Father Hanby showed total disrespect by interrupting Meeko's prayers. He placed his hand on Meeko's knee then affectionately squeezed it, saying, "Come, Meeko. Tonight you will have dinner with me, then we'll watch television together."

Feeling sick to his stomach, Meeko calmly removed Father's hand from his knee and coldly said, "Father, if you ever do that again, I'll kill you! And the next time I hear any of the little boys complain about your hands, I'll see that they're cut off and you're sent away from here."

Without another word Meeko got up and went to his room. He threw himself across his bed and lay thinking about what kind of man this was who spoke for the white God. He watched out the window as the sun faded behind the mountain and darkness covered it, blending everything into a black sky. That night Meeko slept restlessly, fighting off this fearful white God and the demons who were walking on his dreams. After that Meeko distanced himself from everyone and remained in a state of passive rebellion, refusing to work. Each night he would sit and pray as he watched the sun fade from the sky.

Fearing what this young rebel might say and make known to those outside of the orphanage walls, Father Hanby enacted a "hands-off" policy where Meeko was concerned.

Meeko spent most of his time devouring books, finding many of them amusing, especially the ones written by the white race about his people. He found he had a great interest in law books and enjoyed thinking how many ways the laws could be interpreted.

Meeko began to stray further and further from the watchful eyes of the hooded sisters. Each day he would leave before sunrise and run through the fields until he reached the well-traveled pathway that ran along the base of the distant foothills. Keeping to his dreams, he would rest on a large boulder near the river and study the pictures in the clouds. These were the times he could feel Granbear's presence, particularly when he visited Shadow World. One day he heard Granbear whisper, "Meeko, it is time. Place the sun at your back and let it shine over your shoulder until noon. Then bring it to your face and follow the Sun Chief as he travels across the sky. Grandson, find your way home. Find your way back to me."

Still feeling isolated, Meeko walked along the river to listen to the voice of the water. Many times he had come here to throw pebbles at imaginary targets, just to see the ripples return to the shore, wondering if he would ever see Granbear again. Suddenly he felt a tingling chill run up his spine and feared he might have been followed by Sister Teresa. He turned quickly and saw nothing, but heard faint sounds of Sundance songs calling on the wind. With great humility, he dropped to his knees in prayer and felt the vibration build louder and louder in his heart. Unable to control such happiness, tears streamed down his smiling face as he stood up facing the sun and danced to the beat of the entrance song.

To gain control over his feelings, he climbed the embankment and came upon an eagle eating a rabbit. Neither moved! It seemed time stood still, when without warning, the eagle began to flap its wings in a rhythm that challenged gravity. As Eagle lifted high above the ground, Meeko heard his challenge, "Hey, little sparrow! How high do you dare fly?" Meeko watched in shocked silence until the eagle became a mere black speck in the sky, then disappeared. Again he heard Eagle's voice say, "You can never fly with me, my little friend, as long as you think as a sparrow."

Meeko feared his mind was playing tricks on him, but the echo of Eagle's voice continued to ride on the wind. "Someday you will fly with me, Little Brother! Someday you and I will become one," screamed Eagle as Meeko searched the skies, desperately trying to find him. He saw Eagle riding on the unseen currents of air and became enraptured by the experience. As he heard the familiar sound of an eagle diving toward him, Meeko looked up and dropped to his knees in reverent prayer.

Again Eagle spoke. "I come to join you on this life journey. Listen with your heart, Little Brother, not your ears." Eagle again lifted in flight, soaring higher and higher, riding the sun's rays as his feathers seemingly melted into rivers of liquid gold. The brightness was blinding and Meeko shielded his eyes for protection. As Eagle's shadow crossed over him, he heard, "Meeko! Be attentive. I, Eagle, will teach you how to embrace freedom. I will always soar above you to remind you I am the great messenger of the sky. Rise above your earthly chores and take the freedom that you already possess. See the total picture of life, my little friend. It is you who takes the first step back to *Wakan Tanka*. Your power is in your beliefs, and that is what will set you free. Learn from life's experiences and bless each lesson so that you may build a good soul. But first, answer my question."

"What question, my feathered friend?" yelled Meeko.

"How high do you dare fly, Little Brother?"

"Fly?" questioned Meeko. "I can't fly. I have no wings!"

"Oh yes, you can fly, and you have great wings! A spirit can fly anywhere, and do it quicker than a thought. A pure heart is one with *Wakan Tanka*, and this gives you the right to become one with everything. Do not fear life or death. It is your destiny to accomplish greatness. But first you must learn to conquer all inner and outer turmoil. Rid yourself of the hovering fears of darkness that bind you. Seek the knowledge of the never-ending sacred circles, Little Brother, and spiral upward through the vortex to be with me." Again great Eagle climbed upward, still singing his challenge. "How high do you dare fly? How high, Meeko? How high?"

Meeko ran beneath the shadow of Eagle that raced across the land, yelling in excitement, "I will fly! I will not only fly by your side, but I will fly through the sun with you. At that moment, a gunshot rang out from the valley floor, reverberating off the canyon walls. Great Eagle seemed to hesitate for a moment, then spun downward toward Mother Earth. "Pull up! Pull up! Open your beautiful wings," yelled Meeko as he saw Eagle tumbling from the sky. With a loud thud Eagle's lifeless body fell at Meeko's feet. He picked the eagle up and cradled it close to his heart, crying out, "How can this be, *Tunka'shila*? Who would kill such a sacred bird?"

Meeko instinctively knew the hunter was near and would come looking for his kill. He wrapped the bird in his jacket as his heart pounded to the rhythm of Eagle's call. "How high will you fly, Little Brother? How high will you fly?"

Anger filled his heart and he raced toward the orphanage as fast as a frightened deer. When he arrived, he called to his friends and they went to the barn to hear his story. As he finished his tale, he said, "I found a red tie hanging on a fence today. That tells me it's time to go home. If I can get to the old highway, then I know I can hitch a ride with the people that will be returning to the reservation to Sundance." His friends agreed to help him escape as they hid the sacred bird between the bales of hay and returned just in time for dinner.

After the nightly duties were finished and the lights went out, the older boys gathered around Meeko's bed, asking, "How do you know it's Sundance time?"

"They always Sundance when it's Summer Solstice," answered Meeko in a soft whisper.

"Maybe someday we'll see you there," said one of the younger boys.

"Yeah, maybe," Meeko answered, turning over to get some sleep.

The next morning everything seemed overly peaceful at the orphanage. The younger boys kept the good sisters distracted while the older children did their daily chores as expected. By lunch everyone knew that Meeko was leaving and said their goodbyes either through eye contact or a touch. Meeko took his meager belongings and the carefully packed eagle and headed toward the back of the orphanage, then over a hill.

When he reached the main road he searched for the discreetly placed strips of red cloth that he knew would be hidden along the highway. His heart skipped a beat when he saw the first hidden streamer to direct those who wanted to attend the upcoming Sun Dance. Meeko hid himself in the tall grass along the road, watching closely for the right truck to come along. When he saw braids hanging from under tall black hats, he jumped from his hiding place, smiling and waving. The truck pulled over and he jumped into the back, nodding his respect to the old people. He sat at the foot of their wooden benches and asked, "Where you heading?"

"Fort Peck. We're picking up relatives, then we're going to the Sun Dance at Pine Ridge."

Meeko yelped like a puppy. He was finally going home!

Morning light was barely touching the sky when the truck drove through Wolf Point, Montana. Meeko saw Renna staggering down the street and ducked down in the bed of the truck. When they neared Frazer, he tapped on the window to signal the driver this was where he wanted off. Thrilled to feel his land under his feet, he breathed deep to touch his spirit roots, then headed across the field toward Granbear's house, his heart pounding nearly out of his chest as he turned the doorknob.

When Auntie Lizzie saw him, she screamed and rushed to his side to embrace her grandson. Granbear looked up from his rocking chair and smiled. "How was your trip, Grandson?" he asked, laying his glasses and newspaper aside before standing up to lovingly embrace his grandson, tears blurring his sight. Meeko carefully took the eagle's body from underneath his jacket and handed it to Granbear, then sat down to breakfast. As he ate he told Granbear and Auntie Lizzie the story of his life with Renna.

Not wanting to speak of Renna, Granbear picked up the eagle and said, "Grandson, you have learned many things since you've been away, but mostly you've learned to see with your heart. Eagle has brought you a great honor and a heavy responsibility. To have your name called by the great sky teacher is very rare. We will prepare a sacred ceremony in his honor so he will fly with you always."

After the ceremony was completed, Granbear taught Meeko the sacred way to dissect the bird, keeping each piece separate to be used sometime in the future to manifest Eagle power. Once this was completed Granbear wrapped the pieces together then placed one of his own eagle feathers inside the bundle, saying, "We are both connected to Eagle. It was told to me that someday you would capture an eagle, and when this happened I was to adopt you." Granbear pulled a paper out of a yellowing envelope, adding,

"You will no longer have to fear not having a father. This paper says I'm your father. I will send word to the Bear Clan and get this completed."

The following morning the house was once again filled with Bear Clan members. After Granbear discussed his will and Meeko's adoption, he was very happy that every family member openly agreed. Meeko cried thankfully, once again feeling safe in his loving family. To celebrate this glorious occasion, the best quilt makers set up their frames. The beaders, leather and quill workers got together and offered their skills for the big giveaway. It wasn't long until everyone knew of this upcoming event. Auntie Lizzie and other relatives cooked for days to prepare for the biggest giveaway ever seen on the reservation. During that week Granbear ran many sweats and many other celebration ceremonies. A whole month passed before things settled back into a normal, peaceful life for the Bear Clan people.

One day when Granbear was out shopping he heard bad rumors about Renna. Coming home extremely angry, he pushed the door open with his walking cane, walked into the house and threw his packages on the table in a fit of temper. "That girl has no respect for anything. I've heard too many bad things and I'm stopping her disgraceful behavior!"

Auntie Lizzie hung her head in shame and busied herself in the kitchen. Meeko watched from a far corner of the room, his anger boiled at what he was witnessing. He saw sadness unfolding in his home once again and felt the suffering, shame and embarrassment of the old ones. "Renna was never respectful to the family," stated Meeko with contempt. "Why bother with her? Let her problems remain hers. Why care what happens to her, Granbear? I know her and she's no good!"

Shocked by his abrasive words, Granbear looked long and hard at Meeko before answering. "Grandson, you speak as though you have knowledge, but *Wakan Tanka* does not teach us to hate. We know that Renna's spirit is ill. How can we, as humans, condemn a sick heart which is filled with sorrow? We must pray her soul finds its freedom." Granbear's patience with Renna had always angered Meeko, but he sat quietly and listened.

Early the following morning he walked to the highway and stuck out his thumb. A truck, driven by an Indian, pulled over and Meeko hopped into the back, waving the driver onward. He rode to the edge of the reservation then tapped on the back window to signal he wanted out.

He zipped up his jacket and began searching from bar to bar, looking for Renna. As he entered each smoke filled barroom, he slunk close to the walls trying to blend into the crowd. His heart felt heavy as he relived the shame and degradation coming from the drunken behavior of his people. Ready to give up, he walked into the last bar bordering the reservation. His heart skipped a beat when he saw Renna draped over the end of the bar. Bitterness and hatred walked with him as he touched her shoulder and said in a demanding voice, "Renna, come with me. Granbear wants you home."

Renna slowly lifted her head and scowled at him. Focusing her eyes, she saw it was Meeko. "Hey, Kid. Heard you were back in town. So the old man wants me, huh?"

"Yes! Granbear wants you home," replied Meeko coldly.

"And what do I care what he wants? Hey, you little shit, you're getting awfully big," she smiled, climbing off the barstool and grabbing hold of his arm. "Hey, everybody, look who's here. Can you believe this shit? The great Granbear is demanding my presence, and my son has come to take me home. C'mon, everybody, let's celebrate my new importance. I'll buy," she yelled, swinging her beer in the air and spilling most of it.

In a hushed voice Meeko said, "Shut up, Renna! You're making a fool of yourself. As far as I'm concerned, I don't care what you do! It's Granbear who wants you home!"

"Well, well," Renna replied in a mockingly regal manner. Then coldly she spit in Meeko's face. Meeko maintained his stoic manner, controlling his rage. He firmly took her arm and guided her toward the door. "Get your fucking hands off me," she screamed, jerking loose and bolting out the door. Meeko chased her across the parking lot where he saw her climb into the back seat of a car with four men. He opened the car door and brazenly slid into the front seat.

"Go away! Get out of here. No one tells me what to do." Meeko refused to respond to her and sat quietly, letting Renna poke fun at him. "Hey, Kid, wanna learn how to party?" she asked, playing with his hair while exposing her left breast.

A man from the back seat was passing the ever present brown paper bag to him for a drink when Meeko noticed a familiar truck turning into the parking lot. Out stepped Granbear with a very determined look on his face. He walked directly toward the car and jerked the door open. He grabbed Renna by the hair and dragged her to the ground. She let out a bloodcurdling scream before she realized it was Granbear. Without a word, he hit her repeatedly with blows from his walking cane, then forced her to his truck. Meeko smiled with great pleasure, as he got out of the car, and chuckled as he watched Renna desperately trying to dodge Granbear's cane. He had heard many stories about Granbear's famous walking stick, but this was his first opportunity to witness it in action.

Yes, the stories were true. Granbear did have the power to clean out all the Indian bars. It seemed everyone came to witness the drama when Granbear's anger drove him to correct his bad children. "Come here, Boy," stated Granbear, walking toward Meeko, raising his cane and bringing it down hard across Meeko's back. "We do not use deception or make decisions for others. Get in the truck!"

Still determined, Granbear strolled arrogantly toward the men sitting in the car. He paused for a moment and stood in front of the car, then suddenly his eyes flashed with mischief. "Boys, I knew your grandfathers, your grandmothers, your fathers and your mothers. They were a proud people and I know they would agree you have a crazy sickness. In fact, they would see you as useless people, and would take joy in killing you to rid your souls of its filth and misery. I feel sure they are joining me in spirit when I do what I am about to do." With these words, he raised his cane and smashed the windshield, chuckling as he walked around the car shattering each window. "The next time you want to be foolish and get drunk, it would be best you stay hidden behind the protection of your woman's skirt."

Shocked and without a word, the men quickly drove away without a windshield, windows or headlights.

Granbear laughed heartily when he thought of what these men were going to tell their wives. He walked proudly through the crowd of onlookers then got into his truck and drove away. During the ride home, Renna felt humiliated and remained silently submissive until Granbear pulled to a full stop at home. As they entered the house, Auntie Lizzie saw what had happened and quietly brought Granbear a cup of steaming hot coffee. He greeted her with a knowing smile and gently thanked her for her kindness. "Tomorrow the family will be here and we'll have a long talk to work out Renna's problems! In the meantime, she will not leave the house. To make sure we have a peaceful day and a good night's rest, I'm chaining her to the overhead rafters," chuckled Granbear, remembering an old gift of handcuffs that he had received from his friend the sheriff.

Getting up from the table, Granbear went in search of the cuffs and in locating them, he also found an old logging chain and brought it with him. Renna sat quietly watching him as he tossed the chain over the ceiling roof beam. Once it was secure, he gently placed the handcuffs around her wrists, giving her plenty of movement. "There! That should keep you safe until we decide what to do with you," he said, stepping back and chuckling at the pathetic figure sitting on the floor.

The house remained quiet for the rest of the day. That night Granbear tossed Renna a blanket, cupped his hands over the smoke-stained kerosene lamp and blew out the flame as the house was instantly consumed in darkness. Feeling the stillness settle over the house, the old medicine man smiled, knowing another bit of hell in an old traditional Indian family had just bit the dust.

Everyone was up very early the following morning. It was a cold, gray, dismal day and as each Bear Clan family member arrived, you could feel their hostility matching the angry mood of the morning prairie winds. While everyone sat in silence around the kitchen table, the nearby trees used their branches to beat against the house as though they too hated this turmoil. Renna shivered from all this coldness as Granbear approached her, saying, "Come, Renna, have some breakfast," then gently uncuffed her hands.

After everyone had eaten, Granbear said, "Long ago we were a good people and followed the old ways. There was no such thing as alcohol or reservation people. As Bear Clan, we have always understood the power of medicine. We are honorable people, but one of our family members is very ill in spirit and must be healed so she can become a good human. She was taught honor and respect, but she refuses to take her place in our family circle. When she refused to honor our ways, I knew she had to be stopped before she destroyed any future generations.

"Today we suffer because Renna has forgotten the importance of her duty to the family as well as to herself. As family, we stand together and accept that her spirit is crying out to us for help, and we will provide the support needed to heal this broken soul."

They nodded their heads in agreement as the Fire Chief entered, saying, "The *Inipi* is ready." After many hours in the sweat, Renna agreed that she needed their help and would do as they asked. Everyone was pleased when she agreed to go to the rehabilitation center with Uncle to solve her problem.

"Wait!" said Granbear, "before she goes, I want her to know about my plans for the family's future. All of you know the land holds the bones of our forefathers and it will be divided among you. The old place will go to Lizzie, and when she joins me on the Other Side it will belong solely to Meeko. My children, always keep the land for our children's children, and never sell your Mother. The land is what bonds families together. The Bear Clan has never been like a pea that pops out of the shell to roll away. No! The Bear Clan bonds us like the layers of an onion, and we are known to carry the responsibility of the past, present and future generations. Remember my words, and at my death, go to my lawyer friend and he will give you the papers."

By late afternoon Renna was packed. As the Bear Clan left the yard everyone was contented and very proud she had honored their decision. A dear uncle, who had made all of her arrangements, drove her to the government rehabilitation center in Seattle.

Almost a month had passed when Granbear announced at a family gathering that Meeko was almost thirteen winters and it was time for him to begin his boy training with Shadowhawk. "He will be picking us up tomorrow and we will be leaving for Rosebud. Lizzie will be joining us once we are settled."

The family grew very quiet and held a heavy sadness in their hearts. Many eyes filled with tears as they readied Granbear for his trip to the Rosebud Reservation. That evening there was a chill on the wind as the little family sat around a good, hot fire. Meeko lay on the floor curled under his blanket listening to the wood crackle in the fireplace, watching the fire's dancing shadows play on the living room walls. Feeling peaceful, he closed his eyes while pondering the outcome of his upcoming journey to learn the old ways.

The Medicine Wheel

After driving through countless rolling hills on a narrow two-lane road, George Shadowhawk smiled in anticipation as he crossed the rusty steel bridge leading to the Fort Peck Reservation.

Auntie Lizzie was anxiously waiting for her ex-husband to arrive, and when Shadowhawk pulled into the yard, she ran to greet him. He was still the same tall, handsome, charming man she had married long ago. Shadowhawk smiled at her warmly and opened his arms. As they embraced, memories of their shared life suddenly rekindled the old flames of their love. Hearing him sigh as he held her close, Auntie Lizzie slowly pulled away, fearing her feelings. Shadowhawk understood and gently took her hand as they walked to the house.

Granbear and Meeko exchanged warm greetings with Shadowhawk as they entered the house. After they had all eaten a hearty breakfast, Shadowhawk loaded Granbear's and Meeko's things into his pickup truck, graciously accepting the basket of food Auntie Lizzie handed him with the promise that she would visit soon. Tears rolled down her cheeks as she watched the truck fade into the distance. Seeing her sadness Granbear waved, then turned his thoughts to the many relatives who were waiting at the Rosebud Reservation to celebrate his return.

Shadowhawk had driven less than an hour when the open plains gave way to big sky country, renewing their sense of freedom. Granbear felt lighthearted as he inhaled the exhilarating aromas of sage and sweetgrass. In the distance he spotted a large herd of deer grazing lazily on the slopes, and overhead were magnificent raptors circling high, waiting for their next kill. With a thrust of his chin, Granbear issued a silent signal for Meeko and Shadowhawk to share in the beauty of the moment.

It was late afternoon when they pulled into Shadowhawk's yard. Granbear's friends and relatives who had gathered to welcome them carried his things into his quarters while Shadowhawk delegated other tasks to make sure Granbear had every comfort due such a respected holy man.

People began to approach Granbear for advice and healings and by evening many were gathered listening to his enchanting stories of long ago. After the others had retired, Granbear and Shadowhawk discussed plans for Meeko's future.

"As you know, Shadowhawk, Meeko's life with Renna was very sad. He's been forced to do bad things that a child his age should never have been exposed to. He carries many scars from those experiences, and his hatred for Renna is eating away his spirit. As his great-grandfather, I've brought him here to get rid of his anger and help him return to the good way of life. As Medicine, I want all of his training guided by the rules of the old traditional ways. If he is to learn, he needs to give up this ownership of me and accept that I am Medicine. I want you to help him make this change." Reaching over and patting Shadowhawk's knee, Granbear added, "This won't be an easy job for us. We'll both need to be very patient and reach him with kindness."

"I understand, Granbear. I agree there are many things that need to be changed, otherwise I fear Meeko may end up like Renna."

"Tomorrow I'll begin teaching the ways of the Medicine Wheel. I want him to learn the importance of morning and evening prayer. If I walk the land with him, he might get back some of his good feelings. After all, nature is our best teacher," said Granbear, preparing to retire. An affectionate smile crossed Shadowhawk's face as he watched this wise man, who was so deeply loved and respected, walk to his quarters.

At sunrise the following morning, Meeko joined Granbear in a pipe ceremony. After the pipe was cleaned and put away, everyone stood around waiting for the sweat to begin. Meeko, instead, went to the arbor for breakfast. When Shadowhawk saw this, he approached Meeko, saying curtly, "Good morning. I thought you were going to sweat with Granbear this morning!"

Meeko looked at the ground and answered lamely, "I thought I had plenty of time to eat before the sweat."

"You seem to care more for your stomach than your soul. Since you're no longer a child, you will show Granbear the respect a medicine man deserves. See that you remember this conversation." Turning abruptly, Shadowhawk went to the *Inipi*. Shocked by Shadowhawk's scolding, Meeko quickly followed him to the morning sweat.

After the fourth round ended and everyone had left the *Inipi*, Granbear talked to the old people about the gifts they had received during the sweat. Meeko, seeing an opportunity to have some fun, raced to the river to join his friends. When the elders returned to the arbor for breakfast, Meeko joined Granbear and Shadowhawk to listen to what they had to say.

Granbear spent the rest of the morning teaching Meeko the sacred way to gather sage and sweetgrass.

"Granbear, does a plant think like a human?"

"Yes, Grandson, the animals and plants don't trust humans, but they can think like humans. The sad part is that humans can't think like them. Humph, most of the time humans are confused about how they should act or think. You must pay attention to what you're thinking, because the little bird perched in that tree, or even that flower over there, is listening to everything in your mind. They know what you're feeling too, and pass on those messages to all who understand their language."

When Granbear felt they had enough sage and sweetgrass for the evening sweat, they started home. Taking a trail that curved along the river bank, Granbear motioned to Meeko that they would rest under the swaying branches of a big old shade tree. Meeko ran ahead and spread a blanket on the ground, then waited for Granbear to sit before joining him.

"Today, I'm going to introduce you to Father River. I was about your age when Father River taught me how to overcome my fear of water by flowing with the silence of its movement. Even today when I seek understanding, I come to the river and offer a gift to *Wakan Tanka*. I place a small piece of meat in the river bank to show my respect to his life giving waters. Ah, Grandson, when you listen to the sounds of the river, you can hear secrets in the movement of the water.

"To feel the life and beauty of a river, you must follow the motion of its water. Watch how it moves around and over the rocks that block its flow. Likewise, when something such as a person, place, or thing, blocks your life's flow, you have to move around it, just like the water.

"Do you mean if I think badly about somebody, they're controlling what I think?"

"Yes, and it's time to find a way to move like the water around your problem with Renna, so you can go on with your life's lessons and be happy. Many times I've asked myself why you let her control your thoughts and feelings. If you keep following this path, you will become your own worst enemy. I want you to get rid of those bad feelings about Renna so you can become a good servant of *Wakan Tanka*."

Meeko sensed that Granbear was speaking the truth and answered, "You can stop me from hating Renna?"

"Yes, Grandson. That's why I brought you to Father River. Renna has closed her heart. Her drinking and drugging have made her irresponsible toward all of life. She was not taught these ways, but something captured her spirit, turning her into an angry woman who enjoys hurting herself and others. Renna is cut off from life and has forgotten that life should be used for the benefit of all.

"Meeko, a single kind word can take a person higher than any mountain, just as a harmful word can make a person too afraid to even try to climb that mountain. At those times it takes great courage to make the needed changes to have a good life. There are always people who misunderstand our ways, and there will be many who will try to confuse and hurt you because of these ways. But it is you who must find your way and allow the heart of all things to teach you. Grandson, always be on your guard with people who do not know the difference between the mind and the heart.

"In time, Grandson, you will understand that Renna's problems are hers. I'm sorry to say, she has infected others with her hateful ways, especially those who love her. She lives off her memories and blames others for her problems.

"When your mother was born, she was sickly, and we spoiled her. Since then, she's demanded that everybody take care of her. But when the family refused, she became mean and hateful. Renna has chosen her way, and there's no need to be a part of it unless you want your life to be as painful as hers. Your time with her was regrettable, but it doesn't have to make you a bad person."

"Renna is a drunken, useless woman. I hate her and won't ever be like her! I don't want to talk about her anymore," pleaded Meeko, breaking into angry sobs.

Granbear soothed him, saying, "I know she still lives in your heart, and these thoughts hurt you deeply. If you face the hate you feel, it will release its grip on you. Together we'll kill those bad thoughts and change your way of thinking. Now, stop worrying about Renna and think of the freedom that the Medicine Wheel is going to give you. When you learn our ways you will heal those old wounds. Grandson, someday you will walk in courage and become a devoted servant to *Wakan Tanka*."

The old medicine man handed Meeko a handkerchief and after wiping his eyes, Meeko said, "Are you sure that the Medicine Wheel can take away my bad feelings?"

Granbear nodded and returned to the lesson. "Did you know that *Taku Skan Skan* creates the movement in all life? Did you know that as you breathe *Taku Skan Skan* is moving in and out of your body in the air you are taking into your lungs? Look around, Meeko. Can't you feel that you are sitting on Mother Earth watching the motion of the river, breathing in the air and feeling the sun on your skin? Isn't that motion? These wonderful gifts are from *Wakan Tanka*.

"There are four elements that control life: earth, air, water and fire, and all these things give life to your body. Get to know them. It will help you change your outlook about all life. That will give you the courage to build strong beliefs in the powers of sacredness.

"Like I said, Grandson, life is movement, and as water, so are you. Watch the river's ever-changing flow. Go stand in the water and see if you can feel *Taku Skan Skan*'s mysteries of motion." Meeko hesitantly waded up to his knees into the icy cold water.

"Now, close your eyes. When you feel the power in the river's movement, let it touch your spirit," said Granbear. Meeko shivered as the cold rushing water pulled and pushed at him, throwing him unexpectedly off balance. Struggling to stay on his feet, he stumbled and grabbed hold of a low-hanging limb. Chuckling at his grandson's frustration, Granbear commented, "Grandson, never be forced down a river that you don't want to travel. Life tends to be easier when we go with the flow rather than fight the currents."

Determined, Meeko stood firm, digging his toes into the muddy riverbed while letting his thoughts drift with the sound and motion of the water. Feeling peaceful, his mind wandered toward the snowcapped mountains in the distance where he saw the sun melting a single snow flake. Suddenly he was a water droplet joining a babbling brook on its way to the rushing river. Rising into the clouds as vapor, he wondered if this was what Granbear meant when he said everything was connected through movement. Smiling, Meeko believed that he had begun to comprehend the powers of life's motion, and he looked to Granbear for confirmation.

"I see you have found that you are the same as a water droplet and that as a water droplet, you have to risk change. Meeko, without taking risks you will never get the courage to explore the unknown. Anytime you think of the river, also think about the mysterious water creatures who live there."

"You mean like the water monsters of long ago?"

"Ah, yes. Everything that has lived in the past or present, and all things that will be born in the future, influence Mother Earth and all her children. Remember the big box of frozen salmon we received from my Alaskan friends? Wasn't that some good eating? Didn't that influence your stomach? Well, since you like the taste, maybe you should think about developing some Salmon power. Grandson, have you thought about the fearlessness of a salmon? Did you know that every year they risk their lives by swimming upstream to return to their spawning grounds? Think of the odds against them making such a journey. A salmon knows it takes great courage to go against the currents of life, but it knows it must keep going to complete its natural life journey. Ah yes, Meeko, a salmon does what it does, because it's a salmon. Would you be willing to risk your life to get what you want, even if it meant that you could die in the effort? Sometimes I worry that your white thinking is going to kill off those kinds of instincts."

"Granbear, I don't know if I have instincts like the salmon."

"You should. It could teach you to swim upstream and get around the clutter in life. When you surrender to the currents of another's will, you're allowing them to throw your life away. Strong instincts build the power to fight against the harmful currents and allow the spirit of life to shine through you.

Cold and wet, Meeko climbed out of the river, frustrated with Granbear's long lecture. Granbear understood and placed the blanket over him, then patted the ground for him to sit. "So, Grandson, maybe you're a little cold, but I know you're a whole lot of stubborn. That doesn't mean that you're stupid. You just need to know more about how to balance your thoughts. It's a bad thing when your feelings won't let you have a good life. Logic has its place too but it can bog down your mind with useless questions and answers. When this happens, you create doubt and distrust in yourself.

"To become a good human, you must have an open heart. Let *Wakan Tanka*'s mysteries of nature teach you how to connect to Mother Earth. Then let each life force give its own lessons in living and dying. The river is one teacher; the salmon is another.

"The Beaver is connected to water. It is another kind of teacher. Beaver is a hard worker. He builds homes and dams; but with all his ambition to cut logs and move them into the water, he makes problems downstream. I remember once watching a beaver build a dam so good that it stopped the flow of that river for miles so nothing could get in or out. That beaver taught me that every action causes a reaction.

"In many ways, humans are like beavers. Without thinking, we end up blocking other's dreams. And when we don't think of others, everyone suffers the consequences, including us, for we become imprisoned in greed and selfishness. So anytime our minds become whirlpools of confusion and self-importance, it is up to us to unblock our selfish thinking. Always understand that *Wakan Tanka*'s purpose is greater than our self-serving needs. When we know that Creator's plans are always bigger and better, everyone benefits. Good thoughts toward all of our brothers and sisters will make for a healthy attitude toward all of Great Spirit's children."

"Am I selfish, Granbear?" questioned Meeko.

"Yes, often you are thankless and selfish. While visiting large cities, I've found people just like you, who would rather be one of the sheep behind the shepherd, willing to be followers, never thinking or acting for themselves. Grandson, life is full of users who hurt others out of lack of heart. Those who get all puffed up with self-importance are just as blind. Meeko, never let another capture your common sense and cause you to reject what you value. Great Spirit teaches us that life is simple and it's people who complicate it. I believe if life can celebrate me, then I can celebrate life.

"Promise me that you won't ever become a human sheep, if you do, you're likely to be sheared or dismembered, or become a leg of lamb on someone's table. Follow the ways of *Wakan Tanka*. He is the greatest shepherd of all."

"Granbear, is this a Medicine Wheel teaching?" Meeko asked.

"Yes. The Medicine Wheel teaches us that those seven holes in the human head are for gathering information. You have two eyes, two ears, two nose holes, and one mouth. Sight. Sound. Smell. Taste. The mind is like a library that contains everything we experience through touching life and feeling its presence. It's this knowledge that frees our spirits and brings value to our every encounter.

"You see, Meeko, all life forces are within the circle of the Medicine Wheel. That is the sacred zero that we share in our collected knowledge. But when we refuse to share, that's what kills the soul. So, Grandson, if you keep your head right, the body will follow. Fix what's broken inside, get rid of the bad thoughts and good things will come into your life. That's when you'll be following your soul's pathway. Now, get back into the water and tell me if it's the same."

Re-entering the river, Meeko replied, "I don't know."

"Grandson, the life-giving waters never stay the same. Watch the movement around your legs. I think it's time you harness your runaway thoughts and figure out how to see that movement is power," Granbear asserted.

Meeko shrugged insolently.

Aggravated by his attitude, Granbear stepped to the edge of the river. "Grandson, your mind is like a dried-up old lake bed. I may be old and my bones brittle, but I don't think my mind has ever been as unbending as yours. Can't you see the river is moving on without you?" Meeko shrugged a second time. In disgust, Granbear silently walked back to his blanket, lay down, and yelled, "Seek your truth in movement, Grandson!"

Frustrated, Meeko knew that Granbear would continue the lesson until he understood. What difference does it make how the river moves? Picking up a stone, Meeko hurled it across the water's surface.

"Don't deny what is, Grandson! Your flow of learning has stopped because you're not willing to accept my teachings. And since you are picking on the Stone People today, get out of the water and gather enough rocks to build a Medicine Wheel.

Meeko spent hours hauling stones to the site selected for the Medicine Wheel, then sat quietly waiting for Granbear to awaken from his nap.

An hour after opening his eyes Granbear examined the stones and said, "Good, Grandson. Ah, I see you have chosen some powerful stones. Maybe they can teach you how to gather knowledge." Granbear studied each one carefully. "See the picture on this stone?" he asked as he handed it to Meeko. "It's as old as first man. I am thankful to our forefathers for leaving us these designs. They tell me that someone wanted to pass the old history on to future generations. A stone is like the human mind. It remembers everything so it can teach those who understand how to touch a stone with feeling to read its hidden message."

Granbear sat down among the stones, arranging them by size in separate piles, welcoming each for the Medicine Wheel. "Before we build the Medicine Wheel, we must think about its purpose and see how it fits into the history of first creation.

"In the beginning, the world was silent. There was no life, no time, no space, no dimension, just the Stone Nation. Meeko, the only way to get any understanding of the sacred birthing of all life is through our strong belief in *Wakan Tanka*.

"One day Great Mystery decided it was time to expand the universe, and that's when the first sacred circle was created. He chose *Taku Skan, Skan*, the Father of all Motion, to establish the directions. *Taku Skan Skan* then assigned this task to *Taté*, the Wind. With great thought and devotion, the spirit world decided that *Taté* would come to Mother Earth and live among the people as *Kola*, a very special kind of friend. Soon after he arrived, the people found him to be a wise and loving friend. In time he took a beautiful human woman for his wife, and she gave him four sons at one birth: *Yatá*, the North Wind; *Eya*, the West Wind; *Yanpa*, the East Wind, and *Okaga*, the South Wind.

"You know, all firstborn children are the leaders in their families when they reach adulthood. But *Yatá*, *Taté's* firstborn, grew into an angry, suspicious, greedy man. Lacking trust, he was cold and hateful to everyone. And since the wise ones wanted the best for all future peoples of Mother Earth, they removed *Yatá* from his position as leader and replaced him with *Eya*, the second son, a curious, adventurous spirit who enjoyed everything about life. Although sometimes careless, *Eya* was fearless. When the four sons reached adulthood, they were guided by many spirits to establish the directions on Mother Earth.

"During that year-long trip around the world, each brother was met by many challenges. *Eya* became a *contrar* pupil of *Wakinyan*, the Thunderbeing, and dedicated his life to helping *Wakinyan* cleanse the world of filth. His powers grew strong under the guidance of the Thunderbeing, who taught him how to use the elements to affect the world. *Eya* also fought many battles with his brothers, inflicting great damage on Mother Earth and her children. He still unleashes thunderstorms, tornadoes, and hurricanes to keep the filth from overtaking our world. He is devoted to his work and he never fails, despite the destruction he often causes.

"The third brother, *Yanpa*, even though good-natured, was lazy and obsessed with food. He didn't like making decisions and let his brothers call the shots as long as all his needs were satisfied. *Yanpa* teaches us what not to do, but also shows us how to have fun.

"The fourth son, *Okaga*, was handsome, kind, patient, and giving. He loved taking care of the people and felt responsible for seeing to their needs. But *Okaga* was easily blinded by love, especially from family members.

"We learn from these brothers not to be too determined, too mean, too lazy, or overly concerned with the well-being of others. By moving too far in any of these directions, we are likely to interfere with someone's spiritual pathway, possibly even our own. *Taté* raised his sons alone, and being a wise father, knew their capabilities and limitations. He decided to keep control of the year, but divided the four seasons between his sons.

"To embrace life on Mother Earth, we must receive the sacred breath. All life forces require this precious gift from *Taté* before beginning their earthly journey around the Medicine Wheel. With the sacred breath, we learn to control the powers that are controlling us, and gather knowledge to master our weaknesses. Meeko, while you earn the right to become a pipe carrier, you will speak these truths before ever placing a pipe of your own to your lips. Before we build this Medicine Wheel, let's share my pipe in a ceremony so we will know what the stones are telling us."

Handing Meeko his pipe, Granbear reminded him how to handle and fill a pipe properly. Then Granbear smoked it, sending billowy clouds high into the four directions, creating geometric symbols that Meeko somehow recognized. After the ceremony, Granbear carefully cleaned the pipe and put it away.

"Grandson, it's getting late. We'll continue at sunrise tomorrow morning. That's all I have to say."

As they walked home, Meeko tried to ask many questions, but Granbear responded only with grunts. At dinner, Meeko again asked questions, but still received no answers, only stern looks from Shadowhawk.

Shadowhawk waited until everyone was through eating, then took Meeko aside, handing him a talking stick. "As of today, you will get rid of your impolite white thinking! You will learn to respect our ways! Granbear is your grandfather, but he is also our medicine man, and you will treat him accordingly under all conditions! When Granbear is holding this stick you will not interrupt. When he is teaching, you will give him your undivided attention and keep a clear mind. You will have the proper attitude and desire to learn these ways. You will observe his actions and listen to his words when he is telling his old stories. That's where your answers are hidden.

"You know we communicate through our attitude, expression, eye contact, and the movement of our bodies. Granbear knows all and more of these silent languages and you will learn to speak them! When the lesson is completed, you will ask permission to discuss a subject matter or ask a question pertaining to your need to know. Medicine has the right to refuse you. When you come right to Medicine, keep your head lowered to show the proper respect to his wisdom and bring an offering of tobacco or the proper herbs to him before you ask for help.

Knowing this to be true, Meeko was embarrassed at having pushed for too many answers, and fearing more repercussions from Shadowhawk, he excused himself and went to bed where he lay thinking. He let his mind drift to what Granbear had taught him and tried to accept the sacredness of the winds' majestic powers. He pondered how hard it would be to find his own truth and make his words reflect honesty again. When he thought of Renna's bad ways, he immediately felt angry. Wondering if he could ever develop enough kindness to forgive her, he offered a prayer to *Wakan Tanka* to help him understand this terrible hatred for his mother.

Before daybreak the following morning, Meeko was up and sitting with the stones. When Granbear arrived he announced, "We're building the Medicine Wheel together so you can see how the sacred circle has many invisible circles within it. In time, this will teach you how to identify all the life forces on Mother Earth and how everything is born from the sacred zero."

Granbear drew a big circle on the ground with a stick. Next, he marked the four directions with four large stones representing the West, North, South and East, then carefully filled the spaces between them with smaller stones.

He then went in search of a special stone. Finding it in the ground near the pile of gathered stones, he asked Meeko to dig it out and bring it to the Medicine Wheel. For almost two hours Meeko struggled but the stone would not budge. Dripping with sweat, he gave up, and in a fit of anger began kicking the stone repeatedly.

Observing this, Granbear called. "Grandson, that stone probably thinks you're not smart enough to study with it. Your mind is fitful and limited. I guess the stone is proving that you control nothing." Then Granbear casually approached the stone, placed his hands on it, and, apologizing for his Grandson's ignorance, began to pray. As Meeko stared in amazement, the stone started floating over the ground and placed itself in the center of the sacred Medicine Wheel. Granbear explained. "Well, Grandson, you lost the battle with that stone because you were closed to its spirit."

Motioning Meeko to sit beside him near the Medicine Wheel, Granbear said, "I never talk just to hear myself speak. I'm not just an old person, I'm a wise old person. You once told me that you heard the call of the drums. What I teach must be used if you are to have a loving heart and a mind free to follow the old ways. Only then can your soul hear your heart. This is the only way to wake up the beauty in a sleeping soul. You can never search a valley, nor climb a mountain until you find the rhythm of the sacred drum that beats in the heart. I pray your heart will hear those drumbeats and guide you back to your spiritual pathway.

"It is this Medicine Wheel that will give you the depths of wisdom you will need for this life's journey," Granbear said, placing seven stones around the center stone. "Grandson, you have much to think about. A willful mind can be magical, but it takes good strong feelings to create power. You must learn to harness mind energy if you're to have that kind of power." Then Granbear gave each stone a name and explained the power it represented. Meeko slowly began to see the Medicine Wheel take form in a spiritual as well as a physical sense.

Granbear took him into the Medicine Wheel to sit with the center stone before continuing. "Meeko, there is no beginning and no end to life's cycles of rebirthing.

These sacred stones will help you understand all the lives you have lived on Mother Earth. As you experience their power, remember your natural power grows from inside you. Don't ever think you're so special that you don't have to work to get medicine power. It is given to all of *Wakan Tanka*'s children, but without commitment and hard work nobody can discover their power. There are many who want to bask in the powers of medicine, but like you, they are too lazy to do the work. They build their lives on fear and know nothing about love. Such people just gather information and will never have any knowledge until they get out of their heads and into their hearts."

"Granbear, I don't understand. You've always told me that I was born Medicine. I don't want to do all this study. I just want to be what you told me I was."

"I see, Grandson. So, without work, devotion and commitment, you expect to magically become Medicine? Do you know what that makes you? Another 'wanna be' medicine person," snapped Granbear, his eyes blazing. "When I take on an apprentice, they follow my rules without question! As Medicine, I will direct your every thought until it is pure enough to never harm another. From now on, you will earn the right to any lesson I give you about this Medicine Wheel. And if you don't give me your full attention, I promise I will make your life miserable. Now go away from me! Tell Shadowhawk you are not ready to learn from this medicine man!"

Meeko was shocked and confused by Granbear's sudden outburst. Reluctantly, he found Shadowhawk under a tree making a pipe. Meeko approached him slowly and sat down sadly, telling him why Granbear had sent him away.

Shadowhawk listened quietly. "Well, you must have acted very stupid for Granbear to send you away. You have insulted a medicine elder. It will take a lot of work to fix this. Personally, I think you should have your ass kicked until you learn to keep your mouth shut. Who knows? If you don't straighten up I might just do that!

"Don't you know that Granbear is teaching you the Medicine Wheel to develop the tools that will identify all the individual life forces on Mother Earth and show you how to use their powers in a loving way? It takes work to understand the power of silence. We've always had to know the sacredness of all things before we could ask for spiritual guidance. Recognize every life force as its own separate entity and value its teachings. Each one must be revered and treated with honor to walk within the sacredness of the Medicine Wheel. Granbear wants you to become good enough to spiral upward with the never-ending sacred hoops to visit the many hidden worlds. Without this knowledge, how can you ever expect to ride with the oneness of all creation?"

Seeing that Meeko was confused, Shadowhawk continued in a more sympathetic tone. "Grandson, I also had problems learning my journey around the Medicine Wheel. Granbear never tried to confuse me, but he did give me many challenges until I learned to walk with truth. It looks like you are the one that's trying to confuse the issue about Medicine. You say you don't understand what Granbear is teaching you. Meeko, we have no written language and our ways have always been spoken. We must memorize each story to understand its meaning and always repeat it exactly as it was told so as not to confuse another. I say your anger and stubbornness come from the white world's influence. No matter what you say, it's obvious you're not coming from a listening heart."

"But, Shadowhawk, Granbear has never treated me this way."

"Meeko, the main problem is your ego. A medicine person would never allow a student to sit on a pedestal of self-importance. I know for a fact that Granbear isn't one of those medicine people who has ever done bad things to others. Your lack of respect is attacking Granbear's integrity. I think he's too patient with you. He probably feels pity because you're so ignorant! It's plain to see that the problem is you're listening to the trickster of your own mind! If you keep playing around with that trickster, you're going to bring a lot of misery into your life."

"What's a trickster?" asked Meeko.

"Don't ask me, ask your medicine teacher. Granbear taught me to trust what I know and to never let another take it from me. Meeko, Granbear knows of your past life and has told me that you were good medicine. He's trying to restore those old medicine memories so you can use that knowledge to walk in this life as a good human being. You'd better wise up and listen to him!

"You've got to accept that even though Granbear is your great-grandfather, he's also a very powerful medicine man. If I ever hear of you acting like that again, I'll take you into the wilderness and leave you without food or water. Maybe then you will learn firsthand about the powers of Medicine—if you survive! I like the thought of letting you fend for yourself surrounded by the wild animals, the rainmakers, the winds, the sky tribe, the air walkers and the fire travelers. And when I'd be done training you my way, you would gladly beg Granbear to continue his lessons."

Shadowhawk's harsh words cut through Meeko's false bravado, and he silently followed Shadowhawk back to Granbear. On their way to the Medicine Wheel, Meeko was plagued by the horrific implications of Shadowhawk's threats. When they reached Granbear, Shadowhawk said gently, "Grandfather, I think Grandson is now ready to learn about the sacred Medicine Wheel." Granbear nodded, and Shadowhawk walked away grinning in a devilish manner as he returned to the shade tree to finish another sacred pipe.

Scared, Meeko stood at the entrance of the Medicine Wheel, offering tobacco as he prayed. When he finished, Granbear said, "Come, Grandson, it's time to meet all those things that live in the Medicine Wheel." Fearful of making a mistake, Meeko quietly sat next to his great-grandfather, keeping his eyes lowered in respect. Unaffected, Granbear said, "Meeko, look up. Can you see the happy spirit of *Wi*, the sun? Someday when you learn about this great chief, you will have the strength to build your power from his rays. Did you know it was *Wi* who created the first human?"

"Oh, I thought humans were always here."

"No, no, Grandson. We were the fifth life force created by *Wakan Tanka* and *Taku Skan Skan*. What I'm about to tell you happened long, long ago when *Wi* lived alone and decided to make himself a companion. He took some mud from Mother Earth and molded it into a two leg. He asked *Taté* for breath, *Taku Skan Skan* for motion and *Wakan Tanka* for a soul, then named his companion Mud Man.

"For a long time, *Wi* was very happy with his new creation, but as time went by, he noticed that Mud Man was becoming depressed. Understanding this emotion, he was concerned over Mud Man's unhappiness. As time passed, *Wi* thought this over then decided to create a companion for Mud Man. With mud from the soil and one of Mud Man's ribs, *Wi* created first woman. Again he called on his friend *Taté* to give her first breath. *Taté* wrapped her gently in his warmth then named her Rib Woman. He took her to Mud Man and both were very happy together.

"One cold wintry night, Rib Woman and Mud Man lay close together to stay warm. They soon discovered they liked this thing called 'warm', and used it year-round. To their surprise a child was born. And later, many more children were born. As these children grew older, they too liked 'warm' and began to have children themselves. Then their children's children produced children. My, my! In a very short time the earth was a very crowded place.

"The children of Mud Man and Rib Woman were a spoiled and lazy bunch. They argued and fought over everything, and this caused many problems. In those times suspicion and jealousy were everywhere. The people had forgotten about the goodness of life and no longer prayed to *Wakan Tanka*, they only worshipped warm. Some of them even molested their own children. Others raped their brothers and sisters. Ah, Grandson, this thing called warm had spread like a bad disease throughout the land, causing many children to be born not right and with mental problems. But no matter what, the people refused to give up this thing called warm.

This was a sad time, for the people had forgotten *Wakan Tanka*. Many unpleasant things happened to these bad children. Confusion grew, and soon Mother Earth was in trouble and she could no longer grow enough food to feed them all. Why, even the plants began to think of themselves as the most important life force and hid their fruits from the people. The animals moved far away in fear of their lives, but still the people multiplied faster and faster, and this was how starvation was created. Because of these bad times, the children of Rib Woman and Mud Man left home and spread all over the world searching for food.

"*Taku Skan Skan* had been watching this evil for a long time and warned the people to change their ways, but the ones that loved warm refused to listen and continued to multiply. Ah, Meeko, this was a pitiful time. Many of the two legs and the four legs lost their homes. The people were starving and their bodies had become nothing but bones and hanging flesh. Ah, this evil thing was destroying Mother Earth and all of her children. That's when *Taku Skan Skan* grew angry and declared first judgment to the people about warm."

Meeko's eyes widened hoping Granbear didn't know he too had this disease called warm.

Looking at him with a knowing smile, Granbear said, "Rib Woman was lonely for her children and felt useless. She thought of having more children, but when she went to Mud Man, they found she had passed the age of birthing. For years they waited in vain for their children to return.

"Rib Woman showed no interest in life. She wanted to experience a new feeling called 'death'. She went to Chief *Wi* and asked him to allow her to experience this thing called death. *Wi*, thought long and hard, and told her he would grant her this request, but warned that once death happened, it could never be reversed. Rib Woman happily agreed and went home to wait. Time passed, and she waited and waited but nothing happened.

"Then one day Rib Woman spotted some of her children on a far ridge. Excited that at last her children were coming home, she ran to tell Mud Man the good news. Together they built homes, gathered clothing, and made great amounts of food to celebrate their arrival. One by one, the children returned, and soon Rib Woman and Mud Man's house was overflowing with people.

"Months later the children were settled into their new homes. Rib Woman's days were filled with all the children and she had forgotten her wish to experience death. One morning Rib Woman rose early to make food for her favorite son's family. She waited until the sun was high in the sky then went to their quarters to find her favorite son lying still and silent. 'Oh, no!' she screamed as it suddenly dawned on her that her son had fallen down to stay."

Granbear looked deeply into Meeko's eyes. "Rib Woman got her wish. Brokenhearted, she ran to *Wi* wailing and screaming in grief, as she begged him to bring back her son. Since there was nothing he could do, he turned his back on her. Rib Woman returned every day, pleading for her son to live again, and each time *Wi*'s response was the same. 'You asked for this gift of death and now that you know the suffering that death creates, these feelings will forever be connected to death.'

"From that day on, Rib Woman prayed for the life in all things. But death stayed on Mother Earth. Even the animals and the plants were learning to fear death's power as it spread all over the land. Since it was a human that brought this evil, the animals and the plants no longer trusted them. Each night they hid in the safety of darkness and eavesdropped on the humans as they talked among themselves. 'We will no longer suffer from starvation. If we are to survive we must use the power of death to rule the land.' All agreed and death became a fearful power as the first human killed and ate the first animal.

"When the animals heard about the killing they ran deep into the forest to hide from the humans. The winged ones hid in the trees and kept listening to what the humans had to say. They grew very angry and took to the skies to warn the others of this horrible tragedy the humans were bringing on all the children of Mother Earth.

"From the sky, *Wanbli Gle'ska*, shrilled in a high-pitched cry, 'Fear all humans! Hide, you four legs! The two legs have lost their respect for life and are coming to kill us!'

"The plants were deeply saddened by *Wanbli Gle'ska*'s message and the Chieftress of all the green things called a meeting. 'We once offered our lives to feed these humans,' she said mournfully. 'Now they're going to kill our four-legged friends.' Cries of anger rose from the plants and echoed all over the earth. 'We must stop this death,' vowed all the green things.

"That day the plant people decided they would no longer share their healing knowledge with humans. Many of them kept their sweet medicines while others became poisonous to fight the human race. Still others stripped their leaves of their healing powers or hid the medicines underground in their roots. The Chieftress of the green ones went to *Taku Skan Skan* to ask for help. He listened and ruled: 'From this moment, all plant life will be reborn from seeds left the year before, so humans will have to study the habits of the animals to learn what to eat and what not to eat from the plant world.'

"As years passed, the earth was shaken again by starvation, turmoil and death. The humans could no longer find where the animals were hidden, and the plants refused to share themselves. Each one chose a season to birth from seed, and lived only a short time to make sure humans never forgot their unmerciful cruelty. Ah, Meeko, there was little left for the humans and they feared they would vanish.

"Those bad times went on until a few people remembered *Wakan Tanka*'s promise to always take care of his creations, so they began to learn how to pray. These few good people reminded everyone that *Wakan Tanka* promised that he would take care of all of his children if they honored and respected each other, sharing in the abundance of Mother Earth. Many animals listened and joined in their prayers to plead for mercy.

"Soon White-Tailed Deer, Elk and Moose stepped forward, saying all together, 'We will die so that the people may live, but you and your children's children must remember to take our lives quickly and painlessly in a sacred, ceremonial way. Nothing can ever be wasted or thrown away from our bodies, otherwise we will walk on the minds of your children's children and they will starve again.

"Our meat will nourish your body. Our skin will cover your nakedness and keep you from the cold. Our bones will be your tools, and our hoofs your glue. Our teeth will remind you to love and respect all life. And when our souls return to the spirit world, you will come to us in Shadow World to learn more about our powers.' And that is how the people survived in first world."

Granbear sat in silence waiting for his grandson's reaction.

"Granbear, why couldn't the people be happy with all the care and love that was given to them? How could the humans do such bad things?"

"Grandson, kindness is forgotten too easily. Ignorance is a terrible thing. It teaches disrespect, and that is unforgivable. Why, even today, people hate and fear what they do not understand. Most people can't appreciate the beauty that *Wakan Tanka* has given us in nature's creations. Remember, it is humans who create ugliness.

"Ah yes, Grandson, it was a sad day when *Wakan Tanka* finally gave up and destroyed first world by fire," said Granbear pointing to the sun that was setting deep on the horizon. "Come, let's go home. We'll talk more about creation tomorrow," promised Granbear as they got up to leave the Medicine Wheel. Meeko followed Granbear to the arbor for supper reflecting pensively on all that had been told to him about creation.

Early the next day Meeko was waiting in the Medicine Wheel when Granbear arrived. They sat in prayer for a long time before Granbear spoke. "Again Creator wanted beauty, so he made second world. After eons of time it became a very uncaring, unfeeling, cold place, and once again it had to be destroyed, but this time by ice. The Wise One grieved over these terrible destruction's, but he wanted beauty, not ugly. You see, Meeko, *Wakan Tanka* is perfect and he never gives up or tires. So he created third world. This time he gave his children an unburdened world so they could enjoy nature and learn from the silence of its spiritual beauty. To a few of his children he gave a very special gift, the power of dreaming. Ah, Grandson, life was good.

"One day twin boys were born into third world, but their poor mother died during childbirth. Not knowing which child had the power of dreaming, *Wakan Tanka* knew he had to find someone to raise these boys in a good way. He decided that Wolf would be the best mother, and sent this earth teacher to raise them. Wolf soon found that one of the twins liked living in the daylight and the other liked living in the nightlight. Oh my, what a dilemma! Wolf could never get any rest and felt sad when she was separated from either boy.

"Then one day she solved her problem. She used her dream power to move between worlds, sending messages to both Nightboy and Dayboy. And this was how Wolf's medicine bundle was created. The vision bundle became so powerful that it could give anyone the ability to become one with unity, devotion, loyalty and pure love. Creator watched this magical gift grow and now knew how to locate the true dreamer.

"Wolf raised these boys well and they were happy, but the people thought this very unusual. As the twins grew older, they loved Dayboy but were unsure about Nightboy. He had power, but was very cruel and cold. He was abusive with his heartless anger and would voice his bad feelings toward everyone. In time the people feared that Nightboy's punishment was taking over the world. Not knowing which boy had the true power, the people became confused. They began lying to themselves and others, saying they too were dreamers.

"To confuse things even more, the third world peoples argued about where they had come from. Some said they came from the sky; others were convinced everyone had come from under the waters; still others fought raging battles to prove that everyone had come from the underworld. But worst of all, the old, ill-tempered leaders believed they were the wisest and insisted that all people came from a hole in the ground. Well, when the younger ones heard this, they too wanted to be heard. They said everyone had come through a hole in the ice. Oh, Grandson, this was a very confusing time. Once again, Creator had wanted only beauty and the people had made ugly so *Wakan Tanka* was forced to destroy third world.

"Great Spirit decided to make fourth world. He wanted Earth Mother to have a brighter light at night, so he made the stars. When he wanted calm, he conjured the night. When he wanted warmth, he created *Wi*, the sun. When he wanted beauty, he envisioned the flying ones and filled the heavens with their beautiful colors.

"But after many moons had passed, again something was spoiling his beauty. Fourth world was filled with so much kindness and generosity, that the people realized Dayboy had been born into this world. The natural dreamers went to check and to their horror they found that Nightboy had sneaked in too. But it was too late, Nightboy had already taught the people to amuse themselves with the power of warm, making sure his bad blood would spread all over the world. Here again, *Wakan Tanka* had to be very careful in knowing whether dreamers had the blood of Dayboy or Nightboy.

"As time went on, the brothers found each other again and they fought day and night. Following one of their great night battles, the people found Nightboy with so many wounds they could not imagine how he had survived. Terrified, the people ran for their lives. You can still see Nightboy's blood stains on the Stone People," said Granbear, handing Meeko a spotted red stone. "Carry this sacred stone as a reminder that when trouble comes into your life, it is your responsibility to bring in Dayboy so he can help you fight your battles with the dark side. Because the Stone People carry the oldest of knowledge, it is important for me to teach you how to speak with them."

Staring at the stone, Meeko shivered, wondering if he might have the blood of Nightboy. Granbear smiled knowingly as he pointed out the many images of people who had been caught forever in Nightboy's power on the stone's surface. "Study this stone very carefully, Meeko. Someday it will tell you all about Mother Earth and what her children have lost by not knowing the difference between Nightboy and Dayboy."

"I never want to meet Nightboy. How can I tell the difference between the two?"

"Oh, that's easy, Grandson. We know if Nightboy's or Dayboy's blood runs in someone's veins by how they treat others. The dark twin knows who has his blood, and keeps them captured by fear, lost forever in the ignorance of darkness. A dreamer who follows the ways of Dayboy is sensitive and gives loving care and protection to all things. When you see someone like that, you will know that Dayboy is teaching that person to shape-shift and go between worlds to fight Nightboy's power. The ones that follow the teachings of Dayboy become true dreamers. Now there's another story you need to know.

"Once long ago there was a bright star in the middle of the Big Dipper. For some reason it burned out and *Wakan Tanka* sent Blue Woman, a powerful spirit, to protect it. When a life force is returning to Mother Earth she assists in its mortal birthing. When a person dies, she helps the soul rebirth back to the spirit world. When you look at the night sky, you can see these souls blazing across the heavens. Why even today, you can go to her in a proper manner, and if she chooses, she can reach down and guide you through many universes.

"Ah yes, Grandson. One must watch closely to recognize the dark-blooded children. Many times I have seen the blood of Nightboy in some of my loved ones. The ruby red glow in their eyes tells me to pray harder. And when I sweat, I talk to the Stone People to keep this dishonor away from the Bear Clan family.

"Besides Nightboy, there was another unhappy, but powerful spirit who sneaked into fourth world. His names are many, but we Bear Clan call him *Ksa*, Wisdom. It is said when first world was born from the void, he was hatched from a stone—already an adult. And it is also said he looked like his father, *Wakinyan*, and was very ugly at birth. *Ksa* wanted badly to be handsome so he would be accepted. But people shunned him, causing him to become angry and deceptive, so he added trickery and folly to his great wisdom. In our world, *Ksa* is also known as *Iktomi*, the Spider. Sometimes it's very hard to tell the difference between *Ksa* and *Iktomi*. Oh, how he loves to trick people and make them act foolish. In my time, I've met many people who carry the power of old *Iktomi*."

Meeko was horrified to find out about such bad spirits, and Granbear silently let him absorb the revelations for several moments before continuing. "In time we will explore everything about Mother Earth and her brothers and sisters who live as planets in our solar system, but first you must grow beyond your needs and learn more about yourself. This kind of knowledge takes time and demands a clear mind and a pure heart. Nature and all the earth children will teach you how to develop your instincts. To seek such greatness, you must have a hunger to learn and be willing to find the knowledge that is hidden within you."

Meeko's face glowed with anticipation, and he excitedly answered, "Oh, Granbear, I want to be just like you."

"That is good, Grandson, but I want you to become better than me. Medicine is born in everyone, but it must be earned before you can join in its beauty and power. Once you have learned to live in the center of all the many sacred circles of the Medicine Wheels, you'll understand this.

"The old teachings require that you know everything about the above and below worlds. Only then can you get the powers of a true dreamer. People work very hard to learn the powers in the Medicine Wheel. This knowledge is multi-dimensional and comes in many ways as you learn to vision the past, present and future as one. When you know these things, you will be aware of the many roads that can direct you into all the circles of oneness within *Wakan Tanka*'s purpose. To reach the highest of spirit, you have to nurture your every potential. Then you will understand that creation is ongoing—that is one of the many secrets that lies in the knowledge of the Medicine Wheel.

"As you walk these learning roads, you will come to respect the power in all life forces. At the same time, this sacred walk will help you find hidden powers and talk with all spirits, the winds, the animals, the trees, the stones, the plants, the flying ones, even the finned ones and the creepy crawlies. This is the walk of the visionary.

"But to do these things in a good way, you have to learn patience with yourself. Nature's simple lessons will let you reach beyond logical thinking and help you control your emotions. To seek such greatness you must explore everything within yourself and find the greater mystery that lies in the four parts of your soul."

"Grandfather, there's so much to learn that it makes me dizzy."

"I once felt the same way until I found that the Medicine Wheel was a sacred zero. It's the oneness that goes right down to a grain of sand or a particle of dust floating in the air. True dreamers can see these things larger-than-life as pictures lying on the back of their eyelids. Feeling the flow of motion as the spirals shift, they can even see the energies of a thought or the soul. Ah yes, visionaries live in many different worlds at the same time.

"Meeko, to become a dreamer with such power, you must pay a price. It takes a long time to spin the many circles, but when true seekers get this limitless power, they know the meaning of humility in the presence of *Wakan Tanka*. When a person is kind, it gives their Medicine kindness. When a person has ego, it drives away true Medicine. A real medicine person never speaks of their powers. Those that can see that power always treat them with respect and consider them holy. Lots of people think of us as poor, but we know that in other worlds we live in glorious mansions.

"I'm sad to say many folks are uncomfortable around medicine power, and try to copy medicine people because of envy and jealousy. When this kind of person is filled with fear and ego, the power uses them like a tool, then discards them and lets their power leak away until they become a sniveling idiot.

"Why, even a thought has power, and with it comes responsibility. We have to accept all knowledge learned from life's lessons and share it with love for the growth of others. In my experience, I have found that true dreamers are childlike. They have a twinkle of mischief and they look through eyes other than their own. They can be sweet, abrupt and sometimes even harsh. They relate to everything, because everything speaks to them. They play with life in ways that only a dreamer can understand. To them life is like waves rolling across the sea.

"Wise dreamers are communicators who bridge many worlds. Their minds are always traveling to unknown places and transforming energies into matter. People should protect these dreamers from the world's harshness, for it will break their spirits and they will die unless they choose to gather strength and renew their life. Dreamers are amazing people, they truly rule their lives."

"Granbear, please teach me how to become a dreamer."

"If you follow my ways, you will learn how. But first let's learn some simple things. Every color has a meaning and a sound. See that blue shirt you are wearing? I see more than a blue shirt. I see a reflection of the sky in the sacred waters, along with *Taku Skan Skan*, who, as you have learned, is the motion of all living things. I also see this color in the North Door on the Medicine Wheel. See those yellow flowers over there?" questioned Granbear, thrusting his chin toward the river. "I see the sun on Mother Earth, and its glow from the stones in the *Inipi*. I see this color in the East Door on the Medicine Wheel." Then Granbear scanned the area with his half-closed eyes, saying, "Tell me, what do you feel when you see all these green things around us?"

Meeko looked and answered, "I see trees and grass, and I think I feel love and peace from them."

"That is good. I see healing plants, nurturing earth power. I see this color in the South Door of the Medicine Wheel. Every color speaks with its own tone, and has a place in the Medicine Wheel. When we are aware of the sound each color makes, we can hear all the sweet music created between Mother Earth and Father Sky.

"A true dreamer must travel far into the mind to find these things. Someday you will be able to relate all things by knowing the sacred language of mathematics, then you can understand the meaning of the old sky calendars. When that day comes, I will know you are walking strong on the good Red Road."

"How can numbers have anything to do with me being a dreamer?"

Granbear looked away and did not speak again for over an hour. Then he fixed his eyes on Meeko and said, "Opinions have no value when they come from a lack of knowledge. I teach flow, not a closed mind. With such disrespect you will never be able to enter Shadow World. Until you can connect to nature, the elements, the two legs, the four legs, the no legs, the flying ones, the standing ones, and every plant life, you will know nothing! Until then, honor what I'm sharing with you.

"Medicine demands a pure heart before it will help you go beyond our world. Think of the many lessons Renna taught you. Look how she forced you to develop your instinct. Great Spirit put her in your life to make sure you would be strong and independent. You see her as a bad mother, but I see her as a good teacher. I know you don't like her, but those experiences are usable tools.

"Now, go from me and live with your ignorance, you bad person! Don't come back until you can bring me the nice boy that came out of those times with Renna. That's all I have to say!" exclaimed Granbear, throwing his hands up in disgust.

Before Granbear had reached the arbor, Meeko realized the impact of his words. He ran after him begging his forgiveness, but Granbear ignored him as if he was not there. Meeko went to Shadowhawk who sternly warned him to stay away from Granbear. No matter who he approached, they looked at him in disgust then turned their backs and walked away.

In desperation, Meeko spent two days in Shadow World at the Sundance tree that he and Granbear had sat under so many times to pray. On the third day, he had a new awareness about his situation. He thought of Renna's hatred for Granbear and the family, and saw that to him she meant cruelty, anger, hunger and prostitution. Fear struck his heart as he wondered if he and Renna carried Nightboy's dark blood in their veins.

Granbear saw Meeko praying and felt satisfied, knowing his great-grandson was beginning to recognize the parallels between his life and Renna's. Now it was up to Meeko to correct his bad ways.

"Grandson, it's good to see that you're heart is becoming kinder. Living in the good way leads to a spiritual life. First trust in *Wakan Tanka*, then trust in nature to find the sacredness in yourself. Have good thoughts and never come to me without a pure heart. Waste no more time hating your mother, and let me teach you a new direction for you to grow. Renna's hard lessons were a gift that can become a good teaching."

"Granbear, sometimes it's hard not to have a mother and father like everyone else. I've always wanted a happy family."

"Meeko, who cares who your parents are? In reality, we all have the same father and mother as everyone else. They are Father Sky whose home is the blue dome above and Mother Earth who feeds and heals her children with the life-healing waters given by Father Sky. It is *Taku Skan Skan* who rules the sun, the moon, and the stars and all things that move." Granbear gently placed his arm around a tearful Meeko, saying,

"I'm your great-grandfather, grandfather, great-grandmother, grandmother, mother, father, brother, sister, and teacher, and I'm trying to become your spiritual friend. I have always been there for you, and will still be there after I die. You are one of the special ones, and I know Creator sent you here on an important mission.

"When you were born, your spirit walked on my dreams. You were born on a cold, snowy night in the alley behind Joe's Bar. I, Renna, and many rats and field mice were there to see your remarkable birth. I saw a strange blue ball of light hover over you as you entered the world. I saw your spirit enter your body. I strongly believe you were born with a dual soul. I gave you my breath. Ah, Grandson, it was a great night of miracles."

Early the next morning the sun rose on the shadowy figure of Granbear standing in the West Door of the Medicine Wheel. Showing proper respect, Meeko waited in the distance, hoping he would be allowed to continue his studies. As his morning prayers were completed, Granbear motioned him to enter the Medicine Wheel and sit quietly by his side.

"Grandson, this sacred Medicine Wheel is very ancient and has many invisible circles to teach you. It will reveal all its knowledge as you learn to walk in balance and harmony with Mother Earth. But first we need to get rid of false ideas about ourselves so we can be aware of the true spirit of life. It is nature that teaches us survival and opens the door to our hearts."

Thrusting his chin forward, Granbear indicated the four directions of the Medicine Wheel and said, "The good Red Road runs North to South, and the Black Road of experience, runs East to West. Now, that's the four directions. The spiritual Red Road is long and walked by few. If you are among the special born ones who complete this difficult journey, living between worlds will bring you much beauty.

"But let's start at the beginning. Before entering the Sacred Medicine Wheel, we purify ourselves with sage since *Wakan Tanka* wants us to come to the sacred spirit beings with a pure heart." Granbear took a pinch of tobacco and offered it in prayer to the West Door where he would begin Meeko's training.

With hooded eyes, he looked at Meeko, saying, "Grandson, long before the white race came to our land, the people lived in a good way and walked the sacred wheels of life in prayer, always honoring the teachings of Mother Life and the sacredness of silence. We know the West is the home of *Wanbli Gle'ska*, who speaks to us from where the sun goes over down. So we enter at the West Door, since it was the first direction established, then we travel clockwise. When we lift our eyes to the sky looking for the great Sun Bird Chief, he makes us search until we find the excitement of him in our hearts.

"Being the highest flying bird in the world, *Wanbli Gle'ska* tells his earthbound brothers and sisters to fly high so they can see the bigger picture of life before making decisions. Grandson, life's hesitations create fear and procrastination, and these surely confuse the mind. Eagle power can stop this uncertainty once you rid yourself of useless beliefs. This sky patroller tells earthbound children to go forward and expand their horizons, to express themselves simply and beautifully while accepting the harshness of life. Eagle also tells you to look at a situation according to its merits and never allow anyone to discourage you from your goal.

"If you listen to *Wanbli Gle'ska,* you will feel him forcing you to refine your feelings as he moves through your heart, piercing your soul with such beauty that you will understand his great wisdom. Freedom is letting Eagle draw you into flight and guide you to the unlimited power of the spirit world. This opens your heart and lets you transform your weaknesses into strengths. Only then can you understand the humility one needs in order to fly with *Wanbli Gle'ska.*

"Once you can see the ever-changing cycles of your life and be willing to face the unexplored questions in your mind, you will be able to take a weakness and turn it into a strength. But if you keep harmful thoughts, your mind will create a bad life for you and those you love. You see, a person is never just their past. They become who they are by the way they think about their past.

"Ah, Meeko, Eagle shows us his teachings in how he lives and dies. Did you know that Eagle only works about fifteen minutes a day, then spends the rest of his day grooming his mighty wings to be ready for another flight? Think of how Eagle made you feel as you watched him soar high above in his many flying designs. He can see the smallest of movements and when he folds his wings and drops from the sky, he knows that Great Spirit has given him food so he can live for another day.

"Remember how Eagle came to you in your hour of need and gathered you up in his powerful wings to bring you home? What you heard was his sacred truth calling you back to the drum. You flew high above with Eagle that day. It's once again time to listen to this king of the sky and search to find the raw beauty that sleeps in your soul.

"They say this multi-colored bird flew so close to the sun that his magnificent wings started to melt and caused his colors to run together. That's how he got the name Golden Eagle. It was *Wakan Tanka* who made *Wanbli Gle'ska* his bravest sky messenger. He takes our prayers on his feathers to the spirit of Red Rope who goes between Creator and all the earth children. It takes great preparation to fly with *Wanbli Gle'ska*, Meeko, for he commands that seekers understand the above and below powers. Eagle says, 'Before you can fly with me, you must find that power within yourself.'

"It's an honor to wear an eagle's feather, and it takes an act of bravery or a great deed to be worthy of such an honor. We, as a people, never give anyone a golden eagle feather unless they have proven their worthiness.

"Why, even our Dog Soldiers and medicine people must earn the right to carry this sacred feather. Because eagle's strength and swiftness is matched by no other, we always trust the wearer. In the old days, an eagle feather was its owner's greatest possession, and the loss of an eagle feather brought dishonor. A warrior would rather give up his wife or his horse than lose one," said Granbear with a twinkle in his eyes.

Meeko watched closely, for behind Granbear's gestures and amusing smiles, trickery could be hiding. Thinking of Shadowhawk, he quickly searched his mind to make sure he understood the lesson. Feeling assured, Meeko started to ask a question, as Granbear brought his hand up to his mouth. "Be silent as Eagle. I'll be back this afternoon." Meeko remained silent with eyes lowered for he knew if he didn't he would be there for who knows how long. It was almost dark when Granbear returned. "Did you enjoy your day with Eagle?"

"Oh, yes, Granbear, especially learning about the sacred feathers. You have so many, why even your war bonnet has two stringers that reach to the ground. You must be a very important person."

Granbear smiled, "Ah yes, and I earned every one of them. These feathers give me the strength to fly with Eagle and study the world from high above. One must search a long time to see beauty through the eyes of Eagle. When you grow into this kind of power, Meeko, it will take over everything in your life." Getting up to leave, he told Meeko, "You stay here for the night. I'll see you in the morning."

Meeko was confused about why he had been left without food or blankets since he had shown no disrespect. Feeling rejected, he curled up in the West Door and pouting, cried himself to sleep.

Meeko awakened at daybreak, his body shaking from the cold. He was grateful when the sun rose and warmed him. Granbear arrived and motioned for him to leave the Medicine Wheel, then handed him an egg sandwich and a cup of hot coffee. "Meeko, when you finish eating, get cleaned up and come back. Now hurry! We have a lot to do today."

Granbear was just putting away his pipe when Meeko approached the Medicine Wheel, waiting to be invited to enter. They sat in the West as Granbear began the day's lesson. "Grandson, long ago I wanted to become an eagle catcher. I spoke with Medicine about earning this gift and spent many moons learning about Eagle. Finally I was chosen with the greatest of care by an old chief who had decided that I was smart enough to capture Golden Eagle.

"I fasted for four days and did many sweats to prepare my mind. When I was ready, I stalked Eagle. When I found his favorite hunting grounds, I built my shelter near the water to learn how to blend into his territory. Only with great patience and will was I able to handle the elements. Many times I thought I was on an impossible quest, but in time we became adjusted to each other's presence. I learned I could mimic eagle's screaming, shrill voice and when I called to him he would answer. I lived the way he did until I too was an eagle. Then I knew I was ready to be an Eagle Catcher.

"Early one morning I took my bear knife and dug a large pit in the ground, then cut many branches to cover the hole. I then smoked my pipe, asking *Wakan Tanka* to help me on my mission. Once satisfied I was doing the right thing, I took my bow and arrows and went in search of a rabbit. In late afternoon I returned to camp with a dead rabbit hanging over my shoulder. After carefully checking the blind, I tied the rabbit to the top and crawled inside to wait."

Meeko, living every word of Granbear's story, was spellbound and excitedly blurted out, "Granbear, why didn't you ever tell me this story before?"

Granbear abruptly left the Medicine Wheel, sat under a nearby tree and lit his happy pipe, ignoring Meeko, who again was baffled by his grandfather's behavior. The wise old medicine man smiled at him with a knowing look as he finished smoking his pipe and returned to the Medicine Wheel. "Meeko, if you don't get out of your head and listen with your heart, you can never connect to the heart of Eagle. It's sad you waste so much time asking questions instead of listening. Lack of knowledge can stunt your thinking and leave little room for your mind to work.

"Eagle is a wise stalker of thoughts. I know this, because that old bird watched me from above and kept me waiting in that pit for four days. Boy, did I ever learn patience from that master teacher. A few times he flew close, eyeballing the rabbit. And on the fourth day, I was thrilled to hear the singing winds rush through his wings, telling me that he was landing.

"It seemed like forever as I waited inside that blind. My heart pounded so loud that I feared it would destroy the silence. Then suddenly the eagle jumped to the top and moved toward the dead rabbit. I rose to my knees, reached through the branches, and with lightning speed grabbed his feet, pulling him into the pit. Once inside, though, he broke free of my grip and backed into a corner. Then we studied each other as still as could be. I knew if I made one wrong move, he would rip me apart.

"At this moment I too was Eagle and knew that to stay alive I would have to call forth the warrior in me. He charged, and I grabbed him without crushing a feather, then quickly broke his back. Crying out to *Wakan Tanka*, I asked forgiveness for taking Eagle's life. A minute later, while I was still holding this beautiful sacred bird, the sky opened up and Eagle's soul was released. I cried with joy as I heard his shrill, voice calling out to me, and I knew this sacred sentry of the sky was heading home to the Eagle nation.

"When I returned with the bird, there was indeed a great celebration among the people. I went directly to the medicine man, who had a sweat ready for me. I spoke to Eagle through my prayers and promised that every part of his body would become a strong spiritual tool for the people. As I left the sweat, I knew that Eagle had eaten my heart and we would always be one. I wrapped that sacred bird in sage for protection, and ever since I've used Eagle's mind-heart power. Once touched by *Wanbli Gle'ska*, Meeko, your spirit will always track the wisdom in your soul through his flight."

Granbear slowly handed his grandson a beaded golden eagle feather with red markings, saying, "Take this warrior feather. The mark of red paint means it was earned from a killing during battle. I hope that someday it will take you through the sun. When the right time comes, Shadowhawk will awaken the warrior that sleeps deep inside you. Once you have done battle and taken a life you will never forget it."

A strange power surged through Meeko as he took the feather. Holding it close to his heart, he trembled for he felt the vibration of death roll over his body.

"Now that you have felt the power of *Wanbli Gle'ska*, Gatekeeper of the West Door, I will leave you to think about his gift."

Meeko thought about the superiority of Eagle, whose powers far surpassed human capabilities. He cried as he remembered the magnificent bird that had once called out, "How high can you fly, Meeko?" His heart gripped by talons of terror, Meeko knew he must change his feelings about Renna if he was ever to connect to the heart of Eagle. Not knowing how to release his pain, he raised his eagle feather in the air and prayed to *Wakan Tanka* to help him rise as the Thunderbird from the ashes of his past.

To escape the incessant flow of bad memories, Meeko left the Medicine Wheel, feather in hand, and began running. Not until long after dark did he return home, still filled with sadness. Pulling out the old eagle bundle from under his bed, he placed it beside him and crawled under the covers hoping to sleep. But he was restless, so he began caressing each bone and feather, reliving the helplessness he felt while watching Eagle fall from the sky. Suddenly he realized this sacred bird had sacrificed its life to help him attain freedom, giving him the courage to escape the orphanage and return to the reservation. And although he did not know it at the time, this same eagle would someday give him the power to return to *Wakan Tanka* and serve under the Law of One.

After breakfast the following morning, Meeko hurried to meet Granbear at the Medicine Wheel. They sat together in silence at the West Door. "Ah, Grandson, I'm proud of your efforts to connect to the power of Eagle, but there are many other flying ones who live in the West. You will learn that each one of them has very different abilities," said Granbear as he continued to unfold the knowledge of the flying ones through his time-honored stories.

As a sparrow hawk flew nearby, Meeko smiled at the fierceness of his little face and immediately recognized his courage. With childlike excitement, Granbear said, "Thank you, little one, for sharing your gift with my grandson." Then turning to Meeko, he explained, "Sparrow Hawk's gift is the mind, and he knows all about your past lives. His graceful flight teaches us to take control of our thoughts and actions; in fact, he won't be around anyone who runs in fear. To see Sparrow Hawk's commitment in hunting, you must go to the grassy plains, because he lives mostly on insects and rodents. Grandson, when you want to do anything, you'll need to know Sparrow Hawk's power.

After lunch as Granbear and Meeko were walking along a new trail, they had a chance encounter with a red-tailed hawk. Granbear pointed in excitement. "See that warrior bird? We sometimes call him Little Eagle because he's so fearless. Good warriors carry his honored feathers while searching out a hidden enemy since he teaches us to be aware of everything. He can attack an enemy of any size with perfect accuracy. There's no mistaking the roaring thunder of his savagery when he folds his wings inward and falls from the sky.

"Each time our Dog Soldiers carried this winged warrior's feathers with them into battle, they knew they would bring home victory. To be accepted by all the flying ones, Meeko, you must become sensitive to them. The winged ones demand you stalk yourself and find your truth before they will let you sit at their feast of knowledge. Only then can you feel the spirit of these beings and understand their shrill messages riding on the winds."

It was almost dark when they returned home, tired and hungry from their long day's journey. Granbear instructed Meeko to sit in the West Door of the Medicine Wheel and reflect on his new knowledge. Listening to the night creatures as they awakened, Meeko thought about hawks. Then he felt a chill of fear run up his spine as he heard one say, "Take pity on this puny human." Disregarding Granbear's instructions to stay in the Medicine Wheel, Meeko ran to the house and crawled into bed for the night, but he was still pursued by dreams of birds.

Before going to the arbor for breakfast the following morning, Meeko apologized to Granbear for his lack of courage, telling him of his dreams. "Granbear, Raven walked on my dreams last night. He took me to a world of darkness and spoke of things to come. Flying right ahead of me, Raven said, 'You must know hawk and learn to battle your fears before you can fly with me,' then he took off. Can you tell me what this means?"

"Ah yes, Grandson, I know much of this talking bird," sighed Granbear, lighting his happy pipe. "He dares us to go into the invisible darkness of our feared future. Raven is the power of the prophet. He sees the past, present and future and speaks to us in Shadow World about how things are born into being. It takes a mighty worthy person to fly beyond time with him. Raven can fold time. It's like watching an eclipse of our sun. He demands we have complete awareness of our thoughts.

"You must be able to spiral directly into the void before you can approach Raven, so he can show you how to attain your most desired dreams. Ah yes, Meeko, Raven commands that you build strong beliefs before he will teach you to manifest your dreams from a future that is not yet created. The power of such a powerful spirit speaking to you lets me know that you may have great intelligence and leadership abilities, but it will take much thought and courage to cross into the blue-black darkness of Raven's unknown space.

"The old people always say that dreamers must be willing to walk between the known and the unknown worlds before Raven will even bother with them." Granbear smiled mysteriously and leaned close to Meeko whispering, "Watch the sky. If you see two or more ravens flying restlessly, know you are in danger and go home to fight another day. Always listen closely to Raven, for he speaks the magic of the old language of the Shamans."

Meeko's eyes grew wide with fear as Granbear continued. "It was your choice to follow the old ways. But you can do nothing with Raven power until you learn to believe in yourself. Don't be afraid, Grandson, someday you will accept the responsibility that comes with knowledge. I pray that you will have a strong mind with a good heart. The old ways demand discipline to build power. This is what drives us to our spiritual growth and makes life an exciting adventure."

At that moment, a butterfly landed on Meeko's left hand. As he sat admiring its beauty, he saw a woman's face and felt a strange memory from another time and place. Granbear saw this and knew Meeko had made a connection to his soul's purpose.

"Grandson, that butterfly is telling you to become persistent so you can understand his gentle message of love. Think of him as an ally in completing your transformation to a good life. Butterfly must go through four stages, and each carries many lessons. The first stage is the egg with its protective covering, teaching us to protect our plans and ideas. There is a hardened circular hole in the top that gives it time to think and prepare for its birthing as a caterpillar. Once it fattens up, the caterpillar weaves itself into a cocoon. There it must eat the knowledge before splitting open from its shell and emerging into our world as a beautiful, elusive butterfly.

"Those four stages of Butterfly teach us to be aware of the four seasons and the four stages of humanity. The first twenty years of our lives are spent in preparation. Over the next twenty years we become responsible for ourselves. The third twenty years teach us to become good adults. And the fourth twenty years teach us to become wise old people. Making the right transformation in every season of our lives prepares us to return to the spirit world." When Granbear had finished speaking, the butterfly gently flew away.

"Granbear, how did you learn all these things?"

"As a young warrior, I talked to everything. So I asked Butterfly and he told me there was a gentleness in trust. I have always liked observing things. I had to commit to all of my learning with humility and thankfulness. Everything in my life demanded that I learn from my feats and defeats," said Granbear, matter-of-factly. "Meeko! Don't move! Another lesson is waiting. Look slowly to your right, and you'll see a little chickadee."

Meeko turned his head, whispering, "What does that mean?"

"Grandson, Chickadee is the power of joy. This little bird is always happy, you can hear it in his songs. Long ago he wanted all the knowledge and flew to every camp and listened without ever uttering a word. This taught him to listen to others and never interrupt. The Chickadee knows everything. He's one of the smallest birds, yet he carries great power. That's why he never fails himself. His happy little voice invites everyone to come and dance with him in celebration of all life's changes. I honor the little feathers of Chickadee because he also teaches us the beauty of life, and reminds us that no matter how hard our life's experiences become, they are merely lessons for learning.

"I remember once my father gave me a chickadee feather, and said, 'Son, make plenty of friends, for they will become your human power.' Someday, Grandson, I want you to become as fierce as Hawk and have the strength of Eagle, yet always touch life as gently as Butterfly. Only then can you say that you have entered the veil of Chickadee's reality.

"As time goes by you will learn best in the silence of the Medicine Wheel. I want you to find the silent voice of your inner, untouched wilderness. It is that grand vision you must encounter to meet the most feared and dangerous beast in the world. That is yourself. When you can accept the beauty and the ugly that is hidden inside of you and challenges all that you are, then you can see your true self.

"Someday you will have to battle with two ravaging beasts, Greed and Destruction. Every life force lives with the unrest of these unscrupulous monsters. People with these demons do not understand that their dangerous thoughts and actions are destroying our planet. You must learn to fight and win the battle of ignorance so that *Maka-Akan*, Earth Spirit, can be brought back into balance. Someday you must make the people aware of the importance of Creator's bigger plans for *Maka Ina*, Earth Mother.

Alarmed, Meeko asked, "Granbear, do you think the world will be destroyed?"

"Maybe, Grandson, I pray for the day when everyone wakes up and sees the grave damage that is driving Mother Earth into helplessness. Come, we'll go sit with *Tunka'shila* and ask him to show you these many truths that I've explained." Granbear picked up his cane and headed toward the Medicine Wheel.

Granbear sat down quietly across from Meeko and took a deep breath. "Today you will join with my mind so you can see all the life forces of creation." Seeing the worried look that cut a deep crease across Meeko's brow, Granbear extended his hands cautiously and began to chant an old song. Slowly Meeko folded into many ecliptic dark pools with swirling shades of midnight blue. As he spun amidst the dark circles he heard Granbear's voice tell him, "Relax, Meeko. We're just creations from the paintbrushes of *Wakan Tanka*'s hand."

Then another voice spoke from afar. "Welcome, Child. You have arrived in the heart of *Wakan Tanka*'s blessings. Your happiness comes from the ever-flickering light of truth that radiates from your mother, the Earth. When you can accept this, you will be able to speak directly to the talking shadows of all life's reflections. Stop being afraid. Taste the black of darkness to learn the beauty in Good and Evil which is just a tool to teach you the power of your will. Build your strengths in love and goodness, and you will feed the lightning in your blood. This wisdom was fed to you from your people of long ago. Let me enter the stillness of your heart so we may bond in the space of all inner wisdom."

Suddenly Meeko was falling. As he spun out of control, he saw his people dancing through time, removing the boundaries of fear that held him in bondage. He felt courage and trust break free from his slumbering soul and heard the stars speak of the old knowledge while he walked as a spirit through a veil of mystic shadows.

"Let the past hold you in peace under this blanket of pure sacredness," whispered Granbear's voice.

Meeko felt strange as another void of blackness engulfed him. Again, he spun out of control, screaming helplessly until he joined in a dance of circling winds that whipped him into a spring day. He saw a leaf grow from the center of another spiral and was swept up with it. Suddenly, the leaf turned into a field of fallen leaves covering the ground like shining crystals. He reached for one and instantly a tree filled with golden leaves sprang forth. Astonished, Meeko watched the sacred cottonwood tree turn into crystal-like cathedrals emerging from Granbear's head.

"Use the secrets of breath that come before sunrise and you will visit many worlds," said Granbear as he touched Meeko's chest. Meeko felt his breath leave his body as he watched thousands of sun rays melt into streams of brightness flowing into Mother Earth's body. A feeling of joy pierced his heart and Meeko felt his soul open into dimensional time, space. He screamed until he heard Granbear's voice urging him toward a tunnel surrounded by shades of many dense colors.

As he entered the tunnel he melded with Granbear's mind and tracked the spirit of Eagle. He knew Eagle's touch and flew comfortably with him on webs of shimmering light energy that swirled through them. When they neared the center of everything, Meeko covered his eyes, fearing blindness from the brilliant light as they entered into the power of pure spirit love. Moving at light speed along shining filaments of pure energy, Meeko saw a group of strange looking people who were also working to return to the love of *Wakan Tanka*.

Spiraling outwardly upon these filaments, Meeko, Granbear, and Eagle rode the solar winds. While soaring, Meeko heard many birds speaking to the life-giving rains. Then many hills burst forth with blooming flowers as the flowing grass caressed the ground and the trees shouted in a glorious explosion of purified air. Suddenly he was surrounded by his long ago ancestors and heard an unfamiliar voice say, "Grandson, go back to the beginning of creation and know you will always be one with your people."

Meeko's body jolted forward, and he abruptly opened his eyes, knowing Granbear had shown him the power that lived in the sacred West Door of the Medicine Wheel.

Granbear let go of Meeko's hands and they left the Medicine Wheel in silence. While they quietly ate their evening meal, Meeko knew everything was the same, yet incredibly different. As darkness covered the sky, he walked Granbear home under the light of the night sun. "Tomorrow we will begin our journey to the North Door," Granbear smiled as Meeko helped him up the steps.

Meeko opened the door and turned on the light. "Granbear, can I sleep under the stars tonight? I want to think about what I saw in the West Door." Granbear smiled, nodding his head in approval.

Later that evening, Shadowhawk stepped from the bushes. "Grandson, I'm glad you're not asleep. I want to give you something that will help you understand the history of Eagle. Long before Europeans stepped on our shores, we had a strong relationship with Eagle. There is, and has always been a bond between the Red man and the Eagle nation. Since the beginning of creation, most every tribe has embraced a time-honored relationship with *Wanbli Gle'ska*.

"The founding fathers wanted Bear to represent their new country, but since Russia already claimed that symbol, they considered Eagle and sent out a select group of men to research this bird. When they found the eagle living in high fir trees and fishing along river banks, they all agreed Eagle was both powerful and beautiful. Eventually the white members of the Freemasons decided the bald eagle would be the best symbol to represent America. "In 1798 *Wanbli Pey'ska*, Bald Eagle, became the symbol of the American people. We knew *Wanbli Pey'ska* represented feminine power, and as a matriarch society we were proud this new nation honored women. Later, those same people came to believe that Bald Eagle's habit of eating rotten flesh was disgusting, but our people admired this trait because it kept our shorelines clean of decaying fish and helped nature stay in balance. In time they learned she was a courageous bird and a fierce warrior. That's when they decided to award those brave members of the armed forces with a symbol of Eagle power. Later, Boy Scouts earned the rank of Eagle Scout.

"A few years after my discharge from the service, I researched this further while visiting an old war buddy who loved golf. I found that he tried to get two strokes under par to gain his Eagle power. Then on a bet, I found out that a ten dollar gold piece was also called an eagle. Eagle is so connected to America's people, that I can't believe this sacred bird has become an endangered species. It makes me wonder whether we're on the same course as the eagle."

Shadowhawk shined his flashlight on a brand-new one dollar bill and handed it to Meeko, saying, "I carried a bill like this during World War II. Everyday Eagle reminded me that if I managed to survive this terrible war I had to stay in contact with Eagle power. I give this to you, not for spending, but so it will always remind you the Eagle flies in the hearts of every American. Every life force is born equal, and we have the responsibility to represent America proudly, no matter where we are in the world.

"The green side of the bill represents Mother Earth's nurturing ways and her ability to produce food for her children. It is of great concern that the elders who run the world allow constant abuse of Mother Earth. Just think of the destruction the white forefathers have caused to the nation of the Standing Ones. They forget how many trees must die to produce paper, and if this is allowed to continue, she will no longer have the ability to fill future generations with her beauty. Sometimes I also wonder about the power of this piece of paper. Many say it helps families live a good life, but I think it mostly fulfills selfish whims.

"Grandson, I fear for the future children of the world. Your generation will see the world's children go hungry, many starving to death because no one cares. It seems the world worships this external power called money. The few who hold it, feel no guilt about enslaving their brothers and sisters just to get more."

"Shadowhawk, what does this have to do with the Medicine Wheel?"

Taking the bill, Shadowhawk answered, "See, the dollar bill has four sides. This says to me it has a West, North, East, and South direction. If you look close at the writings you can see 'In God We Trust.' Did the forefathers expect this dollar bill to co-create in trust with *Wakan Tanka*? Did they ask him to smile on their endeavors as they gathered wealth? Is this not a prayer to remind us to keep a good relationship with *Wakan Tanka* since he is our partner in life?

"Examine the banner in the eagle's beak. It says 'E Pluribus Unum', that means 'one out of many' and has thirteen letters. This is good if we have an unselfish leader who works for the common good. But I fear our white leaders have forgotten we are under *Wakan Tanka*'s Law of One, and many people suffer from their greed and dishonest leadership.

"Now, look at the shield on the eagle's chest. Those thirteen stripes remind me of the first farmers, all the plants, and about protecting our wild plant medicines. There are thirteen tail feathers on the eagle, which means I can move myself away from any dangerous situation. In the eagle's left talon are thirteen arrows. That means a warrior fights to defend his country and home. This also reminds me to pray for those who have been wounded or killed in battle. In its right talon, there's an olive branch with thirteen leaves and thirteen berries. Granbear used the oil of this fruit in his medicine to help remove the scars from rat bites when you were a baby. Your Auntie Lizzie uses olive oil in her cooking to aid digestion. The branch means peace and spiritual harmony, and that's how a person should carry the pipe.

"If you look closer, you will see thirteen stars over the eagle's head. Historians say these stars represent the original thirteen states, but I say it stands for White Buffalo Calf Woman, who brought our sacred pipe and the herbs that give us our smoke knowledge. To be responsible to our medicine ways, we must stand in honor and integrity as a people, a country, and a world. We are all under the Law of One."

Turning the bill over, Shadowhawk commented, "See how this side is black and white? Look how Grandmother Spider's web holds it together. It reads 'Annuit Coeptis' and again has thirteen letters. They say it means 'God is smiling upon all our undertakings'. I agree that *Wakan Tanka* always smiles upon his children. But does he smile upon us when we kill and rob other countries in the name of power and money? Look under the pyramid that says 'Novus Ordo Seclorum' which means 'the new cycle of ages'. I agree we should all follow the sky maps to know when to do our sacred ceremonies during the year's seasons. The pyramid has seventy two stones that are placed in thirteen rows. They say the sacred *Wakinyan*, the thunderbird, rises from its ashes. We also know that a pyramid unfolds into a Medicine Wheel. The eye on top reminds us that to have a vision we must look from behind our eyelids.

"I understand the power in numbers. But while studying mathematics in school, I didn't know why the numbers made me feel controlled and useless. When I was visiting some Mayan brothers, I learned that mathematics is the sacred language of *Wakan Tanka* and these mathematical designs help us understand sacred sky knowledge. So, why are there so many thirteens? I want you to think about how we demonstrate the sacred mathematics through our paintings and prayers. We have always depended upon Eagle to carry our prayers up to *Wakan Tanka*. The old people teach us that drumming, dancing and singing are like magnets pulling us back to *Wakan Tanka*'s blanket.

"And now, my little fledging, I know that someday you will see this bigger picture as *Wanbli Pey'ska*, Bald Eagle. Pray from your heart, and let *Wakan Tanka* use you to fulfill his purpose while you're living on Mother Earth. Listen to Granbear, and learn in silence like the eaglet who sits in its nest quietly until it learns to fly. Use discipline to find the stillness within your heart. Like Eagle, never waste your time and energy on things you cannot change. Think as Eagle, and search deeply for the hidden mysteries about yourself. Change your attitude so you can work better with Medicine. Next time you have a problem, dive-bomb it like Eagle and kill the bad thoughts that are trying to destroy your soul. Grandson, soar with Eagle tonight and fly among the stars."

Meeko watched Shadowhawk disappear into darkness. Then he carefully folded the dollar bill and placed it in his wallet. Stretching out on the ground, he stared at the stars, envisioning himself as one with Eagle as he flew through the invisible passages of his mind. His thoughts melted with the vastness of space and followed the pathway that reached to the sky. When he crossed the Milky Way, he felt at peace and drifted off to sleep. Embraced in the arms of *Hanwi*, the Night Sun, he traveled with her on her nightly journey across the sky, knowing that today he was merely an eaglet waiting in his nest to be fed, but someday he would answer Eagle's call."

Meeko awakened to see Granbear sitting in the North on the outside of the Medicine Wheel. He jumped up excitedly then ran to the river for a quick morning bath. On his way to the Medicine Wheel, he teased some of the girls by shaking his long wet hair.

They screamed, "You dirty, wet dog!" as they wrapped themselves in their blankets to escape the ice-cold water droplets. Meeko laughed, then saw an old grandmother removing a batch of fry bread from an iron skillet. Mischievously, he grabbed one and stuffed it into his mouth. The old woman raised her fist and scolded him teasingly as he dashed onward to the Medicine Wheel.

Granbear, who was in an enthusiastic mood, said, "Today, I'm going to introduce you to our relatives of the North. We will start this journey by visiting Bear, Buffalo, Wolf, and his little helper, Coyote. These gatekeepers will help you find another way to guide your life. Handing Meeko a thick grizzly bear robe, he added, "But first Grandson, since you've been sleeping outside so much lately, you'll need this to keep you warm.

Knowing this robe had been his grandfather's for as long as he could remember, Meeko wondered how he could be worthy of such a prized possession. He held it close to his heart as he murmured a gentle word of appreciation. He then sat down next to Granbear, hoping to conquer his fear of the responsibilities demanded of anyone who carried the powers of *Mato*, Bear.

"Grandson, Bear is curious and affectionate, and sometimes acts like a clown, much like humans. Bear power teaches through discipline, and demands that we set strong boundaries.

"It was Bear who taught me how to build a strong body, mind, emotions, and spirit. *Mato* taught me to eat good foods and gather the right herbs to heal illnesses. Like Bear, I am strong, I have a powerful mind, and my heart is steady. That's how my spirit soars with the above powers," said Granbear, swelling his chest and flexing his muscles. Without warning he let out a loud bear growl, grabbed Meeko, and pinned him to the ground. Meeko wriggled and cried out for Granbear to let him go. When he was finally released, his expression was one of hostility.

Granbear took a stoic approach to his grandson's reaction as he watched him trying to cope with his frustrations. "Grandson, I've lived a long, healthy life by knowing Bear's teachings. You've got to watch Ole Bear, Grandson, he's a tricky sort, just like me when I pinned you to the ground. It's a good thing you tried to set a boundary for yourself with me, but it has no meaning since you don't respect another's boundaries. Maybe I should give you some of my bear blood. Otherwise, you're going to stay as helpless as an untrained cub."

Meeko wondered if his great-grandfather had bear blood in his veins since he was as strong and healthy as a man half his age, and could go without sleep or food for long periods of time.

"Grandson, compared to animals, humans are powerless. It is Bear that gives us true ownership of ourselves. He says that we should mind our own business and expect others to do the same. When you learn to carry Bear power, you will fear nothing, including yourself. The more you watch Bear's actions, the more you'll accept this happy, playful soul." As the lesson ended, Meeko went for a long walk to reflect on this unusual morning.

Weeks passed and Meeko began to isolate himself, sleeping under the stars every night. One morning, Granbear grabbed him by the foot, yelling, "Get out from under that robe before you smell like an Ole Bear. Today I'm getting rid of that grumpy attitude you've had. You and Crazy Bear have too much in common. So, little crazy cub, today there will be no food or water until after sundown.

"Grandson, bears are half-human and allow us to share *Maka Ina* with them. They teach us to honor the lessons given through the life we choose, and they are our very good teachers. We have to understand the emotion in each painful lesson and never allow that kind of hurt again. That's when we learn to honor all that we experience. I've learned much from my emotional pain. Without it I would not be who I am today.

"Bear is a masculine power that connects us to our manhood and can help us get down to business when necessary. It is the custom for an uncle to give his nephews their boy training, but I have asked Shadowhawk to take charge of yours."

"Why Shadowhawk? I want you to teach me, Grandfather."

"It is your dislike of authority which makes you reject Shadowhawk. You are learning the traditional way. Sometimes this needs a Dog Soldier, like Shadowhawk, to help a student have proper respect toward our teachings. And besides, he too is my student and has lots of experience with Bear power." Meeko sulked in silence, angry that Shadowhawk would have anything to say about his training.

"I was about your age when my father decided it was time for me to become a man and spoke to his brother about this. Being a good son, I wanted to please my father and was grateful to my older brothers for their earlier training. I already knew it was important to be a responsible member of the Bear Clan family.

"To this day I honor Uncle for sharing the old ways with me. Because of his training, I am a good man and the humble leader of the Bear Clan. He believed it was best to learn from experience, so I learned by hunting, fishing and living off the land. It is because of that training that I learned to understand the lesson of providing for and protecting the Bear Clan.

"I remember one scary hunting trip with Uncle. It was a very cold winter morning, and we had walked far to reach bear country. I took pride in following his orders, but on that day I showed my ignorance by ignoring his words. I was walking ahead of him so wrapped up in the beauty of nature, that I wandered off into territory claimed by grizzlies.

"Uncle yelled a warning, but it was too late. A bear bolted and chased us both up a tree. At first, Uncle scolded me for my stupidity, but as the day wore on and the bear waited at the foot of the tree, Uncle entertained himself by making wisecracks about my fears of that bear. It seemed like forever before that bear grew bored enough to leave. When he was finally long out of sight, Uncle decided it was safe for us to climb down. I hesitated, still too afraid to leave that tree, while Uncle laughed at me then climbed down the tree and headed for home, leaving me alone.

"As the sun began to set, I knew I was in trouble. Oh, Grandson, I was freezing cold and hungry. That is what made me climb down from that tree and run like a scared deer all the way home! I could hardly breathe, and when I finally entered the tipi everyone began laughing. My father chuckled, 'Son, don't you know it's black bears that climb trees, not grizzlies?' It took a long time to live that one down. After that experience, I didn't care what color the bear was, if I saw one I ran, just in case it was in a bad mood." Laughing with Granbear over his hunting story, Meeko soon forgot about Shadowhawk.

They left the Medicine Wheel and during lunch Meeko continued to pester Granbear to tell another story until at last the old man pushed his plate away in frustration. "Grandson, one must learn to appreciate each gift a medicine person gives them. Why, even a bear demands that kind of respect," said Granbear returning to the Medicine Wheel. Granbear made it a point to take his time until he was seated comfortably on his blanket. "It was Bear who taught us the proper foods to eat and how to use the herbs to heal ourselves. My Uncle was stern and demanded discipline from me as I learned to honor the ways of a warrior. This is what made me a strong Bear Clan member. Someday it will be your responsibility to pass this knowledge down to the next gencration.

"Grandson, you must learn your place and stop asking questions. I'll share my stories when I'm ready. This Ole Bear is tired of your self-importance, and you'll get nothing more from me until you can give me your full attention. My peace of mind is far more important than trying to teach an idle brain, Grandchild! That's all I have to say!" With these words, Granbear left the Medicine Wheel and joined his friends in the arbor.

Shocked, Meeko sat in the Medicine Wheel not knowing what to do. He hadn't meant to be disrespectful, but Granbear didn't understand the best way to teach him. After several hours of sitting alone, Meeko was more willing than ever to listen to one of Granbear's lectures.

Finally one of his friends came by to tell him to clean up for supper. Meeko hurried to the arbor, glad he would be allowed to eat with the others. At dinner, to regain his great-grandfather's favor he sat next to him, and waited for Granbear to take the first bite, signaling all to begin eating.

Again Meeko spoke. "Granbear, I love your story telling, but Bear doesn't make sense to me. I can't see why I have to learn the weaknesses and strengths of Bear when it has nothing to do with me."

Shadowhawk, hearing this remark, glared sternly at Meeko and thundered, "You ignorant fool! Who are you to tell Medicine what you should and should not learn? Get away before I remove you from this table!"

Silence filled the arbor, but Granbear continued to eat as if nothing had happened. When he saw that Granbear would not support him, Meeko felt betrayed. Humiliated and fearing repercussions from Shadowhawk, he left the table in disgrace and headed for the river. While kicking every stone on his path, he wondered what he had done that was so terrible to cause Shadowhawk to embarrass him in front of everyone.

Meeko's disgraceful behavior had humiliated and embarrassed the Bear Clan. Not being able to eat a peaceful meal, they went to Shadowhawk to demand that Meeko change his behavior in the presence of the head of Bear Clan. Granbear smiled with satisfaction, glad that his grandson was being held accountable for his disrespect.

At the end of the meal, a married couple approached Granbear and spoke to him of their troubles. He spent the rest of the evening discussing what they should change, and the couple left smiling. Granbear sighed as he reflected on his mistakes during his own marriages. Overly tired, he struggled to his feet. Shadowhawk quickly appeared, as if from nowhere, and walked his medicine teacher back to the house.

Meeko went to bed angry at how the people had turned on him. He hated Shadowhawk for interfering in his relationship with his great-grandfather. Still restless two hours later, he dressed quietly, then slipped out of the house and headed to the Medicine Wheel, hoping to feel less betrayed. That night he prayed hard to *Wakan Tanka* for guidance.

When Granbear arrived at the Medicine Wheel for his usual sunrise prayer, he was surprised to find Meeko. After his prayers, he sat in the Medicine Wheel enjoying the beauty of the morning. Clearing his throat, he said, "Meeko, everyone must experience the bad and good things in life. These experiences are our best tools for learning. I'm willing to share my experiences with you so you will not have to suffer as much as I did to become wise.

"Our ancestors were always connected to life. They grew in spirit by walking with the strength of Bear. To follow Bear's ways, you must become conscious of boundaries and be a fearless survivor. As a people, we have many secret societies named after Bear. You were born into Bear Clan, and I think it would be wise to practice Bear's habits.

"*Mato* never bluffs, and makes us walk with honor and courage. The old hermit allows no creature to cross his boundaries. Why, only a fool would get into his space. If you do, that mean old cuss will get his dander up, and fight to the death, destroying everything in his path to get you. His temper is much like Shadowhawk's was last night. Bear speaks his own language through grunts and body movements. If you're ever in danger of overstepping Bear's boundaries, remember he will warn you by giving a cough or a low growl.

"But don't ever think that *Mato* can't play, too. He can be boisterous and frisky, but in the blink of an eye, he can become fierce. Sometimes an apology offered with a little honey can sweeten a bear's bad temper. *Mato* walks through life tearing up and discarding things. You must learn to recognize the dangerous side of his medicine. If you listen to my words and work hard to get a kinship with Bear, maybe he'll touch you in a good way.

"Grandson, I have spent my life learning about this sacred brother. You must trust in this medicine man if you expect to learn the truth of Bear medicine. And as for Crazy Bear, well he's just crazy. You show his traits by wanting your way all the time. One minute if someone goes against your wishes you're angry, and the next minute you're willing to do anything to keep peace. You just can't react badly because of another's opinion. This is something you do because you have no strong belief in yourself. You need to learn that acting for the good of *all* lets you control your emotions and make wise choices."

Observing Meeko's lack of interest, Granbear shouted fiercely, "Grandson, you carry so many silent opinions, that they are getting loud enough to hurt my ears. You'd better learn to listen! Don't ever think you can outsmart this Ole Bear, or I'll walk on your mind and rip the flesh right from your bones!"

At the thought of another mauling from Granbear, Meeko reflected on the proper response to this ultimatum. It seemed that since he had been learning about Bear, his great-grandfather was continually switching from threats to kindness, keeping him very confused. Maybe he should take a greater interest in Bear to comprehend what was happening.

"Granbear, why do you call bear our two-legged brother?"

"Grandson, *Mato* often walks in an upright position using his entire foot. When you are no longer a fearful human, you will understand this affectionate, adaptable old soul is a true brother." Then Granbear's face softened as he said, "When you were a little boy, I enjoyed taking you into the high mountains in winter. Those trips awakened your instincts, forcing you to learn how to survive under hard conditions. Seeing you so willing to accept life's challenges and changes, I knew you could face life's cruel lessons with courage. Go back to that time, Meeko, and remember that was Bear power."

"Granbear, if I become a bear person, will that keep Renna out of my life?"

"No, but when you learn to think of her with love rather than hate, you will know how to accept who she is and keep your own boundaries."

Nearly an hour passed without another word from Granbear while he let Meeko ponder this thought. Meeko knew that Granbear was right, but had no idea how to conquer his violent behavior. He wanted to correct his actions, but shame and fear kept him bound in a prison of self rejection.

Finally, Granbear smiled knowingly as he continued to deliberately step across his grandson's boundaries. "Look how you refuse to share your thoughts with me. Why are you afraid to share yourself? I hope your disinterest in people doesn't isolate you from the rest of the world. Where is your trust?

"Since birth you have shown the dual traits of Bear. Sometimes you have his courage and stamina, but you also have his laziness and you tend to dawdle. As a child you responded to gentleness, but lately you've been acting like Crazy Bear.

"I've seen you flirting with the girls. One day I even saw a girl bring you homemade cookies, and you acted just like an Ole Bear that had found a tree with honey. You better control your Crazy Bear nature before one of those girls gets jealous and turns into Crazy Bear and teaches you a lesson about rage." Meeko never had realized that Granbear knew about this and turned red in embarrassment.

"Grandson, I have eyes that see beyond your thoughts. If you can get the same hunger for learning as you have for cookies, I'll be happy. Sometimes I think you are both blessed and cursed with some of *Mato*'s ways. Besides the women, look how you love to curl up by a good fire at night to do your lazy daydreaming. Remember, I'm teaching you about Bear, not Coyote, the Trickster."

Eager to change the subject, Meeko interjected, "Granbear, I'm trying hard to learn. I want to serve *Wakan Tanka*. Until I can do it from my heart, I know you won't let me sing, dance, or share in Bear's sacred medicines. But I really want to know the songs, dances and how to drum."

Granbear took a deep breath. "Grandson, those things are all part of my teachings. The most important ceremony is your life journey. Bear, like Eagle, also demands we become keen observers, which gives us the ability to act quickly in any situation. Don't you understand, even teaching is a sacred ceremony. You're going to listen with your heart not your head, and you will trust this Ole Bear before I will continue."

"But I do trust you, Granbear."

"I hope you do," countered Granbear, in an exasperated tone. "And I pray that you start using what I tell you so I won't have to turn into Crazy Bear. I want you to eat my words until the ways of Bear become second nature to you. I promise that before I'm through you will act in mind and body as Bear."

Afraid of upsetting Granbear, Meeko vowed, "I promise to work harder, but your lessons aren't always so easy to understand."

"Then just give me your attention without your opinions, Grandson. I'm concerned about your lack of respect for Medicine. If you keep going the way you are, you will never understand our ways."

"Granbear, I know you're right, but I can't see how an animal can direct my life."

In exasperation, Granbear answered, "Maybe if you would stop fighting and apply yourself to what you see, we would not be talking about your behavior!"

"Granbear, I try not to get angry and fight, but it's the others who cause the problem not me," argued Meeko.

"Meeko, Meeko. A fight starts in your thoughts before it comes through your fists. Stop fighting what's outside and fight your inner battles. You can't expect everyone to make you the center of their world. People are sick and tired of your temper tantrums. I will not talk with you anymore until you get out of your own way! Now, go away from me you bad person!" stated Granbear with cutting coldness as he got up and left the Medicine Wheel.

For the next two weeks, Meeko saw little of Granbear or Shadowhawk, and was happy to have the control of his time. He slept late each day and spent afternoons either girl watching or roaming around the reservation with his friends. But as time passed, he missed Granbear's teachings. One day he found Granbear in the arbor and went to plead with him. "I know I was wrong. I promise I will show the proper respect and won't interrupt you again. Please let me come back to learn the Medicine Wheel." He then offered Granbear tobacco and sage.

Granbear took the gifts, knowing the time had come to resume their studies. He motioned Meeko to follow him to the Medicine Wheel. "Grandson, you are Bear Clan Sioux! It's time you start honoring your ancestors by acting right! We Sioux want our children to become courageous warriors. That is the Bear way! Like Bear, we gather and store information for future generations. We eat bear meat to get his power, and honor him in all of our ceremonies. Some tribes believe that if they eat bear meat they would get sick and die."

Then Granbear acknowledged, "Meeko, I know how you enjoy my stories, so if you promise to listen closely, I will tell you some of my favorite ones." Meeko listened intently as his great-grandfather began another fascinating tale.

"Long ago, there was this strong Bear Clan brother who was a powerful bear hunter. Everyone admired but feared Bear Man, and most believed his blood had been replaced by Bear's blood. Each time he brought a dressed-out bear into camp everyone would speak excitedly about his great bravery. Because I wanted to be like him, I started following him around camp, but always at a distance.

"Months passed, then one day he spoke to me about Bear power and said that a good bear hunter was very rare. For about two years I learned from his teachings. Then he gave me a perfect double-edged knife with a handle made from a large bear jaw, telling me to always carry this killing blade when I went alone into the woods. He told me that if I was ever attacked by a bear I must show no fear and respond to this sacred brother as an honorable warrior. I should move in close and stab him in the belly and chest until he fell to the ground. His words filled me with excitement and fear. Believe me, that Dog Soldier taught me that Bear will fight to the death, no matter whether it's his opponent's or his own. After hearing this, I was always cautious when I went into bear territory and was thankful that Bear never challenged me to a battle of life and death.

"One day I thought I was following Bear Man, but before I knew it, he had doubled back and silently walked up behind me. Placing his hand on my shoulder, he offered to tell me the secret of killing a bear. 'You must pray, then ask brother bear for his life, promising to always honor his ways. You must be very careful when you kill him. If you take his life correctly, he will not return and take away your spirit. The moment Bear is dying, you must be brave enough to kneel down and take his last breath. You must be very careful, or he may fool you and take your breath instead. If this happens and Bear kills you, you will lose your soul'. He also told me that when the breath ceremony was finished, I should skin the bear out and wrap myself in its hide to become Bear medicine. I was also told to cut off its soft paws and ask it to teach me how to dig for the sacred medicine roots. I was then to return to camp, taking all of its body parts to use in my honoring ceremonies.

"Ah, Grandson, once a person kills a bear, he becomes a Bear Warrior and a great healer. Bear medicine lets him know the secrets of the sacred herbs and the skills of bone setting. After earning these rights, he can make the claws into a special necklace to show everyone he is Bear.

"That great warrior taught me so much about the sacredness of Bear medicine. Anytime he killed, he did it right so he could fill himself up with the spirit of Bear. I remember him walking through the camp wearing his many bear symbols; the women lusted after him, the children followed him with excitement, and the men made sure he was their friend."

For once Meeko had listened intently to Granbear's every word. The old medicine man's eyes twinkled as he walked away, leaving his grandson eager for more.

Early the following morning Meeko was waiting to join Granbear in his prayer ceremony. As the sun peeked over the horizon, Granbear put away his pipe and went back to the arbor to visit with his friends. Disappointed, Meeko entered the Medicine Wheel alone to reflect on what he had already learned about Bear.

It was late afternoon before Granbear returned and found Meeko still sitting in prayer. Pleased Granbear said, "Grandson, I left you this morning because Bear is a wanderer. Did you know Bear taught us the lessons of following the seasons by moving around? We learned when it was time to leave the land so it could heal itself from our stay. When the season was right, we'd always return to find Mother Earth once again full of life, ready to take care of her children.

"The great grizzly is called 'Old Man of the Claw,' and is also known as the 'Son of Chiefs.' As the Gatekeeper of the North, his job is to protect our ceremonies, rituals and medicines. Ah yes, the Son of Chiefs shows his power by his unpredictable ways. He is a strong, spiritual animal and one of the finest shape-shifters on Mother Earth, but he refuses to speak to anyone who doesn't follow his ways of life. Once Bear knows that you have made strong boundaries against all your intruders, including your own bad thoughts, he will teach you. You must know who you are before he will come to you, and if you try to trick him, it will be you who will suffer the consequences.

"Today I'm going to tell you how my uncle introduced me to a female bear."

Meeko was thrilled at the prospect of hearing another true story.

"It was a cold winter day when Uncle and I were out on a hunting trip. We had enough supplies to last for two weeks if we lived off the land. We had spent two hard days traveling into a whipping head wind, when suddenly the clouds dropped to the ground and we couldn't see our hands in front of our faces. A moment later, Old Cold Maker covered the land with a blanket of snow. Uncle said that we were in grave danger and could go no further until the storm had stopped. He quickly built a lean-to while I looked for dry wood to start a small fire. There we sat, huddled together for warmth, waiting for Father Sky to clear.

"Uncle said, 'Nephew, don't worry. We can't argue with nature. If this storm keeps up, it will drive all the bears into their dens to begin their winter sleep. And this is good.' He went on to say that their wise mothers taught them to be good survivors.

"As winter went on, we traveled deeper into the mountains looking for bear signs. When we finally got to their territory, we set up camp and scouted for empty dens. Uncle spotted a bear in the distance and said we better get downwind and hide. I saw it stand upright and stretch one big paw into the wind, then sniff it. Uncle said in a loud whisper, 'She's checking to see if anyone has crossed her boundaries. I think she's going to have babies this year.'

"Uncle felt I needed to learn more about women and that this she-bear would be my best teacher. He said that this bear could teach me how to relate to the spirit world and that I should begin my visionary work with her. Every day for weeks we visited that spot, so I could learn her ways. We even found her den, and Uncle was glad to see the cave was empty except for dried leaves and pine boughs.

"Before leaving the mountains, we ran into another blinding blizzard and set up camp to wait it out. As we sat by the fire talking, Uncle told me that since there would be plenty of snow to cover the bear's tracks, she would probably head for her den soon. Within a week, Uncle said it was time to visit her again. When we got to the cave, she was curled up, drifting into her winter sleep and waiting to give birth.

"On one of our visits, Uncle told me that female bears have great wisdom when it comes to their children. He explained that female bears can control their body functions. He also told me that during hibernation they stop eating and eliminating waste, but their bodies continue to build bones and lean muscle. Their body temperature lowers, and the sugar and fat levels in their blood are the same as a person with the sugar sickness, diabetes. That's when bears are most vulnerable.

"Bear uses its mind to control its every need. I was amazed when I learned that a female is able to control her pregnancies. Uncle explained to me that a she-bear will not bring a new life into this world unless she is in good health and there is plenty of food for her cubs in the coming spring. If not, she will stop the pregnancy and give birth at another time. Human females could learn much about being good women and mothers if they would follow the ways of Bear.

"One night sitting around our fire, Uncle told me that it was the male bear who chooses the cave for the family, but when the cubs are born, Mama Bear chases him away, so he won't eat her babies. You see, Meeko, bear cubs and human cubs are not able to survive without their mothers. Both must be taught these skills if they are to carry on their race.

"Now, Mama Bear knows what it takes to become a good bear and she is very strict with her cubs for about two years. The difference in a human mama and a bear mama is that when Bear speaks, her children listen! If a cub does not heed her every command, she will instantly swing a mean paw and correct the situation. She takes great care to see that her cubs live and become strong old bears.

"I became very excited about visiting the bear to see if she had cubs. One day when we went to her den, Uncle noticed the snow was melting away from her body and whispered, 'She will wake up soon. Just to be safe, let's move to another spot.' We climbed high above the cave until we reached a place where Uncle had carved a small hole in the stone right over her bed. He motioned for me to look inside, where I saw the she-bear and her two cubs. I was surprised to see the cubs were almost hairless and shaped like blobs. Then Uncle told me bears are blind at birth, and that the mother licks and molds them with her big paws until she shapes them into proper-looking bear cubs. Through the peephole, I watched this shaping and heard Mama Bear grunt as she worked. Uncle described her grunting sounds as a secret bear chant.

"Why, Meeko, even male bears fear she will go on the warpath and kill them if they dare come too close during that time. That evening Uncle warned me never to go near the cave entrance again unless he was with me because Mama Bears are very dangerous after giving birth.

"About two weeks after I first saw the cubs, Uncle told me we must hurry to the bear cave because he had dreamed Mama Bear would take her cubs into second birthing. You see, a bear is born from the darkness of Mama Bear's womb into the darkness of Mother Earth's belly. When the cubs reach a certain age, Mama Bear takes them out of the cave to enter first light on Mother Earth and that is called second birthing.

"That day we rushed to the top of the cave, then Mama Bear stepped out, and moved quickly away from the cave entrance with her cubs staying close as shadows. I heard her growl as one wandered from her side. When she slapped it with a thunderous paw, the cub screamed as it went tumbling ass over tin cup. Boy, was I thankful I wasn't one of her cubs. From then on, those cubs mimicked her every move.

"Uncle decided to hang around for a few more weeks so I could watch Mama Bear teaching the new cubs. One day we saw her leave the cave without them, and after rubbing ourselves with dark, rich soil to give off an earthy smell, we scooted down to the entrance and looked inside. I had to hold back my laughter as we watched the cubs gnaw on the branches and twigs of their bed, playing with their feet and practicing their bear growls. Then, knowing Mama Bear would soon return, we went back to camp.

"Oh, Grandson, what pleasant memories I have of that beautiful spring and summer with Uncle and that bear family. I soon learned Mama Bear didn't fool around when teaching. Work was work, and play was play. Each cub had definite duties to perform, and when one was defiant or lazy, she would knock it head over heels to get its attention. When this happened, the cub would run back to her, begging forgiveness. It took only a few of these harsh slaps for it to learn to stay close to her side. But I also knew her heart was warm toward her cubs. Bear teaches us to learn quickly and listen to what's being said, so we can make good decisions.

"One sunny day I watched Mama Bear teach her cubs how to fish. Using their claws as fish hooks, they swept their forepaws through the water, quick as lightning. They also caught fish in their mouths and chomped them right down. Uncle explained that once they grew up, fishing would be about the only time they would tolerate each other. When those bear cubs were fishing, they taught me what real patience was. I pray for the day that you will get enough patience to catch what you want in life," Granbear chuckled.

"By fall the cubs were roaming around alone. Uncle told me it was time to stop our visits because they were learning to check out each scent in their thirty-five mile territory. But despite his warning, one day I went close to my favorite cub and saw him stretch his paw into the wind and bring it back to his nose. He caught my scent and charged in my direction. Knowing his eyesight was poor, I ran downwind to get away. Uncle chuckled over my stupidity, saying, 'I see you've learned to respect the boundaries of Bear.'

"I had bonded with this family of bears, and as the next winter came, I surely missed them. One day in early December while close to their territory, I spotted my favorite cub playing with an old water-soaked log down by the river. He kept throwing it in the air, and when he didn't catch it, he got so angry that he would try to stomp it to pieces.

"As I grew older, I began to track Bear, looking for the highest and deepest claw marks on the trees to tell its size. Once I traveled beyond the timberline to follow a bear. That's when I learned about Bear's great endurance and need for space and solitude. Grandson, you must learn to respect everyone's privacy if you expect to become one with Bear.

"Meeko, at first I too wanted to please my father and become a Dog Soldier like my older brothers. But Uncle saw me as Medicine and told me I was going to be a different kind of warrior. In time, he trusted me to go into the mountains to study Bear. Every year after that, I tracked Bear alone.

"My brothers, knowing that I was not a warrior, would always tease me about my fear of smacking a bear. Then one day I was given the perfect chance to prove them wrong. A bear was up a tree, stealing honey from the bees. I sneaked up on him and smacked him hard on the butt, then ran as fast as a scared deer all the way home. Believe me, Grandson, that was not an act of bravery, that was an act of stupidity! When I told Uncle what I had done, he grinned, saying, 'Well, I bet your brothers won't tease you again about being afraid of bears.' Meeko, I believe courage is born from a coward dying a thousand deaths. As a child, I knew I would never become a bear killer. Besides, there were more than enough warriors in our camp wearing strings of bear claws and bear teeth around their necks.

"Once I had made up my mind to become Medicine, I went to Bear Man and told him that I wanted to learn how to track the Spirit of Bear. He said I was already a very brave Spirit Bear hunter and to prove it, he gave me my first bear necklace. Since bear claws are used as digging tools for gathering roots and herbs, he told me to wear them when I hunted plant medicines. He said if I would honor Bear in this way, he would always show me to the right plant medicines, and someday I would become a good healer. That wise old warrior taught me plenty about gathering courage to hunt Spirit Bear. And that was the sacred knowledge I needed to have to become Spirit Bear medicine."

Meeko's eyes were filled with awe and respect. "Grandson, since your birth I have studied you as my uncle studied me. I know you have courage and you are learning how to build strength and endurance. It makes me happy when I see you act as a good bear cub. I want you to walk as Bear, think as Bear, and be ready to change as quickly as Bear.

"Meeko, there are times when you act like Crazy Bear. I see you teasing the girls, and it makes me wonder if you aren't mixing your blood with Coyote power. Everyone around here knows that you can be controlled by your stomach. But don't worry, Grandson, before I'm through with you, you'll be as proud as I am to be an Ole Bear. Look at me. I look like Bear, I think like Bear, and sometimes I even smell like Bear! Why, I wouldn't have these handsome, long thick braids if it weren't for bear grease."

Granbear became serious. "I think it's time we talk about your appearance. Your hair is a mess! If you don't want to take care of it, why don't we cut it off like a white boy's?" With this, Granbear pulled out his bear knife. Shocked, Meeko quickly spit in his hands and smoothed his hair back with his fingers, tying it with a strip of deer hide he had pulled from his pocket.

"People who carry bear power are well aware of their good looks, so keep it that way. I advise you to be careful when flirting with girls for only a plate of cookies. Try to become their friend. That way, you will learn how a woman feels and thinks. I learned the hard way about being with a jealous Crazy Bear woman. You will find that female humans, like female bears, love the gentle and sweet things in life. Sometimes a man must suffer a few bee stings to get to that sweetness in a woman, but it's worth the pain," remarked Granbear, recalling some of the hard times he had with the women in his life.

"Granbear, can Bear medicine protect me from marrying a Crazy Bear woman?"

Amused, Granbear laughed. "It'll be hard, Grandson." Meeko blushed at his answer and together they walked to supper.

Meeko was feeling good about the day until he heard that some of Granbear's old friends had come to visit. For the next three days, he could feel his jealousy returning and would go to the Medicine Wheel to wait for Granbear to come. Knowing he must rid himself of these bad feelings, he reflected on Granbear's teachings, trying to connect with Bear. He began to mimic Bear's growls and movements and soon he believed he was thinking like Bear. On the fourth day at sunrise, Meeko was happy to see Granbear coming to join him.

"Meeko, sometimes we must experience a near-death situation before we can understand the power of Great Spirit. I've known many great medicine people who could eat the poisonous bear root plant without harm, to bring on a trance-like state. These past few days, it made me proud to see you practicing the traits of Bear. If you keep working, you will build a strong relationship with Bear and will not need to use this root to talk to him. Bear has chosen you to be a Bear Dreamer if you keep up your hard work."

Pleased, Meeko said, "Granbear, strange things have been happening to me. Bear has been walking on my mind. I'm seeing many things, but when I wake up I don't remember most of them. Bear is telling me about animals, stones, trees, and the white man's thinking. One white man told me he was moving the water. I don't understand. Where do they move the water?"

"Behind a large wall they call a dam. It holds all the water where they want it to be, until they send it where they think it should be. The white man thinks *Wakan Tanka* made a bad plan and put everything in the wrong place."

Meeko was amazed at the white man's arrogance and questioned Granbear further. "What about Mother Earth?"

Impressed with the depth of Meeko's question, Granbear answered, "Grandson, by the time you reach manhood, the waters and the air will be polluted. New dams will have been built that will change the courses of the rivers, shifting nature's natural flow. Future generations will see many court battles over these uncaring ways. For some animals it will be too late, but like the bears they may be lucky enough to survive."

"Granbear, do you think I could become strong enough to change things for *Maka Ina* and all her children?"

"Grandson, when you have enough insight you will understand how to correct these bad things. There are many battles you will fight for the good of all life if you are to serve *Wakan Tanka*'s wishes. And for this you'll need a good education so you can change the laws and help all of Creator's children. These same questions came to me when I was a young man learning about Bear. I also worried that the changes the white man was making would affect all life on Mother Earth." Feeling he had given Meeko enough information for the moment, Granbear left the Medicine Wheel. Glancing over his shoulder and seeing his grandson deep in thought, he knew his words were having a profound impact.

It was late afternoon the following day when Granbear called Meeko to join him in the Medicine Wheel. "Grandson, you must know how to act as quickly as Bear in spirit, mind, and body. Bear's ways must become second nature to you if you are to ever claim him as your spiritual protector. Someday you will paint your body with bear signs and adorn it with bearskins and a bear claw necklace. And when you are older you will become a strong Bear Sundancer. I have seen you in that sacred circle dancing with courage and carrying a strong pipe with a bear symbol carved deeply into its bowl. When that day comes, you will dance like Bear and know all his power songs.

"For now I want you to learn to walk in life as a brave bear." Removing his bear hunter's knife from his belt, Granbear held it out to Meeko, saying, "After my death, this knife will be yours to remind you that you are a member of the Bear Clan people. Use it wisely, Grandson."

Meeko carefully pulled the double-edged blade from its sheath and looked at the intricate markings carved into the bear jaw handle marveling at any warrior who, with only this weapon, would venture that close to a bear. Shivering at the thought, Meeko slid the knife back in its casing and returned it to Granbear.

That night while lying under the stars at the Medicine Wheel, Meeko knew that Bear would help him prepare for his future. He had finally accepted that Granbear had always walked in his mind so that he could accept the sacredness of becoming a Bear Clan member. He remembered Shadowhawk telling him that some tribes believed the first shamanistic powers came from Bear. He knew that Bear Dreamers carried a certain power that allowed them to live between worlds like shadowed ghosts, and wondered if he would someday have the ability to embrace that kind of solitude. Bear's teachings, he was sure, would serve him well if he learned to use their powers.

Suddenly Meeko remembered Granbear speaking in the *Inipi* about *Tob Tob*, Four times Four, the power that governs all things. He knew he would have to remember to always call *Tob Tob* in a sacred manner if he wished only the good spirits to help him. Granbear had also called on *Hu Nunpa*, Spirit Bear, who could be addressed only in the sacred language of the Shaman. Meeko then thought about the old people's ability to speak directly to all the spirits and wondered if he would someday become a holy man who could speak with those sacred beings.

A little later Granbear joined Meeko to continue his lesson, saying as he pointed to the sky, "That's the Big Dipper. If you look to the side of it, you will see Bear's tail and a bit of his backside. You see, he lives in the sky as well as on Mother Earth. It is Bear who protects our ceremonies and makes sure we do them correctly.

"Long ago our people followed the old sky maps, which told them when to perform the sacred ceremonies. That's how we know in mid-summer that it's time to follow the sun as it moves into Bear Lodge, and prepare to go to Devil's Tower to Sundance.

Satisfied that someday his great-grandson would follow in his footsteps as a good Bear Clan member, Granbear ended the day's lesson saying, "Tomorrow we'll get acquainted with our brother Buffalo. Now it's time to rest and get some sleep."

A soft morning breeze blew gently across Granbear and Meeko as they crawled from their bedrolls and sat listening to the chirping birds while watching the sun rise. Granbear placed a buffalo skull in front of the North Door and smiled as he watched Meeko's excitement over his forthcoming journey with another four legged brother. He sat beside Meeko and began the day's lesson.

"Grandson, it is our sacred brother *Tatanka*, Buffalo, that we honor this morning. The old ones always told us that as long as the horns remain on a buffalo skull, the spirit of Buffalo will be there to help the people. The people and Buffalo are one and share in the gifts given from Mother Earth and Father Sky for our survival. Not only did the buffalo herd feed, house and clothe us, but their bones were used as knives, shovels, and other tools. It is Buffalo who taught us the true meaning of 'Giveaway.'

"Grandson, we were as much a part of Buffalo as the trees are of the landscape, or the streams are of the water, or the birds are of the air. When we were a free people, we were carefree and loving. We followed great Buffalo who taught us that life was a cycle of learning and giving. We understood this cycle and honored our relationship with all of Great Spirit's creations."

Meeko could almost see himself straddling a paint, riding as free as the wind across the open plains. Granbear, seeing his great-grandson's eyes and knowing he was reliving those long ago days through his stories, continued. "After the foreigners came to this land, the buffalo and the Indian began to slowly fade away. The old people had predicted that when the buffalo disappeared from Mother Earth, so would the Indian. And indeed with the loss of the buffalo, we became a different people, for without him, our way of life could no longer be. White society has no regard for natural living things, which is why the buffalo and the people have lost their value.

"While the white man was busy slaughtering the buffalo through train windows, it was not only the Indian who was losing but also the new white nation. Since those days, the white man has been forced to live with his shameful lack of honor which will be written for all time in the pages of history. Today, the buffalo and the Indian people suffer because we no longer have the Great Plains to roam. We both live on reservations with a white name and a government number, but we both know that someday we will again roam freely across our land.

"I predict that in the future the white man's offspring will understand what their forefathers did to the Indian and will follow our way of life. Surely the young minds of the Indian will never forget the old teachings. Tomorrow's young will bring back the ways of Buffalo and come together giving proof that *Wakan Tanka*'s way is a pure gift of love for all his children."

Meeko nodded in confirmation and said, "*Hau*, Grandfather." For the first time, Granbear felt comfortable that his great-grandson could envision the old Indian world.

"The animals of the North Door teach us hard lessons, but such brutal experiences are what build our strongest beliefs. The Moon of the Strong Cold, the month of January, reminds us to muster the courage to follow our way of life. The spirit helpers from the North teach us to never forget who we are. The constantly swirling winds tell us to correct our mistakes. When we don't listen to them, life becomes cruel, forcing us to open our eyes and find a better way to live."

With the winds rustling the leaves in nearby trees, Meeko wondered about this message.

Granbear lit his happy pipe then continued. "When I was a child, we followed the buffalo herds. Sometimes they were so large that they covered the Great Plains as far as the eye could see. Our people shared everything for the good of the tribe. We lived a nomadic lifestyle and we walked within the sacredness of Mother Earth. We knew that everything was spirit, not just flesh, to fill our needs. We knew how to see and listen to all life from the heart, keeping everything in balance. And we never forgot to take care of Mother Earth's children in a proper manner.

"I remember some tribes used the buffalo jump to kill herds of buffalo. They would drive the poorly-sighted buffalo over high ledges, forcing them to fall on pointed staves that pinned them to the ground, causing them a lingering death. I never accepted this way of killing, it seemed wasteful and disrespectful of *Wakan Tanka*'s four-legged children. It made the buffalo a victim, and caused the same thing to happen to the Indian. We Bear Clan people believe hunting is a tribal effort and a sacred act. It is our duty to take only what is needed and never cause unnecessary pain.

"In the fall we would burn off the dead grass so the rich new grass would provide plenty of food for the buffalo in the coming spring. I remember the excitement as the people prepared for their return. You could hear them coming from miles away. I recall some of my best eating was during Buffalo hunts. When my father took down a Buffalo, my mother would grab me and rush over to skin the dead animal. I would sit near the head, and many times I saw another world in the buffalo's beautiful big eyes.

"It was my sweet mother who taught me to look into Buffalo's eyes to touch its sacredness. She would feed me raw pieces of buffalo heart and tongue, and laughing, say in her gentle manner, 'Child, you have enough buffalo tongue in you to last two lifetimes. When you grow up you will surely become a good talker. I just hope you will speak with Buffalo wisdom.'"

Granbear's eyes glistened with tears of happiness at the fond memories of his childhood as he continued. "We were a loving family. I remember how my grandfather bragged about me as a young brave. Sometimes he even said that I would someday have the skills of a brilliant Dog Soldier and would become a kind and good provider who always protected the Bear Clan people.

"I loved my grandfather in a very special way and wanted to offer him something very special at the giveaway after the next Sun Dance. I spent weeks thinking of a worthy gift for him. Remembering how much he prized the tail of Buffalo, I asked my father to help me make his gift. He smiled, nodding in his patient and loving way. Then one day after a buffalo hunt my father took me aside and showed me how to properly remove the buffalo's tail and make it soft. Then my grandmother helped me decorate it with bones, beads and pieces of hides. It was beautiful, and I was proud to be giving such a gift to my grandfather.

"When the day came, I waited in line with the others until it was my turn to present a gift. As I offered my grandfather the decorated buffalo tail, he smiled with great pride and proceeded to show everyone this special gift from his youngest grandson.

"After that, whenever he was sitting with his friends I would sneak close, hoping to hear him say good things about me. Pretending he did not see me, he would pick up his buffalo tail and flick it back and forth, saying loudly, 'My friends, I have a good grandson who has the heart of *Tatanka*. He made this fine gift for me to keep away the pesky flies. Someday he will speak strongly with the tongue of Buffalo and become a brave warrior like his father and a great leader among our people.' Now, go to the house and get my buffalo tail, Meeko."

Returning, Meeko handed the tail to Granbear and asked, "You're not going to swat me with that, are you?"

"Who knows, Grandson? You might think about keeping yourself out of situations where I would have to swat you," laughed Granbear. "Ah, Grandson, back in those days life was simple. When the seasons changed so did the lifestyle of the Bear Clan. When the first snow fell, the Bear Clan tribe knew it was time to travel to our winter camp. I once packed the sled too high with buffalo hides and wasn't watching the dogs close enough, when the sled tipped over, spilling everything on the ground. It took me and my mother over an hour to reload it and catch up with the people. My father gave me a very stern look and I never did that again."

"Granbear, why do you collect so much buffalo stuff?"

Flicking the old buffalo tail across his body, Granbear explained, "You could find everything you needed on the buffalo. Why we even used the buffalo chips to make very hot fires. The buffalo was kinda like a commodity store is today. My father knew how to make glue from its hoofs to repair broken things in our home. Did you know that the buffalo has sewing thread hidden in its body?" Then Granbear told the story of how this thread was discovered. "Long ago, a very thrifty and hardworking woman was skinning her husband's kill and found a peculiar mass in the hump. She laid it out in the sun, and once it dried she found that some pieces were good for sewing clothing, while others were strong enough for a bow, or for lacing tipis together.

"Women today could sure use some of this old sewing knowledge. I remember a very embarrassing thing that happened after Auntie Lizzie had used the white man's weak thread to sew up my pants. I was speaking to some important people in Washington, when I knocked over a glass of water and it fell to the floor. I quickly bent over to pick it up, and my ass fell out of my pants. It is because of that experience that I won't wear clothes patched with the white man's thread."

Meeko broke out in uncontrollable laughter at the thought of Granbear showing the great white fathers in Washington his bare ass. Without missing a beat, Granbear joined in the fun as they ended the day's lesson.

After a late breakfast the next morning, Granbear and Meeko went to the Medicine Wheel to continue their study of *Tatanka*. "Long ago the people and *Tatanka* were as one, bonded in spirit. They understood that every thing must be given respect, and shared equally in the responsibility of the sacred gift called life.

"It was Buffalo who showed us how to face the harsh lessons of life, and taught us to stand strong and face the bitter cold north winds. Meeko, always stand as Buffalo and face life's cruelties. Keep good thoughts and know that Creator will give you the power to withstand all your battles. A good enemy holds great value. They teach us to stay alert and to act wisely, while a dumb enemy is dangerous, because you never know what they'll do."

At that moment, Meeko knew he had to learn to be as strong as Buffalo and face his enemies, even if the enemy was himself. He then reflected on his coldness toward the harsh lessons Renna had taught him. A shiver raced up his spine as he realized that someday he would have to become kind and giving, yet stand strong and face her as an enemy.

Realizing the impact of his words on his great-grandson, Granbear hesitated for a moment before going on. "Meeko, there was a time when the *Pte Oyate*, the Buffalo People, spoke directly to the two legs, four legs, creepy crawlies, flying ones, and all of the great spirit helpers. These people told us about huge herds of buffalo that lived under the great waters. Many heard their thundering hoofs when they stampeded under the lakes. It was a rumbling that lasted for many moons until suddenly they started coming up from the underworld. The earth shook for days as these herds grew so big that they covered the land. Many of the sacred beasts roamed freely among our camps. From that miracle, the people saw the importance of this gift and felt a humble appreciation for sacred *Tatanka*. Many societies and ceremonies were created in honor of Buffalo.

"Ah yes, Buffalo is good medicine. He teaches us to remember to be kind and giving to others, expecting nothing in return. It's Buffalo that opens the Sun Dance. It's Buffalo who gives the true meaning behind our giveaway ceremonies which honor the never-ending gifts from Great Spirit. And it's Buffalo that brings life to our rituals and ceremonies. The old people always said that when you have a personal problem, you are to go to Buffalo and give it up in prayer. Otherwise, it will keep you from stepping onto the good Red Road.

"I was about your age when I first accepted the power of Buffalo. My father told me if I went to the buffalo wallows on a moonlit night, I would see *Tatanka* dancing across the prairies. For many moons I searched but never saw one. Finally my father told me to look for the sunflowers growing in the wallows where the buffalo had come to roll. I did as he told me, and had been waiting in prayer long into the night, when I finally saw my first spirit brother, *Tatanka*. I watched him roll from side to side, cleaning his shining fur. Then, just before the red that shines at dawn, I saw many sunflowers blooming from seeds that had fallen from his coat.

"I rushed home and told my father about this experience. He smiled, saying, 'Son, it takes time, patience and wisdom to know the hidden teachings of Buffalo. When you truly honor this grass eater, you will always do the right thing. It is good to know that someday my son will become a Sundancer.' I've never forgotten his words, and in the future you too will walk the hard road to the Sundance trail. When you're out walking the land, watch for those wild sunflowers. Who knows? Maybe Buffalo will come to visit you in Shadow World. Someday our brother Buffalo's spirit will rise again and walk around on Mother Earth, the real tipi of Creator."

"Granbear, I wish the buffalo still lived with us," said Meeko longingly.

"Grandson, Buffalo does live with us today. Think how its skull is connected to all our ceremonies, proving that there is an ongoing kinship between Buffalo and Indian. They say if you smoke with Buffalo, he will become your relative and feed your spiritual survival."

Meeko felt a grave sadness over the vanishing of the old ways and said, "Granbear, I wish that I lived in those times."

"Grandson, a great honor was given to those who happily shared Mother Earth with the Buffalo nation. You and I are sharing those times through these teachings. Through your memories of them you will someday grow wise. When you know the history of our people, you will understand the purpose of both Buffalo and Indian."

"Granbear, why did the white man want to destroy the buffalo?"

"The government wanted our land and knew that if they destroyed the buffalo there would be no Indian. They even used the old buffalo trails to build their railroads that brought the white man across our land in the safety of wooden boxes. They called the slaughtering of the buffalo a sport and they came by the thousands to take part in the game. I remember the decaying stench that filled the air as herds of skinned buffalo lay rotting in the hot sun.

"The white man's evil plan was to kill off the buffalo and destroy the Indian. Many of our people died from starvation while others stood by helplessly watching our way of life disappear. The white man then drove the rest of the downtrodden hungry people onto reservations. The plot was to blend the survivors into their society through mixed marriages, destroying our race through interbreeding. Ah, yes! The white man's plan was simple...Isolation, Degradation, Integration, Annihilation.

"Those were pitiful days. But despite all of this, our elders made sure Buffalo would never be forgotten by retelling the stories of his greatness. They spoke of the day the herds would return and take care of the people. Everyone knows that when Buffalo returns, the Indians will rise up beside him and take back their land to roam again as a free people.

"As I told you earlier, this was not just a loss to the Indian, but to the future of the white race as well. The slaughter of the buffalo and the Indian will live on as an embarrassment to the white man's descendants, and someday their system will fall as their white children begin to think like Indian people." With a tear in his eye, Granbear silently got up and left the Medicine Wheel. Meeko followed at a respectful distance, knowing the heart of Buffalo had been in Granbear's words.

The following morning Meeko awakened to the sound of the rain beating on the roof. After breakfast he and Granbear were on the porch swing enjoying the sounds of the wind and rain when Granbear spoke. "*Tatanka* lives as a reminder that *Wakan Tanka*'s great love is given freely to all his earth children. *Wakan Tanka* has instructed Father Sky to feed Mother Earth with his blessing of life-giving waters. Think how the rain reaches deep into the ground to nourish Mother Earth, allowing her body to once again become covered with all the green things. Only when you give from the heart can you truly say you understand the power of Buffalo." Granbear lit his happy pipe, silently reminiscing about how the people had shared so freely in the ceremonial taking of Buffalo.

While Meeko's mind and heart were open and receptive, Granbear took this opportunity to tell another story that contained a lesson beneficial to his great-grandson. "When I was a young boy I went on many buffalo hunts. We hunted the big males, the old, the tired, and the weak. We never killed the females or the young ones. In this manner the herds were kept strong and free from disease. I never ceased to be amazed at how these giving creatures seemed to know when it was their time to die and graciously stepped forward to give their life so the people could live.

"Taking this gift carried a great responsibility. A hunter needed excellent skills to take down such an animal. The kill had to be accurate, quick, painless and performed in a sacred manner. The tribe members who were lazy and thoughtless were considered cruel and disrespectful of the sacredness of life and were not allowed to join in the hunt.

"Your great-great-great-grandfather carried Buffalo power and was a strong leader of the Bear Clan. He always spoke highly of my father's bravery and bragged to everyone that my father was a good provider and protector of the family. The Bear Clan was large in those days, blessed with fertility from the bull buffalo.

"Meeko, you are good with your hands. Maybe if you learn to make some of our ceremonial things it will help you create beauty in your life. When I was growing up, I learned to make many beautiful things to help my mind grow. I remember helping my father make my first pair of moccasins. Following a big buffalo hunt, he asked me to help him skin the hind legs. After we had finished brain-tanning the hides, he shaped them into a pair of long, soft moccasins and taught me how to sew them.

"Approving of the stitches, my mother took her polished bones and dyed porcupine quills and taught me how to decorate my moccasins. She then took the tips of two bull buffalo tails and sewed one onto the back of each moccasin. I tried them on and found they fit me perfectly. My mother smiled, saying, 'Son, when you wear those moccasins, know you are walking with the wisdom of Buffalo.'

"And my father said, 'Son, wear those moccasins as an honorable and proud man.'" Granbear sat for a moment reliving this childhood memory. Then from under the blanket on his lap, he removed a beautiful pair of beaded moccasins, saying, "Shadowhawk made these for you. When you wear them, remember to walk proudly as Buffalo in all that you do."

Filled with shame over his many mean thoughts about Shadowhawk, Meeko declined the gift, saying, "Granbear, I have not liked Shadowhawk for a long time. I want the moccasins, but I'm not worthy of his gift."

Granbear smiled knowingly. "Grandson, Shadowhawk loves you. He is Buffalo and this proves it. Now see if they fit."

Meeko slipped his feet into the moccasins and walked around, grinning from ear to ear. "Granbear, they're just right!"

Granbear smiled in return. "Grandson, those moccasins look fine on your feet. Come, let's find Shadowhawk so you can thank him for this kindness." Meeko strutted proudly to the arbor, showing everyone his new moccasins. When he saw Shadowhawk, he apologized for his disrespectful thoughts and ignorant ways.

Shadowhawk nodded and calmly answered. "Wear them well, Grandson. Come, we'll walk to the river so we can speak in private." While silently approaching the water, Shadowhawk pointed to a tree that hung over the riverbank and motioned Meeko to sit down. Lighting a cigarette, he began, "Grandson, I know you have many problems. Renna created much heartache in you. Many times I have tried to help my daughter, but she was not willing to help herself. Now you have an opportunity to heal these old wounds by following Granbear's teachings and taking advantage of his short time left on Mother Earth. He is the walking history of our old ways.

"If you want to truly know Buffalo, look closely at Granbear, the most loving human you will ever know. I remember when I first came to him to learn the old ways. He told me there were two kinds of Buffalo, the good one and the crazy one. I knew about the giving heart of Buffalo, but Granbear pointed out that everything can be taken to extremes. He said if I sacrificed too much, I could destroy my life because I had ignored my own needs. It was Granbear who taught me never to depend on another to fulfill my own life. That's when I knew I could no longer help your mother, because she would have caused my downfall.

"One of my favorite Buffalo stories is about how Buffalo is connected to Magpie. This bird is a cousin to Crow and demands we think intelligently before speaking. Magpies are curious scavengers and thieves, but they use everything they steal. Sometimes they are called the 'dirty bird' because they keep their nests so filthy that they must lay their eggs in another's nest. The old people say magpies are lazy irresponsible parents.

"Magpie has both good and bad magic, and you never know which gift he is going to give you," said Shadowhawk, handing Meeko two magpie feathers. Not wanting them, Meeko hesitated, but Shadowhawk pushed them his way, forcing him to take them. Then smiling mischievously, Shadowhawk added, "I can't tell you which feather will bring you good or bad luck." Meeko was confused and fearful about what to do with these gifted feathers.

Shadowhawk noticed his dilemma, and said. "If you lie and deceive, you are using the wrong feather, and it will bring Crazy Bear or Crazy Buffalo power to you. However, if you have good thoughts for others, then all the parasites of the world will stay away from you. Grandson, you have never known trouble until you use the wrong magpie feather.

"Once I thought of myself as a fierce warrior and felt kindness was a weakness. I had no idea it would become my strength until Granbear told me the story of how Buffalo and Magpie got together in the beginning of first creation. Like you, Magpie was a lazy, but a very smart bird, who was always looking for a deal. He flew throughout the world until one day he came upon a buffalo herd. Knowing Buffalo could not see well, Magpie said, 'Oh, Great Buffalo, I think we can serve each other well. I know it is hard for you to raise your heavy head up to watch for danger while you are trying to eat. Why not let me sit on your back and feed on the insects that get caught in your furry coat? If you allow me do this, then I give you my word I will act as your eyes and warn you whenever danger is approaching.' Well, Buffalo thought Magpie had a good idea and agreed. From that day forward, Magpie is always found near Buffalo.

"Over eons of time this arrangement was comfortable for everyone until the herd traveled far into the North Country where *Wazi*, the Old Man from the North, resided. One day while Magpie was sitting in *Wazi*'s house and feeling too lazy to fly outside, he took a shit right there. *Wazi* was very angry with this disrespect and placed a curse upon all magpies, saying, 'From this day forward you will always keep a dirty nest and the world will know you as the dirty bird.' So let this be a lesson, Meeko. Never shit in your own house." Shadowhawk chuckled and walked Meeko back to the arbor.

At the arbor, Shadowhawk told Granbear with a wink, "I took our grandson to the river to tell him about the deal between Buffalo and Magpie, and I gave him two magpie feathers to remind him never to become Crazy Buffalo."

"I see," laughed Granbear. "That's a good teaching story." Granbear then told Meeko to go sit alone and think about his new magpie feathers.

Late that evening Granbear unrolled his bearhide next to his great-grandson, saying he was going to sleep there under the stars with him. Since the wind was chilly, he asked Meeko to build a fire. Thrilled that Granbear would be with him for the night, Meeko built a happy fire, then remarked, "I sure wish we had some Buffalo chips around here."

"I don't think you're going to find any around these days, Grandson. But don't worry, someday our brother Buffalo will rise again and fill the plains with them."

As both lay quietly staring up at the heavens, Meeko whispered, "Granbear, can you tell me what to do with these magpie feathers? I sure don't need any more bad luck!"

"I can't talk about your feathers, Grandson. They are yours and they will teach you what you need to know," answered Granbear.

"Granbear, are the people from the North as cold as their weather?"

"They can be, since the North teaches us hard lessons. I use the Night Sun. It reminds me to keep my beliefs strong during long cold winters. But don't worry, Grandson. Old *Wazi* loves directing us toward tasks that help us build strong convictions. He waits for you to make mistakes so he can teach you another hard lesson. Meeko, it doesn't matter how you learn, as long as you open your eyes to get the view of what life is all about."

Lying down and gazing overhead, Granbear thought about the changes taking place in his great-grandson, then whispered, "Meeko, see that circle with a dark spot at the center in the starry sky? That's the Milky Way." Pointing in another direction, he added, "See Buffalo? It too lives in the sky. Always look to the sky and you can see what *Wakan Tanka* is telling his children to do. Tomorrow we'll speak of Wolf and his little helper, Coyote." With that, Granbear rolled over to get some sleep leaving Meeko with many things to ponder.

The next morning before sunrise, Meeko awakened Granbear to listen to the howls of what he thought was a coyote pack in the distance. Granbear smiled at his great-grandson's curiosity and, cupping his hands to his mouth, lifted his head toward the sky to answer the mournful cry of *Sunká Manitu*,Wolf. Meeko, feeling a wildness as he listened to them conversing, asked, "Granbear, teach me how to talk with coyotes."

"Grandson, that's not *Mica*. I was talking to *Sunká Manitu*. But before we speak about Wolf, please go and bring my breakfast."

After eating, Meeko and Granbear sat in the North Door. "Grandson, I want you to think about how you were fooled earlier. When you listen to a howl, remember that Coyote sings a little off-key and his voice seems to come from many places at the same time, but Wolf's voice is very clear and has a harmony. Both teach inner strength, but there's a difference in the way each teaches you."

"I'm trying, Granbear. I really thought that was a coyote."

"So, Grandson, tell me what you know about these two animals."

"I know they both run in packs and start their days with prayers to *Wakan Tanka*. I also know they greet their brothers and sisters with nips and whimpers."

"Yes, but they each teach from a different point of view, and it's important to learn the difference."

Just then a pickup truck sped into the yard and stopped abruptly. Flying Feather's nephew had come to inform Granbear that his old medicine friend was very ill and needed him to come quickly. Granbear hurriedly gathered his medicine things and told Meeko to stay with Shadowhawk until his return.

Knowing that he must be on his best behavior, Meeko went directly to Shadowhawk and was assigned to morning chores. But within two days he became bored, and returned to his campsite near the Medicine Wheel to think about the difference between Coyote and Wolf. Each night thereafter he listened carefully to their howls amidst the surrounding night sounds, and every morning he awakened with a deeper appreciation for these two animals' teachings. His dreams were becoming more vivid, and he was beginning to realize the powers in the Medicine Wheel were heightening his awareness of his own life.

After two weeks Granbear wearily returned and reported on Flying Feather's condition. "My old friend is feeling better, but he has heard his death song and is preparing to begin his journey back to the spirit world."

There was a sadness among the people at the thought of yet another elder leaving this world. Concerned for Old Grampa Flying Feather, they made an offering to

Shadowhawk for a healing sweat. When he went to Granbear for approval of the people's request, the medicine man smiled appreciatively. Accepting the role of Fire Chief, Shadowhawk built the fire for the stones while the others gathered all the sage needed. Everything in the *Inipi* was ready as the last rays of *Wi* sank below the horizon.

During the sweat, many prayers were said for Flying Feather, and as the flap went down on the last round, Granbear was overwhelmed with gratitude that so many spirits had come to visit on his friend's behalf. There was a peacefulness among the people as they offered Granbear many heartfelt wishes for the well-being of his medicine friend before heading toward the arbor for supper.

Late in the evening Granbear told Meeko to get his bedroll. "I'll join you shortly at the Medicine Wheel." Thrilled that he would have his great-grandfather to himself, Meeko quickly took Granbear's bedding to their campsite, where he built a fire and waited. When Granbear arrived, he lay quietly curled up as the night descended. Only when the echoing cries of Wolf broke the silence did Granbear speak. "Meeko, while I was gone did you discover the difference between Wolf and Coyote?"

"No, Granbear. I did spend the nights listening to them, but I couldn't reach the spirit world through them."

"It takes time to understand their ways. My friend Flying Feather uses Wolf power. When he does his healings, he calls Wolf to enter his body and fight the evil spirits that are making the person ill."

Meeko interrupted. "Granbear, teach me to howl like Wolf."

"Grandson, you're still not hearing my words."

"But I thought you were going to teach me to howl like Wolf and Coyote as soon as you got back?"

"Silence! Stop fearing death!" commanded Granbear. Suddenly a melodic, mournful cry pierced the air, prompting Granbear to answer first as Wolf, then as Coyote. Hearing Meeko's pitiful attempt to mimic him, Granbear laughed at his futile efforts. "Not yet, Grandson. I want you to go far out of earshot to practice the language of these two animals. Even though both communicate with their voices, Wolf speaks more strongly and uses body movements, like his head, tail, and expressive eyes to reveal his thoughts. This beautiful animal shows best how a thought can be transferred to every member of its pack and is immediately acted upon by all.

"Sometimes when wolves are far from their families, they howl in a certain way to tell the others that they miss them. Grandson, it's not wise to enter the territory of these animals until you understand their ways. I promise you Wolf will demand great patience. They are capable of watching you while you're not even aware that they're there. Wolf thinks. Wolf plans. Wolf makes decisions and acts on them! Wolf also has honor and warns intruders with a low, threatening growl. Ignorance of these two animals can mean your death."

"I thought wolves and coyotes ran together," said Meeko, still not understanding the difference between the two.

"Grandson, Wolf and Coyote have traveling blood, and will go great distances from home just to see what is there. Coyote is Wolf's helper, not his companion. Crafty Coyote lives a shameless life and openly shows his deceit in cunning ways. It's his nature to fall victim to his own tricks, and he never seems to learn from his mistakes despite the many painful and funny experiences. Coyote is sly, gullible and indestructible. He can get bruised, burned, smashed, drowned and almost killed, but he still comes back none the wiser from his misfortunes.

"Can you see the humor in this clever one's teachings? He goes through life as a trickster, and gains endurance while suffering from his own follies. Why, I've seen this scavenger become so confused by his shenanigans that he ends up the prey of his own hunt. You must be careful when this shortsighted clown touches your life. Since he's up to no good you'd better get ready for turmoil and pain. Coyote thrives on mischief and thievery, and will only fight when the stakes are in his favor. Coyote will fake being hurt, just to lure his prey into the pack.

"As a young boy I enjoyed following Coyote. It was Coyote who gave me my sense of humor, teaching me never to take myself too seriously. He's called the trickster because he can escape most anyone and shape-shift himself into anything. He could even be that stone sitting over there by the fire listening to us."

"Granbear, is coyote just dumb? Why would anyone want to make the same mistakes over and over again if it keeps hurting them?"

"Coyote isn't dumb. He's brilliant, but a twisted critter disguised to trick the world. He lives on deception but never thinks of himself as a troublemaker. He goes through life blaming others for his problems, but most times it's his own actions that bring those bad consequences. Sometimes it makes me wonder why he can't see how smart he is and use that power to help others, instead of for destruction. Meeko, when you find yourself in a bad situation, know Ole Coyote's walking on your mind," cautioned Granbear.

"Do you think I have Coyote power?"

"Absolutely! Look at your life. Coyote teaches us the duality of life. He's a survivor and can adapt to any situation. Because of his many magical powers, the old people consider him the Sacred Medicine Dog. One minute he acts superior to others then the next minute he's very humble. This way he keeps you confused and before you know it, he's outwitted you. I think it will be a toss-up between Coyote and the cockroach to see who will be the last survivor on Mother Earth. Just remember, when you hear Coyote's voice riding on the winds, get ready for trouble, because that crazy joker is loose and running wild again," said Granbear as he crawled into his bedroll.

The next morning Granbear insisted that Meeko join him in the Medicine Wheel earlier than usual. When they arrived, Meeko went directly to sit in the North Door with head bowed, and Granbear began the day's lesson. "Grandson, soon you will be studying with Shadowhawk, who will take you on trips into the deep wilderness. I'm going to prepare you for those trips, so listen closely. Coyote uses his mind, not brute force. But if you ever see a hurt or trapped coyote, don't go near, because it will tear the flesh from your bones. And always look around with great caution, because these animals tend to hunt in pairs.

"Coyote has a good hunting relationship with many of the flying ones and some four legs. Coyote eats rabbits, ground squirrels, rodents, quail and the remains of others' kills. Once, I saw him working a kill with a badger, a no-nonsense animal that fears nothing and is very confident. The two stood very still for a long time, staring at each other. Suddenly, as if they had reached some kind of agreement, they turned and traveled in opposite directions, then turned again and cautiously moved back toward each other, flushing a bevy of quail and a rabbit from the bushes. Well, Grandson, that Badger grabbed that rabbit, and one unlucky quail became Ole Coyote's meal."

Meeko's eyes widened in amazement at the descriptions of Coyote's survival instincts, and he wondered if he had some Coyote blood in him as a result of his life with Renna. As if reading his thoughts, Granbear said, "Grandson, you have traveled great distances from home and have learned how to survive in the streets. This makes me wonder sometimes if you're not related to Coyote."

"Granbear, I had the same thought. Do you think my living with Renna has something to do with who I am?"

"If you've accepted some of her bad thinking, you might have future heartaches with Coyote. I do agree that you have gotten Coyote's attention," said Granbear, emphasizing his point by making soft yipping sounds near his great-grandson's ear. "This is how Coyote tells you he is finished talking." Then without another word, Granbear got up and headed for the arbor to welcome Flying Feather, who had just arrived.

Meeko, angered by the disruption of the lesson, sat alone for a few minutes, then walked to the river to soothe his frustration. Returning to the arbor, he felt totally rejected as he watched Granbear and Flying Feather conversing happily without inviting him to join them.

Soon afterward, Meeko drove to town with Shadowhawk to get the mail and some vanilla ice cream for Granbear and Flying Feather. Late that afternoon, Flying Feather's nephew picked him up and the medicine men said their goodbyes, then Granbear excused himself to rest until morning. Feeling abandoned, Meeko went to the campsite and lay thinking about his life with Renna, wondering if he had walked too long with the powers of trickster Coyote to be able to change. As he fell asleep, he heard coyote's howling and thought he might be one of the pack. The following morning, Meeko was up before sunrise, eager to tell Granbear about his dreams of Coyote.

After breakfast, Granbear motioned him to the Medicine Wheel, where he sat quietly in the North Door to learn. "Meeko, a wolf is an agile beauty and has a strong sense of order within the pack. He also roams freely over the unspoiled wilderness remembering what his ancestors taught him. Due to his early rigid survival training, he can run about forty miles an hour and can cover around fifty miles a day. In olden times our warriors learned endurance from Wolf, who taught them how to balance their strong bodies and run in silence. As I told you, Eagle is the sky teacher and now know

Wolf is the earth teacher. This graceful soul demands we are physically, mentally, emotionally, and spiritually strong so that we can complete our life journey.

"When a pup is born, it is nurtured and protected by all members of the Wolf Clan while it builds great stamina in puppy horseplay. Wolf teachings build strong, independent leaders. As Wolf they give freely of themselves and go far beyond their own needs in order to do what is best for their family.

"The Hidatsa tribe believes that Wolf offers power in the secrets of breath. They say anyone who carries the power of a wolf bundle practices breath control rituals to complete very long journeys. Grandson, someday the breath of Wolf will teach you these secrets for becoming a strong man. The Hidatsa also say that if Wolf disappears from the earth, we humans will no longer know the way to use the powers of Mother Earth or find our place in life.

"I once heard an old Blackfoot say they too follow the Wolf Road to wisdom. The old ones say anyone who kills a lone wolf will bring bad medicine and they will lose everything. Why even a mountain in Glacier Park was named Wolf Rising to honor the sacredness of Wolf.

"It's necessary to know the ways of a wolf family before you can understand the spirit of this animal. For their survival, wolves must have family loyalty and cooperation. The pack starts each day with a gentle howling prayer to *Wakan Tanka*; then they greet one another by nipping and whining affectionately to re-establish the importance of family unity and rank.

"There is one way that you can spot the wolf that rules the pack. Look for the tail that is raised the highest, that is the leader. That wolf must be very courageous and is always the first to step forward to protect the family. The leader can be male or female and it makes the decisions of where and how the pack lives and hunts. It has the responsibility for the pack and faces the danger first when the pack is threatened. When challenged, Wolf gives off a low, deep growl. Then to prove its point, Wolf grabs any challenger by going for its throat. Wolf says, 'I could kill you, but this is just a warning. Leave the pack or next time, you will die.' Ah, Grandson, that is why the pack shows great respect to their leader."

"Granbear, would they really kill one of their own?"

"Like Wolf, our people once banned tribal members who didn't act for the good of the whole. The tribe would line up at the exit of the campsite and cover their heads with blankets of shame as the Dog Soldiers drove that person away to live alone.

"A lone wolf cries out in a low-spirited voice in late winter, telling all that he's looking for a young lady wolf. If she answers his call, the two will continue this communication while traveling toward each other until they finally meet. But mating is never done hastily. If she accepts the male, they will hunt and play together during their courtship, and when the time is right they mate for life then begin their family.

"Grandson, every tribe has its own beliefs about Wolf. The Cherokee never kill wolves because it would ruin their weapons. If they were forced to kill one, they would take their rifles to a medicine person and have them spiritually cleansed, otherwise the gun could never shoot right again. They believed that if they killed a wolf, a dark cloud would drop over them and eat their soul along with the souls of their future generations, and that the waters would sour and they could never taste the sweetness of pure water again. I think it's interesting that they solved the problem by hiring white men to kill the wolves for them."

"Now, the Cheyenne say they know for a fact that if the sun rises on a sleeping wolf, it will die before the sun goes down. That's why wolves get up before dawn and only feel safe to take a nap in the afternoon. Meeko, if you look at the Milky Way, you can see the tail of the Dog Star, Sirius. That's called the Wolf Road. The Pawnee say the Red Star of Death is in that southeastern sky and on a clear dark night you can see wolves coming and going on the road from the earth to the sky world. Remember, I told you that Wolf helped take care of the dreamers in the creation of Second World. They say Wolf is still roaming between worlds. Still others are sure if you kill a lone wolf, you will run in fear for the rest of your life, never finding your place in any world.

"When you know all of wolf's habits, you will be able to see the humans that have wolf souls. Southwestern tribes believe some of their people can practice Skin Running and can shape-shift into a wolf by using certain rituals. I've heard of many mysterious deaths in that part of the country. Ah, Meeko, Skin Runners are very bad medicine."

"Granbear, can people really change their shape and kill as a wolf?"

"That's what they say, Grandson. That's what they say. I've always had a great interest in wolf power, but never for bad medicine.

"I remember one day when I was about fourteen years old and came to know a family of wolves that I visited for many years. They taught me how to follow a wolf trail. Ah, Meeko, when you learn how to read a wolf's paw print, you will know every member of that pack. The prints tell you if they are hunting, moving, or just playing around. If I found blood, mud and grass left in some of their prints, I could tell if the pack was dragging home a kill or if one was injured," said Granbear, as he drew an adult wolf print in the dirt.

"Granbear, that paw print looks the size of a man's hand!"

"That's true, Grandson, and don't you think its shape looks like a tipi? Did you know wolves have very intense, penetrating eyes and they are set facing forward like a human's? When they're hunting they use their eyes to search out their victim and lock onto its mind before they begin dancing the death ceremony. There is nothing more beautiful or frightening than to watch a wolf pack work a kill to its death. If you watch closely, you can see when their prey accepts death.

"They circle their victim and take turns biting its ankles or hindquarters, to wear it down. Wolf's jaws can crack the leg of a buffalo. If they have young pups, they drive their prey close to the den before they make their kill. Sometimes if they are too far from the pack and have to take it down, they will swallow the food and take it home, where they heave it up to feed the pups.

"Meeko, I want to tell you a good story about Wolf, Raccoon and Red Bird. One hot, sunny day, Raccoon was bored and decided to aggravate Wolf. Wolf was tired and wanted to sleep, but that harebrained Raccoon wouldn't leave him alone. Wolf got so angry that he chased Raccoon up a tree near a river. Being upset, Wolf sat at the base of that tree for hours until he was so thirsty, he gave up on Raccoon and went to the river for a drink. Then feeling better, he decided to take a nap next to the river.

"Raccoon seeing that he was safe, came down from the tree thinking, 'I'll fix that old wolf.' He filled his little hands with mud and cautiously sneaked up to Wolf, carefully placing the mud all over Wolf's eyes.

"When Wolf woke up and couldn't see, he grew afraid and ran and ran in circles, howling and begging for help. 'I can't see! I can't see!' yelped Wolf as he continued running in circles and falling down.

"Now, since everyone was afraid of Wolf, they stood back at a safe distance. But Little Brown Bird grew curious and flew close to him, asking, 'What's the matter?' Wolf told his sad story. Little Brown Bird being very considerate understood his problem, but needed time to think. Finally he chirped, telling Wolf if he helped him get the mud out of his eyes, he must promise not to eat him. Wolf made a solemn vow not to eat Little Brown Bird.

"Little Brown Bird remembered that Wolf had medicine power and asked timidly, 'Wolf, I have no bright colors, but I would love being colorful like my friends. It would be nice if you could help me find the beautiful red color that lives in the clay.'

"Wolf did not hesitate. He gave his sincere promise to take him to the place where the sacred red clay was hidden. Little Brown Bird believed him and flew down, landing on Wolf's face. He began to peck and peck at Wolf's eyes, throwing beakfuls of dried mud to the side. He worked all that afternoon removing the dried mud, but had to stop many times to go to the river for a drink. Finally when the last piece of dried mud was removed from Wolf's eyes, Little Brown Bird flew quickly to the nearest tree and watched as Wolf jumped with joy.

"Wolf was so thankful that he told Little Brown Bird to follow him along the trail that led to the sacred red clay. Excited that Wolf was keeping his word, the happy Little Brown Bird flew over Wolf's head until they arrived at the secret clay pit. Wolf stood back and watched him peck and peck until he had loosened the right amount of red clay. Then Wolf ran to a nearby stream and brought back mouthfuls of water to help Little Brown Bird apply the clay to his feathers. When they had finished, Little Brown Bird flew close to Wolf as he trotted to the river. Both stood looking at their reflections as Little Brown Bird marveled at his new beauty. He chirped a sweet thank you to Wolf and boasted of his good looks. And that's how the cardinal got its beautiful red color."

"Granbear, are you saying that if I cut a deal with a wolf person, I will get exactly what we have agreed on?"

"Oh, Meeko. Wolves are secretive creatures but keep their word. They possess the highest form of integrity while keeping themselves as the wild spirits of truth.

But never forget! Don't ever sleep under a tree with a raccoon overhead unless you want to go blind."

"Oh, Granbear," giggled Meeko.

"Who knows, Grandson, maybe you too can be an honored member when you earn your place in our pack. Another thing you should know about Wolf is its body language. If it's annoyed, its tail raises halfway up, its hackles go up, and it moves its ears forward while retracting its lips to bare its long, curved white teeth. The more docile Wolf will flatten out it ears and lower its body while lifting a paw in submission. Sometimes it will start a licking motion to appease the stronger animal.

"Meeko, you must have a good mind, nose, eyes and ears to share with this special kind of four leg. Who knows, if you learn the powers of Wolf, you may someday find happiness with a Wolf Woman," chuckled Granbear, promising that if Wolf ever walked with Meeko, he would never carry another scowl on his face without good reason. "Once you understand the language of Wolf, you will know the value in Wolf's strict rules."

"Granbear, I didn't know that wolves were so close to their families."

"Ah, Grandson, humans could learn much from watching them. The pack I used to visit had a female leader, and one day I watched her prepare a birthing den. She dug a long tunnel back into her cave, making it very comfortable. When at last she went into labor, the entire pack gathered at the entrance and sang to her. It was amazing to know that she could control her labor by licking her body into relaxing.

"I knew when the first puppy was born, because the pack howled loudly, and wagged their tails furiously when they heard its small voice. After the birth of each offspring, the mother would bite off the cord, clean the pup and move it to suckle. For days the pack brought food so the mother could have enough milk to keep her four babies healthy. When they were a few weeks old, I could hear them growling and playing in the den. Then one day she brought them into the sunlight and on that day the entire pack waited outside to greet each new pup.

"After a couple of weeks they all moved to another home near an open range where there was plenty of food and water. While playfully snapping and tumbling, the pups sniffed the air to see if anything was around. As they grew older they chased and ambushed each other in mock fights. Sometimes the mother would let me come fairly close to the pups as they explored their new surroundings. I especially enjoyed watching them learn about Wolf's social behavior. In less than a year those pups were scent-marking their territory, making strong family ties and doing what wolves do best.

"Wolves are very devoted to their young, always encouraging their pups to find their place in the pack. The aunties, uncles, grandmothers, grandfathers, and brothers and sisters help train the young pups showing great patience until they reach the age of responsibility. And that's when the older pack members become strong taskmasters, demanding that each find its place in the wolf family.

"Ah yes, *Sunká Manitu* is a resourceful hunter. He is a determined predator. Wolf teachings demand that you control your violence and use that energy to build the courage of Wolf. I have no doubt that as you come to know Wolf's traits you will learn to respect, honor, and love them. They will teach you how to grow into a strong and confident man. But always remember that as Wolf, you must set aside your personal feelings and do what is right for the good of the pack.

"Now you once asked if I thought you had Coyote blood in your veins. I've been watching you run lately, and I don't think so, because Coyote moves with fairly stiff legs. You run with graceful strides, holding yourself proudly, like Wolf. If you took your running more seriously, you could probably have Wolf breath. That would help you know Wolf."

"Running makes me feel free," answered Meeko, envisioning himself with a wolf pack.

"I remember when Wolf taught me something about running. I was coming home from a hunt and had a young deer strapped to my back. Being tired and careless, I didn't hear the pack moving in on me; had I been paying attention, I'd have known they'd been tracking me for miles. As they slowly circled me, I could see they were hungry and determined. I stood very still, watching their every movement until I located the highest tail, a scrawny, determined female. I knew if I was to survive that day, I would need much courage to face this fiercesome lady. I watched her closely for any signal to attack, reminding myself to stay alert or I would be a dead man. Meanwhile, I kept a respectful distance, trying not to cross her boundaries.

"I knew the pack was starving and that she was going to take my deer. As she signaled for the others to tighten the circle around me, snapping their jaws and growling, I slowly cut my kill loose from my body and let it drop softly onto the snow-covered ground. Then she let me move slowly away. From a safe distance, I looked back to find her still watching me with penetrating eyes. While the others tore at the deer's flesh, I could almost hear her say, 'My pack is hungry and the babies are starving. We need this food.' Even today, I can still see her determined eyes.

"After that narrow escape, I became very interested in her eleven member pack and spent many days watching them. One afternoon, I saw her become ferocious as she faced a challenger. Her powerful jaws grabbed him by the throat, killing him instantly. Standing by his dead body, she howled in sadness.

"When I look at Wolf, I see a friend and a predator. More than that, I see the sacredness of their teachings which are found in the substance and shadow of all life. Wolf teaches us to stay in good standing with our family, to become a fair and just leader, and to pass down our knowledge for future generations.

"Meeko, I remember when our clan trained its young men. The men had to learn all the ways of Wolf, including the excitement, strategies, and abilities for battle. A Dog Soldier is a powerful warrior and an expert in war. Once a young man was accepted as a Dog Soldier, there was a big celebration. The old society members dressed him in the finest of clothes and taught him Wolf's power songs. Then the new member had to spend one winter living with Wolf to learn its ways. After the snows had gone and the sun brought the new warm spring, everyone knew if he lived to return he would be loyal and fight to the death for the people.

"I remember the old ones saying a good Dog Soldier had to know the smells of the land. He had to be a wild-spirited man with a nose so sensitive to sickness and trouble that the odor of humans was almost unbearable to him. In spring, as the people returned to the summer camp where all the new Dog Soldiers were waiting, the new ones would say, 'We knew you were coming because the wolves taught us that the terrible odor we were smelling was coming from the people.' So sensitive to smell were these warriors that sometimes two weeks would pass before they could move back in to their tipis with their families. Grandson, if you can develop the nose of Wolf, you will be able to sniff out any enemy."

"If a person takes a bath do they still stink?" questioned Meeko, smelling his armpits.

"Oh, yes, people always smell, not only because of what they eat, but also what they think. If you stick your nose up in the air like Wolf, you might be able to smell trouble on the wind and know how to head it off. My nose often tells me what kind of day is ahead of me."

"Granbear, what happened to the warriors who spent a year training with Wolf?" asked Meeko, intrigued by the Dog Soldiers.

"Ah, Grandson, they were great fighters, and after many battles they became great leaders. Did you know that Shadowhawk is particularly close to wolves? Can you sense his wolf spirit? His observation skills will show you the way back to the trail of inner peace. Haven't you noticed that he drives you into the Medicine Wheel for safety? Aren't you learning your way to the cave of silence? I believe he has committed himself to making you a good man. Shadowhawk has no interest in anyone who does not practice the old ways.

"When I was a young boy, my grandfather told me a story about such people. One year the tribe had a very hard winter, and the people were starving. They roamed for months across the cold plains looking for Buffalo while living off scraps. Soon they came upon Raven Boy, and one of the wiser young boys, called Indian Boy, made friends with him. After hearing Indian Boy's sad story, Raven Boy wanted to help and took the tribe to his father's camp to get food. For many moons Chief Raven fed them and let them stay warm around his fire.

"Then one day Chief Raven complained about the visitors staying too long and told them to leave. This saddened the tribe, but having no choice, they left. Indian Boy, fearing the starvation of his people, made a plan. After they left, he hid in the bushes and turned himself into a wolf pup and became known as Wolf Boy. Then when Raven Boy came out to play, he joined him. Raven Boy liked Wolf Boy so much that he forgot about Indian Boy, and they became best friends.

"Every night, Wolf Boy lay on the side of Raven Boy's bed and kept a close eye on Chief Raven. One night Wolf Boy saw him sneak out of the tipi and followed. He watched Chief Raven approach a big stone, roll it back, let out a buffalo then quickly place the stone over the hole before creeping back to bed.

"As weeks passed, Wolf Boy waited for a moonless night, then quietly left Raven Boy's bed a second time. When he arrived at the big stone, he shape-shifted himself back into Indian Boy and rolled the stone away from the hole. The Raven Tribe heard the commotion and flew all around, trying to stop the whole herd from getting away.

"When the last buffalo had escaped through the hole, Indian Boy went to find his tribe and lead them to where the buffalo were grazing. For weeks, his people watched over the buffalo to keep Chief Raven from trying to recapture them. Then Indian Boy went to speak to the wolves about his release of the buffalo herd and told them that he felt bad about tricking Raven Boy into sharing his father's food. Why even today Raven flies close and pecks at Wolf just to watch him jump and snap. But being a smart bird, Raven always stays just out of Wolf's reach. And this is why Wolf and Raven declared: 'From this day forward, we will share our food.'

"According to another story about wolf's relationships with other animals, the young and old wolves, together with all the other animals, met at a river to discuss their needs. As they sat in a circle waiting their turn to talk, one lone wolf insisted on leading everyone in song. But his singing went on for hours until it became a horrible nuisance.

"Finally some of the animals could not stand the sound any longer and ran to the mountains. Others crawled under stones, and the creepie-crawlies dug deep into the sand to find silence. The fish were so upset that they swam upriver, and it is said that's how the salmon learned to leap the rapids.

"Even *Wi* grew tired of the lone wolf's howling and placed a large cloud in front of himself to dull the sound. But still the wolf continued his concert day after day. Finally, no one was left to hear his songs, and he became very sad. But then Grandmother Moon bent down closely to listen because she understood Wolf's song. And that's how Wolf became connected to the moon. When she arrives full and beautiful, Wolf looks up and howls a greeting to this loving grandmother."

"Oh, Grandfather, I really like the stories, they help me understand."

"Meeko, you've let me trick you again. Don't you know that Wolf and Coyote both howl at the moon? And don't you know that all the animals are so busy living their lives they couldn't care less if humans learn or not? Let's just hope that one of these powerful gatekeepers takes pity on you and teaches you something. But don't worry, Grandson, I'll put in a good word for you," said Granbear coyly as they left the Medicine Wheel.

After supper, while Granbear and Meeko were sitting on the front porch silently pondering the day's accomplishments, Shadowhawk approached. He greeted Granbear, then handed Meeko a gray wolfhide, saying, "As is Wolf, so will be the warrior. When you wear this hide, speak to it and ask to share in the intelligence of Wolf. Always remember Wolf sizes up his battles without ever being detected. Use your feelings, and if something doesn't feel right, walk away. And when you reach a safe distance from the problem, always turn and, like Wolf, look over your left shoulder, promising your opponent that you will be back to fight another day. Keep this skin close to you, and remember to think as a Dog Soldier."

Meeko accepted the gift with profound gratitude, pleased to receive this sign of respect from Shadowhawk. Just then Flying Feather's nephew pulled into the yard.

The tears in his eyes let Granbear know his friend was leaving this earth. Telling Shadowhawk to get the truck started, Granbear gathered his medicine bundle.

When Granbear, Shadowhawk, and Meeko arrived at Flying Feather's home, many relatives and friends were gathered in mourning. Seeing the chaos, Granbear asked Shadowhawk to take Meeko for a long walk, then went directly to the bedside of his friend.

Setting off through the field behind the house, Shadowhawk said, "Meeko, smell the air."

Meeko inhaled deeply, then answered, "Smells damp or rotting."

"It's the scent of the Three-legged White Wolf coming for Flying Feather. This spirit vanished long ago from Mother Earth. During Flying Feather's last visit, he told Granbear that he had heard the Three-legged White Wolf quietly singing his death song. Because of these signs and the medicine bundle brought by Granbear, Flying Feather will leave this world before sunrise. We must accept this so Grandfather Flying Feather will be safely returned back to the spirit world. Granbear is concerned that you might see the Three-legged White Wolf and does not want you to be frightened."

Fearing his words, Meeko cried out then bolted. Shadowhawk grabbed his arm and pulled him back. "Meeko, accept what I'm telling you."

"Shadowhawk, Granbear, knows that death scares me! Why did you bring me? I don't want to be here! I want to go home."

"Grandson, stop running with Coyote and instead run with the truth of Wolf. You know Flying Feather is returning to his relatives. Life and death are the beginning and the end of an ongoing cycle of renewal that every life force faces. Come, we'll sit with Grandmother Moon and listen to the wolves throughout the land welcome the banished one back from the spirit world."

But Meeko was filled with the fear of death, especially since he was now plagued with thoughts of losing Granbear. Feeling helpless, he went to sit alone under a nearby tree, while Shadowhawk left to join the prayer ceremony.

Around three o'clock in the morning, a pack of wolves suddenly began howling in unison from a great distance. Meeko's eyes widened in fear as a glowing, vapor-like energy shaped like the Three-legged White Wolf floated past him, then stopped at the front door of Flying Feather's home. Within seconds, Meeko saw Flying Feather's spirit leave the house with the Three-legged White Wolf and heard all the people trillo his passing. Meeko returned to Flying Feather's house in time to hear Granbear lead the parting prayer. He could tell that everyone felt a deep loss over another elder's departure to join relatives in the spirit world.

After the ceremony was over everyone left for home, their hearts filled with sadness. Upon his return to Rosebud, Granbear spent a few days alone in quiet prayer thinking of the wonderful days shared with his good friend. Shadowhawk understood his need for privacy and took Meeko to help rebuild fences around the pastures.

At the end of each day the two rode horses, discussing the clues that would help Meeko learn to be a good tracker. He was surprised to find that he enjoyed these times with Shadowhawk.

One evening as Meeko left the pasture he saw Granbear in the arbor talking with Shadowhawk and joined them, eager to hear their conversation.

"Did you hear Night Stalker calling last night?" asked Granbear.

"Yes, that old Chief Bird was really talking. Made me wonder who the warning was for," answered Shadowhawk.

"Night Stalker? Chief Bird? What kind of bird is that?" asked Meeko.

Shadowhawk gave Meeko a stern look for interrupting. But Granbear remarked, "It's okay. He doesn't know we're talking about Owl."

After Shadowhawk left to do errands, Granbear handed Meeko a stick, saying, "I've made this talking stick for you. Shadowhawk told me he explained to you its meaning, but it seems you have forgotten. When you see this stick in my hand, never speak unless I hand it to you." Meeko nodded and dropped his eyes in respect, but he wondered why he could not speak as openly as others.

"Meeko, I find it interesting that Owl has caught your attention since he has night vision. He lives in the East Door of the Medicine Wheel and is the messenger for *Yanpa*, the East Wind. Long ago, when *Yanpa* was establishing his direction, he could not find his way through the night and cried out for help. Hearing this, Owl flew quietly over to see who was in trouble. When he saw it was *Yanpa*, Owl agreed to guide him through the darkness and help him establish his direction. For this good deed, *Yanpa* chose Owl to be his messenger. So, Meeko, if you're ever lost, call upon Owl and he will guide you out of darkness.

"This night hunter teaches us about night vision. He can weave his way through a dense forest in complete silence, seeing where every sound comes from. Owl is conceited and loves to hear his name spoken. The old people say if you speak his Sioux name, *Atsitsi*, he will answer you. If you repeat it over and over in a gentle way, he will joyfully fly close and let you touch him."

Reaching for the talking stick, Meeko asked, "You can actually touch an owl?"

Taking back the talking stick, Granbear replied, "Ah, yes. If you have the touch, Owl will share his magical powers with you. And if you carry Owl power, you can hear the thoughts of others. Long ago our warriors used Owl's voice to bring the wisdom out of the darkness so they could signal their position to others as they moved into battle. You should also know that sometimes this enchanted one is called Night Eagle. Many fear he carries black magic and believe his feathers can make us very deceptive.

"One particular owl that people fear is the screech owl. They say he brings bad news and warns us of an approaching death. I remember one man who hated these owls so much that whenever he heard one, he would hunt it down and kill it. The last time I was in his house, an entire wall was lined with screech owl carcasses. Now, that's a superstitious man! Personally, I feel kinda sorry for this little *Stiginney*. Makes me wonder if he's going around doing normal owl business and gets himself killed just because people fear him."

Picking up the talking stick, Meeko asked. "Can we talk about something besides death? It makes me afraid."

"Meeko, lessons do not come as we wish, but as they are needed. You must learn to accept that death is a part of life, and we cannot change the time we are given to die."

"I know, Granbear. I just don't like the feeling of death being linked to Owl. Why, even his hoots make me feel sad and lonely."

"Maybe Owl is trying to get you to reflect on your thoughts so that you never doubt your decisions. I think you need to speak with Owl so you will know what he means when he asks, 'Who?'"

"I don't want to learn about Owl, I just want to know how to say his name so I can touch him."

"We'll see, Grandson," said Granbear, pointing the talking stick at Meeko as a reminder that he had spoken out of turn. Granbear walked home as Meeko submissively followed close behind.

Several days had passed when Granbear called to Meeko to follow him into the Medicine Wheel to continue yet another lesson. "The Gatekeeper of the East Door is *He'aka*, the Elk. He shares this sacred doorway with Moose, Deer, Antelope and all of the rest of the hoofed ones. Our history teaches us that these plant-eating creatures were our first meat, a sacred gift from *Wakan Tanka*.

"Although Elk is related to the deer family, he has a much larger brain, which gives him a greater ability to learn. He has special gifts of sight and hearing. He can see and hear better than any human and can instantly smell an unnatural odor in his territory."

Reaching for the talking stick, Meeko said, "Shadowhawk once told me that Elk has a keen sense of smell and strong front legs for fighting. He warned me to always be careful around them. He once saw an elk kick a wolf so hard that it broke its back, then the elk stomped it to death."

"He told you right. An Elk can kill a cougar, or even a grizzly, with his powerful front legs. When the bears awaken from their long winter's sleep, they search for elk carcasses and live off the bones until the spring brings sprouting plants. That's why we find very few elk bones returning to Mother Earth's soil.

"Before the white man came, herds and herds of elk lived in the grassy meadows of the lowlands. But many were slaughtered with the constant raping of the land by farming and careless hunting. The white man then drove the surviving hoofed ones into the high country where they met Bear and Cougar, two very strong predators.

"Meeko, always be especially careful around a bull elk, he can be very dangerous when he senses his herd is in danger. At these times he bugles a warning so the herd can run to safety while he hangs back as a decoy. This great hoofed one will fight to his death to save his herd, and yet his face holds gentle, kind eyes. I like watching him stand on the edge of a high cliff, sniffing the winds as he surveys all that is around him. I can't help but laugh as I see those long, skinny black legs holding up such a big body. Ah, Grandson, I've watched those legs jump over huge fallen trees and plow through the deepest of snow to escape danger. Why, Elk can run up to thirty-five miles an hour, and by pacing himself, can keep that speed for a long time. I've seen whole herds run full-out through a dense forest while maneuvering their huge racks with ease. What a sight to behold when he uses his speed as another defense. And Elk, like Buffalo, never changes his route of travel, even if he has to swim through frozen rivers to reach his destination. *He'aka* teaches us to pace ourselves in life so we too can reach our destiny.

"*He'aka* is truly one of the rulers of the forests all over the world. His beautiful hide is tough, and goes from shades of beige to black. This impressive four leg travels many miles to reach the lush green meadows that lie between the tall mountain peaks. This is the best place to find these grand creatures, standing knee-high in tender grasses enjoying the bounty of Mother Earth. Sadly, many hunters kill these sacred animals just to collect their racks as trophies to prove they have a power over this animal.

"Once a year elk lose their old racks and start growing new ones. We use their old racks to make jewelry, charms and medicines for ceremony. When elk's new antlers break through the skin, they are soon covered with a soft velvety material that supplies the blood for the new growth. Elk rubs them against trees and bushes to remove this coating, and when they reach maturity the antlers harden into bone. I've seen racks weigh over sixty pounds and stretch a good six feet, carrying up to forty points. Meeko, can you imagine that short, thick neck carrying such a heavy load and still gracefully outrunning a hungry cougar?

"The males and females live together only during rutting season. The bulls are very competitive as they gather their harems, and will fight to the death to keep their females. Ah, Grandson, when I think of the bull elk's strength, stamina, speed and courage during this season, I can't help but be amazed by the beauty of such a passionate animal.

"I've witnessed many fights among the bulls, watching them prance around in circles, tearing up trees and the ground to show they are the best bull of the herd. They attract a female through touching and bugling. I've heard their beautiful low-throated voices riding the wind all night long. At first it sounds like a bugle that goes flat, then it starts all over again, getting louder and higher until it reaches a certain pitch, then the song ends in a short cough. When a cow hears this, she perks up her ears and goes running to that bull. So if you ever hear an elk call during that time, you will understand the true magical powers in Elk's mating ritual.

"When a person carries Elk power, he is expected to accomplish his goals and above all take care of his women. Grandson, that wise old Elk can teach humans much about romance and passion. A man can learn many things about a woman if he knows the ways of Elk. I think you should learn the flute so you too can woo the women like Elk."

Meeko giggled, wondering how Granbear, at his age, could ever think such things.

"Grandson, this noble animal is truly a master of lovemaking, but I kinda feel sorry for him during rutting season. Oh my, does he have problems with other males trying to steal his women! But he's smart and herds his cows near a river that is wedged between hills. You see, an elk cow watches the handsome young ones, and like some women, she tends to wander off with one. Why, he's so busy with his harem that he can't take time to eat. Many bulls die happily during rutting season, knowing their bloodline will keep the future herds strong.

"I know the secret medicine of Elk," whispered Granbear. Meeko's ears perked up and he leaned close. "The old people say if you grind the antlers into a powder, it will bring back your sex drive. And if you secretly sprinkle some of this powder on a woman's food or in her drink, she will love you forever," chuckled Granbear, reaching into his pocket and pulling out a little package which read 'Elk Love Potion Medicine.'

Picturing a huge harem of beautiful girls catering to his every need, Meeko blushed, saying, "I don't need that stuff! I know all the girls like me. Besides, I'm not gonna love just one woman—I'm gonna love them all."

"Grandson, someday you may find much pain from that statement. When you can appreciate the power of one woman's love, you may need this powder and even a string of elk teeth to keep her. I think you already need help with that silly harem that you've collected. But there will come a time in your life, Meeko, that you will tire of the many, and want real love from only one woman. In my experience, I think you should keep this powder for that one special lady that will come into your life someday."

Meeko took the bag knowing Granbear was telling him to start controlling his flirtatious ways. As he set the bag aside, a strange chill ran over him as he thought about loving only one woman. He picked up the bag and placed it in his pocket, asking, "Granbear, did you ever capture love?"

Granbear grinned. "Oh yes, Grandson, I captured love many times but until I found the right woman I never knew love. My truth about love came from watching another's pain. That's when I knew I was not the only imperfect man in the world. Since those days, I've always carried a large bag of Elk powder to guarantee my success with women."

Meeko cringed at the thought of Granbear ever having had the disease called warm.

Granbear saw his reaction and whispered close to Meeko's ear, "Once, Meeko, I heard Elk's slow, low-toned voice calling to me. I jumped out of bed, ran outside and saw a herd of females gathered around a striking bull that had mastered them with his haunting call. As long as I live, I will not forget that moment. I am thankful that Elk taught me the power of sweet speech when talking to a woman. That's why many women find me irresistible," boasted Granbear, showing Meeko a necklace of elk teeth. "Grandson, these teeth carry power, prestige, and the promise of a long life of warm."

Meeko examined them closely, finding they were about the size of a man's thumb. "Grandson, these teeth will outlast you. We collect elk teeth to give to our women to sew on their deerskin dresses. When I was young it was not unusual to see our women's dresses covered with them. When a woman wore such a dress, it meant her man was wealthy and loved her dearly. But love, like the wind, comes and goes. So, when a man finds a good woman, he must take pride in his treasure. A man of honor will always open his heart as big as the sky to give his woman an honest, heartfelt love, because then he knows she will never be taken away from him. It is Elk who teaches us the importance of sharing ourselves and our passion."

As they left the Medicine Wheel, Granbear smiled, saying, "Ah, Grandson, romance and love are good talking, but right now I'm hungry for food, not the company of a woman." Feeling disappointed that the lesson on his favorite subject had been cut short, Meeko had to admit that his hunger did outweigh his need for the company of girls.

Early the next morning Granbear, Shadowhawk and Meeko drove to find a herd of deer to study. After reaching a deer habitat, Shadowhawk guided the others to the top of the hill, where they sat under a tree to wait. The sun was just breaking over the horizon when the misty profiles of a herd of white-tail deer slowly filled the meadow below.

"Today we are here to observe the deer people. We humans have much in common with these hoofed ones. Look at those very intelligent, gentle souls. Since the white-tailed deer eats in the day, we know it carries the daytime powers, unlike the black-tail deer that feeds at night and carries the nighttime powers. Deer families live by the laws of a matriarchal society. Deer, like elk, are also swift runners and graceful jumpers. I've seen huge herds swim great distances without ever showing tiredness. These beautiful plant eaters also have keen hearing and smell."

"Granbear, is it true that they are colorblind?"

"I've heard that," answered Granbear, tapping the talking stick to remind Meeko to be quiet. "See their tails flagging? That's how they communicate. The herd knows we're here. If they sense danger, they will lift their flaring tails, then give off a high, nasal whistling sound and start running to safety.

"Deer are very elusive and sure-footed. These hoofed ones are shape-shifters and many hunters claim they can vanish before your eyes. That's why it's necessary to become a clever tracker before hunting. A good hunter knows how to read the signs and track everything in nature. Shadowhawk, since you're a fine hunter, tell our grandson what it takes to become as good as you," requested Granbear, handing Shadowhawk the talking stick.

Leaning against a tree, Shadowhawk smiled, "Grandson, when I was learning to hunt, I made many mistakes. I was ignorant and wanted too much too fast. I've let many a deer lead me astray, and the slightest sound can start a herd running. When this happens, it's time to go home and hunt another day." Shadowhawk picked a blade of grass and stuck it in his mouth, before continuing. "Deer power teaches us to never waste time by following false images about ourselves. To remove clouds of doubt, we must place our lives in the trusting hands of *Wakan Tanka*. We must recognize the sacredness in all things before ever thinking of taking a life.

"There is much you must consider before you can ever become a good hunter. First, you must remember the spirit of the hoofed ones. It was Deer that gifted the people with their first animal food. The people promised this creature that if it would die so they could live, they would always show respect and make sure its death was swift and painless.

"The old ones would always speak to *Wakan Tanka* before ever taking a life. It was those medicine people's prayers that caused certain deer to willingly step forward and give their lives so the people could live. A good medicine person could even tell a hunter where to find his particular deer. I became a good hunter when I finally listened to what Medicine had to say. Now I always find the right place and make a swift, clean kill, then immediately do the proper ceremony before dressing it out and taking it home.

"To hunt deer, you have to think like a deer. You've got to know the animal's eating habits and where and how it lives. When I'm hunting, I study the deer droppings. If they're piled high, then I know the herd is relaxed and senses no danger. But if the droppings are piled very high and wider, I know the baby fawns are not yet strong enough to keep up with the herd. Now, if their droppings are scattered, I know the herd is running. That's when I know another predator is around and I could be in danger. I'm a very good tracker and am always aware of my environment. I keep my mind focused and move in silence, reading every sign as I track my prey, watching to leave no signs that would tell another where I am. Over the years I've learned how animals survive, and that tells me their weakness. To become this kind of predator you must know everything about the animal that you're hunting because if you don't, it could be stalking you.

"Granbear once took me hunting to teach me how to find a buck. I knew to look for the scarring on the young saplings and how to find the heart-shaped hoof prints, and it was Granbear who taught me how to follow a cold trail. A deer will avoid a fight unless the human puts the leader into a situation that demands he protects his herd.

"Meeko, before you ever kill, know the spirit of that animal, otherwise you will create pain and suffering for your victim as well as yourself. Granbear taught me that the hoofed ones can teach us many secrets about ourselves. I find it funny when a man foolishly believes he has power over a woman. It's the male hoofed ones that teach us men never to fight with a woman unless we want to lose. Any wise man knows to think with his big head, rather than the little one that hangs between his legs." Shadowhawk and Granbear smiled as they watched Meeko's embarrassment at the blunt remark.

A silence reigned as Shadowhawk poured Granbear a cup of coffee. As he sat sipping, Granbear said, "I think we learn best through trial and error. I was about eight years old when I foolishly killed my first deer. It was not a clean kill, and I caused that poor deer a great deal of suffering. I sat next to its head and prayed to be forgiven for my stupidity. As its breath grew faint, I looked deep into its eyes and heard it ask me in a loving manner never again to kill a member of its family until I learned the proper way to take a life. I promised that deer that I would never hunt again until I knew the sacred way to kill any animal.

"When I told my brothers what I had done, they helped me dress out the deer and brain-tan the hide, and my sweet mother made me my first buckskin shirt out of that deerskin. Whenever I wore it, I could feel the spirit of that deer. As I grew older and became a good hunter, my father taught me how to clean my animal skins with white clay and water. And to delouse the hide, I found an ant hill and let the ants do the work."

During lunch, Granbear asked, "Meeko, did you know that I can make it rain?"

"It's true, he can make it rain," mused Shadowhawk.

"How can you do that, Granbear?" questioned Meeko.

"I learned it from the pronghorn sheep. They shared with me the secrets of rainmaking."

"Will you teach me?" asked Meeko.

"No! If you want to know about the rainmakers, then I suggest you go talk to a pronghorn sheep and let him teach you. Right now, we're sharing our stories with you so you can live more honestly. The Medicine Wheel takes a lifetime to learn. There are thousands of wheels and you've barely touched the first one. Understand, Meeko, that knowledge grows on knowledge, and you have a very long way to go."

Shadowhawk spotted a group of fawns and whispered, pointing, "See the babies? Maybe Granbear will tell us the story of how the fawns got their spots."

Granbear smiled, cleared his throat, then said, "Great Spirit came to Mother Earth to teach all the animals how to protect themselves against their natural enemies. One by one, he gave each animal a gift for protection. To some he gave claws, to others he gave blunt or pointed teeth and still others he gave poisonous bites.

"A shy mother deer stood off in the distance, deeply concerned for her fawn. Mustering all of her courage, she went to Great Spirit, saying, 'Oh, Great Spirit, I thank you for giving the deer family the gift of speed, perfect eyesight and a keen sense of smell.' Glancing toward her fawn with soft, loving black eyes, she pleaded, 'Great Spirit, I do not question your great wisdom, but I have only my sharp hoofs to defend my young. I beg you to consider a gift of protection to keep our babies safe from the hungry wolves and the determined cougars. I try to hide my newborns in the high grass, but it is not enough to keep them safe.' The Great Spirit heard the sweet words from the timid deer. He thought and thought, trying to find the perfect solution to resolve the mother deer's problem.

"Now, the Mother Deer did not want Great Spirit to think her impolite or impatient, so she busied herself with cleaning her fawn. She washed the little black circles around his eyes, then ran her tongue down the bridge of his shiny black nose, checking everything, as mothers do, while cleaning his reddish-brown coat. As his coat grew wet from the moisture of her tongue, there appeared light and dark patches over its little body. Well, when Great Spirit saw this, he knew exactly what needed to be done. He quickly took out his paintbrush and began to paint white spots over the fawn's body.

"When he had finished, he stood back to admire his work, then proudly announced, 'There, Mother Deer, your babies will always be safe. The white spots will blend with the tall grass and when the young become strong enough to run with the herd, their spots will vanish and they will look like all the other deer.'

"When the rest of the deer mothers saw the white spots they came running to see what had happened. They stood around in amazement, listening to their sister deer speaking with Great Spirit. 'Oh, thank you, Great Spirit, for this wonderful gift.' Once the deer mothers understood, they too were grateful for this sacred blessing. And to this day when a fawn is born, its tiny, reddish body is covered with little white spots. And that's why, Meeko, you can see all the mother deer grazing near their babies without any worry." Meeko remained quiet in thought. Granbear smiled at his grandson's reaction, then picked up his blanket as the trio walked back to the truck.

After they had eaten a hearty meal, Granbear and Meeko sat on the front porch. "Grandson, thoughts change like tides in the ocean, but Medicine remains steady. When you learn to live by the principles of your beliefs, you will have a courageous heart. Deer teaches us to be good and giving. That is the order of things. Deer says, 'If I don't love myself, how can I love another?' Deer are not people pleasers; they are survivors. Deer power teaches us to be prepared for every occasion. Life is demanding, and we must know if a person is worthy of our sacrifices. Always remember, Grandson, we learn best from those things that hold our interest. Always bend down humbly and touch Mother Earth every day, thanking her for her gift of caring. In taking one step toward *Wakan Tanka*, we have just taken two steps back to ourselves."

Meeko's mind whirled in a state of confusion. He knew little about loving others and less about sacrificing himself or protecting himself against the pain of rejected love.

"Grandson, every life force has predictable habits. And we, like any hunter, must develop our skills to capture and kill. When we have emotional problems, it is our responsibility to kill whatever is destroying our happiness. Creator has painted us a beautiful world, and has filled it with magnificent colors giving each a duty and a voice. Someday when you become a Sundancer, you will understand the light and the warmth from the sun comes from an act of love. Let the sun turn on your heart to help you see what I am saying.

"It is *Tunka'shila* who helps us see clearly and gives our thoughts direction. We should be thankful for his gift of caring. It is our greatest source of power and gets us past our bad feelings. Love is our greatest gift of power, and giving love is a way of helping the spiritual growth of another. But until you can love yourself and accept others without judgment, you will have nothing. Hating Renna will cause your life's lessons to be harder and your evil thoughts will waste your life. I pray that you will accept your feelings and learn to make good choices in your life's journey.

"Someday you will understand that life is an exciting growing process. I remember a wise medicine man once telling me that everything was created from the spiraling circles of the sacred hoop of life. I would sit and watch him scratch his knowledge into pictures on the stones. He once painted a wheel that told about the four races of man, giving great details of how these related people were born from the same sacred circle.

"Grandson, you too are a part of that sacred wheel. In this life, your journey, as well as all others', comes from within the never-ending sacred hoop. Every life force is individual and separate, yet intertwined, as part of the whole which makes us all one. Therefore we are all related. Creator asks us to revere and love all life, and that includes Renna. Someday when you are willing to forgive her, Creator will gift you and let you use your paintbrushes to place our old knowledge on canvas for the world to know us as a people."

Seeing Meeko's thoughtful expression, Granbear felt gratified that he had learned from the lesson and told him that tomorrow they would visit the South Door and meet the gatekeeper called Cougar.

During the night, thunder awakened everyone at Rosebud. Lightning struck all around as the winds whirled in fury, ripping huge trees from the ground. A torrential downpour rolled across the land, giving rise to chaos and terror in the people. For the next two days the storm continued, causing the river to overflow its banks. Hoping to stop the water from flooding everything, Shadowhawk gathered the people together to build a makeshift dam.

Days passed, and they were desperately in need of supplies and food. Shadowhawk, Granbear and Meeko prepared to fight their way through the storm to replace the needed commodities. After four men pushed Shadowhawk's truck out of the mud-filled yard and onto the flood-damaged road, he drove Granbear and Meeko through thick pockets of ground fog while battling gusty headwinds.

He was forced to drive with his head hanging out of the window, while fighting the steering wheel to keep the truck from sliding into the ditch that ran along the side of the road. Unable to ignore the people stranded along the way, he would stop to help get their cars started. For others the situation was useless and they could only be driven to safety. Granbear voiced his fears for those who lived deep in the interior of the reservation and had no transportation. Shadowhawk assured him that upon their return, he would send a Bear Clan member to check on them.

Almost three hours had passed before they arrived home with fresh supplies and by then, the rain had stopped. As they pulled into the yard, they were shocked at the chaos left by the heavy winds. The arbor had been ripped away, and benches, tables and chairs were scattered everywhere. Shadowhawk and Meeko ran to the river to help sandbag the bank. Granbear instructed the older women to take the groceries inside, while he and the others gathered the damaged furniture and tied it to nearby trees.

Once Granbear had finished, he began to wade across the yard through knee-deep water toward the river. Shadowhawk, fearing for Granbear's safety, insisted that he get the supplies ready instead to send to the people in the interior. Frustrated with Shadowhawk's direct orders, Granbear left in a huff and returned to the house to find everyone was busy in the kitchen preparing the food for the working crew.

Worried, Granbear stood at the window watching the water inch its way higher toward the house. He gathered his most trusted pipe carriers for a prayer ceremony, then asked those who had trucks to deliver supplies to the interior before the rain returned.

Barely an hour had passed and the air was dangerously still, then darkness slowly crept over the reservation. As the winds began to build funnels from all directions, everyone took shelter in Shadowhawk's little four-room house, praying that another severe electrical storm would not hit. The momentum of the howling winds began ripping sheets of roofing from the house as heavy rain once again soaked the ground, causing the river to creep close to the back door. The people sat in silent prayer, knowing at any minute the house could be destroyed. Gripped by futility, everyone fought hard to protect the house. Shadowhawk knew that they were all exhausted, so he set up shifts to sustain their makeshift dam.

This relentless routine continued for four grueling days. Finally on the fifth day, the sun poked its head from behind a dark cloud, bringing intense humidity and creating a heat that bore down on the people and the waterlogged land. The river dikes were still holding as the people began to clear away the fallen trees and debris. Seeing things were safe, Shadowhawk took two more truckloads of supplies to the people in the interior, and while he was there, trees were cut and loaded to rebuild Granbear's arbor.

Two weeks later, life was slowly getting back to normal. And once again everything was good. Granbear sat in his new arbor enjoying a cup of coffee with Meeko, thankful that everyone had weathered the storm and there had been no deaths.

After the people had been fed, Granbear and Meeko went to check on the condition of the Medicine Wheel. Granbear stood quietly, smiling as he looked and said, "I see the Stone People weathered the storm. Grandson, life offers many surprises. We've had a busy two weeks, but there is one thing about the Bear Clan, we always help our people. It's strange how life guides us in so many different directions, merely to bring us back together as a loving people."

"Granbear, you've always cared for the people, and it's nice they built you a new arbor," added Meeko as they neared the South Door of the Medicine Wheel.

Suddenly something moved. Granbear knelt by a stone, placed his hand under its slightly raised edge, and chuckled as he gently pulled out a baby mouse. "What have we here?" Meeko saw its big pink ears as Granbear stood up with the little creature in his hand. "Grandson, this is a good sign. This little fellow knew to come to this sacred space for safety. Amazing! You know he lives here in the South Door with the Gatekeeper, *Igmu*, Cougar. Grandson, see if you can find his loosely woven, grass-like nest."

Meeko looked around until he found a few pieces of what was once the little mouse's home. Picking them up, he went to Granbear, asking, "Is this what you were talking about?"

"Yes, Grandson. Now go to the kitchen and ask one of the grandmothers for some milk and a small piece of bread. And pick up that empty matchbox sitting on the kitchen table so we can make this little fellow a new home."

When Meeko returned, he watched with great interest as Granbear fed the famished little mouse who ate until his belly was full and fell fast asleep in Granbear's hand. Fascinated, Meeko giggled as he watched his grandfather gently place the little one into the matchbox on the loose pieces of woven grass, saying, "This will make him a good bed." Handing the matchbox to Meeko, he continued, "Grandson, this is going to be a very interesting study for you."

"Are you going to tell me about Cougar?" questioned Meeko.

"In time, Grandson. First, we must speak about what is now. This mouse has brought to my attention that your lack of caring for others is a lesson we can't ignore. He is a distant relative of the ones who surrounded you at your birth. Mouse teaches you to watch for details so you will not become prey to everything around you. I believe Mouse showed up to say that it's time for you to pay closer attention to the details in your life.

"Grandson, this little one can teach you that freedom comes from the smallest of details. Mouse lives very close to the ground, which helps him see things others miss. He has a certain kind of bravery that allows him to travel to small places and find new things of interest. Everything is Mouse's enemy. Even domestic animals like to play with him and when they tire of the game, they kill and eat him. Take that young, helpless mouse for instance. He, like you, is a child of *Wakan Tanka*. Right now he has little knowledge of life, and no family to teach him. Without proper care and training, he will not survive. Surely you know that you must take care of him until he is old enough to understand the life of a mouse. This is why I give him to you.

"Maybe Renna never took care of you, but your family did. I give you the job of taking care of this mouse until he is old enough to go back to his people. This will help you understand more about the responsibilities of being a parent. I think this is good because it will stop your scattered thoughts from falling on barren soil. The South Door and Little Mouse are going to heal what is wrong between you and your mother."

Meeko hesitated. Deep down he did not want to change his thoughts about Renna because he liked hating her and using her as an excuse for his behavior. In addition, he was skeptical any animal as small as Mouse could teach him anything. He asked Granbear, "What kind of power can a mouse have anyway?"

"I see you are refusing the lesson that is right in front of you!" Not knowing what to say, Meeko removed the little mouse from the box and began to play with it, wondering why Granbear was so upset. "To appreciate its power you must be aware of how this creature is connected to your birth and Renna's treatment of you. I remember the cold, snowy night you were born. I was home sleeping when a blue light came and told me that Renna was giving birth. When I finally found you two in an alley, there were mice scampering all around while one rat was feeding on your arm. That's how you got that scar," said Granbear, touching it.

As many sad memories came alive in Meeko's mind he pulled away with embarrassment and covered the scar with his shirt. Seeing his shame, Granbear added, "When I picked you up and filled your lungs with first breath, you cried loudly, expressing life and causing my heart to fill with joy. Grandson, that was a night of miracles!

"Now, this little field mouse is a relative of those that were present that night, and you must take responsibility for its life to get free from the prison of your bad feelings about your childhood," said, Granbear motioning Meeko to leave the Medicine Wheel.

For the next two days, Granbear constantly compared Renna and the mouse, but Meeko persisted in rejecting the lesson and became increasingly angry. He hated taking care of the mouse because of its associations. One day he tried letting him go, but the mouse stayed close, always looking into his eyes. Frustrated, Meeko decided to leave him closed up in the matchbox without food and water.

Several days later Granbear opened the matchbox to find the mouse had died of starvation. Taking the box, he went to Meeko and said, "Your carelessness has sent the mouse back to *Wakan Tanka*. What a shame—you killed one of his children. I had no idea you were fighting this hard to keep from learning."

"Granbear, I'm sorry. I didn't mean to kill it. I just don't have an interest in mice. I want to study Cougar, like you taught me about Eagle, Bear and Wolf."

Granbear exploded. "So your lack of love for yourself and others made it okay to kill an innocent mouse? And you say you want me to help you learn? If you like the predators so much, then why didn't you eat the mouse instead of making it suffer through your careless ways? Now take this little mouse and give it a proper burial."

As he took the dead mouse, Meeko's hand shook, for he knew that Granbear would not easily forgive him. As he walked sullenly by the house, the grandmothers turned their backs on him and covered their heads in shame. Meeko's sense of guilt made him respond in anger. Abruptly turning away from them, he walked across the back field until he saw some other field mice climbing among the tall grasses. For a moment, he wished he had brought the mouse here to be with his relatives rather than let him die. Then, as he placed the matchbox carefully in the ground, he tried to convince himself it was just another stupid mouse. So what? The mouse should have been able to take care of himself.

Returning to the Medicine Wheel, Meeko was surprised to find Granbear was gone. Hesitating for a moment, he entered the Medicine Wheel and sat in the South Door, hoping Granbear would forgive him and return to talk.

When two days had passed with no sign of his grandfather, Meeko became increasingly concerned. But as the sun rose on the third day, he heard Granbear approaching. Relieved that he had returned, Meeko jumped up to greet him. But instead of returning his greeting, Granbear kicked him hard in the butt. Shocked, Meeko began to apologize. "Granbear, I'm so sorry. I promise I'll never do anything like that again. I should have honored that little sacred animal and learned to live by its principles."

"Grandson you're not a bad person, but you are a stupid and heartless one. Why should I spend my time with you? In fact, I've enjoyed making you go without food and water for the past two days. Maybe you've learned something about caring for others' needs. Why I was given a grandson that could make an animal suffer is beyond me! This kind of behavior from anyone that has my blood leaves me in disgust." Furious with his Grandson, Granbear walked away.

Meeko struggled hard with Granbear's harsh words, and for the rest of the day and into the night he thought only of the mouse and its relationship to him. He remembered how Renna had left him alone without food or a place to sleep, and how unloved that had made him feel. He also thought of all the times the white people's cruel words had hurt him deeply, especially, 'You dirty Indian. I think the lot of you should be gassed before you reach the age of five.' Slowly he began to accept, that he too had become a cruel person, allowing the mouse to experience a torturous death by going without food and water in that little matchbox. At that moment Meeko knew if he did not change his ways, he would end up just like Renna.

The following morning Granbear found Meeko sitting in the Medicine Wheel, crying as though his heart had broken. When Meeko saw him, he dropped to his knees and pleaded, "Oh, Granbear, I've done a terrible thing. The mouse died because I didn't want to take care of him, and that's exactly what Renna did to me. If it hadn't been for you, I too would have died, locked away in a world I didn't understand. I know I deserve to starve to death just like the mouse, but please help me."

"Yes, Grandson, you did a very bad thing. You killed an innocent animal because you refused to be responsible for another life."

Hearing these words, Meeko began to pray from his heart for the first time, begging *Wakan Tanka* to forgive him for this awful deed.

Granbear listened closely to his grandson's prayer, then sat down next to him. "Meeko, you now understand how long Renna has kept your feelings trapped in your cold heart. Maybe you weren't locked in a box like the mouse, but Renna holds the key to your feelings, and they're still locked up inside of you.

"*Tunka'shila* did not give you a life purpose and then tell you to give it away to someone who would imprison your growth. When someone gives you love, it must be honored. Thoughtless people will never have good friends or real love. You can either look at your time with Renna as a gift for your spiritual growth, or you can go on resenting her, never fulfilling your life purpose. This is your life, not Renna's, yet you insist on keeping your mind locked in hatred. If you keep it up, you will have no loving friends and you will remain an ignorant, selfish person. The little mouse gave his life to help you understand what happens when you refuse to take responsibility for yourself and others."

Seeing that Meeko's sorrow was genuine, Granbear put his arms around his great-grandson's shoulder. "I'm glad you have chosen to look closer at your feelings. I think you will find that respect and consideration are what life is all about. A person can never be happy if they leave Great Spirit out of their life. The little mouse helped you see your flaws and made you realize that your identity goes beyond Renna's influence. Creator allows us to find our life's lessons in many ways, so we can see the bigger purpose he has for us.

"I knew you would come to find all of your answers in the Medicine Wheel. You are now looking at your bad experiences yet there are many circles to walk before your heart can be cleansed of all your problems. If you reflect with concern on every problem you encounter in life, you will grow in knowledge. But if you choose to ignore what I say, life will continue to give you painful lessons until it destroys you."

"Granbear, I will never doubt the sacredness of *Wakan Tanka*'s children again. I will be responsible and will never be cruel to another living thing."

"That is good, Grandson. The more you know about yourself, the better you'll be at directing your life. Your heart must grow in a good way before you can become a caring person. Although your experiences with Renna were sad, I will not allow you to deny what you have learned from her. She is a bad mother, but a good teacher. Renna is very ill, but she is still family. During your time with her, you shut down your feelings and lost yourself. But it is up to you and *Wakan Tanka* to get rid of this grave sickness.

"Meeko, for your own sake you must remember that Renna gave you life, and you must respect her. But she is not a mother, only a parent. Since you are a member of the human race and related to all life forces, you know your real mother and father are Mother Earth and Father Sky. So, why is it so important for you to know your human father? What does it matter? You are alive and you are here. Look up! See that beautiful blue sky? That is your real father! See how he touches Mother Earth? That is a true marriage. See how Father Sky brings the life-giving rains to help feed all their children? Honor and respect these two forces, for they are your survival."

As Meeko accepted what Granbear said, the two held each other. Then Granbear told his great-grandson, "I want you to stay here for the night and let these feelings help you overcome your sadness. Consider your experiences, and let them make you strong. In the morning let the beauty of dawn awaken your soul as you embrace the rising sun, allowing its warmth to open your heart.

As a moonless night approached, Meeko listened to the strange night sounds while praying for forgiveness. Suddenly he felt something crawling on his leg. As an intense terror gripped his heart he opened his eyes wide to see Little Mouse scurrying across his lap. Meeko thought he saw it smile at him and knew at that moment that Little Mouse was happy to be back in the spirit world. Then, amazingly, the mouse spoke to him, saying, "Its okay, big brother. I gave my life so you could have a heart. You must now pay close attention to the little things in life, and never harm another of Creator's children through lack of caring." That night Little Mouse led Meeko to many different places where he saw numerous four legs who had sacrificed their lives so the human race could learn the beauty in caring for and understanding all life.

After sunrise the next morning, Granbear appeared with food for Meeko and quickly observed a change in him. "I see your vision has expanded, Grandson, that you're observing what's around you and your mind is connecting to your heart. This will help you get rid of your bad feelings as you walk with each animal on the Medicine Wheel. Today I'll tell you a story that reminds me of the problem between you and Renna.

"One day long ago, there was an old female Cougar who was close to giving birth. Being ill and not strong enough to hunt, she knew she was starving to death, but her divine will kept her fighting for life. This day she could go no further and lay down near a sheep pasture to rest. She would occasionally struggle to her feet, hoping to kill a sheep, but try as she might she was too weak. Finally realizing she could do no more, she took her last breath in prayer just as she gave birth to her new cub.

"The cub meowed for days, and finally when an old mama sheep sniffed around, she found the little cub lying very still. Seeing the newborn was in trouble, she felt sorry for the little one, and let it nurse. In six weeks the cub was following her everywhere, and in six months he was learning how to eat grass."

Meeko's eyes widened skeptically. He had never heard of a cat eating grass. Granbear smiled, then continued. "Two years passed, and the cougar grew big but acted like a sheep, bleating and grazing with the herd. He had forgotten who he was and had become a sheep-thinking cougar.

"Then one day at twilight time, an old cougar was out hunting and saw this young cougar living as a sheep. He could not believe what he was seeing—a fine young cougar eating grass with a herd of sheep. Everyday he came to watch this strange behavior, until one day he boldly asked the young cougar what he was doing.

"The old cougar was shocked when the young cougar began to bleat pitifully and ran with the flock to escape. He grabbed that young one by the nape of the neck and shook him, but the young cougar refused to fight back and kept bleating, begging for his life. The old cougar roared in anger, then dragged the young cub deep into the forest, demanding he stop his pathetic behavior. The young cougar shook in terror as he explained his life's story.

"Understanding the young cougar's problem, the old cougar decided to teach him how to become Cougar. Each day he would roar and sharpen his long claws, but the young one refused to learn. Then the old cougar decided he would tell him the history of all cougars, but still the young cougar would not believe him and continued begging to return to his flock.

"After weeks of trying, the old cougar finally gave up and again grabbed the young one, this time dragging him down to the lake and forcing him to look in the water, saying, 'You bleating fool! Can't you see your reflection is the same as mine?' But the young cougar would not open his eyes. In disgust the old cougar threatened to throw him in the water if he didn't open his eyes. With this, the young cougar opened his eyes and saw he looked just like the one he feared.

"Within a week the young cougar began to understand what it was to be Cougar. In time, he liked the taste of raw meat and learned how to hunt for his food. He was thrilled he could see in the dark and proud he could stalk and kill his prey without being caught. The young cougar gained new confidence and soon loved his new world of Cougar power.

"Over the next year, the old cougar became proud of the young cougar and said, 'It is time we return to the flock.' As they walked together into the meadow, the old cougar commanded, 'Go kill that mama sheep that raised you.' The young cougar begged the old cougar not to force him to do such a thing, but the old cougar started killing all the sheep onc by one to prove that Cougar does not allow emotion to rule his life. Hating to see the sheep die, the young cougar approached his adopted mother and roared, 'Mama, you kept me alive when I was young, and I thank you for that. But you trained me to be a sheep and that is not who I am. I give you my word that I will never kill sheep for my food, but if the flock is to survive, I must kill you because I am Cougar.'

"The mama sheep understood and said, 'For a long time I have known this day would come. You are my sacred enemy. Take my life and eat my flesh so that I will become a part of you. I know that as Cougar your ability to kill is swift and painless. It is time for you to do what Cougar does best.'

"Without hesitation the young cougar killed his adopted mother and offered her as a gift to the old cougar for his teachings. The young cougar said to the old cougar, 'Today I am Cougar. I will see you no more. I will establish my territory, and if you ever cross my boundaries, I will kill you, just as you have taught me.'

"The old cougar answered, 'I expect that from Cougar. And if I ever see you again in my territory, I will kill you.'"

Meeko was appalled at the cruel ways of Cougar power and said, "Granbear, I don't want to be as coldhearted as Cougar."

"Grandson, when you understand the teaching of all animals, you will know everything about yourself. You're afraid of Cougar, and sometimes you act too much like a sheep. Cougar power will help you grow from the harsh experiences of life. You, like the young cougar, got mixed up and became something that you were not. You've learned too many bad things. Sometimes you act too white for an Indian boy. Everyone must learn their hardest lessons from their own kind.

"*Tunka'shila* sits in the heart of every child, no matter if it is a two leg, a four leg, or a creepy crawly. Because this is so, they listen with a loving and curious heart while following *Tunka'shila*'s voice. In the beginning of life, that's how babies are. They quickly learn who their natural enemies are so they can survive on Mother Earth. Like any other child, Grandson, you must keep *Tunka'shila* close to your heart if you expect to have a good life," said Granbear, loading his pipe and asking Meeko to join him in a healing smoke.

When the ceremony was completed, Granbear offered the ashes to the four directions, saying, "For now, think on my words and see how they affect what you have experienced in your young life." Granbear left the Medicine Wheel, telling Meeko to think of what he must do to become a good human.

Early the following morning, Meeko sat waiting as Granbear joined him in the South Door of the Medicine Wheel and said, "Today we open the last doorway of the animal traditions in the Medicine Wheel. "Grandson, Cougar and Bear are bitter enemies, but if both are starving, they will share a meal. As you have found, Cougar takes charge of its life. When you can walk in silence with the power of Cougar, you then can say you have control of your life. As long as you use common sense, Cougar will speak to you with these words, 'I got mine, now go get yours.'

"Cougar teaches that truth brings the power to make us independent, alert and aware of our surroundings. If you want to be a leader, Cougar demands you value your freedom and enjoy solitude. Grandson, becoming a leader does not mean that others will follow you.

"Long ago, some of our medicine people lived alone in isolation and collected Cougar bones and paws for healing the sick and wounded. Most people feared them because they were truthful and defended their convictions, regardless of the consequences. Cougar taught them that if they had the slightest fear, they would lose their Cougar medicine. If you choose to follow the way of Cougar, know it will be a hard journey.

"Meeko, I have always known you to be fascinated by the big cats. But I warn you, once you touch Cougar power, she will destroy you if you do not use her medicines to eat the habits that have caused you so much pain. Only you can call on the power of Cougar, but you'd better have the courage to awaken her in your heart when you do. Cougar will not live in a coward's heart. You must know how to focus on your spiritual strength to achieve self-love and self-respect."

"Granbear, how will I know if Cougar will accept me?"

"Grandson, I too know about bad feelings. I remember a sad, lonely night when my first wife left me for another man while I was hunting. I found some cat droppings, and decided to track this killer. I shape-shifted and became Cougar, and found out my prey was female because I could feel her in my body. My mind was totally absorbed in finding that cougar when I saw a faint trail left by her long, moving tail. I knew she was hunting and totally absorbed in her next kill.

"Suddenly a bloodcurdling scream came from behind me. She was so close that I thought the earth had opened up and a thousand demons had risen from the ground to devour my soul. I was in serious trouble because that cougar was now tracking me! She let out another loud scream and, believe me, I was so scared I froze in my tracks. Then silence! I knew she was crawling on her belly, inching closer to me. Then I let go of my fear and charged her, running past her as fast as I could, until I entered my house. She jumped onto the old roof and clawed at it, tearing it open. Knowing that cougar is afraid of fire, I took the kerosene lamp and held it up to the roof.

"I didn't sleep a wink that night and was thankful when the sun came up. I was still so afraid she might be near that it took me almost half a day to go outside. Meeko, I sure learned a good lesson from that big cat that night. After that, I never went near Cougar again, whether she was raising babies or not. So remember, if you ever meet Cougar, make plenty of noise and fight unless you want to die. Cougar teaches confidence and demands you stand up for your life without hesitation, doubt, guilt, or fear! And do it with dignity!

"I want you to truly understand the powers of a female cougar. We call her *Igmu*, and she is the Gatekeeper of the South Door. Some people call her Mountain Lion, or Screamer, and to others she is known as Puma, or Panther. No matter what she is named, *Igmu* protects all the medicines of the South Door. This fierce, mysterious lady shows very little emotion, but that does not mean she has no feeling. She shares her emotions only with those she chooses.

"Cougar has no patience with stupid or stubborn people. She trusts no one and holds a defensive attitude at all times. That's why this loner is always patrolling and marking her territory with piles of dirt, mixed with leaves and twigs that she has pissed on. To find her, you would have to climb the highest mountain, search deep in the desert canyons, or cut your way through the dense tropical jungles.

"Cougar is fascinating. Her sleek coat ranges in color from ash-beige to a grayish silver, or even golden brown. When sunlight touches her body, the colors blend into the many different shades of Mother Earth. Her black-tipped dark brown tail that she uses for balancing, resembles a thick rope about the size of a man's forearm. The old people say that her whiskers bring good luck to artists, but I don't think Cougar will give one up too easily. She uses them to measure spaces to feel if they are big enough for her body to enter safely. The muscles in her shoulders and legs ripple with power, and she is always prepared to stalk or attack. This animal commands attention since no other has such confidence. It must be this that attracts so many admirers. Meeko, don't you wonder how she got this kind of power?"

"Granbear, I thought she was just born that way."

"No, as a baby she has to be taught to be Cougar. Then she teaches humans many things. If they want to be successful, they must leap forward and grab every opportunity that comes their way. She has purpose behind every action and, if attacked, will not hesitate to fight to her death. Cougar always does what Cougar does, no matter the price.

"My brother once told me that her hind legs were slightly longer than her forelegs, making her walk with a slight sway that I thought was funny. I once saw Cougar use those hind legs to leap off a high boulder. She stretched her body out like she was flying and landed perfectly. I'd never seen such power in my life!

"Grandson, you don't ever want to be on the receiving end of Cougar's claws because one swat can bring serious injury or death. One time I saw Cougar stalk an elk. She slunk forward inch by inch toward her prey, often freezing in place, her tail twitching back and forth. Suddenly, as fast as lightning, she sprang onto that elk and broke its back, then ripped its neck open with her swift claws. Cougar *does* give a merciful death.

"Cougar can also teach us about romance and relationships, although her many courtships are still strange to me. She mates about every two years, romancing several possible mates, then picking the strongest one. You never want to be near her during this time because violent fights break out among the males and many are injured or killed. Once she becomes pregnant, she chases her mate off, finds a shelter, lines it with dead leaves, then waits for her babies to be born. Cougar cubs are born blind, but in about two weeks their eyes open to their new world. Their little bodies are covered with tiny black spots that disappear in about six months.

"Like Bear, a mother cougar raises her cubs alone. When they are about two months old, she takes them out, still bringing them food while she trains them to hunt for themselves. Recognizing her voice—that goes from a hiss to a growl to a loud purr to a scream—they know when she makes a shrill, whistling sound, she is warning them of danger. Her cubs live with her for about two years, before she demands they get their own territories to begin the cycle all over again.

"Cougar's special senses are keen hearing and eyesight. Her small round ears move, taking in sounds from all directions. Likewise, she can expand her pupils to fill her entire eye, giving her powerful night vision. Cougar is an excellent hunter usually killing her prey in the early morning or the late evening. She is very wise and only kills the old, the weak or the sick among the deer, elk, moose, wild sheep, goats, rabbits, wild turkeys and ground squirrels. Like a house cat, Cougar hates getting wet. But if a duck is near and Cougar is hungry, she'll become a swimmer real quick. I've seen her powerful jaws grab a duck out of the water, then sinking her long sharp teeth through it, she will tear it to pieces in seconds. Now, that's what I call a quick dinner," chuckled Granbear.

"This silent-footed one is clever and shows us how to have our own territory while living on Mother Earth. Cougar knows nature's secrets and is truly the master of her world. She is feared, hated and loved. When you meet her in Shadow World, she will share those deep mysteries with you. But if you enter her domain with fear, she will capture your soul. The solitary life of this mountain lion is sheer, raw power that is always in control," concluded Granbear, reminding Meeko as they left the Medicine Wheel to spend time in Shadow World visiting this mysterious lady of the night.

For the next four days, Cougar seemed to walk on Meeko's mind. Once he felt her eyes piercing him and grew afraid, pulling himself out of Shadow World in a cold sweat. But with the next encounter, he forced himself to face this open-mouthed Cougar. Hearing Meeko scream in terror, Granbear rushed in and remarked, "I see Cougar has walked on your mind."

"Yes, Granbear, I've never been so afraid."

"Grandson, Mountain Screamer is making you feel what's in your soul. You fear her because you do not accept that you have fear in your life. The human race and the big cats avoid each other because humans do not want to face their truth and expose their weaknesses.

"*Igmu* is hunted by Bear, Wolf, Coyote and other big cats, but her greatest predator is man. Humans hunt this mysterious creature because they fear her and want to pretend they have her power. Using trained dogs and guns, men drive Cougar up a tree and shoot her down, proudly claiming their bounty and boasting of their bravery.

"Grandson, I teach you these things so you can become a good spiritual human and use the sacred powers of the animals to serve others. Without knowledge of people and animals, you cannot recognize beings with these kinds of powers. Someday when you become an artist, you will need to know these things if you are to paint what the spirits tell you.

"Ah yes, Grandson, all animals can teach you about relationships with yourself and others. But when you build a relationship with Cougar, you will understand the kind of relationship you can have with another while having your own freedom. The day will come when you choose a mate. If she is destructive, Cougar would say, 'Let go of the emotional ties and do what is right for you.' Cougar demands that you leave any relationship or thing that is destructive to you.

"Look at how destructive Renna has been with you. Cougar would quickly demand that you take control and never allow anyone to use your emotions against you. Meeko, let your emotions be yours, not what someone forces on you. As Cougar, you may sometimes feel cut off from the world; but by using Cougar's intelligence, competitiveness and love of solitude, you can act correctly—if your beliefs and convictions are strong enough.

"The Medicine Wheel teaches us there is a time for everything in life. A time to pray. A time to fight. A time to play. A time to be gentle. A time to love. A time to talk. A time to be silent. And always time for the betterment of yourself. Now that's Indian Time.

"In everyone's life there are times for change. When I was young, I loved a woman who was like Renna. After six months of marriage, I felt I could not live without her. But she loved another, and I lost my home, my self-respect and my self-love. That was a lonely time in my life, and I felt there was no reason to live. I even forgot about *Wakan Tanka*. If I had listened to my heart, I would have heard Cougar saying it was time for me to take back my feelings, just as you must do with yours for Renna. It is time to get back the feelings that were ripped from you. Once you rid your mind of your bad feelings toward her, you will be free of the hatred in your heart and can begin to rebuild your feelings of love and respect. I believe Great Spirit put you with her to teach you to be strong and free. Now, that's Cougar power!

"Let's look again at the Sacred Medicine Wheel, and tell me how you use the animals to know people."

Meeko sat up straight and said, "The West People, like Eagle, teach me to fly high and see the bigger picture, so I can look into the future and see a problem coming. *Wanbli Gle'ska*, takes my prayers to *Wakan Tanka*, and if I sit in Shadow World long enough, I will be given all the knowledge I need. Eagle tells me that I can develop the ability to get through hard times without getting caught up in bad feelings and demands that I seek my true self. Indian Time means no time. It's how I spend my time that counts. If I use my creativity to find *Wakan Tanka*, I will have power and confidence in every song and prayer. Eagle says I must speak in truth and be watchful, and follow the cycles of the seasons. Once I find the rhythm of life and understand nature, my quest will always grow by my knowledge. My heart has to be healed before I can dream with hope. If I want to call upon the spirits, I have to find the doorway to them through praying, drumming, singing and dancing.

"The North People, like Bear, teach me not to cross their boundaries. Buffalo says I must be kind and giving to all life. I must learn to get past my feelings and hunt for the spiritual fire in each person. When I'm following Wolf, I have to be a loyal family member of the Bear Clan people and unite all of them to do what is best for the tribe. But I need to always be very careful if I am talking to the trickster, Coyote.

"The East People, like Elk and Deer, teach me to love myself in spirit and have a forgiving heart.

"The South People, like Cougar, teach me to get rid of my sad feelings and remember I always have the right to make good choices in my life. Cougar will give me the power to control my feelings. It is the warmth from my heart that makes me happy and that's when Cougar will let me be an artist."

"Very good, Grandson. Come, look at the sky and let that blanket of stars cradle you in life," commented Granbear, pleased that his lessons were taking effect.

"Granbear, while I was searching my mind for Cougar, she gave me a dream. I heard a flute playing while I was painting a woman's face. I seemed to know her."

"Is that so, Grandson? Maybe this woman will believe in your art and give you a cougar whisker. I know someday you will see people's traits as surely as you'll be able to express your feelings, and that's when you will be an artist."

"Granbear, are you telling me that someday I will see people like animals?"

"Absolutely! Their traits are easily recognized. Some people, like some animals, are very sociable. Others are like the cats and don't want to be bothered. Some have a great confidence, while you must approach others very carefully because they don't know who they are. A good artist can see these things and paint their meanings with deep emotion. But until you learn to accept your own feelings, you won't be able to paint any emotion. Don't let your sadness eat away your peace. Once you realize that knowledge is not repeating the words, but becoming the words, you will see that the sun shines equally on everything. When this happens, you will feel the special love in all of *Wakan Tanka*'s creatures.

"Meeko, free yourself from what imprisons you. Let this Medicine Wheel training become your guide in all walks of your life. Breath is the secret passageway to enter Shadow World and that is where you go to find all of your answers. You were born from the land and you will return to the land, but know that your soul will live forever far beyond the pines."

Boy Training

It was long after breakfast when Granbear called Meeko to the arbor. "Grandson, you are nearly fourteen winters and it is time to accept the responsibility for your life. Let the Medicine Wheel training help you walk with respect on your sacred earth journey. Soon you will be learning a deeper understanding of nature. Shadowhawk will demand you know all the symbols that are hidden in the unspoken languages of the natural world. What a wonderful adventure you are going to take with your grandfather, a man of great honor.

"Shadowhawk will share his warrior experiences with you and demand truth in your words. He will use the traits of the animals to build your courage to face life's dangers. He will insist on the silence of Eagle so you can learn the power to examine all that is around you. Shadowhawk will use Bear to establish strong boundaries. Buffalo to teach you patience. Wolf to demand loyalty. Coyote to become a clever survivor. Elk to develop keen listening skills and passion for understanding. He will expect you to look from your heart, rather than your eyes when you search for truth.

"Shadowhawk will use Cougar to help you conquer your rage. He will never allow you to judge or qualify your actions in any given situation. As you learn from these things, remember thoughtfulness reaps the greatest harvest."

"When I see Shadowhawk waiting for the sun to rise to smoke his pipe, I smile from my heart, knowing this happy man is giving thanks for living another day. Shadowhawk will always know your intentions and if you are feeling joy or sorrow. You may not agree with his ways of teaching, but never cheat yourself from learning a different way to survive.

"Ah, Grandson. Life can be as clever as Coyote, and many times it is best to walk in silence and keep a good sense of humor. I've lived through many experiences in my life. They have taught me to appreciate a good night's sleep and a good meal. I also know that my real food comes from Great Spirit, and that's what feeds my soul."

"Life can be a very lonely walk if you choose to surround yourself with dark clouds of confusion. It is you who must feel worthy of Creator's gifts and accept the happiness in being his child. Remember Meeko, life is simple; it's people who complicate it."

Although Meeko was apprehensive about training under Shadowhawk, he knew this man would demand strong principles and many responsibilities from him.

Understanding where he was in life, Meeko asked, "Granbear you know I've always wanted a father in my life. Do you think it would be okay if I ask Shadowhawk to be my *Hunka Áte*, adopted father, during my boy training?"

"Do you think you are ready to become a *Hunka Towa*, adopted relative child?"

"Yes, I'm ready to ask for the ceremony of making relatives and feel that Shadowhawk would be the right person to guide my manhood years."

"Well, Grandson, there is a way to do everything." Granbear gave Meeko a pipe then explained what he must do. "Go talk to the grandfathers and get their advice about how to earn the right to receive this ceremony."

Meeko went to speak to many of the elders about his situation and found an old Sundance leader who smoked the pipe with him then explained what a *Hunka Towa* ceremony would require from himself and Shadowhawk.

Following his instructions, Meeko chose three trustworthy men to become his advisors. After gathering more information from them, he was advised to take his pipe, sweetgrass and sage to Granbear, and ask in a proper manner if he would be his medicine man for the *Hunka* ceremony.

After the pipe ceremony, Granbear advised Meeko to find two *Hunkapila Kola's*, relative friends, to speak on his behalf to Shadowhawk to see if he would consider becoming his *Hunka Áte*. Taking his pipe again, Meeko chose two Dog Soldiers to speak for him. They sat with Meeko under a large shade tree listening.

"*Kolas*, I give you this filled pipe along with this willow bark and sweetgrass to offer to Shadowhawk to become my *Hunka Áte*. I know what I do is right. I know you both are *Hunkas* and I want to speak to you about the *Hunka* ceremony."

They spoke for some time about the loyalty and responsibilities to become a *Hunka Towa*, then by late afternoon they agreed this was a good thing. When they left on their mission, Meeko wondered if he had been strong enough to impress Shadowhawk to accept his offer. That evening when Meeko saw the two men approaching he became nervous.

"We have done as you've asked, Little Brother. Shadowhawk has accepted your pipe. He will use it in prayer to see if the spirits wish for him to become your *Hunka Áte*."

Meeko was happy to hear their words and yelled, "*Hau*, thank you."

Granbear heard and said, "Meeko, Shadowhawk makes decisions with great thought, for he is a warrior who carries *Contrar* medicine. What you've asked of him, says you wish to be like him. It means you have to know the old ways backward and forward. A *Contrar* will say 'I hate you' but that could mean 'I love you.' They have the power to stick their hands in boiling water but tell everyone it's ice cold. They can bathe in icy water and scream that it's too hot. To follow these ways, you must be able to completely control your body, thoughts and actions without any fear of failure.

"If Shadowhawk refuses you as a *Hunka*, he can also refuse to guide you across the bridge between boyhood and manhood. Are you sure you want to try to accomplish these two ambitions at one time?"

"Granbear, I know I can do both, but I'll do whatever you advise."

"Well then, if this is what you want, it's time to get your advisors and meet with your desired *Hunka Até* in the proper manner."

Shadowhawk smiled as the four entered his house. Granbear spoke first. "I bring you my great-grandson. He wants you to become his *Hunka Até*."

Then each man stepped forward speaking in Meeko's behalf. Granbear stood up to go saying, "We all want the best for Meeko. So, I will say goodbye to the boy and soon let you introduce Meeko, the man, to the Bear Clan." Granbear winked in a knowing way at Shadowhawk and both agreed that this training would be beneficial for Meeko.

As they were leaving, Granbear hesitated at the door, saying, "I'll be visiting some friends for a few days. They will drive me to the bus station to pick up Lizzie, then bring us home. Meeko will stay and begin his duties to become a *Hunka Towa*." Turning to Meeko, he said, "Grandson, don't let your shortsightedness aggravate Shadowhawk while I'm gone."

Meeko felt intimidated with Granbear's words, yet full of anticipation as he sat alone with Shadowhawk, a man he had feared since age three. He remembered Shadowhawk scowling at his *Alo Wanpi*, Sing Ceremony, when he cried getting his ear pierced. But now, he felt somewhat more confident about facing Shadowhawk's challenges.

"My Grandson, you have always been strong in my heart. But are you sure you are ready to leave behind your childish thinking and become a good man? I know you have always missed having a father, and I can be that father. My question to you is, can you be a son? I have taken counsel with Granbear, my *Hunka*, and he has advised me to consider this matter carefully before I make you my *Hunka Towa*. I have chosen three elders to assist me before I give you my final decision.

"The *Hunka* ceremony is only given to a special few. You were taken away from the reservation very young and many of your thoughts are still too scattered. There will be many responsibilities demanded from both of us to build a strong *Hunka* relationship. We must ask *Wakan Tanka* if this ceremony should be granted.

"Before I can agree to become your *Hunka Até*, I will explain the responsibilities so that you understand what it takes to be a *Hunka Towa*. As a *Hunka Towa*, you can never lie or deceive me. Nor can you question my decisions. Whatever I ask of you, you must do, even if you disagree. Your loyalty is to be given without question. If you are accepted into a *Hunka* family, you are related to all *Hunka* families. The honor of being a *Hunka Towa* goes far beyond any position of a birth son. A *Hunka* family is your first family, and you must always be generous and protect them. Not only will my children be your brothers and sisters, my wife will be your mother. And if I choose another woman, she too will be your mother.

"Once the ceremony is completed, we must always respect and never dishonor one another. Such loyalty is stronger than blood and you, like me, will honor the people and condemn every bad thing thrust upon them for all time," stated Shadowhawk, looking deep into Meeko's soul.

As Shadowhawk continued to probe the boy's mind, Meeko felt intimidated, his mind racing as if he was riding chaotic waves in a sea of flames. He knew deep inside that being Shadowhawk's *Hunka Towa* would bind him forever to this man, and this scared him.

"Meeko, in the old times I would have demanded a *Hunka Towa* to take many wives. Now I ask you to take one good wife. In the past I would also have demanded you to help me steal many horses as well as women. Now I ask you to never steal. I would have insisted you fight and kill my enemies and take many scalps. Now I ask you to not harm another. These are my rules and once we're bound together, it is for life. Know this bond can never be broken, nor can either of us withdraw from this relationship unless we both give our consent in front of council. It is they who give the last word."

He started to speak, but Shadowhawk put his hand up for silence. "Before you speak, I have things to say that must stay locked in your heart and never become spoken words. Do you understand?"

Meeko nodded obediently.

"Granbear is a most highly respected holy man. He is the only one left that can incite the magic voice in this ceremony. He knows the great Sun Chief, and when he enters that doorway, this powerful man of reverence knows how to ride with the above powers. Since I cannot teach these things, I insist you learn as much as you can before he leaves us.

"When Auntie Lizzie and I had your mother, Granbear became my *Hunka Áté*. You are my grandson, and naturally I want you as my *Hunka Towa*. I have watched you closely, and I know you can become a good man. But I have also seen how you like the girls. Two of those young girls are my daughters. There will be no more looking at your sisters in a wrong way if you are to become part of my *Hunka* family."

Meeko gazed at the floor in shame, hoping Shadowhawk would accept his ignorance, wondering why he had never been told of these things before.

Shadowhawk knew he had touched Meeko's heart and dismissed him curtly. "Go pray to have the ceremony sanctioned by the Great Spirit. I will go to the hills for a *Hanblecheyapi*. When I come back, I will be ready to give you my answer."

Grateful for his instructions, Meeko spent the next four days praying and awaiting Shadowhawk's return. On the fifth day, Shadowhawk arrived with a broad smile on his face. "Start planning for the *Hunka* ceremony. Invite everyone to celebrate this great occasion."

Meeko was ecstatic that *Wakan Tanka* had sanctioned the ceremony and knew there was a great deal of work to do before the ceremony. It was Granbear's responsibility to find the mysterious sacred ear of corn then paint it in alternating red and blue stripes, leaving some rows in their natural color. He also supervised how to make the secret wands to send to certain guests.

On the day before the ceremony many people began to arrive and offered to help. Certain ones were chosen to help with the last-minute details, and by late afternoon the tipi held all the needed items.

When the sun went over down, Shadowhawk sent word for the participants to meet in the tipi for the night ceremony. Meeko arrived with willow bark, sweetgrass, tobacco and his pipe. Everyone waited in silence as the fire burned down to hot coals. Shadowhawk and Meeko sat at the West Door of the tipi while Shadowhawk's advisors sat in the other three directions.

Then Meeko filled a special pipe and handed it to Shadowhawk who, in turn, sprinkled sweetgrass over the coals and waved the pipe in a circular motion through the smoke. "Oh, Great Spirits of the West, North, East, and South, give us your warm and unselfish blessings for this ceremony." He then offered the pipe up to *Wakan Tanka*. "Oh, *Tunka'shila*, Grandfather, I humbly offer this smoke up to you. Oh, Spirit of the West, we appeal to you. Oh, Spirit of the North, we plead to you. Oh, Spirit of the East, we draw upon you. Oh, Spirit of the South, we urge you. Oh, sweet Spirit of Mother Earth, we ask much of you." Then with the pipe over his head, Shadowhawk stood and called upon *Wakan Tanka* to sanction the ceremony for all the people to witness.

As Granbear entered carrying the counting sticks and one fire stick, his helpers placed a painted Buffalo skull on the altar. While Granbear chanted an ancient song, Meeko's advisors brought in two *Hunka* wands decorated with horsehair and two eagle feathers swaying from each end. They also carried two rattles and the sacred corn adorned with two white eagle plumes hanging from the end. When the song was finished, Granbear lit his pipe and prayed as he walked in a sunwise manner around the tipi. A helper followed him, holding both wands in one hand and the skin of a mallard duck in the other, calling to *Okaga* while offering the corn up to Father Sky. Granbear called out, "May this sacred corn represent our *Até*, *Wi*, and *Maka Ina*."

Granbear took the mysterious ear of sacred corn. "Give this family plenty of food, *Tunka'shila*, and take this dried meat to please *Tatanka*. Let these gifts, along with our prayers, reach to the spirit of the animals so they may always take care of the people." Taking the painted tail feathers of a young eagle, he waved them above Meeko's head, shouting, "May the spirit of *Wanbli Gle'ska* ride in this tail. Let these feathers make a brave man who will bring peace and happiness to all who know him."

Granbear took the wands, and waving them over Meeko's head, shouted, "Oh, fire of the light, see these four quills..I offer this gift from *Wanbli Gle'ska*. Let them hang as a sacred fan always, so this young man can speak to the spirits of the Sun Chief and *Tatanka*." Again Granbear waved the wands over Meeko. "May you always have plenty to share with your *Hunka Até*."

The old medicine man took two buffalo scrotum rattles which were painted red with blue stripes, and again called out, "Oh, *Tunka'shila*, Grandfather, we offer up these two rattles to please the good spirits and to drive the bad ones away. We call upon the Two times Two, the day and the night powers. Let them give us two good blue days and two good red days."

Granbear brought out a mysterious pipe that was seldom used and lit it. Offering it up to the spirits, he softly prayed, "Oh, Great Spirit who lives in the Buffalo skull, tell the animals and the plant people to please take care of the children." He then burned sweetgrass to summon all the spirits to join in the ceremony and lit sage to drive away the bad spirits as he sang songs recounting the history of all the *Hunkas*.

When Granbear had finished, Shadowhawk handed Meeko a large Bear medicine bag, saying, "You will stand like Bear, and you will never sleep with Coyote."

Granbear shouted out to Meeko, "My moccasins are old. I have none to take their place. Take off your moccasins and give them to me." Meeko obeyed.

"I am cold and hungry. I have nothing to wear. Take off your clothes and give them to me," demanded Granbear in a forceful voice. Meeko handed him food and stripped down to his loincloth.

Granbear smiled, then yelled out, "You have proven you are a *Hunka*. See everyone, he has given up everything for a *Hunka* in need." He painted the right side of Meeko's face with a red stripe from his forehead to his chin. "This is so no one will ever forget who you are. I now place such a stripe on your *Hunka Até*." With steady hands Granbear painted an identical stripe on Shadowhawk's face. Thunderous drumming rang throughout the tipi, driving the *Hunka* members to their feet while they lifted their voices as one in a *Hunka* honoring song.

Shadowhawk shouted, "*Hunkas* are willing to die for each other! Look everyone! There is an enemy in the camp! Who will help me capture him?"

Meeko bolted to his side, and together they crouched down into the stance of stalkers. Moving silently around the outside of the tipi, they slashed at all that was near, and when they re-entered the tipi, everyone let out the *Hunka* warrior's cry then burst into their victory song.

Meeko was offered the place of honor next to Shadowhawk who said, "I take this young man as my *Hunka Towa*."

When the advisors heard this they rushed at them, wrestling both to the ground, binding their arms and legs together. Shadowhawk and Meeko were stood up on their feet as Granbear waved the *Hunka* wands over them. "You are bound as one for life. What you have will be his. What he has will be yours. If anyone tries to harm your *Hunka*, you will seek revenge. I bless this joining."

It was sunrise before the ceremony was completed, and everyone shared in a special feast to celebrate this sacred ceremony. And for the first time, Meeko was moved by the commitment of such a ceremony and proud he had participated in this ancient custom.

Time passed as the hot summer winds blew steadily. Every afternoon rainstorms swept over the land, making Meeko more aware of the cycles of life caused by water. His knowledge grew as he observed every aspect of nature. In the evening the old people would sit listening to the night sounds, often speaking softly to Meeko to help him understand his own life dance.

When Summer Solstice arrived, Granbear, Shadowhawk and other Sundance leaders began preparing for the sacred Sun Dance. Meeko wished he could participate in this sacred ceremony, and spent days walking into the interior of the reservation thinking about his desire. He walked to a high point overlooking the vastness of the hills and valleys to listen to the messages of the winds, praying the spirits would embrace his needs. Trying to absorb nature's innermost secrets, he remembered

Granbear's words, "First know yourself, then you can connect to the spirit that moves in all things. Only then will the Great Spirit assist you in placing one foot in front of the other without ever leaving a bad mark on the land."

Slowly Meeko began to merge with all life around him like an invisible being with no thought, breath or sound. Meeko heard his inner voice whisper. "Let the animals, plants and trees guide you to the pathway of a good heart." Suddenly in a terrifying voice that penetrated to the core of his soul, the winds warned, "Run, Meeko, Run." Feeling unsettled, Meeko sat that evening with the elders, listening to Granbear speak about their days of collecting old bones in the Badlands and the deep significance of this one hundred and twenty square miles of barren land that held the history of First Creation.

He felt the presence of these old spirits, just as he had while listening to Granbear's campfire stories about all the aspects of the Medicine Wheel. But this time he experienced a revelation—the world had new meaning and everything had a purpose when he saw that everything was connected to spirit. Thinking of how Red Cloud and Crazy Horse had fought to save their way of life, he wished the land was once again filled with buffalo and tipis. Yearning for more knowledge about his people, Meeko went to Granbear. "Why do we place our dead underground instead of above ground, like long ago?"

"Some people do place the dead above the ground, but most do like the white man and bury their dead. I do not believe in that way. The soul must be given the time to find its way back to the spirit world. The Keeping and Releasing of the Soul is the first rite on the pipe. To be a strong pipe carrier, we do as the pipe tells us."

"Granbear, if I chose to walk the Sundance way, would it help me build a stronger pipe?"

"Meeko, many things are considered when learning to track the beast that lives inside. The Sun Dance teaches us to track ourselves and return with all knowledge of our soul's existence. A good Sundancer tracks himself without disturbing another's world, just as Shadowhawk tracks animals without disturbing the land. Each of us finds our own way."

That night Meeko lay awake reflecting on the potential growth that might await him if he became a Sundancer. Long before dawn the next morning, he joined Shadowhawk to help gather firewood for a sweat. "The *Inipi* reminds us to always give thanks to *Wakan Tanka* for all life and pray for spiritual guidance in all that we do," said Shadowhawk.

"Shadowhawk, I wonder if I could Sundance this year?"

"Have you discussed this with Granbear? You know you must pledge one year before participating in the Sun Dance. Did you do this?"

"No," confessed Meeko. "But I would like to dance while Granbear is still alive."

"That would be a good thing. We'll pray over this in tonight's *Inipi*."

Three weeks before the Sun Dance, Meeko helped set up security, placing a long pole across the road to control the entrance. As he did so, Shadowhawk outlined the rest of his duties. "You must know everyone who enters, and no matter who it is, search every vehicle for alcohol, drugs, or cameras before putting a red cloth on the antenna."

Coming home from a hard day's work, Meeko was surprised when Granbear handed him his piercing ropes. Knowing this meant he had been sanctioned to Sundance, Meeko thanked Granbear profusely and hurried off to ask an old grandmother to make him a Sundance skirt.

The night before the Sun Dance, the grounds were filled with many new tipis and tents. Very early the next morning forty men went to get the sacred cottonwood tree that had been selected the year before. Shadowhawk motioned two men to climb up and place ropes among its branches to keep the tree from touching the ground as it fell. As the men carried the sacred tree on their shoulders back to the Sundance circle amidst much singing, an old Sundancer invited Meeko to join them. Thrilled to be one of the new pledgers, he sang proudly along with the group. When they entered the sacred circle, Shadowhawk invited Meeko to walk by his side to the front of the tree.

Granbear met them with his Staff of Life and placed the tobacco, buffalo meat and water into the hole that had been dug for the sacred tree. The people lined up to give flesh offerings as they prayed. Many prayer flags and tobacco ties were placed in the tree's branches, while Shadowhawk hung the handmade leather images of a bull buffalo and a man. He then placed four Chokecherry branches into the tree to symbolize abundance for the world, while the Sundancers fastened their piercing ropes to the tree. Following Granbear's signal, the men stood the sacred tree in the hole. As the wind slowly began to dance with the colorful prayer flags, Meeko stood next to Granbear and felt a power growing from the joyous faces of the people.

Later as Meeko wandered through the campgrounds, the grandmother presented him with a beautiful blue Sundance skirt on which was painted a bear face with many ribbon streamers. Granbear joined them, admiring her work, then handed Meeko his piercing sticks along with an eagle fan and an eagle bone whistle.

Meeko entered the Sundancers' lodge and began to twist pieces of sage into wreaths, wrapping them carefully with blue material. He made one for his head, two for his wrists, and two more for his ankles.

"My name is Crow. Is this your first year to dance?" a stranger asked.

Feeling insecure, as he noticed the many scars on the man's chest, legs and back, Meeko said softly, "Yes."

"You'll do fine," encouraged Crow.

Following the sweat the next morning, Meeko silently went with the others to the Sundance tipi and dressed for his first day in a Sundance circle. Crow smiled and placed a Golden Eagle feather on each side of Meeko's head, saying, "These eagle feathers will help you be strong through your first Sun Dance."

When Meeko walked into the Sundance circle, skirts of many colors came alive with the rising sun. The symbols of Eagle, Bear, Buffalo and Lightning Man moved on the garments as the drums called to the dancers. The high-pitched sounds of their eagle bone whistles connected the dancers as they raised their eyes toward the sun.

Meeko blew his eagle bone whistle with every step, letting his feet glide to the rhythm of the drum's beat. At the end of the first endurance, Meeko left the circle to go and rest under the arbor where Granbear quietly acknowledged that he was doing well.

A helper approached each dancer offering them burning cedar. Meeko inhaled deeply to feel the smoke's power touch his soul. When the dancers returned to continue the Sun Dance, Crow walked over to the Tree of Life and lay down on a bed of sage. Shadowhawk knelt over him and pierced Crow on the right and left side of his chest, placing his hanging sticks through each slit. After his ropes were hooked over these sticks, he stretched his arms outward as they hoisted him up into the tree. There he hung for the rest of the day. Slowly *Anpetu*, the red that shines at twilight, painted its colors across the evening sky signaling for the serene glowing Crow to be lowered to the ground.

As Meeko tried to sleep that night many pictures danced on the back of his eyelids. He saw people of long ago being pierced at the tree, dragging behind them as many as twelve Buffalo skulls hooked to their backs. He cried with joy, knowing that he was gathering power in the same way as his ancient ancestors had done long ago.

On the second day, Meeko danced in view of Crow, who was once again hanging in the sacred Tree of Life with outstretched arms looking directly into the sun. That evening as Meeko listened to other dancers complain of hunger, thirst, exhaustion and sunburned bodies, he was thankful that Granbear and Shadowhawk had prepared him well.

On the third day prayers were said for the fallen dancers who were either taken to the tree to rest or left to sit with their heads bowed in shame. Granbear or Shadowhawk spoke for a long time with the dancers as they left the circle. Meeko was exhausted and worried if he could continue.

Crow, reading his thoughts, encouraged him, saying, "Once I too, was afraid of piercing, but I wanted to dance for the people. I found that Father Sun offers his rays to climb upon. After they paint the red piercing circles on your chest, go to the powers of *Wakan Tanka*, and when you are pierced you won't feel anything."

On the fourth day, Meeko entered the Sundance circle with two red circles painted on his chest which indicated to the Sundance leader where he wished to be pierced. Mid-afternoon he noticed an eagle flying overhead and remembered his first call from Eagle. 'How high can you fly, Meeko? How high do you dare fly?' He felt a strength beyond his knowing surge through him as he glanced toward the tree to see Crow break free from the ropes. Crow dropped to the ground and landed on his feet with a peaceful face that reflected spiritual beauty. In the traditional way Crow ran clockwise four times around the circle then returned to the line of dancers. Meeko, inspired by Crow who looked at him with spirit eyes, left the line to be pierced.

As Meeko lay down on the bed of sage, the appointed grandmother caressed his forehead and spoke to him encouragingly. Granbear placed a bundle of sage in his mouth as Shadowhawk pinched his skin, lifted it from his chest and slipped a knife into it. Shadowhawk helped Meeko to his feet and carefully hooked the ropes to the sticks now protruding from his chest.

The ropes pulled against his flesh, causing a burning sensation. Meeko stood still until his body adjusted to the pain, then danced toward the tree, placing both hands on it in prayer. The tree came alive, its bark felt like soft skin and its movements like human breath. Meeko blew his eagle bone whistle as the beat of the drums drove his pounding feet. Four times he danced to and from the sacred Tree of Life, causing the ropes to stretch his skin outward from his chest as he filled his heart with the strength of Great Spirit.

The last time Meeko danced away, he held his head high and faced the sun, staring unflinchingly as he rode its rays. He danced backwards until his skin stood out four inches from his chest and yet he felt no pain. All of a sudden his skin tore free and the piercing sticks flew into the air as his spirit soared. Meeko ran at breakneck speed four times around the circle, with many friends and family following behind to honor him.

When he returned and stood at the sacred Tree of Life, Granbear smiled proudly and handed Meeko the pieces of his flesh wrapped in a square of red cloth. Shadowhawk took special herbs and mixed them with tobacco to fill Meeko's open wounds. After resting for a moment at the tree, Meeko returned to the line of Sundancers, moving stronger than ever.

Although many pledgers had participated in the Sun Dance, Meeko was proud that he was among those who had completed his Sun Dance ritual.

At the end of the Sun Dance ceremony the participants, now considered holy, lined up and lay their hands on the heads of those who wished to be healed. Once this healing ceremony was accomplished, the Sundance leader called the dancers together for their final sweat. This completed another yearly Sun Dance ceremony.

Once dressed, Meeko looked for Crow, but could not find him. After inquiring about his whereabouts, he thought it strange that no one knew of his presence. Puzzled Meeko went to Granbear and asked, "Where is the man called Crow who hung from the Tree of Life for four days?"

Granbear smiled in a knowing way. "Ah Grandson, many have seen this man called Crow, but few have spoken with him. The old ones say he's a spirit who comes each year to Sundance, and they call him the Man Who Carries Many Scars." Chills ran through Meeko's body when he realized he had danced alongside a great spirit warrior.

For a week, Meeko's mind was engrossed with images of Crow. Once all the people had left Meeko went to sit alone in the Sundance circle to relive the days of the Sun Dance. He was astonished to see Crow again hanging from the tree as he spoke to Meeko of his future. "Today's world demands you learn to use many new weapons in battling for the freedom of humankind's soul. The young ones that are being born today will help free a fear-controlled society. In time you will experience this limitation and understand how the human race has suffered from the ruling peoples of the world." Now certain of his calling, Meeko never spoke of Crow again, yet he never forgot this powerful encounter.

The next day Shadowhawk spent many hours teaching Meeko the history of their people. "We come from the stars and we were chosen to take care of Mother Earth. She holds the bones of our ancestors and we should never sell the land. It was these old ones and nature who taught us that we are one with the land. To become a good warrior and hunter, you must know your place in the tribe. I'm teaching you this history so you too can walk like the invisible trackers of old and never leave a mark upon your path unless you choose to do so. Now, go and learn from the coming season."

During the next three months, Meeko came to understand the reality behind the changes of the seasons and how it takes time for all things to adjust to change.

Meeko was sad to see summer waning and fall approaching. The leaves were slowly turning red and yellow and fell to the ground in brown brittleness, a signal to certain birds it was time to fly south. Meeko felt the anger of winter, knowing *Yatá* was killing everything in his path in order to lay his blanket of winter snow across the land.

Soon winter arrived and Shadowhawk began to teach Meeko new hunting skills, pointing out the importance of the signs left by the animals and the characteristics of plants and trees. While they were tracking one morning, Shadowhawk said, "Everything has its own language. Learn to observe and understand how to speak without the use of words. Learn to feel a presence, then look for the obvious. There are always signs if you are aware of nature's rules. Study each mark left on Mother Earth's floor and know whose footsteps are walking the same trail. Know that the winged ones live above and below and when there is a disturbance on the earth's floor, something is out of balance. Eagle looks for these things and considers them as food, a gift from Creator.

"Sounds are another way to understand nature's laws. Listen to everything and know each message the voice gives you. Study the trees, bushes, stones and animals for the answers you seek. If you become worthy of nature's knowledge, you will understand the lessons that *Wakan Tanka* has provided for all beings." Shadowhawk shared his excitement as he spoke of nature's laws, giving Meeko a deeper understanding of the skill of observation.

"Remember when I sent you to watch the beavers build their summer home?" questioned Shadowhawk. "Did you see why the young must learn to follow the rules of the elders? Beaver teaches her young to grow strong and independent. When she is finished training, she chases them from the home—something human parents could learn. Beaver may teach a harsh lesson, but it is for survival. Pay attention and you will live. Break a rule and you die. Everything in nature is willing to share its teachings, but it takes a wise student to benefit from them.

"Meeko, I tell you these things so you do not become a foolish hunter. Taking a life is done for survival. It's only common sense never to hunt alone. In old times someone who hunted alone was seen as breaking a tribal rule because they would scare away the game needed by others. If this happened, the people would tear up the hunter's tipi and take away his food, or they would demand a public beating.

"In the past a man's words and deeds gave him honor among his people. Sharing and caring was *Wakan Tanka's* way of teaching the people to love one another. This is why we teach our boys to become good, caring men and expect them to pass these values on to the next generation. You must know of all these things, or *Wakan Tanka's* creations will not speak to you."

Arriving home in late afternoon, Meeko and Shadowhawk stripped, gutted, cleaned and distributed two freshly killed deer. The women filled the drying racks and the old men prepared the antlers to be used for carrying the sacred stones into the *Inipi*.

Once the work was completed, Shadowhawk presented a beautifully hand-carved ash bow with arrows to Meeko, who felt honored. Granbear placed the bow stave across Meeko's chest, then down his right side, making sure it was properly sized, stating, "In my day, the bow was our most powerful tool. It kept us from exposing ourselves to the white man's rifles in battle. We would stay well hidden until we were close enough to send our arrows to the target, sometimes as far away as fifty yards. A good warrior knew his weapon and made his arrows deadly. As he rode his war pony, he could shoot faster than a pistol. During battle our men sent arrows to the enemy like a swarm of mad hornets."

At dawn the following morning, Shadowhawk gave Meeko his first lesson with the bow. "Become one with the bow. Feel what the bow is saying to you, and let the arrow be an extension of you," said Shadowhawk as he painted a round target on a tree stump. In time Meeko developed the strength to pull fast and release quickly, hitting the target three out of five tries.

One day Shadowhawk demonstrated his own skill. Meeko watched as his arrow shot high above their heads, then downward, right where he was standing. As Meeko jumped out of the way, Shadowhawk chuckled, saying, "Handle the bow more gently and become one with it before you break its spine. Feel the power in its body and listen to what the bow is telling you."

Meeko was awed by Shadowhawk's skill. Shadowhawk continued the lesson, saying, "Long ago, the tribes tortured enemies' souls by shooting their bellies full of arrows. This practice ensured their children would be born deformed throughout eternity. Our warriors knew their enemies could never take revenge until we released their souls."

Week after week Meeko tried to shoot his arrows into the target. When he could finally plant every arrow precisely, Shadowhawk challenged him further with a rolling hoop, and in a short time his arrows landed in the center of the moving object.

Granbear then added another challenge. He put a small stone between a split stick and had Meeko spin around and shoot, telling him, "When you learn to feel its presence, just turn and release." For weeks Meeko missed because he could not understand how to feel its presence without seeing it. Then one day he felt a surge down his arm, and as he shot the arrow, he split the stone and understood what Granbear had been saying.

Meeko bragged until Shadowhawk took his bow and arrows from him, saying, "Now let's see if you can throw a spear." Shadowhawk heaved forth a heavy spear, and hit the center of his target, then asked, "Did you watch the motion of my body?" Meeko just shrugged, so Shadowhawk demanded he stand by the tree. Shadowhawk arched his back and threw once again. Meeko froze as the singing spear landed between his feet. Horrified, and vowing to get even, he began to practice with the spear until he was sure he could place it between Shadowhawk's legs. When the opportunity came, he aimed it carefully at Shadowhawk's legs and threw, but Shadowhawk caught it in midair and hurled it back between Meeko's legs, saying, "A little more to the right." Stunned and feeling powerless, Meeko knew he would pay dearly for his challenge.

At four o'clock the following morning Shadowhawk woke Meeko and led him to the icy river saying, "A swim in cold water is good for the soul." No sooner did they step into the river than Shadowhawk swam away. Meeko followed submissively, his teeth chattering.

"You sound like an angry squirrel. Where is your stamina?" demanded Shadowhawk, testing Meeko's dedication to his training. As they climbed out of the river, Shadowhawk grabbed Meeko and wrestled him around in the fresh fallen snow. Meeko fought back but nevertheless he lost. Laughing, Shadowhawk tossed Meeko a towel, saying, "After breakfast we'll go hunting," as he raced Meeko back to the house.

At dawn Shadowhawk and Meeko were trudging through the snow when Shadowhawk said, "Today we'll practice tracking so you can learn the right way to kill. For us, killing is never a sport. We kill by first asking permission from the animal. Once given, we take its life quickly and painlessly. An animal should never suffer from a hunter's lack of knowledge. The cleaner the kill, the better the meat. A bad kill results in tainted meat, and we would not want to feed our loved ones spoiled food."

Eager to learn this spiritual way of hunting, Meeko paid close attention as Shadowhawk called to Coyote and then Wolf, both of which answered him. "If you hear a wolf howl a little off-key, something is wrong. And if you hear a magpie chattering too loud," he explained, "you know something is wrong and it's time to go home."

Fascinated, Meeko expressed his appreciation for Shadowhawk's lessons, knowing that someday he might need to know these ways for his own survival. He noticed his feet were crunching in the snow, while Shadowhawk's footsteps were noiseless. He began emulating Shadowhawk's every move. When Shadowhawk imitated an owl, Meeko copied. Shadowhawk smiled, knowing he was finally getting the full attention of his grandson.

Gratified that Meeko was now ready to learn more, Shadowhawk proceeded with another lesson. "To locate water in the summer, find light green growth. That will tell you that you are near a watering hole. When you find dark green vegetation, this says water is close to the surface. Also look for the cottonwood tree, as it can hold up to five buckets of water. Now, if I was thirsty, I would watch for a dove because it waters daily. Also watch for swallows, they fly very low and straight when going for water. If a swallow's mouth is filled with mud, I know he's flying away from water. This would tell me which way I should walk. If you see a mustang's tracks, remember he usually stays within three miles of water. When you find water that's muddy or filled with bugs, grab a clump of grass and dunk it in the water then suck through it or you could eat bugs for dinner. Remember, it's nature that holds the secrets of all survival," continued Shadowhawk stopping to notch a tree. Meeko watched him peel off the bark in a certain way or break a branch, never leaving an obvious mark that would allow another to track him.

"At that moment they spotted a trail of blood on the ground. Examining it, Shadowhawk said, "This blood is from an injured doe that passed this way about half an hour ago. It tells me there is a stupid hunter in the area. We've got to find this animal." As they followed the heart-shaped footprints, the trail of blood became darker. Shadowhawk now moved more cautiously, whispering, "Never trust a wounded animal. If there are hungry predators tracking this trail, we could be in serious trouble."

Shadowhawk slashed the air with his left arm, signaling for Meeko to wipe out all sound. As they approached a thicket of trees, they saw the wounded doe collapsed on the ground, heaving for air. Shadowhawk raised his rifle and with a grim look on his face, fired. He gutted her and took her blood then smeared it over his arms and face letting out a war cry of sorrow. He gently closed her eyes in silent prayer, saying, "I hated to kill such a young doe, but I couldn't let her suffer. She has run in fear so long that her body is filled with blood and her meat will be tough—only good enough to feed Creator's animals."

"C'mon, we have something more important to track. A dangerous hunter is out there and might shoot us if he sees any movement. Meeko, I'm going to teach this white man never to hunt on this reservation again."

"How do you know it's a white man?"

"You can know a person by how careless they are with knowledge," said Shadowhawk. "This man doesn't know how to move with the land. Look at his tracks. He's wearing new boots and walks heavy and scattered. He's heading for the main road, toward that truck we saw this morning," added Shadowhawk, picking up his pace. As they moved as one across the open field, Meeko could easily see nearby stones had been moved along with many broken twigs and frozen blades of flattened grass which told the story of the man's stupidity.

They both saw the hunter at the same time. As they crept in closer, Shadowhawk asked, "What are you doing hunting on reservation land?"

Shocked, the hunter looked hard at them. Then realizing they were just Indians, he snapped back, "What the hell does it look like I'm doing, Chief?"

"Did you know you shot a doe back there?"

"Yeah, I missed her. Couldn't find a blood trail."

"You hit that deer. We don't take to people coming on the reservation out of season, wounding animals and leaving our food to rot." Meeko watched Shadowhawk's temper flare as he moved in closer to the man, adding, "I don't think you'll leave this reservation alive if you keep on acting as you are. I suggest you give me your goddamn gun and bullets. Then maybe I'll guide you back to your truck instead of burying your sorry ass on this Chief's reservation."

Unnerved by these words the hunter handed over his gun and shells, then followed Shadowhawk and Meeko back to his vehicle, promising never again to hunt on reservation land. Afterwards, Meeko and Shadowhawk shared a good laugh, then headed home.

Another day, after hearing that a baby boy had been born, Meeko hung around the new mother's house and listened to her sing warrior songs to her infant, wishing that Renna had sung them to him. As the nights grew even colder, he began to stay home and spend his time listening to the old ones tell their war stories. Every night the elders came to visit, bringing their coup bags to tell another story. As each spoke of the old battles, he would lay down a stick or feather that would prove what he said was true. Granbear's stories were always the best—always bigger, braver and more daring. Meeko never tired of this wise man's words.

One day, much to Meeko's surprise, he received the unwanted attention of an old medicine woman who mysteriously approached him, her head covered by a blue shawl. Everyone knew of Wicahmunga, the short, chunky, toothless, bushy-haired witch with the lazy-eye. She dropped her shawl and glared at him, saying, "Here, Dog Turd! Take this lizard skin. Its power will guarantee you a good woman, if you ever become a good man, that is. If I decide to like you, I'll tell the women you can make plenty of strong babies." Meeko was terrified and afraid of her bad medicine and knew he did not want to get on her bad side.

"Humph, so you're afraid of me! Well, you'd better be! You tell everyone that you've come under the eyes of Wicahmunga," she cackled, grabbing him and pinching his arm hard before running off into the bushes.

As if frozen, Meeko held the lizard skin in his shaking hands. He knew people went to this woman for powerful love potions, and he also knew she could put spells on people. Finally he gathered his wits together and ran off to find Shadowhawk and Granbear to show them the gift.

Granbear smiled and asked, "How did you ever get her attention, Grandson?"

"I don't know. I always run when I see her, but today she came from nowhere and gave me this! Is it bad medicine?"

"I suggest you watch yourself and don't anger her," came the reply.

Still afraid, Meeko took the lizard and ran to Auntie Lizzie. When he showed her the bundle, she pulled back, refusing to help. "Meeko, you know Wicahmunga is *contrar* power, and she can do as she pleases."

Meeko moped around Shadowhawk's house the next day, hoping to escape another chance meeting with Wicahmunga. He asked Shadowhawk what to do, but instead of answering, Shadowhawk grabbed Meeko's left ear and cut the string that held a small stone. Shadowhawk then inserted a hammered silver earring shaped like a hawk feather in Meeko's ear, saying, "Don't fear Wicahmunga. She may be hard to understand, but she is powerful Medicine. Walk with the protection of Hawk; it will keep you safe from Wicahmunga. Here, take this matching earring to her and make her a gift of peace. If you become her friend, she might teach you something." Then Shadowhawk held out two woodpecker feathers, saying, "Granbear left these for you. He said they will keep you close to home and you won't have to worry."

Although Meeko felt safe with these gifts, he still feared Wicahmunga's bad medicine. Many times he had heard her threaten others, making them give her something to keep her silence. For weeks Meeko knew Wicahmunga was walking in his dreams. When he heard she had left the reservation to visit friends, his fears and nightmares subsided.

Throughout the winter Shadowhawk remained a hard taskmaster. Many times Meeko heard Granbear's words repeated from Shadowhawk's mouth. He was beginning to be thankful for his Medicine Wheel training and realized that the Bear Clan had always demanded unwavering honor from the Sioux. Crazy Horse, Red Cloud, Sitting Bull and Spotted Tail were all men of great leadership and honor. When he asked to know more of these men, Shadowhawk was especially pleased.

One day as spring was approaching, Granbear called excitedly, "Meeko, come quickly. Follow me!" Both walked sprightly to the pasture and leaned on the fence. "See that black stallion over there? He's yours, Grandson," announced Granbear with a big smile.

Meeko was speechless. He had fed this black stallion for over a year and it was his favorite. When he called to him, the stallion popped his head up and proudly tossed his long mane as if in defiance. Meeko grabbed a pan of cracked corn and as they neared this black beauty, the horse lifted his tail high and moved away. Meeko spoke softly and continued to follow until the horse allowed him to gently rub his nose. "Granbear, I've always wished he was mine. I've always called him *Hanhepi Sapa*, Black Night."

Meeko felt carefree for the first time in his life. From that day on, he and Sapa were inseparable. From daybreak to dusk he would ride Sapa bareback, guiding the stallion with his knees through mock battles. Within a few months he was mounting from the left or right side and over Sapa's rump. On some mornings he would jump from Sapa's back and race alongside him across the fields. On others he would practice war tactics, often hanging from Sapa's belly like the warriors of long ago. When exhaustion had taken its toll, Meeko would take Sapa to the tall grass, stretch out on the ground and leave his horse to graze freely as they shared moments of stillness. Many a nightfall would find them still in the pasture fighting imaginary battles with make-believe shields, bows and arrows. Meeko knew that Sapa was helping him birth his warrior spirit, and that was good.

Sometimes Meeko's friends joined him in imaginary battles, often galloping across the plains, counting coup on each other. Proud of their abilities, Shadowhawk and other boy training men organized a competition for their apprentices.

The boys were excited, and knew they would be up against some tough competition. The trails became more strenuous each day as they tracked both on foot and on horseback, smelling the blood from the long-ago battlefields. Meeko became the leader of the party and began to wear an eagle feather in his hair and to carry his eagle bone whistle around his neck to signal his teammates. The boys shared knowledge freely with one another. Some were good with birdcalls or wolf and coyote howls, while others knew how to use mirrors, hands, or arms for signaling. Still others showed how to communicate silently by laying a circle of dust. Some even knew how to make lightning bolt patterns on the ground with their horse's feet.

One day Granbear, who coached from the sidelines, instructed, "Grandson, move quicker, and pay closer attention to the sign language so you will know your next move. Stop looking, and feel your teammates! Our family holds a certain importance in the tribe as medicine men, warriors and horsemen, and I want to keep that place of honor. As Bear Clan, you must always practice honorable principles in order to become a responsible leader. If a friend falls from his horse, take a rider and double back for him, drop him a rope and keep moving as you hoist him onto your horse. Now go, and remember my words."

Shadowhawk called all the young men together and said, "Our Granbear wishes much more from us and I intend to see that his wish is fulfilled. We'll go over the four levels of manhood that you must accomplish before you can be recognized as a man in our clan. One, you must respect your family; two, you must respect the community; three, you must respect your tribe; and four, you must respect your society. Each of you know many songs and dances, but until you learn them all, you will not get the full meaning of manhood.

"From today on, you will start to practice our customs and priorities more thoroughly. Since each of you know it is impolite to call a person by their first name, you will begin to use a title that reflects the individual's age and knowledge, such as uncle, son, nephew, brother, auntie, daughter, niece, sister, grandfather, grandmother, father or mother. Now the special wise ones such as Granbear, you will call great-grandfather. Or in the case of a woman like Wicahmunga, great-grandmother. This will help deepen your respect for one another. These lessons will be important throughout your life."

Granbear smiled, adding, "We will soon have guests. Never ask why they have come, because that would be impolite. Remember, we are on Indian Time. They will get around to telling us when they are ready. These ways will help you develop patience and consideration toward one another, as well as toward visitors from other reservations."

Shadowhawk continued the training, saying, "Know the rules of a warrior. Long ago, a murderer had to pay with his life or give all his worldly possessions to the victim's family. A thief was made to replace the items he had stolen and had to live in shame. A traitor was considered the lowest form of criminal, and was punished by death. We made cowards wear a woman's dress and they were never allowed to marry or produce a child. And if a woman went to another man's blanket, her husband could cut off her nose or ear, or kill her. A man must always be worthy of this kind of honor."

The young men reflected on these traditional laws. Then Shadowhawk went on, saying, "Starting tomorrow, your training will be more strenuous and time-consuming. The competition is going to be keen, and you must build even more strength to match your opponents. To increase your stamina, we will feed you a special diet and discourage overindulgence. I demand your cooperation so we can make you very competitive young men. Your success will hinge on your skills, dependability and trustworthiness. Responsibility and loyalty are common traits of the Sioux. They give us honor among most tribes, and following these ways assures everyone's welfare."

Shadowhawk's words excited the young competitors, who were all now willing to work harder for the honor of becoming respected Sioux men. Yet despite the feeling of group unity, Meeko began to feel insecure and became aggressive toward the others.

Shadowhawk noticed the change and said, "Life is simple! Do not complicate it, Meeko. What you have, we have; and what we have, you have. This is the attitude of a loving *Hunka* family member. Now forget your street ways and follow the rules of your new family."

At times Meeko still felt intimidated by the other boys, and developed his own rigorous training program to enhance his chances of winning. Each morning he swam in the river against the current to improve his endurance, then rode Sapa until long after dusk practicing his horsemanship.

One morning Granbear, while giving him some pointers to improve his riding skills, yelled, "Push Sapa for more speed!"

Respectfully Shadowhawk asked, "Why are you pushing Meeko so hard?"

"I was thinking we might enjoy a little wager on the boy."

Shadowhawk smiled in agreement and called Meeko over, advising him to spend more time running to prepare for the upcoming footraces.

Meeko started running the following morning. He loved to run but realized he was having problems establishing a rhythm that would allow his mind and body to become one. One day after running the hills, he collapsed in the yard, exhausted. Wicahmunga appeared out of nowhere. Walking around as though she was inspecting him, she mumbled something in her unintelligible voice, her devilish eyes flashing. She plopped down next to Meeko, causing him to jump to his feet with a start. Wicahmunga grabbed his ankle, commanding, "You stay here! I have something powerful for you." She placed a river pebble in his hand and said, "The next time you run, slip this magic stone under your tongue and you will not know thirst.

"Now, I'll tell you the secret of running. Go to the pasture and catch a yellow butterfly. Rub its wings gently on your chest, then let it go. If it flies, you will have quickness and speed. I'm only helping you because I've made a wager with my friends and want you to win the race. So, Dog Turd, if I lose my money, I will put a bad spell on you," she threatened in her mysterious way, then quickly disappeared into the bushes.

Feeling uneasy from yet another encounter with Wicahmunga, but believing she spoke the truth, Meeko went to the pasture the following morning in search of a yellow butterfly. He chased dozens of them unsuccessfully, until finally in the heat of the afternoon, he chose to sit by a sweet flower. Suddenly, his magical yellow butterfly landed and he quickly caught it with his ballcap. Then, ever so gently, he rubbed its wings across his bare chest, asking it to give him the fastest and the strongest legs in the world. As he carefully let it go, the butterfly flew away. Meeko, knowing he had captured its power, decided he would pray to the butterfly before each run.

Eager to test this new magic, Meeko began running and soon found his legs were moving to a different rhythm. After three miles his mouth felt dry, so he stuck the magic pebble under his tongue, and his thirst immediately stopped. Then he ran as if his body was no longer of this world and his mind was free as the wind, allowing him to drift over the hills as gently as a butterfly.

One day as Meeko entered the yard Wicahmunga ran to him with a towel and wiped his face, then studied the cloth. "See Dog Turd, your face is dry. Keep acting tired for the others! But know your puny power doesn't impress me. Gimme my stone, you silly mutt."

Meeko took it from his mouth and placed it in her hand. She examined it carefully, whispered something, then said, "Okay, Toad, I put more power in the stone, but I want it back after the race! If you forget, I'll make your legs so heavy you can't even walk." She punched him hard on the arm, then ran to the arbor and sat very still.

Finally competition day arrived. Everyone met at the local Pow-Wow grounds and joined in the celebration with their drummers and singers as the ceremony officially started. At nine o'clock the whistle blew, announcing for all runners to line up for the first footrace. As Meeko left the starting line he prayed to the yellow butterfly. Again he felt his legs stretch beyond their normal limit, and the winds seemed to push him onward until he felt one with *Skan*.

When he crossed the finish line, he was not fully aware of being the winner until Wicahmunga approached him, saying, "See, I was right. I won! Now, you better win the next race because my monthly check is riding on it."

Meeko felt exuberant as he lined up for the final footrace. Once more running in an altered state of consciousness, he crossed the finish line as the winner. Wicahmunga ran to him and said, "Gimme my stone! I have to go get my money." Grabbing the magic stone from Meeko's hand, she examined it before wrapping it in a red cloth.

Smiling, Meeko reached into his pocket and handed her the matching silver hawk earring, saying, "Great-Grandmother, this is for you."

Wicahmunga stuck it in her pocket, answering suspiciously, "Now, don't ask me for any favors."

"Oh no, Great-Grandmother. This is a gift from my heart."

"No matter, it ain't going to save you from my medicine," she warbled, trotting away.

At just that moment Shadowhawk called out, "It's time to get our horses and challenge our opponents. They're mostly Oglala from Pine Ridge. Remember, the word Oglala means 'the Scatterers.' They're our brothers from the Tetons." Meeko watched the riders enter the field, dressed in colorful ribbon shirts with feathers flying in their hair. The leader, wearing full headdress, looked daunting to the Sioux boys dressed in simple jeans and white T-shirts.

Meeko watched their opponents please the crowd, and shouted angrily to his teammates, "Paint your colors on yourselves and your war ponies. We who represent the Nakota, Lakota and Dakota will look forward to telling our grandchildren how we counted coup on the Oglala."

Shadowhawk smiled as he handed Meeko a special beaded eagle bone whistle, saying to the team, "The eagle bone whistle has its own voice. Listen to its signals. Lie back easy as Cougar, and study your opponents' moves before exposing your strategies. Work together as brothers to win." Then he tied two hawk feathers to Sapa's tail saying, "These will give him more speed and accuracy."

Granbear tied an eagle feather to Sapa's mane, and reminded Meeko, "Grandson, call upon Brother Eagle. His feather will let Sapa run as the wind."

Next, Wicahmunga wrapped two wolf tails around Sapa's neck, saying, "These will make him long-winded." Dipping her fingers into Meeko's paints, she marked her face, then made a handprint on Sapa's chest, adding, "If you get in trouble, call upon the bobwhite. His power will tire the other horses. Now, don't you touch anything I've done, you simple-minded mutt," she grumbled, running off.

As both teams paraded onto the grounds on horseback, the old people began betting heavily, and Granbear offered Meeko a last bit of advice, "Remember, ride light on Sapa's back. Some boys are sitting very heavy. That keeps a horse from running his fastest. Be as one with Sapa's movements when you speak to him. Let him make the choice how best to win."

Meeko watched their opponents remove their feathers and shirts to get ready for the race, then signaled for his team to come together for final instructions. "Remember, good stalking and tracking will get the most red ties. We're a war party. Use the trails as Fox, and mark every opponent's shirt with your coup sticks. Okay, let's count coup!"

As the starting whistle blew everyone rode hard, jockeying for position. Shadowhawk was pleased to see his group riding fast, and as they rounded the last hill he saw fistfuls of red tie markers. Taking a quick head count, he yelled to Meeko that the youngest teammate, seven-year-old Little One, was missing. Meeko and Joe, another teammate, took off to find him and reached Little One just as he was falling from his horse. Meeko maneuvered himself into position to hoist the boy onto Sapa's back as Joe grabbed the loose horse, all racing to the arena.

Little One stood up proudly on Sapa's rump, thrusting his hand in the air showing a fist full of red tie markers. Meeko was elated as he and his teammates paraded into the arena pointing at their unmarked white T-shirts to show the crowd they had no coup marks. As the last of the visiting team entered the arena, their shirts covered with red marks, the crowd jeered enthusiastically and the women stood and gave a trillo for their team.

The crowd settled down once again as the teams gathered around their field leaders to begin the mock battle. Meeko and his teammates turned their horses until the arena became a dust bowl. The people stood and cheered with excitement as the riders performed daring feats.

When Meeko yelled, "War!" the teams began to dismount their opponents. Little One was soon seen on the ground, crying. The team scattered as Meeko and Joe went to his rescue. Meeko dropped his rope and Little One grabbed on, while Joe again retrieved his horse. They told him to be brave and lead all the loose horses to Shadowhawk.

The arena was filled with determined competitors, spinning and turning their horses, as they charged into hand-to-hand combat. The crowd stood watching in anticipation. The rules were getting lost as Shadowhawk's team dismounted their opponents with vengeance. Each time Little One caught a loose horse, he would wave to the crowd as he ran with the horse from the field.

The crowd roared with laughter, then whooped and hollered their war cries of joy, feeling a moment of pride in the younger generation. By this time winning was of less importance than the glory of the Sioux nations and the fact that the spirit of a warrior still lived in their youth. All tribes agreed that everyone was a winner, and celebrated for the rest of the night. By late the following morning, the grounds were almost barren as the last truck left a little dust devil, a reminder they would all be back another day.

A few days later, Granbear announced to Meeko that the Bear Society had accepted him as a member. Meeko surged with pride, knowing he had worked hard to learn the Bear Society songs and dances. After telling Meeko the responsibilities of a new member, the society began its preparations.

On initiation day Shadowhawk shaved most of Meeko's head according to tradition. As Meeko watched his long hair fall to the ground, Shadowhawk took the remaining hair that extended from each side of Meeko's head and twisted it into tight circles to resemble bear ears. Meeko dressed in his perforated bear shirt, and Shadowhawk painted four black stripes on his chin.

Granbear instructed with a smile, "Remember, Bear Society members always grunt like old bears before an attack so people know we mean business." Then he handed Meeko a bear knife, saying, "I promised you this, and now it is yours." Surprised, Meeko mumbled a humble thank you as he strapped it to his side. After the lengthy ceremony, both Granbear and Shadowhawk made a large giveaway to honor the newest member of their family into the Bear Society.

Embarrassment kept Meeko close to home until Shadowhawk finally agreed to shave the rest of his head. Auntie Lizzie made him a special beaded ballcap, and Meeko once again felt comfortable enough to roam the reservation.

One day while riding Sapa along the creek, he stopped and knelt at the water's edge, thinking about Granbear. It seemed that Granbear was spending a great deal of time in Shadow World, which Meeko resented. Angrily scooping up his reflection, he asked himself, "Why do I always paint myself with such distorted truths? Why can't I grasp the meaning of Granbear's words?"

At that moment, an unfamiliar voice answered, "Open your fingers wide. Watch how quickly the water leaves your hand, yet you know its presence by its dampness. Let the water's reflection comfort you." At once, Meeko's thoughts saddened as faint echoes of Granbear's death surfaced to the top of his mind. With a heavy heart, Meeko plucked a piece of sage and rolling it between his fingers, begged, "Oh, heartbeat of Sage, share your secrets of life, not death with me."

"Grandson, why fear through eyes of little experience?" answered the sage. "Things are not always as they seem. Inhale my aroma and silence your mind so you can understand the spiritual protection I offer you."

Meeko breathed the aroma and let its peace permeate his mind. He was so engrossed in the moment, that he failed to hear the thunder or see the lightning bolts racing across the darkened sky. As the winds whipped at the trees, Meeko grabbed Sapa to head for home. But seeing that many trees were already blocking the trail, he grew fearful. Heavy rain soon gave way to floodwaters, prompting the two to seek protection under a group of pines. Meeko pulled hard on Sapa's reins, but the stallion bolted and broke free of Meeko's grip, racing toward the open plains. Disgusted with his situation, Meeko went to the nearest tree to sit. As soon as he sat down, a lightning bolt struck, knocking him unconscious.

Laying in the darkness of oblivion, Meeko heard a voice echoing, "We have come to bathe away your loneliness." Meeko wailed at the words, sensing Granbear's death. Leaving his body, he felt himself floating toward the top of a mountain where he saw Granbear standing. Meeko fought hard against the winds as he crawled toward Granbear, but a gust tumbled him over the ledge. He screamed in terror and tried to grab Granbear's hand, but it went through his body.

As he fell, he suddenly found himself floating over majestic snowcapped mountain peaks, he heard Granbear say, "Let go of your enemy, fear. Stop fighting the mysteries of death and know it is a natural part of life." Just as Meeko was begging Granbear never to leave him, he awoke to see Shadowhawk and Auntie Lizzie leaning over his bed.

"Grandson, we knew something was wrong when Sapa came home without you. We followed him through the storm and he led us to you," explained Auntie Lizzie in a soothing voice.

Later when Meeko told Granbear of his vision, Granbear replied, "I could not go with them to find you, but my spirit traveled to you. I know you are well prepared for life because I have seen your pathway. It can be a beautiful life if you follow the teachings.

"Now this old warrior can go home free from worry. I have heard my death song, and my journey upon Mother Earth is almost over. I am ready to travel through the Milky Way and go Beyond the Pines. Be happy, Grandson, knowing I am getting ready to go home to *Wakan Tanka*."

Meeko's heart filled with great sadness at the thought of Granbear dying, and he wept openly. Granbear understood and said nothing more, returning to Shadow World.

As weeks passed, Meeko often sat beside Granbear's bed in prayer. One morning Granbear opened his eyes widely and declared, "Go find Lizzie! Tell her I must speak of something very important."

When Auntie Lizzie arrived, Granbear said, "Lizzie, when I die, don't let anyone change my wishes. Postpone my binding ceremony for four days. I don't want my body to be bound before I am dead." Auntie Lizzie promised him she would honor his wishes.

Sitting alone reflecting on the situation, Meeko saw Shadowhawk's truck pull into the yard with Renna. Furious, he ignored her presence and walked away to join the many mourning relatives and friends.

At four o'clock in the morning, Meeko heard an eerie howl and saw a darkened shadow appear in the front yard. He realized the Three-legged White Wolf had come to escort Granbear to the spirit world. Meeko watched it approach the front door, scratch, and then vanish. Saddened, he went to the Medicine Wheel and listened to the mourning of the winds.

Soon loud wails from the house confirmed that Granbear had left on his final journey. Meeko stayed in the Medicine Wheel lamenting his loss until the following afternoon when Shadowhawk came to inform him it was time to take Granbear to his final resting place.

It was on a moonless night when the Bear Clan took Granbear's body to the interior of the reservation. Four days of ceremonies were performed, and sweats were held morning and evening.

On the fifth day the Bear Clan held Granbear's farewell. The women prepared his body and Auntie Lizzie dressed him in his finest buckskin, covered his feet with moccasins that had beaded soles and tied two eagle feathers in his hair. Shadowhawk painted four black stripes across Granbear's nose, then turned to Meeko and placed the same markings on his face.

Both wept openly as Auntie Lizzie filled Granbear's pipe for the last time. The Bear Society smoked it, then the clan placed Granbear's war club and pipe next to his body. They wrapped Granbear's body in many fine skins, then covering this with a buffalo hide, they bound everything together and gently lifted it onto the newly constructed burial scaffold. Auntie Lizzie handed Granbear's medicine bundle and shield to Shadowhawk, who tied them above the body along with the many eagle feathers and prayer ties brought by the people.

The tribal pipe was lit, and the drummers and singers brought in the dawn for Granbear's final song. Granbear's flags and feathers flew proudly upon the breath of the four winds telling all that Granbear was going home.

Meeko watched as members of the Bear Clan cut their hair and gave flesh offerings to show their overwhelming grief. He walked to the scaffold, lamenting in prayer as he took his bear knife and slashed four long gashes on each leg. As the blood ran profusely, Meeko had a strong vision and saw Granbear as a young man, riding proudly toward his final destination. He knew it was time to follow the old ways and grow strong as Granbear had taught him.

Later as the family had gathered in silence, Meeko announced in a serious tone, "I am going back to the orphanage to get the white man's education. When I return, I will have the weapons needed to fight for the people." Tears filled Auntie Lizzie's eyes, knowing Meeko was doing what Granbear had wanted.

The following morning, Meeko hugged his grandmother goodbye and Shadowhawk drove him to the edge of the reservation where he could hitch a ride. As Meeko disappeared over the horizon, Shadowhawk prayed, "Oh, *Wakan Tanka*, guide my grandson so he may become the man who was predicted by our loving Granbear."

Meeko Learns to Fly

Upon arrival at the Sisseston, South Dakota Indian Orphanage, Meeko felt apprehensive when he found most of his old friends were gone. As he walked over the grounds, he found nothing had changed except that the faded facility looked even more weathered. The same bigoted sisters were still in charge, assigning the same demeaning chores to the residents.

Meeko hated the structured rules and recognized that most of these discarded children did not know the difference. He looked to Father Sky and wished the others could know of their people's glorious past. Feeling alone and unsure, he walked to a nearby field. He could feel the influence of Granbear in every wildflower and tree. Even the winds seemed to speak to him of the medicine man's spirit in all things.

After weeks of struggling to make a decision, Meeko realized if he was to ever fulfill his dreams, he must find his own pathway through this complex organization. He thought carefully before he spoke to Father Hanby. Meeko sat across the massive desk from the priest and stated, "Father, I chose to return here to get an education to help fulfill my dreams, but your classes are too limited. It's a constant battle inside of me. I want to learn everything. Still, I don't understand why my people's ways are not taught since there are no white kids here. Why can't we also learn about our God?" Then he explained the medicine people's belief that all gods are one.

Father listened, yet remained stoic, saying, "Meeko, I do not question nor do I care about the gods of your people. Surely you know you cannot live in two such diverse cultures at the same time. Here, there is no choice. You learn our way or leave. Stop living in the Indian world, I think that is what's confusing you."

Meeko realized the situation was hopeless; he thanked Father Hanby for his time and left the room. To stay here, I must live in their world. To go back to the reservation means no education. There's got to be a way. Why can't I use what I know to live in both worlds?

Meeko knew he had to play the white man's game if he wished to fulfill his dream. After several weeks of pondering and planning he approached the other Sioux students and persuaded them to establish an underground study movement so they could focus on their heritage. The group met secretly in the library, where they would research their history. However they soon discovered that the library contained little material about their culture, at which point they continued their studies by sharing their history orally.

Running had helped him focus and integrate his physical and mental abilities, so Meeko decided to discuss the possibility of establishing a running program with Father Hanby one afternoon. To Meeko's surprise, Father Hanby agreed that a running program would be good exercise, and Meeko volunteered to share his skills with the other students.

Within three weeks Father Hanby saw Meeko's leadership abilities were causing the students to question his authority and he began to regret his decision. He immediately removed Meeko and took over the new running program himself. This caused Meeko to rebel against Father Hanby's teaching methods, and as an outlet for his frustrations with the system, he started running everyday before daybreak. It felt good to re-discover that he could fend off fatigue and develop a more peaceful attitude by being in his Indian mind. As he began to process new thoughts, every snow covered day seemed more beautiful than the last. And as his speed increased, he moved beyond his fear toward a heightened awareness of natural phenomena.

Early one Saturday morning while watching the rays of the sun pierce the shadows and cast a glowing radiance across the hills, Meeko knew his soul had connected to the day in a ceremonial way. As *Wi's* hand nobly reached down and gracefully scattered the frozen fields with many shining diamond-like crystalline patterns, a voice emanated from somewhere deep inside and his loneliness cried out for something beyond what was there. Meeko remained enveloped in the power of an unknown presence until the cold air penetrated his wet shirt and brought him back to reality.

Spring had finally arrived and Meeko was just finishing his morning run. He drove his hands deep into his pockets, tucking his head into his chest as he struggled against the wind that was kicking up loosely plowed ground. Each day for the past month he had sat on an old stump watching with curiosity the changes a farmer was making to his newly planted fields.

But on this morning things were different. There were trailers, trucks and planes moving in on the far side of the field. A water truck caught his attention as it moved at a snail's pace toward a makeshift hangar in the far distance. By noon Meeko had gathered enough courage to walk near the ground crew that was mixing crop-dusting chemicals. The foul odor of sulfur that drifted his way caused him to wrinkle his nose as he wondered what they were doing.

He heard engines revving up in the distance and felt their guttural sound churn deep inside his stomach as he walked to the edge of the dirt landing strip where two crop-dusting planes were jockeying into place. The winds were building power, and Meeko felt a certain excitement in their defiance. One by one, the planes lifted from the ground with gut-wrenching roars of explosive energy. Meeko felt connected to them as if they were kindred spirits. It was like watching a pack of wolves readying for the hunt, knowing they would catch the prey of the day.

Meeko spotted Jake, a pilot he had met while running, and waved then walked near. "Hey, Meeko, long time no see. Can you believe this wind? It's definitely gonna be squirrelly today," said Jake, zipping up his jacket. "What are you doing out here without a jacket?"

Meeko was offended and took a cocky stance. He glared at Jake before answering sarcastically, "I don't need a jacket. We Sioux don't feel the cold." Inwardly he wondered who in the hell did that white man think he was?

Jake continued to pre-flight his plane as Meeko stood in awkward anger. After thinking over the situation, he realized Jake had spoken from a white man's point of view and let it go, saying, "I don't own a jacket."

"Sorry," answered Jake.

"No problem. Have a safe flight," replied Meeko, stepping away from the plane.

He watched Jake climb aboard Seven Two Charlie, open the side window and yell, "Clear." Meeko saw him pat Seven Two Charlie on the panel before hitting the starter button. The engine sputtered, then kicked over and burst into a loud, thundering roar. Jake scanned the panel, kicked the rudder pedals and flipped the ailerons then taxied toward the runway.

Meeko ran across the field to an old broken-down fence and climbed up for a better view. Enthralled, he watched the plane respond to Jake's every command, and thought someday he could learn to respect this man's knowledge. Jake pushed the throttle to full bore, and Meeko smiled as Seven Two Charlie roared rapidly down the dirt strip. Meeko quietly offered tobacco to the spirits as he prayed for Jake to have a safe flight.

The plane was squirrelly as Jake fought the strong quartering winds that lay hard against Seven Two Charlie's nose. Lifting the left wing into the air, Jake threw her into a skid and pulled back on the stick, bouncing her sideways into the air. The engine let out an eerie scream and Meeko's stomach trembled as he held his breath. Jake popped her nose down to gather the air speed he needed, then up into the sky they climbed. He turned sharp, dropping the right wing when he entered the flight pattern. At that moment, Meeko knew Jake was a kindred spirit of Eagle, and wondered when he had heard the call.

Jake came in hot over the field, barely missing the tops of the trees as he dropped very fast under the power lines. Meeko listened to the growl of the engine as he watched the flag boy line up his flags to guide Jake safely through his first pass. Steady and forward, he directed the flags. Jake poured on the coal and dropped close to the ground. He opened the spray jets at the beginning of the run, and Meeko could see him giving a thumbs up as he left the field to ready for another pass.

Meeko was intoxicated with the whole process. Jake and Seven Two Charlie were indeed partners. As the chemicals floated down in a showered mist, Jake just barely cleared the tall trees that loomed at the far end of the field. Meeko watched the spiral of the invisible vortex move the leaves on the trees, then raised a clenched fist toward the sky, yelling, "Now that's Eagle power!" He was impressed that Jake could thumb his nose at danger, and knew the pilot was not only riding with horse power but also the spirit of the flying ones. The sky people were guiding man and machine in a choreographed waltz of simplistic beauty. Meeko could feel the connection between Jake and his plane, and he wanted to explore how they had become one in spirit.

Meeko knew that for a white man Jake was different because he honored the winds and was connected to Father Sky. He felt the winged ones had given him these capabilities, otherwise why would he have chosen to challenge the sky? He saw Jake as a free spirit, merely using Seven Two Charlie to control the invisible unbridled power of the winds, and this oneness fed Meeko's dreams with ambitious flames. He concluded that Jake was precision in motion, and from that moment learning to fly from this man became one of his dreams.

As days drifted into weeks Meeko spent all of his spare time watching the crop-dusters launch into euphoric pleasures in the air. But when each day ended, he was forced to return to the orphanage where he kept his heart in seclusion, just waiting for the next day to arrive. He was determined to maneuver his way into a job, any job, just as long as he could become a part of their flying world. Everyone at the makeshift hangar soon knew "the hang-around Indian kid." Meeko silently vowed to become connected to the flying world and made friends with all the flag boys, pilots and crew, taking every opportunity to assist Jake whenever needed.

When the sun went over down in the South Dakota sky, Jake taxied into his tie down spot and killed the engine. Meeko grabbed the ropes and tied the plane down. "Thanks, buddy," said Jake as he walked away and turned his attention to the crew. "I noticed some bees at the end of the runway. That's a sign a front's moving our way. They looked pretty thick for this time of year, so we'd better fly tonight if we expect to beat the weather. It'll probably hit sometime tomorrow."

As Jake hopped into the jeep he noticed Meeko still leaning against Seven Two Charlie's struts and said, "Hey, Meeko, how'd you like to join me for dinner? I'm hungry as an old bear." Meeko had not heard that expression since he left the reservation and he jumped at the invitation, thinking it was a good sign.

Heading toward town Jake said, "Need a flag boy. I think you've got the knack to be a good one." Meeko's heart raced with excitement. Minutes later they stopped in front of a small, plush restaurant bearing a sign that read, "Fine Food and Spirits." Meeko had never been in such an elegant place, although on occasion he had peeked through the windows. Aware that the restaurant was for white people, he felt out of place but was curious to see if they would serve an Indian. The waitress led them to a candle-lit back booth, then courteously handed a menu to Jake and tossed another on the table for Meeko. He glared at her and she promptly returned the gesture. Jake, ignoring the situation, ordered two large steaks and a bottle of red wine.

"Tell me about yourself and what you want to do with your life."

Although Meeko felt uncomfortable with Jake's questioning, he wanted the job and told his story. When he finished, Jake told him he could start the next day as his flag boy. "It's not flying, but it beats the hell out of sitting on that old fence post every day dreaming of flying. Maybe someday we'll talk about you learning to fly." Meeko was thrilled and accepted the job but secretly he wondered if Father Hanby would allow him to work while living at the orphanage.

That night as Meeko lay in bed he could not help but be concerned about becoming too close to a white man and reminded himself to be more cautious. He was ashamed of his intentions to control Jake, so he took a pinch of tobacco and offered it up to Creator, asking forgiveness for manipulating the situation. Then he called upon Granbear, saying, "I think our dreams are beginning to happen. Jake may think this friendship is real, but to me it's an illusion. I know the flying ones have directed me to this man as a teacher, so why does it scare me?"

Granbear's voice answered, "Your happiness is too limited, Grandson. Try to see the beauty in what you are experiencing. Call upon the clouds and let *Taku Skan Skan* direct you. It was Creator's power that drew this man into your life. There's nothing wrong in sharing his gifts. Allow them to help you take wing and fly. Chase your dreams, find your place of greatness and remember what you have learned, never forgetting the love of Great Spirit."

Responding to Granbear's words, Meeko bolted beyond time and sailed across the sky in an attempt to avoid facing the truth. Suddenly he circled downward into a spring day where he found a hawk that demanded space within his wintry soul. They journeyed as one through the four seasons and watched together as a flock of swallows ate the fire of self-mastery. Meeko recognized that he was not chasing his dream, but leaving it to chance.

Long before dawn the next morning, Meeko sneaked out hoping to avoid a confrontation with the sisters, and raced off to meet Jake.

"You ready?" asked Jake. Meeko nodded and fell into step with him as they walked toward the makeshift hangar. "I hope you know what I expect from you. I don't want to crash and burn on your first day," Jake added, chuckling and handing Meeko two brand-new white flags.

He explained, "Your job is very important. This is a hard field. See the barriers at both ends? They are blind spots for a pilot. To get over this field right I have to fly high, then drop under the power lines, cross the field and pull up quickly to clear the treetops at the other end. When I'm on the deck, your flags are my talking arms. If either wing is too low, tell me by raising the proper flag. If I look good, guide me forward with two raised flags. Once I'm aligned with the ground, I'll fly low to get good chemical cover. If the spray is drifting, signal me to move in the right direction to compensate. If I'm too close to the ground or an obstacle is in my way, put those flags in the air quick and wave me outta there." As he turned to walk away, Jake added, "If I'm going to crash and burn, you haul ass outta there. Got it?"

"Sure!" answered Meeko, eager for Jake to get in the air so he could start work.

Meeko's heart skipped a beat as Jake came down fast on his first run, blowing a strong wind over him. Then hearing the backlash of the engine's roar as Jake climbed back into the sky, he felt great excitement. By late afternoon he could sense Seven Two Charlie's every move.

As the days passed Meeko began to feel an even stronger connection with Jake. He was also understanding more about the wind's motion and had more confidence in his judgment.

One calm day Jake decided to play and came in really low and hot. Meeko waved him off, but Jake kept coming. Meeko accepted the challenge and stood his ground. But when Seven Two Charlie forced him down on his belly, he dug into the dirt as the wheels almost rolled across his back. Jake pulled up, flipping the ailerons in a thumbs up approval, laughing as Meeko scrambled back to his feet. Meeko, feeling the power and the exhilaration of the moment, learned the real meaning of counting coup. By the end of the day both felt the bond that was growing stronger between them. As they were tying down the plane, Jake said, "What you did today took guts, kid. Maybe someday I'll make a pilot out of you."

For the next two months Father Hanby allowed Meeko to spend his summer vacation working with the crop-dusters, and it was during this time that Jake, Meeko and Seven Two Charlie became inseparable. When the job came to an end, Jake reluctantly handed Meeko his money, watching him take out enough for a soda and bag of peanuts then tie the rest in a red rag. Jake shook his head not comprehending the way this kid handled money.

Meeko returned to the orphanage, reflecting on his experience as a flag boy. He felt proud that he had found a way to survive in white society and shared his thoughts with Granbear's spirit.

"The plane is a tool, like our war ponies of long ago. It taught me to connect with the air like the winged ones. I watch Jake's spirit grow strong when he flies, and I see the heart of a true warrior as he cuts a deep opening into the spirit world." Meeko felt Granbear embrace his thoughts and said with a smile, "Someday, Granbear, we will fly together in our shared dreams."

The world of flying had become everything to Meeko. As the crew hooked their trailers behind their trucks and prepared to leave, they expressed regrets that Meeko was not joining them on their next job. Meeko smiled knowingly, for he was formulating a plan of his own.

That night after bed check at the orphanage, Meeko gathered his belongings, sneaked out and headed for Seven Two Charlie. After tucking his things into the back of the plane, he crawled under a canvas covering and fell into a troubled sleep. He saw desperate, distorted faces that made him shriek with fear as he was driven beyond the peacefulness of Shadow World. Hazy images appeared, then he heard the sound of flapping wings and felt them wrap around his head bursting into colorful circles that descended throughout his body. One spoke. "Run, Meeko, run. See the enemy of confusion destroying you."

Without warning, a brilliant spirit eagle blocked his sight, saying, "Stop thinking as a sparrow. Life demands strength to conquer turmoil. Use what you know to swoop down and capture the power of flight. How high do you dare fly, Little Brother?" Meeko remembered that same question from long ago and sensed *Wanbli Gle'ska's* presence. He knew this great spirit bird would guide him safely into his future.

At daybreak Meeko heard Jake climb into the cockpit, start the engine, and taxi down the runway. The plane lifted into the air, taking Meeko on his first flight. Initially the sound of the engine soothed him, but as the air became turbulent he began to experience dry heaves and feared becoming sick. Aware that Meeko was on board, Jake startled him by saying, "Come up here, Meeko." His blood ran cold as he crawled sheepishly out from under the canvas and sat, gray-faced, next to Jake. "There's a barf bag in the side pocket. You're gonna make one helluva pilot, flying with one hand on the stick and your head in a barf bag."

"On my word as a Sioux, I won't be sick," Meeko promised, holding his head over the barf bag just in case he had to go back on his word.

"Hey, you're right. You won't be sick, so stop giving me that brave Indian bullshit! Just relax and you'll be fine." Meeko leaned back into the seat and breathed deeply into the bag.

"Looks like you owe me an explanation," growled Jake.

"I just couldn't stay there. If I'd asked to go, you would've said no."

"What the hell do you think that orphanage is going to say about this? Meeko, there's a law against taking a runaway kid across a state line! What happened to your goals? More importantly, what about your education? Have you forgotten all of our talks about your future? Your decision is bound to cause us both a lot of trouble. Who are you to give me problems? Hell, I'm stopping at the next airport and your ass is going back to the orphanage."

"I know it was wrong Jake, but you know I can take care of myself! Look, I have money and I can pay my own way," insisted Meeko pulling his money rag from his pocket. "Honestly, it'll work. You need someone to watch the planes and the spray equipment at night, so I can live at the airport and finish school during the day. Don't worry about me, Jake, they don't care."

"That's what you think."

"Honest, Jake! They won't care. What's another runaway Indian kid? I left the orphanage before and when I came back this last time, the agreement was, when I go, I go!"

"You expect me to believe that bullshit?"

"Wait, Jake," answered Meeko, pulling a crumpled letter from his pocket. "Here's the paper. See, it's okay as long as I go to school. You know I'm an honor roll student. I promise if you let me stay, I'll finish school and everything will be okay. I give you my word as a Sioux. All I really want to do is learn how to fly and be a pilot just like you."

"Well, you're here, but I'm still calling the orphanage. If they say you gotta return, you return. Understood? And by the way, how old are you anyway?" asked Jake staring straight ahead.

"Oh, you know Indians, we don't really keep those kinds of records. I think I'm about sixteen or seventeen," Meeko lied.

"Yeah, I bet," responded Jake skeptically. They continued the flight in silence, taking in the picturesque countryside to escape further confrontation. Finally Jake pointed out the window and declared, "Look, that's California." Meeko studied the neat patches of green and brown land, wondering why people had cut Mother Earth into such small squares.

"Here, take the stick. Let's see what you can do," said Jake. Meeko gently took the stick, wondering if this was what an eaglet felt when it first left the nest. "Feel the plane, Meeko. Respond to it," encouraged Jake. "Now just keep it level. You're doing fine. You have a feel for flying. I saw it in your eyes. But if you want me to teach you, you better damn well learn to think and act like a plane. Crawling into the cockpit is like putting on a second skin," he added, taking back the stick.

Kicking the rudder and hauling back on the stick, Jake let the stall button scream until Seven Two Charlie floated on the whispering winds. "Betcha this is what a bird feels like when it flies," he said, pushing the stick forward, letting Meeko feel the G-forces build. Feeling a sense of unity with the flying ones, Meeko understood why man needed a machine if he wished to play with the wind.

Jake dropped the nose of Seven Two Charlie to restart the engine. Meeko responded like a homesick angel heading for the happy hunting grounds. While climbing, both yelled triumphantly, at which point an exhilarated Meeko knew he was born to be a pilot. As they approached the outskirts of Sacramento, Jake killed the engine and put Seven Two Charlie into a slip, falling diagonally toward Mother Earth. Many times Meeko had watched Jake land with a dead-stick and was excited to feel it for himself. As they neared the ground, Jake leveled off and rolled onto the runway in dead silence. Meeko climbed out of the plane with hope in his heart for a bright future.

The ground crew approached smiling and grabbing Meeko's belongings took them to the hangar. Proud, Meeko carried Jake's flight bag and set it down in his office. "Why don't you look around and get acquainted. I've got some work to catch up on."

Meeko obediently followed Jimmy, one of the crop-dusters, up the stairs and into a spare room. "This is your home, kid," said Jimmy as he pointed to a single bed, chest and bathroom, then left the room. Meeko quickly placed his things in the chest, saving the bottom drawer for his Indian medicines. He then wandered throughout the hangar and found it was much different than he had expected. It was a very big metal building, housing many offices, a restaurant, living quarters, a flight training and ground school. Meeko was overjoyed as he strolled toward the mechanic's bay where he saw many large and small charter planes. He realized Jake ran a very large business called a fixed base operation.

Meeko glanced around to see a brown mongrel was following him at a distance. "Looks like you've met Manfred, our mascot," said Jake, catching up to Meeko. "He's the official welcoming committee around here. Pay attention to him, he can teach you a lot of things. Hell, Manfred has more time logged in the air than some of these pilots around here, and he has his own log book to prove it. Right, Manfred?" said Jake, scratching his back.

Laughing at the dog's name, Meeko said, "Well, Manfred, you must be a special kind of dog. I hope we'll be good friends."

During the next few days, Meeko hung around the airport lounge listening to the crew grumble about the rain that was keeping them on the ground. Then he heard his name over the intercom. It was Jake paging him to come to his office. As he entered, Jake handed him some documents, saying, "I contacted Father Hanby, and he and my attorney friend put this together."

Looking through the papers, Meeko noticed that Jake would now be his legal guardian, which made him feel accepted in the white world. He folded the papers, put them in his pocket and grinned at Jake, saying nothing. After that, Meeko enrolled in school and continued working as a flag boy after school and on weekends. On warm, sunny days he and Manfred explored the nearby fields or played ball, and when night came he spent hours sketching his favorite planes with Manfred now always by his side.

One rainy day months later, Jake looked over Meeko's shoulder at the many planes he had drawn, saying, "These are great sketches. You must love that Cessna 180 tail dragger we call Seven Two Charlie."

"I'm gonna buy one someday," answered Meeko shyly.

"That's one helluva plane, but it's expensive. "I think you better learn to fly one before you buy one. C'mon, the sun's out, let's get in a little flying time."

From that day forward, Meeko flew daily, eventually completing his forty-hour training requirement. This particular morning, Jake asked Meeko to follow him as he headed toward the Cessna 150 training plane. Meeko pre-flighted the plane as usual, kicked the blocks free from the tires and waited for Jake to get in the plane. Jake smiled proudly saying, "I'm not flying with you today. Let's get going! I want to see what you can do on your first solo flight."

Meeko could not believe Jake's words and yelled, "Solo! Jake, are you sure? I don't think I'm ready."

"Yep, you're as ready as you're gonna be. Hey, let's see if you're as good as you think you are. Now get going, before I change my mind."

Meeko was nervous at the thought of flying again. He hesitantly climbed aboard, touched the rudder pedals then gently moved the wheel and yelled, "Clear." Turning the engine over, Meeko taxied down the runway, filled with excitement, yet still feeling unsure of his readiness. He opened the throttle full bore and continued down the runway. Watching his air speed build, Meeko pulled her off and into the air. He pushed the wheel gently forward to drop her nose to gain enough air speed to climb to twenty-five hundred feet right above the airport runway. He flew downwind and lined up on final for his first touch-and-go. As he touched down, the plane bounced slightly upward.

Jake hit the mike button, saying, "Watch it! Are you trying to tear up my new radio gear?"

Meeko picked up the mike and gave a nervous laugh, saying, "Sorry."

"Be alert and watch your rpm's. It'll help you climb out smoother. You've got three to go before you leave the sky."

Meeko did the second touch-and-go, then climbed back into the flight pattern for his third and final one. Flying straight and level, then downwind, he turned on base and lined up for his final approach. Suddenly he broke out in a cold sweat, until he heard Jake's voice somewhere deep within saying, "Easy, relax. Easy on the pedals, boy. Start your flare-out. Pull back gently. Now c'mon, grease those wheels onto that runway."

When Meeko's wheels touched the ground, he grinned and picked up his mike, saying, "Smooth as silk." Again, he pushed in on the throttle and raced down the runway, knowing he had the first step of his dream in his hands. He repeated another touch-and-go for good luck, then taxied toward Jake and the waiting crew.

As he stepped out of the plane beaming with pride, the crew slapped him on the back congratulating him as Jake recorded Meeko's first solo flight in his log book. Everyone gathered close around as Jake suddenly grabbed Meeko by the shirt and cut it off up to the pocket. Meeko looked at everyone in confusion. "Old flying tradition, my boy. We always cut the shirttail when you solo. One helluva flight, my friend. C'mon, let's go hang your shirttail up with all the others."

From that day forward, Meeko began accumulating the cross-country hours he needed to make sure he could get his private license. Finally the day came for his flight test. Meeko was nervous when the FAA examiner climbed on board with his pad, pencil and an expressionless face, asking many questions. Meeko fumbled with the gears and the examiner sensing his nervousness said, "Meeko, relax. Fly like any other day. Forget I'm on board and you'll do fine."

Meeko scanned the panel, yelled, "Clear," and taxied down the runway. The examiner watched every move as they left the flight pattern. Meeko flew straight and level, turning right then left, responding smoothly to each request.

"Let's head in," said the examiner, calmly reaching over and chopping the engine. The plane stalled. Meeko casually put the nose down to regain his air speed. As the engine started he resumed a straight, level flight. The examiner kept writing on his pad as Meeko trimmed her out and lowered the flaps to land. The wheels breezed onto the runway and rolled out as Meeko chopped back her power. He had a knot as big as a football in his stomach as they stepped out of the plane where Jake was waiting. Meeko thought he would surely explode in anticipation until the examiner smiled and offered his hand, saying, "Congratulations! Let's go to the office and complete the paperwork." Meeko let out a war whoop and Jake laughed.

As they left the FAA office, Jake said, "Okay, rookie, take us home." On the flight home Jake spoke of his earlier flying days. "Meeko, when I was a child, I was poor. I always knew that someday I'd be a pilot. I've worked hard for what I've got, and the day I got my private license was the greatest day of my life. Since you've graduated from high school with good grades and now have your pilot's license, I think you just might get your dream.

"The man who taught me how to fly told me a good pilot must be friends with the wind. The wind is like an invisible ocean wave. The only difference is, you have to feel it, rather than see it. The air currents demand respect, and you should never go beyond your experience. The sky's a safe and peaceful place, but it can become a living hell if you make bad decisions. Remember, a good pilot should always be a man of honor and integrity. That's why so many kids look up to pilots to help them pursue their flying dreams. Now that you have kept your word, it is time to learn the flying business." Although Meeko had always hoped this day would come, he could only acknowledge Jake's proposal with a smile as they landed.

One rainy Saturday an unimpressive brown package arrived in the mail, but to Meeko it was Christmas in July. Jake watched him tear open the package and carefully scan the manual for a Cessna 180 tail dragger. Jake wheeled around in his chair and unlocked the shelf that held all of his model airplanes. He took out a model of Seven Two Charlie, saying, "This one built this business. She has taught me the most about flying. Yep, this little lady and I have reached quite a few goals together. She was my first tail dragger, and will always be my best gal." They spent the afternoon discussing various aircraft and how each had its own personality.

Jake pulled out another model, saying, "I've waited a long time for this one," and set it in front of them before sharing a faded manual.

"Is that the manual for a Beech 18?" asked Meeko excitedly.

"Yep, she's a converted tail dragger and a bush pilot's dream. I want to buy her to take the rich folks back into the primitive areas. I'm trying to cut a deal on her today."

As the discussion closed, Jake placed the model back on the shelf and locked the case, saying, "Well, c'mon, gotta pay the crew before I can go pick up my dream."

Jake handed Meeko his pay and threw his hands in the air in exasperation as he watched him tie the money in the red rag and stuff it into the lining of his jacket.

"Meeko, how much money do you have in that rag?"

"About eight thousand, four hundred dollars."

"That's too much money to carry around in a rag. Why don't you let me open you a bank account, and when you find the plane you want to buy, let the bank give you a cashier's check?"

"Nope, I want to always know where my money is."

Jake shook his head, saying, "I swear, Meeko, for being so smart, you do the damnedest things. I'll never understand your reasoning. Might as well go with me to pick up the new plane," Jake offered, grabbing the keys to Seven Two Charlie and heading for the flight line.

There sat Seven Two Charlie on her oversized tires, looking proud. "Charlie was made for a bush pilot. She loves the dirt strips and country roads. She'll look out of place in the big city," chuckled Jake. As they strapped in, Jake yelled, "Clear" as the prop turned over. He went through the ever familiar checklist and ran her up to 1700 rpm, saying, "She's purring like a kitten." He reached down and set her trim as he grabbed the mike to call the tower. "This is Niner One Seven Two Charlie, calling tower."

"Go ahead," answered the tower.

"This is Niner One Seven Two Charlie, filing a VFR flight plan to Santa Monica airport. Could you give me the weather?"

"Roger, Seven Two Charlie. Weather clear. Have a good flight."

Jake clicked the mike button twice in response as Seven Two Charlie lifted off the runway. Once in the air, Jake reminisced. "When I think of all the times I've spent with Seven Two Charlie, it makes me sad to think of giving her up. This was the first plane I ever owned. It was just us who tackled the jobs no one else wanted. We both should have been dead a hundred times over. She's taken me through blinding snowstorms and flown when the birds were walking. Hell, I remember once up in Canada, we landed with so much ice on the wings that the tower thought we were an illusion.

"Many strange and funny things happened when I was flying people back into the primitive areas. Once I had a trapper chop away the timber to make me a short strip to bring in hunters. I was flying a rich cigar-smoking hunter into the area on a squirrelly day. Seven Two Charlie's wings barely missed the tree stumps, and that was the first time I ever saw a man so afraid he bit his cigar in half. The guy didn't know he was on fire until I told him," roared Jake. "But old Seven Two Charlie has always had a strange sense of humor. I've seen us lost on moonless nights, and when I was low on gas, I've landed on highways and taxied to gas stations. Yep, this gal has flown a lot, and she always gets me home safely. It's always been me, God and Charlie," said Jake, fondly patting her panel.

He pushed the wheel forward and took her down for a little hedgehopping. Meeko knew this was his last flight with Seven Two Charlie and remained quiet. Both enjoyed the excitement as Jake flew low, almost touching the sage on the ground. Meeko loved his front row seat and dreamed of the day he too could fly this well.

Jake pointed to a shepherd's camp off of the left strut as they dropped low and buzzed him. "It was Seven Two Charlie who taught me to fly on the deck when we were hunting lost sheep. Many a time we've climbed the steep canyon walls like a mountain goat. Old Seven Two Charlie's stall warner was screaming like a mad cougar as we barely crossed over the top of those steep mesas.

"Yep, gotta be thankful for the Wright brothers. Don't know how I could live without flying. I'll miss Seven Two Charlie, but someday I'll buy her back," said Jake as a lump settled hard in his throat.

Both sat in silence as Jake flew over the last mountain top and entered the Los Angeles basin. As they dropped into the smoggy brown valley, Jake explained how this beautiful city once had pure, clean air. As both sat thinking of losing Seven Two Charlie, they entered the flight pattern at the Santa Monica airport. Jake reached for the mike to call the tower for landing instructions. He held Seven Two Charlie high over the field and suddenly chopped the engine, letting her slip quickly toward the ground. Jake lowered the flaps, flared out and greased her wheels onto the runway. "Okay, Charlie girl, do your stuff," said Jake as he paraded her on two front wheels and into position next to the Beech 18. For a moment she teetered, as Jake slowly dropped her tail proudly to the ground. Meeko watched Jake pat Seven Two Charlie on her panel and shut her down for the last time.

Meeko stayed with Seven Two Charlie while Jake and Keith, the salesman, looked over the new bird. Jake ran his hands along her leading edge as they walked around the plane. Meeko watched and immediately got out of the plane. Glancing sadly back at Seven Two Charlie, he saw a proud peacock sitting on oversized tires, and wondered if the new plane could match her heart.

"Well, Meeko, don't you think she's pretty? Got one helluva payload."

"Yeah, she's pretty and all that, but if you ask me, those twin engines seem like double trouble," answered Meeko, as Keith handed Jake the papers to sign.

"Jake, I've always wanted to own Seven Two Charlie and this should be enough money to take care of it," offered Meeko, handing Jake his red rag. Jake rolled the keys to Seven Two Charlie around in his hand as he studied the situation.

"Okay, you got a deal,"he responded, handing Meeko the keys. After Jake and Meeko had signed all the necessary papers, they walked happily toward their planes. "Think you can fly old Seven Two Charlie home?"

"C'mon Jake, I cut my teeth on her struts," laughed Meeko, climbing in and buckling up. Meeko watched Jake fire up the Beech 18 and taxi her toward the runway. As Jake popped her into the air for a fast climb out, Meeko was cleared for takeoff, and both planes headed home. When they crossed the first mountain range, Jake picked up the mike and asked Meeko how he was doing. "Hey, Old Charlie knows what to do. She knows her way home. Hey Jake, that new silver baby is sure pretty in the air."

"Yeah, I like her. Handles good."

As they arrived home, Jake lowered the landing gear. Meeko grabbed his mike, saying, "Don't see any wheels coming out of the well."

"Yeah, can't seem to get them down. I'm gonna use the hand pump. Let me know when you see rubber."

Meeko watched closely and radioed back to Jake, "You got a little over half of a tire."

"Running low on fuel. Gotta try it anyway."

Meeko watched Jake wrestle with her as they touched down, and was relieved when he saw the plane was safely on the runway. He brought Seven Two Charlie in and taxied next to the Beech 18, shutting her down. Meeko unbuckled his seat belt, patted the panel and approached Jake.

The mechanic worked on the Beech 18 until long after dark before the landing gear was workable. "We'll check it out tomorrow, Meeko. I'm tired. Need some shut eye."

One morning Meeko awakened to the sound of a radio announcer speaking about a war in Vietnam. He was concerned about the country, but he was more worried about the draft. Taking Manfred, he walked into the field behind the hangar and built a small fire. He sat studying the talking fire and pulled out a hot coal. As he blew on it glowing images appeared, telling Meeko it was time to return to the reservation. Back at the hangar, Meeko told Jake he needed some cross-country time. "I'll be flying back to the reservation. I'll be gone a few days. I need to talk to Shadowhawk about this war. I am thinking about enlisting in the Marines rather than being drafted into the Army."

Meeko flew in silence toward the Great Plains, listening to the sound of the winds blend with the droning engine of the plane. A tail wind caught him near the Dakotas, as if offering assistance to accelerate his flight home. Meeko chased his thoughts but there were too many possibilities racing in his mind to focus on his future. He hoped he would receive direction for what he was about to do from Shadowhawk.

Meeko gazed out over the valley and saw the reservation airport looming ahead. Old feelings stirred, as he thought of the days spent with Granbear and Shadowhawk. He could still hear Granbear saying, "Everything is a part of the whole. All answers are within. You must be high above before you can see the total picture. Life has many choices. You must choose what is right for you. If you choose to fight for your country, will the experience harm or help your life? Listen to the inner voice, Meeko, and let spirit guide you to your decision. These worldly challenges are merely tools created to help you grow from each life experience."

He felt Granbear's presence and as he stepped out of the plane he once again embraced the plains as they touched his soul. Even the wind brushed against his skin to welcome him home, and Meeko knew the reservation was alive and well. After tying down Seven Two Charlie, Meeko hitched a ride out to Shadowhawk's place.

"My son, we've prayed for your safe return," said Shadowhawk.

"It's good to be home. I've come to visit Granbear's bones and ask you for a *Hanblecheyapi*," stated Meeko, handing Shadowhawk many new blankets. After speaking for hours about the Vietnam War, Shadowhawk and Meeko went to visit Granbear's burial site where both felt his presence. The elements had taken nearly everything, and Granbear's flesh had departed to the four winds.

As they sat talking late into the night, Shadowhawk said, "I am glad you came to speak with me. I have waited a long time for you to pick up your warrior's shield."

"Shadowhawk, my mind has talked with you many times, and your words have always guided me."

"There's a very thin veil that separates our hearts, Meeko. I will always be with you. You've come because of the war, but it's also time for you to think of your future."

Within the first day, many old friends heard of Meeko's arrival and came to visit, but Meeko avoided them, wanting to see Wicahmunga first. Walking toward her place, he found her waiting at the door. Smiling, she pushed open the screen door and silently invited him in for breakfast. Meeko spoke of his plans and they talked for hours. She went to the bedroom and brought back two feathers, one from a golden eagle and one from a little chickadee. About the chickadee feather, she said, "This little bird sits quietly and listens. It can hear and understand everything. Chickadee knows the languages of all the animals and the humans. Before you make a decision to join the Marines, take this feather and go talk with Chickadee. Let him tell you of the coming events in your life," she said in her mysterious way.

"*Unci*, I have returned to the reservation to gather my power and find some answers."

"You will find the power you seek when you go to war. You will return, but you will have suffered many wounds."

"What do you mean?" questioned Meeko.

Disregarding his question, she glared at him in disgust and continued, "Take this golden eagle feather and spiral upward through the hole in the sky until you find your way through the sun. It is Eagle who teaches your spirit to soar in life. Carry his feather in battle and use his powers of sight to help you move between worlds. Now, go," she said handing him her favorite stone. Meeko knew their conversation was over and said goodbye, then walked back to Shadowhawk's.

Finding him waiting under the arbor, Meeko approached. "Shadowhawk, I need a *Hanblecheyapi* to help me make a decision. I feel a need to serve my country. My logical mind says if I do this, my college will be paid for by the government and then my decision would be wise. My question is, do I have the heart and the courage to become a warrior?"

"*Hau*," answered Shadowhawk. "First let's go to the *Inipi* and pray for these answers." After the sweat Shadowhawk continued, "Since *Wakan Tanka* possesses all knowledge, and you wish to take the war trail, I advise you to begin your *Hanblecheyapi* before sunrise in the morning."

Meeko took the necessary things and began his lamenting, offering many prayers as he waited motionless, searching for the entrance to the Great Mystery. Crying, he prayed desperately, trying to see with his heart rather than his eyes. Begging the spirits to have pity on him, he called upon the elements and all the animals. Bear came first, standing tall on his hind feet, roaring with fierceness, saying, "I have nothing for you. You already have the power and the will of the fearless."

Then Wolf came, saying, "You have the brotherhood. Sharpen your hunting knife as it will sharpen your shrewdness. Use what you already know!"

On his last night in the vision quest, Meeko saw a spirit warrior with red eyes. "Leave me, evil one," he yelled.

"Am I evil? Or are you seeing the other side of yourself?" laughed the spirit. "You seek, and I come. I can give you wealth, fame and power. Why not make it easy on yourself to learn the power of duality before you complete your life's journey? Take what I offer, and I will make you powerful beyond your wildest dreams," tantalized the spirit.

"Go from me! I have no need for evil! I will not be tempted by you." The spirit disappeared, and Meeko stayed in the hills for an extra night. When Shadowhawk came to get him he was tired, but anxious to tell him about his vision. After a sweat, Meeko and Shadowhawk spoke for many hours about his experience.

"At first I was tempted by a powerful demon who offered me the world, but I drove him away. I saw much dying and know this war will bring disgrace upon this country. The people will reject all who serve, which will cause great illness in the men, signaling the beginning of a decline in our power around the world. I saw myself in Vietnam fighting alongside many Indian brothers. I saw us fighting for a people who looked like us, but smaller in stature."

Shadowhawk went immediately and prepared a special *Inipi* asking Wicahmunga to bring her special medicines. By the fourth round, she had cleansed away the bad spirit and taught Meeko a special war song for his protection. Wicahmunga and Shadowhawk then made Meeko a special medicine bag and gave him a small object from Granbear's medicine bundle to protect him on his warrior journey. Meeko accepted these gifts with gratitude and took a piece of hair from Sapa's mane for safety upon his new journey.

When he arrived at the local airport, he found many relatives and friends had gathered to say goodbye. Wicahmunga, stepping out from the crowd, handed Meeko a hawk feather, saying, "Find the clues, Grandson, and know your enemy."

After his return flight, Meeko and Jake talked long into the night until Meeko was sure he had made the right decision. Early the following morning he made arrangements to rent Seven two Charlie to Jake until he returned from the war. The next morning Meeko and Jake flew Seven Two Charlie to San Diego where he enlisted in the United States Marine Corps, knowing this was his first step in becoming a true Sioux warrior.

Vietnam

In July of 1967 Meeko was loaded onto a bus to be sent along with the other recruits to a receiving station at Camp Pendleton in San Diego. The recruits were apprehensive as they stood in formation listening to a very large black man named Sergeant Tibbs address them with contempt.

"You bunch of spineless, gung ho pussy debutantes! God knows why you joined the Marines. No one is born a Marine, but you'll know what it is to be a Marine when I'm through with you. You'll forget every pre-conceived idea you ever had about serving your country. I am your mother, your father and your god! Accept this as a fact! So, wire your heads onto your ass because you don't know jackshit about the Marines! I'll tell you when and how to do everything, including when to take a piss! If I tell you ladies to eat a shit sandwich, you eat it! Ninety days from now, you will be a lean mean fighting machine that protects Mother Green, or you'll be history! Am I understood?"

Intimidated by his overbearing manner, the recruits marched to their assigned barracks in silent confusion. Up before daybreak the following morning, they were processed, classified, given medical checkups, and issued uniforms and field equipment. That afternoon, under the intolerant eyes of Sergeant Tibbs, Meeko sat in a barber's chair and watched his waist-length hair fall to the floor. He remembered the day Shadowhawk had shaved his head for his boy training and wondered what Granbear would think of the kind of training he was about to get.

The sergeant's harsh voice intruded on his memory. "I guess you think you're pretty? Well, you're not pretty enough for me, Chief." Turning to the barber, he continued, "Now, shave Tonto's locks to the scalp. I don't tolerate fucking hippies in my platoon!" Meeko immediately hated the Sergeant for his derogatory remarks and silently promised his time would come.

Within a month Meeko had adjusted to the physical fitness programs, circuit courses, drills and weapon instructions, water survival, and hand-to-hand combat with the use of pugil sticks. Meeko was also assigned to a class in sight and triangulation pictorials, but his excitement disappeared when the sergeant criticized his drawings.

"Listen, Skin, this isn't a fucking art class! This is the Marines! Now draw me a goddamn simple map without the fucking frills," bellowed the sergeant.

Meeko refused to let the black son of a bitch intimidate him and calmly drew another map. He contemplated his knowledge of animals and wondered which one Sergeant Tibbs resembled. Perhaps a hyena, since it would never attack anything bigger than itself. When the opportunity presented itself, he decided to test his theory on the good Sergeant to see if this was one of Tibbie's guiding principles.

This day Sergeant Tibbs stopped Meeko on the pretense of checking for dress code. Finding nothing wrong, he sadistically brushed a lit cigarette across the front of Meeko's shirt, saying, "Indian, you're dirty! Drop and give me fifty!"

Meeko remained dignified as their eyes locked in a cold stare. Then he curtly saluted the sergeant, saying, "Sir! No one calls me a dirty Indian, Sir! Not even a fucking sergeant in the United States Marines. So go fuck yourself, Sir!"

Sergeant Tibbs' mouth dropped open in shock as Meeko casually walked away, assured the sergeant was indeed a hyena and would not attack him. But the good sergeant understood the game, and kept pressuring and insulting Meeko with ugly remarks. "Hey, Skin! It takes intelligence and courage to be a Marine. We reserve that right for those who can meet our standards. Personally, I hate Indians! The government should have gassed all of you before you reached the age of five! Now, double time and give me five miles with full pack."

Although the sergeant tried to push him beyond his physical and mental limits, Meeko was determined to win this battle. He fought day after day until his energy was drained, but just when he thought the sergeant could not possibly demean him any further, Meeko had to endure yet another barrage of macho arrogance and bigoted racial remarks. "When you're an old man, I want you to remember me as you sit around your campfire telling how your people lost this country to a better race of men." Even though Meeko remained at attention during this emotional punch, it caused his fists to clench and his jaw to tighten. He knew he was losing control.

"Gotcha, you Red bastard! You're not only a dumb Indian, you're a fucking arrogant, dumb Indian." Meeko's blood boiled and he knew he was headed for a violent confrontation.

"Drop and give your black master fifty, or it's the brig," challenged Sergeant Tibbs. Meeko dropped to a prone position, determined the black scumbag would not kick his ass. The more he focused on his hatred, the faster he popped out the push-ups. In that moment, Meeko became determined to become the best Marine in the Corps, although at times he was unable to control the challenging smirk that would cross his face when he looked at the sergeant.

"Are you a fucking queer? Did you make a pass at me? Gimme another twenty-five! On one arm!" bellowed Sergeant Tibbs, his face twisted in rage. It made Meeko happy that the sergeant was out of control, and he gladly did the push-ups, all the while hoping the sergeant's bulging neck veins would explode.

After this confrontation the antagonism between them grew even greater, but Meeko was committed and finished in the top ten of his platoon. After graduation he took great pride in wearing his Marine uniform.

With twenty days of leave, Meeko boarded a bus to San Francisco hoping to contact Jake and get in a little flying time. A pretty hippie girl with long hair intertwined with flowers took a seat next to him, and without saying a word, placed a string of beads around his neck.

By the time they arrived in San Francisco, Tina had invited Meeko to stay with her until he could find Jake. He gladly accepted the invitation because he wanted to see the sights. On their cab ride to the Haight-Ashbury district he became angry when he saw the streets lined with long-haired hippies carrying anti-war signs. When they arrived at Tina's house, Meeko was introduced to young people of many different races who strongly voiced their opposition to the Vietnam War over the blaring sounds of Janis Joplin.

Distraught at their talk of a new revolution, and trying to escape their opinions, Meeko asked to use the phone. Unable to locate Jake, he decided to depart. Not wanting him to leave so soon, Tina seductively motioned him to follow her to a second-floor bedroom where she turned up the radio and danced around the room, undressing both of them.

"I've never done an Indian before. Always wanted to," she giggled, running her hands over his body and caressing his crotch. Meeko, embarrassed, wished the room was pitch-black. Then overcome by his sexual desire, he hesitantly responded to her touch. Tina sensed his awkwardness and asked, "Your first time?"

"Kinda," he answered.

"Wanna burn one first to relax?" she asked, motioning for him to sit on a bare, thin mattress in the middle of the room.

"Sure." Meeko watched her fingers quickly roll a joint. When she passed it to him, he inhaled deeply, and by the time the doobie had been reduced to a roach, they were comfortable with each other.

The room was in disarray, clothes strewn everywhere except for a small table where there was a syringe, candle, bent spoon, red balloon, belt, and several small white bags. Seeing Meeko's fascination with these items, Tina sprinkled a dark coffee-colored powder into the burnt spoon, drew water into the syringe, and made a colorless liquid. She lit a candle and held it under the spoon until the liquid was almost boiling. She dropped in a frayed cigarette filter and then, reaching for the syringe, sucked up the liquid. She strapped a belt around her upper arm and flexed her hand while smacking her arm trying to pop up a vein. When the needle entered a vein, she got ready for the run.

The drug soon took effect, transforming Tina into a very aggressive woman. She smiled with lust, and put her head between Meeko's legs, wrapping her mouth around his penis. Meeko lost control and quickly ejaculated with a deep moan.

Tina continued to tutor him in the art of sex for the rest of the afternoon until he fell asleep. Meeko awakened to find several other couples lying around, at which point, he dressed quickly and bolted out of the room saying he was hungry. In the kitchen he met an Indian girl named Mary who reminisced with him about life on the reservation.

As night rolled over the busy city, Tina's home turned into a party house. Meeko was surrounded by booze, drugs and group sex as well as loud debates on freedom and human rights. He watched many naked bodies intermingling and writhing on the floor in a circle of ecstasy, reminding him of a den of snakes. Although he felt the urge to participate, his mind rejected this strange behavior.

Instead, he took refuge and joined Mary and her friends in another room. Understanding, Mary smiled and placed a small sugar cube in his mouth for him to suck on as they discussed world events. Soon his mind was engulfed by vividly colored images that kept appearing and transforming before his eyes.

When Meeko awakened the following afternoon in a disoriented state, he found Mary and asked, "What did you give me last night? I can't remember a thing, except I saw many beautiful colors."

"That was acid," she smiled, handing him a cup of coffee. "Today me, you, and Tina are going to the park. I scored last night and we're splitting a four-way."

On a grassy knoll in the park Mary cut an orange barrel-shaped pill. Within twenty minutes the world around Meeko once again became distorted. The blades of grass turned into little people and the roots of the trees rose out of the ground emblazoned with monster-like faces. To his dismay, Tina suddenly transformed into Renna and began to sexually caress Meeko. Thinking his mother was trying to have sex with him, Meeko grabbed Tina by the throat and started to choke her. As Tina fought, Mary pulled Meeko off, demanding, "Let her go. She's not your fucking mother. You're having a bad trip!" Trying to break his rage, she sought to distract him, speaking more gently. "Brother, remember how the buffalo herds once wandered across the land and how we talked about their return? Remember how the sage and sweetgrass smelled after a summer rain?"

"All that shit is gone and will never return," growled Meeko, still in a daze.

Mary and Tina took Meeko to the ladies room to pull him out of his bad trip. They steered him into one of the stalls and Mary commanded, "Tina give him a blow job, while I cook up this shit."

Although Tina was frightened, she pushed him against the wall while she unzipped his pants and did as she was instructed. While Meeko was distracted by the sexual pleasure, Mary worked quickly with the Mexican mud. She hoped it was cool enough to insert the needle into his arm, saying, "Damn it, hold still. This will take away your demons."

Meeko's eyes rapidly glazed over and he threw up. Tina raced out of the stall and Mary led Meeko back to the grassy knoll where she held and stroked him. Meeko, trying to clear his fogged mind, asked, "Mary, how long have you been doing drugs?"

She offered him a line of coke before answering. "A couple of years ago I came here to get a job and couldn't find one. So I started selling drugs, and pretty soon I was using. I got two kids back home with my folks, but no husband. When I get straight, I'm going back."

"How old are you?" Meeko asked after snorting two lines of coke.

"Twenty-eight."

"This kind of life is okay for honky broads, but not for an Indian woman. Why don't you quit drugs and find a good man? You know you belong home with your children."

"Hey man, I was a junkie before I left the reservation, so don't talk shit about my life. Hell, I wouldn't be alive right now unless Tina had helped me. I'm a mule, man! I stole the last load of drugs and right now I'm hot. If I hadn't gotten another load of Mexican mud, I'd probably be dead."

"What's Mexican mud?"

"It's horse—the shit I put in your arm to take away your demons. Come on, we're going home. You've ruined the day," growled Mary.

It was dark when they returned home to find Tina was waiting at the door. "I delivered the stuff, Mary, and everything's cool. They still want you for a run next week. I went shopping and here's what's left of the money."

"Thanks," answered Mary, stuffing it into her pocket.

Meeko noticed Tina was dressed in a short red oriental robe which barely covered her naked body. As they sat smoking a joint, he was flabbergasted to see Mary making sexual advances towards Tina. Uneasy, he snorted a line of coke then headed to the side porch to regain his composure.

Although his favorite drug was heroin, Meeko indulged in all varieties, using his Indianness to support his addictions. He soon found that if he fed their curiosity about Indian philosophy, all of his drugs were free and this gave him many hours of entertainment.

Late one afternoon Meeko awoke somewhat clear-headed. He was shocked to see the floor filled with drugged-out, foul-smelling naked bodies. A girl he did not know was lying in his arms, her body covered with dark needle holes and bruises. He realized three months had passed and he was overextended on his leave. This was big trouble.

Disgusted with himself, he walked to the police station and turned himself in. Three hours later he was shackled and on his way back to Camp Pendleton as ABSENT WITH OUT LEAVE. Meeko was immediately taken to the rehabilitation center at the base hospital and treated for withdrawals. As nausea, diarrhea, and cold chills violently shook his body, he lied to himself insisting it was the flu, but his convulsions convinced him otherwise.

After weeks of detoxification, Meeko was still confined to the base, but he nevertheless found ways to entertain himself. At the base bar one night, he spotted two old- timers from his unit sitting at a table. He joined them and became privy to a grim hour-long discussion about the large number of body bags coming back from Vietnam. Then Dave, a sergeant, raised his glass in a mock toast asking, "Aren't you with the second battalion, ninth Marine, third division of Golf Company?" Meeko nodded yes. "Well, drink up, Chief. You never know when it'll be your last."

Meeko's division received orders in the middle of the night and by sunrise they were on route to Vietnam. Soon after arrival in Da Nang, it became apparent to him that most of his division used drugs and he was glad that Dave had supplied him several vials of coke. With all the smoking, snorting, and shooting up, no one seemed to mind the fact they were being sent to Camp Carroll deep in the Demilitarized Zone.

At first Meeko's use of drugs masked the brutal reality of the war. The day his division pulled onto base, there was a mortar attack. Everyone hit the dirt except Meeko who had dropped acid minutes before. He stood there watching the pretty colors and envisioning John Wayne chewing the ring off a hand grenade, thus saving the day. A moment later when he saw a man get blown to bits, Meeko came to the realization he could get killed and dove headfirst into the nearest bunker.

When the attack was over, the marine lying next to him said in a thick Alabama drawl, "What the hell's wrong with you? Only a fool would stand and watch mortars come in!" Meeko felt foolish and in celebration of his craziness, offered the medic a hit off his joint. After they smoked together, Meeko had made a friend and was rewarded by an introduction to the dispensary. From that day on, he feigned any sickness to get free drugs to support his habit. He had downers to sleep and uppers to wire for battle. His drug of choice was a speedball of China white and crystal meth.

One night, after coming back from a dangerous patrol, Meeko and his partner joined six others in sharing a needle, after which they sat smoking some really good weed. Soon stricken with a bad case of munchies, they searched their lockers for something to eat, but came back empty-handed.

"I heard the army artillery unit has plenty of food and beer. Why should we Marines have to drink this brown shit they call water, when those army bastards get cold beer? I think we oughta do something about that!" proposed Meeko.

"It's your idea, man. You do it," dared the group.

Meeko accepted the challenge. He passed an Army officer's hooch and noticed a second lieutenant's hat on a cot. He placed it on his head and marched to the supply house. As an Army private saluted him, Meeko demanded, "Give me two cases of beer and a ten-pound can of Spam."

"What unit are you from, sir?" the private asked, scrutinizing him.

Meeko barked, "I didn't come here to get a fucking third degree from a dumb-ass private. Give me the beer and Spam, or I'll walk out of here with your ass!" Silently, the private handed over the provisions. Taking the bounty, Meeko strutted back to his unit. The group cheered his success, then partied for the rest of the night, until every beer was a dead soldier.

The following morning Meeko began his new duty guarding the local bridge. He was curious about possible drug connections in the nearby village of Cam Lo. When his relief showed up, he walked across the bridge to investigate. The beautiful little village nestled at the base of forested mountains was populated by simple farmers who reminded him of Indians. He soon learned they too saw themselves as caretakers of the land. Upon further visits to Cam Lo, he discovered their language was similar to his, and within a month he was speaking Vietnamese fairly well.

The local Chief, Ong Nguyen, invited him to attend a religious ceremony for Spring. Meeko became good friends with him and they spent hours discussing their similar spiritual commitment to the people and the land. One day the two were drinking rice whiskey at a local bar when Ong explained, "I'm from the mountain people. We are called the Montagnard tribe, but most refer to us as the Moi, which means savage, because we are descendants of the Mayayos and Polynesians, rather than Chinese."

Meeko felt a kinship with this simple man. "In my country we have the same problem. The French named us Sioux, which means savage in English, but amongst ourselves, we are known as the Nakota, Lakota or Dakota."

Understanding, Ong smiled and continued, "Long ago, I came here to take a wife. After our marriage, we decided that since we could have no children, we would stay and help these people. After my wife's death I thought of returning home, but instead I stayed on to help the people through this time of crisis.

"We continue to struggle with the North Vietnamese Army and now also the United States military. We mountain people are forced to defend ourselves with only crossbows and spears, when what we really need are firearms to stop the soldiers from taking our food and raping our women. Too many of our women have become whores or drug dealers to support their families. Our land is all we have. It is being destroyed and no longer able to yield good crops."

Meeko was horrified at the impact the war was having on these poor people. As he prepared to leave, Ong said, "If you hear of orders that might threaten our village, you can send messages to me through the little girl Suzie Lin, that lives with me. Her stand is right by the side of the bridge. She is very independent, trustworthy, and wise for a ten-year-old. Her village was destroyed and she was raped. She became just a street urchin. I took her in and have seen to her education as best as I can."

"Oh, yeah, That's where I get my joints and anything else she has to sell for the day. My friend, I fear what happened to my people is happening to yours. Still, I will do what I can," promised Meeko as he walked away.

Three weeks later Meeko returned to Suzie's stand with dreaded news. "Tell Ong the bridge will be closed tomorrow," he whispered in his now fluent Vietnamese.

Meeko was familiar with most of the villagers and he felt badly about executing the orders to stop them from crossing the bridge. One day a stranger with a water buffalo and an overloaded wooden cart got to the center of the bridge before he could stop them. When Meeko told him the bridge was closed, the old man bowed and apologized for the difficult situation. "We have walked this bridge for many years to sell our vegetables in the next village. The buffalo does not understand that we cannot cross."

"Let me help," answered Meeko. The old man graciously accepted his offer, whereupon Meeko grabbed the ring in the buffalo's nose and, hoping to turn the beast around, began pulling him with authority. To his dismay, the buffalo remained determined not to reverse his direction. In an effort to outwit the creature, Meeko shoved his shoulder into the animal's ass and pushed. When it still did not move, he twisted its tail and shoved with all his might.

"My friend," the farmer said to the animal, "it is imperative we move forward before this crazy man twists off your tail." As if understanding, the buffalo plodded forward, and Meeko knew he had no choice but to let them continue their journey. The old man bowed graciously and thanked him. As they passed, he reached into his cart and handed Meeko a mound of fresh vegetables, then continued his journey across the bridge. Meeko stood laughing, his arms full of vegetables, as his relief approached.

"Man, what the fuck are you doing?" asked the marine. "You can't let those slope-heads cross this bridge."

"Yeah, but you go tell that fucking buffalo he can't use the bridge," chuckled Meeko, heading for Ong's house. There Meeko found his unit Captain and Ong drinking together. As Meeko shared his story of the buffalo, the Captain roared and pointed at Meeko's shoulder which was covered with buffalo shit.

Later that night in camp, Meeko was startled awake by gunfire. Grabbing his M-16, he ran outside to investigate. "Fuckers got through the perimeter," someone yelled, as Meeko caught a glimpse of the Viet Cong about a hundred yards away. Shrapnel was flying everywhere and a moment later Meeko saw the little village of Cam Lo go up in flames.

"Ong is dead!" screamed Suzie, running toward him across the bridge.

Meeko saw Suzie and ran to bring her to safety. He put her into a bunker, telling her not to move until he came for her, then ran toward the sound of machine guns as bullets continued to rip sporadically through the air. Meeko looked at the river and saw dead military personnel floating like fallen leaves. Madness gripped him and he began firing wildly into the wooded area.

The next morning, the river was red with blood as the troops searched for bodies. While he carried the remains of friends who had been cut in two by machine gunfire, Meeko raged at the senselessness of the war. By late afternoon, his division had rounded up sixty prisoners, and because he spoke their language, he was asked to help with the interrogations. As one prisoner was questioned by Lieutenant White, Meeko translated the reply. "He says for you to go fuck your mother, Sir!" The Lieutenant's expression froze as he blew off the front of the prisoner's face. The rest of the prisoners quickly dropped to their knees, pleading for their lives.

After the attack, security was tightened, and the Lieutenant was sent along with the three Viet Cong officers to Da Nang where the prisoners were further interrogated. Meeko placed Suzie with another Vietnamese family then left with his unit to stabilize their perimeters, all the while mourning the death of Ong, knowing he had lost a good friend.

Soon time and order meant little to Meeko. He stayed in the bush until his drugs ran low then stopped at the dispensary to replenish his supply. Late one night after night patrol, the captain, concerned that Meeko was endangering others, issued orders to detain him. When Meeko arrived, drugged as suspected, the captain invited him for a drink. The moment Meeko passed out, the captain had him taken in for drug rehabilitation.

Meeko woke up strapped to a bed in a Da Nang Hospital. He was not only enraged, but was wrestling with withdrawal symptoms, including incessant delusions. Three months later, a counselor reviewed his records in disgust, saying, "Your behavior is incorrigible! Some of your actions could warrant prison time and a possible dishonorable discharge, but your records also show you're one of our best behind enemy lines. I could arrange to have prison bypassed if you'll volunteer for a new Special Forces program. I understand you have many Vietnamese friends and can speak some of the dialects. Accepting my proposition would help you resolve your problems."

Knowing he had no choice, Meeko's hatred for the government flared and he answered coldly, "Sure, I'd love to die for my country."

Within two weeks, Meeko was in the Special Forces group referred to as the 'marine fuck-ups.' Although their common status created a bond among the men, they were also aware that anyone of them could flip out and go on a killing spree. To guard against this possibility, the ten Indians and one white boy were put under the direct supervision of Tony LaVette, a hard-nosed expert from Special Forces. Although he respected the fighting abilities of this unconventional group, he frowned on some of their war tactics.

"I've reviewed your service records and consider you all corrupt degenerates. I have little respect for you irrational loonies," he told them as they glared back with contempt. "You misfits are in this program because you aren't worthy of the Marine uniform. My assignment is to make you an elite fighting unit and I intend to fulfill my orders. You will earn back every rank and privilege you threw away. If you think you have it bad now, wait til I'm through with you. You'll be on your knees, praying to be back home with your mamas.

"Everyone here has had jump school and has served more than two years on active duty. Yes, you've been in some of the hottest areas, but your motivations were based on self-destruction. I expect each of you to operate at one hundred-and-fifty percent efficiency. Whoever doesn't will be dishonorably discharged and given fifteen years of hard time in prison. Every one of you come from a bad background and you all lack a formal education. My orders are to redirect your thinking and make you into robotic fighting machines.

"This program has three phases. The first will bring back your memory skills. The second will improve your abilities in weaponry, communications and engineering. The third will demand teamwork and promote independent thinking and well-developed instinctual survival skills."

Thereafter the group began each day with a fifteen-mile run which they were eventually expected to complete in ten minutes per mile or less. After weeks of running, they beat this time, but Captain LeVette only smiled and had them add full packs. Once their bodies grew strong, the captain stepped up the pace of the assignments, and as a result the training became harder, with respect to handling live ammo and conducting patrols, raids and ambushes. One morning he ordered the group on a dangerous assignment. "Today you will jump from a C-130 over unknown territory. You are to use the buddy system, and if you're still alive, be back here at zero four hundred."

The following day the men listened to the captain congratulate them on their safe return and in the next breath outline the next phase of the program. "In the second phase of your training, the subjects will be engineering, communications, special weapons and medical treatments. I know every one of you are experts around water. It is imperative that you use your instincts and good judgment to practice teamwork effectively."

Dave LittleFeather, a Blackfoot from Montana whom everyone called Savage, said, "Hell, most of us come from reservations. We been doing this survival shit since we were born. What's the big deal?" All the Indians chuckled looking around in agreement.

"You will become state-of-the-art fighting machines. And when I'm through, this unit will be Four-O in every aspect of down and dirty warfare. All of you men must commit to a different thinking, because there will be no racial or cultural prejudice here! You will work together, in spite of your differences," stated the captain as he handed Patti Snowman, a Mescalero-Apache, a handful of sealed envelopes. "Read these papers and answer every question, then we'll discuss your answers."

Meeko opened the envelope and read:

1. If you are behind enemy lines and you find an old or a pregnant woman with small children or young girls, what would you do?
    A. Kill them.
    B. Take them with you.
    C. Leave them.
    D. Rape them.

2. If one of your team breaks a moral code by engaging in rape, child abuse or killing senselessly, what would you do?
    A. Turn him in.
    B. Kill him.
    C. Accept what happened.
    D. Hold a grudge.

3. If a teammate froze in battle, what would you do?
    A. Turn him in.
    B. Keep the information to yourself.
    C. Deal with it on your own.
    D. Kill him.

As each man voiced his opinion, the group understood what they might expect from one another. When it was Meeko's turn to speak, remembering that Suzie had once been beaten and gang-raped by six marines, he empathetically stated that he would kill any man who raped a woman or a child.

During the next five weeks of training, the skills and tools Meeko had been introduced to in childhood took on a different meaning. The knife and the hatchet became his means of survival.

Charles, a northern Cheyenne from Montana they called Dog, joked, "Hell, in the old days they rode into battle naked, unless they had a little dick, and then they wore loincloths." Meeko appreciated Dog's dry sense of humor and thought they might become close friends.

Arnie West, known as Hillbilly, grabbed his dick to emphasize his point and answered, "Shit I ain't fighting nobody unless my family jewels are protected. Where I come from, those briar bushes can cut off your balls."

"Hell, I thought you southern boys kept your dick hard to hold your pants up," chuckled Bait, a Seminole from Florida, whose real name was Alan Fishook.

As the training continued, the captain became increasingly impressed with their skills. When he felt they were ready, he introduced even more advanced strategies. Taking a rolled bandage, he threaded it through the loops of his pants, saying, "This is how you carry your emergency supplies—insect repellent, C-rations, flare gun and nylon suspension rope. Your line maps, code frequency books, and contact times go in your breast pocket. When you're out in the bush for an indefinite time, carry two canteens of water, one on each hip, and tape your purification tablets to them. For special missions, attach a dummy cord, mirror, compass and a penlight to your cammies. Keep all morphine in a protective box somewhere on your body. And make damn sure everyone knows how to use a serette."

Hillbilly grinned, then said, "Well, Captain, everyone knows a good druggie gives the best shots" as the group cracked up in laughter.

Passing around a packed box for everyone to see, LeVette continued, "The web gear is placed over your pistol belt, and everyone better get used to wearing suspenders."

"Shit, Captain, Sir! My ole granpappy's been wearing suspenders since he was born." Everyone laughed as Hillbilly spat tobacco juice into his tin can, noting, "I don't understand why these little slope-head bastards are such a big deal. Hell, it's like huntin' coon. If you got a good nose, you can smell'um."

The captain, ignoring his remark, got everyone's attention by the way he was handling a live hand grenade. "Remember your count, and never carry a grenade on the upper part of your body. Keep your grenades and ammunition, plus your water evenly distributed on your body. Carry an ammunition pouch in front of you, and position all live ammunition downward on a bag of rice to keep you from fumbling when reloading. Always keep at least four fragmentation grenades and inspect the pins daily for cleanliness, making sure that each fuse is secure. I find it best to tape the handles to ensure a faster pull.

"Now, Arnie, let's go back to your granpappy's suspenders. On the left side, you tape your serum container. Right below it, put a snap link and a swiss seat. On the right side, carry a knife and an emergency strobe light for easy access. That's in case you have to operate it without the use of your hands.

"Today each of you will be issued a .45 with a silencer and an M-16. Carry your pistol in the center of your back and your M-16 to your side. While in training, the last three rounds of your clip will be tracers, reminding you to reload. Arrange bullets upside down and pointed away from the body in case a round accidentally goes off during an attack. Remember, a smart enemy is trained to conserve his ammunition. He will look for your mistakes, hoping to injure or kill you with your own ammunition. Use your canteen covers to carry your ammo, and during the rainy season, cut the corners off your ammo pouches. This will give you easier access and let you carry extra fragmentation and smoke grenades.

"To conserve energy and water, always move in the morning hours and use Claymores when camped at night. Again I emphasize, check each other for sterility and remove all ID before any maneuver. When you're in a hot zone, have designated alternatives for rallying points and when you move, move out fast for about twenty minutes, then stop and rest if you can.

"Be alert to all natural sounds before going forward. If you hear anything unusual, check it! If you think you're being followed, change directions and circle back to ambush your tracker. Never take off any of your equipment when you're in the field. For those who insist on carrying gloves to reload, I'll let Hillbilly tell you how to handle a heated gun."

Arnie stuttered out his answer. "Well, Sir, back in Alabama where I come from, if the calluses don't work, you just spit on your hands and sizzle with the fry. Or you could just reach down and use a handful of dirt."

The class roared as Billy Joe "Rat" Archer from Navajo country, added, "I can't see any reason to worry about a hot gun. Just make peace with the fire so it won't burn your hands." The Indians chuckled.

The captain continued, "No more than two will eat at the same time, the others keep tight security. Control all noise and blend with the natural sounds. Become one with that jungle, because it's either your sanctuary or your death trap. Before going on patrol, camouflage your faces and the tops of your hands. Check with the Indians—they can teach you about the meaning of paint."

"Yeah, if you can find any good Indians around," laughed Hillbilly.

Accepting the invitation, Meeko said, "We Sioux are a warring people and have always used paint for power, not for hiding." The class went quiet and Captain LeVette asked him to elaborate.

As a result of his answers, Meeko spent the next two weeks teaching the many aspects of the medicine wheel. By then the other Indians had dubbed him "Bear" and unofficially made Meeko the group's leader.

Each Indian had his own area of expertise, as well as an unspoken understanding that they had to help each other in battle. Dog was most knowledgeable about apparatus and equipment; Snow, about communications; Crow and Drum knew the most about maps, while Ghost and Rat were best at tunneling. Bait was a whiz around water, whereas Bear and Savage were the C-4 specialists.

Each day the captain saw the Indians' cooperation and determination grow. What fascinated him was their use of eye contact, gestures, and grunts to communicate. In the back of his mind, he knew these guys would become his best plastics team.

"Some brainwashing job that guy does, huh," remarked Savage as they met outside of class one evening.

"Yeah, but he's sure earned the right to wear that Q patch on his shoulder," said Drum, an Oglala from Rosebud.

"He makes sense. I even like him—but I still don't trust him," stated Crow from Billings, Montana.

"I don't believe you, man. I never met a Crow who agreed with anyone. Your people can't agree on a damn thing," quipped Bear.

"Fuck all of you! We Crow are smarter than any of you blanket asses," boasted Crow.

"Hey, relax man, we're skin, no matter the tribe," said Bear.

"Yeah, and under these conditions we better stick together as brothers," suggested Snow.

"You're right, man! Let's design a war shield to remind us we're family," said Dog.

"Man, they won't let us do that!" retorted Crow.

"Well, who gives a shit? We'll make the thing, and if we can't have a patch we'll tattoo the fucker on our bodies," determined Bait, laughing.

Everyone focused on coming up with a design. Finally Meeko sketched a circle with red and blue colors to represent the four directions. In the center he drew crossed arrows that held a bear claw and an eagle feather, then bordered it with wolf claws to symbolize the unity of power needed for their special missions. The group adopted this design, calling themselves the Crossed Arrows, which they viewed as an elite brotherhood with its own code of ethics.

Meeko told them about an old Vietnamese woman whose teeth were black from her many years of chewing betel nuts. "She accepted me as a friend when I first arrived in Vietnam and many times I tended her rose garden. One day she asked me about the rose tattoo on my hand. I explained my dream about a woman that would someday bring love into my life. When I focus on the rose, I always feel peace and in control of my hatred. After she heard my story, she enlarged the rose and made the colors brighter." Meeko showed them his tattoo.

After his story everyone agreed she was the right woman to tattoo them. Getting permission from the captain, the group went to visit Meeko's friend at her home. When the Crossed Arrows returned to base their shields were tattooed on their arms, and a close bond of silence rested among them.

One day while flying on a covert operation, the Crossed Arrows sat listening to the plane's droning engines and watching the umbrella of thick jungle below. Bear, reflecting on his many conversations with Ong, said, "In the area where we're going, there are over two hundred friendly villages. If we need help, I have some names."

Crow answered, "I heard those villagers support both sides of the war. How will we know whose side they're on? Get fucking real! We're here because it beats the hell out of rotting in a fucking jail cell. The government needs a job done and if we're killed they won't give a shit! They'll just keep sending more men until the job's done."

"Pleiku's coming up! Get ready to jump!" announced the pilot.

"We're here to mask another mission, so remember, we've gotta get in and snatch a few bodies to extend our perimeters," said Bear.

"Yeah, take no names and kill every fucking thing in your pathway," added Savage.

Within twenty minutes, everyone had hit the Drop Zone and the men smiled confidently as the jungle came alive. Doing double time with full packs, they began working their way toward their destination, wired on government-issued black beauties to help them keep the pace through enemy territory. Three days later they reached their destination and set up camp.

As darkness closed its curtains on the day, Dog whispered, "Gentlemen it's time to burn one." Everyone smiled, lit up, and sat back chilling while listening to the sounds of the jungle magnify.

Bear broke the trance. "What the hell am I doing here? I'm no fucking fighter, I'm a lover." Everyone smirked over his arrogance and Snow thought it needed further discussion.

"This is serious. You know, he could be right. I think the goddamn government should send in a research team to study his sex life."

"I agree," laughed Savage, "we should definitely call Uncle Sam and discuss the error of his ways."

"Lover, huh? You Sioux don't know the meaning of sex. Hell, us Northern Cheyenne took your women and had to teach them how to fuck," bragged Dog.

"I heard different. I thought our women took pity on you and taught all of you about fucking," said Bear.

"Shit, you heard wrong, man. We couldn't chase your women away. I heard you Assiniboine Sioux were so hard up you had to steal Crow women," joked Dog.

"Yeah, the Sioux did that, but they only got the ugly ones because we hid the pretty ones," added Crow.

"I always wondered why you Sioux were so big and ugly," said Ghost.

"Oh, we got pretty women," answered Savage.

"He's right. I remember the pretty ones always had Cheyenne fathers," teased Dog.

"Yeah, and if you fuckers were Crow, you wouldn't have had to worry about your dicks. Hell, our women know how to take care of us," chided Crow.

"Shit! We Sioux can fuck, eat a meal and collect enough fingers to make a necklace before a Crow could get a hard on," jested Savage.

"Hey, will you fuckers shut up before we have to call in the firefighters to get our crotches under control?" laughed Rat, getting to his feet to go take a piss.

Suddenly they heard what sounded like a stampeding herd of buffalo and everyone hit the dirt.

"What the fuck is that?" whispered Savage.

"Something big is going down," whispered Bear.

Rat, belly-crawling back from the bushes, tapped him on the shoulder, saying, "We're within fifty yards of a Charlie scout patrol. One of those fuckers tried to tell me in Vietnamese that I had guard duty, stupid son-of-bitch."

"Holy shit, man! Move! Move! Move! We gotta get outta here!" whispered Bear. Then everyone crawled until they could run safely toward the river.

At daybreak they were surprised to see a newly constructed bridge upstream. Agreeing that the bridge would ease life considerably for the enemy, they decided to make things less convenient. Silently they worked their way toward the base of the bridge, climbed up the main support beams and laid in C-4. Then they headed toward a nearby hill to wait for the excitement to begin.

Around noon, as a convoy of enemy trucks and artillery reached the center of the bridge, the Crossed Arrows watched with fire in their bellies as it blew, filling the air with machine and body parts. The Crossed Arrows watched in delight as death rode heavy with the enemy this day. Their mission completed, they moved on.

After two weeks, the unmerciful, ball-busting emergencies, combined with the ongoing humidity, hunger, and fatigue began to weigh on the men. Worse, they had become so enmeshed in the jungle's dying vegetation that it snared them like a disease, causing the degeneration of their thoughts and feelings. Now the only animals that took notice of them were the insects that fed hungrily on their bodies.

"Hell, we've been tramping through this shithole for too long without a fucking break!" said Rat.

"I've sweated so damn much my fucking clothes are rotting off my body, and my crotch itches so bad, I'm afraid my dick's going to fall off," snarled Dog.

"Man, now that's a serious problem. I think you're right. My little feller seems to need some air," said Savage, dropping his pants.

"What the fuck! If that's all you got, we don't need to worry about it," laughed Bear.

"It's a bitch, man. No dick, and can't leave this shithole to go get some pussy. Yeah man, it's bad" agreed Drum, winking at Bear.

"Shit! My balls have been on fire for weeks," moaned Crow.

"Well, stop whining and get serious. We're all in the same damn canoe," snapped Dog.

"Damn, Bear, your feet stink like they're rotting! I told you to get out of those fucking boots and wear sandals like the natives. You'd probably keep your feet if you'd listen to me," snapped Bait.

"Geezus, get serious. Now, heads up! There's no more smoking, eating, shitting, or pissing. Nothing can be left that can be traced. Now, let's get the fuck out of this misery!" barked Bear.

Everyone realized it was time to focus on the job. Snow again checked his watch and saw it was eleven hundred. "Christ, I gotta call in."

"Fuck, you've been trying for two days and all you get is static," answered Savage.

"Fuck the prick! We've got less than twelve hours. Let's move out," stated Bear. The men fell into a single file run and silently faded into the marrow of the jungle's body.

"Goddamnit!" said Savage, smacking viciously at his neck. "These fuckers are driving me crazy! I'm gonna lose it. I'm gonna have myself a pan full of these mother fuckers for lunch if this keeps up."

Bear noticed blood trickling from open wounds on Savage's neck. He grabbed a nearby wet plant, saying, "Use this, man! Looks like the sky brothers sprayed with Agent Orange this morning." Savage stripped and wiped his body down with the damp leaves, finding it gave him some relief.

By dusk they reached a clearing that overlooked their final destination and everyone knew the importance of claiming this area. Seeing there was too much activity, they decided to wait until after dark before entering the village. "Drum, we've got to know what these bastards eat if we're to stop their food supply. Take the shit detail tonight and collect some samples," said Bear.

"Fuck, man. I did the last three villages. Let someone else collect their maggot-filled shit!" grumbled Drum.

"Hell, man, a shit tribe should do the shit work!" kidded Crow.

Drum pulled his knife, challenging, "Fuck you! You Crow bastard! You're nothing but a shit disturber. I think you're the one for this job," he stated, slicing the air dangerously close to Crow's face.

For a moment Bear feared the confrontation might be fatal. "You sons of bitches," he growled. "What the fuck are you doing? C'mon, Drum, put the fucking knife down! He's still your brother." Drum eased the knife to his side and stepped away to light a joint. As the tension eased, Bear approached him, saying, "You know you can get in and out of that place faster than any of these bastards!"

Drum agreed, saying, "I know it doesn't matter who raids the shitters, but that sonuvabitch pissed me off."

"Hey, man, I'm sorry. I was out of line," said Crow.

Drum nodded, "Yeah, man, no problem. It's me, I'm a little touchy."

About that time a raging monkey jumped through the trees and threw shit at the men. "That sonuvabitch scared the fuck out of me. Shit, man, they seem to have their own war going on," laughed Bear.

"They got good aim," answered Dog, wiping monkey shit from his helmet.

"That sonuvabitch nearly made me piss all over myself. If I get my hands on that little cocksucker, I'm gonna make him a meal," threatened Savage.

"I hope you kill it first," chuckled Ghost.

"I didn't know you were supposed to cook'em," added Savage.

"Shit, man. You damn bunch of dog-eating Sioux are all alike," chided Ghost.

Just then screams and gunfire ripped the air as flames shot upward from the nearby village. The men froze, listening to the voices of Viet Cong and American troops, then ran to join the unit. Three hours later nothing was left, and by ten o'clock that night, dozens of women and young girls had either been raped or brutally murdered.

As the Crossed Arrows began helping the wounded, Bear saw a soldier pistol-whip a village woman and set her on fire. Outraged, and seeing her eyes begging for relief, he shot her. Throughout the night, teams dug ditches to bury the dead. As the last shovel of lime hit the graves, Meeko could still hear the souls of the dead screaming with pain and sorrow.

Three high ranking Viet Cong officers were taken prisoner that day and Bear was ordered to handle the interrogation. As he stood facing their leader, the soldier spat in his face, saying in English, "Your mother is our dog whore and when you are dead she will not weep."

Bear beat him with the butt of his rifle, smashing his head so it resembled a rotting pumpkin. Looking around coldly, he said in Vietnamese, "If anyone else wants some of this, come on and try me!"

"Yeah, please do! I need a few more fingers and ears to finish my necklace," said Savage, displaying his collection.

Snow stepped up, saying, "Easy! We need these prisoners alive to get important information!"

"Sure," smiled Savage, placing his knife at the throat of one of the prisoners. He pricked the skin and let the blood trickle to impress the others, while Bait stripped the prisoners naked to check for any hidden booby traps.

"If you tell me one fucking lie, I'll let this heathen slit your throat and feed your bodies to the pigs," stated Bear.

Snow unfolded a map and showed it to one of the Viet Cong as Bear asked, "Where is your fucking base?" The prisoner pointed directly North. Bear thrust his chin forward, signaling Snow to check it out. Snow confirmed what the prisoner said was true and informed everyone there was another platoon moving in for an ambush. Immediately the Crossed Arrows headed into the jungle to stop them from advancing any further North. Snow tried to make radio contact, Savage popped smoke and Dog climbed above the jungle umbrella to attach a homing beacon. Eventually they met two of their platoon's scouts who escorted them to the commanding officer.

After debriefing, the Crossed Arrows were flown to Cam Lo, glad the mission was over and eager for some rest. The group visited their favorite bar where they met up with their old drug buddies from other Special Forces units. After hours of catching up on all the news, Hillbilly threw a drunken arm around Bear's shoulder, saying, "How you doing, man? Getting any?"

"Only your sister," answered Bear with a big grin.

"Try my mother, man. She's got a helluva lot more experience," laughed Hillbilly. Everyone joined in the brawling hoopla as several women moved in on the party. Booze, drugs and women flowed like water as the men kept the stairs busy running to and from the women's private rooms.

The following morning they all found themselves in the brig, suffering from hangovers, split lips, black eyes, broken bones and bruised bodies. They spent ten days listening to lectures and then boarded a Huey, bound for another suicide mission. Each man held grave thoughts as they flew out of the sun into another heavy attack.

The Huey hovered down to six feet while the men jumped. Below them, amidst heavy artillery fire and villagers dashing in all directions, lay dozens of wounded soldiers. The Crossed Arrows remained pinned down for eleven hours before the Medevacs could rescue the wounded. One helicopter exploded into a ball of fire, then the second took a hit. As it spun toward earth, many ran, but it was no use. The battle continued for two days, the winds carrying the sounds of hideous screams of pain.

Early the next morning Bear picked up a white soldier who had lost a leg. While carrying him toward safety, Bear yelled for morphine. Dog helped Bear put him on the stretcher and popped him with a serette as the soldier grabbed Bear's arm, crying, "Please, man, get my leg. It's over there, someplace in the grass. You've got to find it!"

"Okay, soldier. I'll look! You take it easy," said Bear and went in search of the leg. He returned, saying, "The leg ain't there. It must've been blown to bits."

"You Red bastard! I know it's over there! You're just too fucking yellow to go look!" the soldier screamed, pointing again toward the grassy area. Shaking his head, Bear deposited him in the helicopter next to a mound of body bags, while the soldier continued shouting. Then Bear, now a mainliner, rejoined the Crossed Arrows, took out his rig, and shot up.

"Don't listen to that dumb bastard. He is gonna get us killed," said Savage, pointing to their new Louie as he passed around a joint.

"Who?" questioned Bear.

"That fucking new Shake 'n Bake," answered Savage, referring to the pimply faced Second Lieutenant that just arrived and had never seen any action.

"Hell, the fucker can't wipe his ass, let alone make a decision!" growled Dog.

"If one of us goes, that mother fucker is going to feel my blade in his gut," snarled Savage.

Bear smiled then added, "The problem is, he ain't hot or cold. He's just like my Auntie Lizzie's dishwater, always lukewarm."

"Hell, how can you fight a fucking battle if you can't make a fucking decision?" wondered Bait.

"I say we don't listen to that dumb motherfucker. I'm telling you he's gonna get our asses blown off! I'm gonna fight my own fucking war. At least I'll stay alive!" growled Savage, climbing out of the foxhole.

"Bait, follow him," said Dog. "That bastard has turned into a fucking thrill killer. He's crazy enough to go over there and blow that sonuvabitch to kingdom come." It was long after dark when the two returned to join the unit, now under another mortar attack.

"How many times do we have to take this fucking hill? One day it's ours, the next day we fight to get it back," argued Dog.

"Hey, man, you gotta remember this war is like the rabbit dance—two steps forward and one step back," chuckled Bear.

"Yeah, makes you wonder what's real and what's an illusion," remarked Savage. "Do you realize we've lost over sixty percent of our men in this fucking war? What's the purpose of fighting a war no one wants?"

These kinds of questions were taking a toll on everyone. They searched their hearts for the answers, as they climbed into a foxhole, loaded their guns and prepared for more hell. The men lay wrestling with their thoughts as they heard a familiar sound fill the air.

"Move, Move! Dig, Dig! Here comes Puff!" yelled Bear. Everyone hit the trenches and prepared for the worst. Puff was a special kind of plane. When the enemy had you by the balls, it was old Puff who got your ass out of the jam. She was a beautiful AC-47, with side-firing miniguns attached to the wings. Everyone feared, yet loved Puff. It only took her a few minutes to take down everything in her path. When the smoke cleared and everyone went in search of the wounded, they found the new Lieutenant was missing. Savage and Bait exchanged a look while listening to new orders on the radio telling them to get back on the move.

While they continued to raid many villages, Bear wondered what these places had once looked like when they were beautiful and serene. They entered another village to see piles of dead bodies and spent days burning the rotting flesh. The Crossed Arrows had grown accustomed to the swarms of large black flies eating from the open graves.

"Goddamn these fucking flies," screamed Bear as he ran, slapping at his body.

"Grab him! He's gone *dinky dau*," yelled Dog. He and Savage wrestled Bear to the ground and held him, while Bait filled his arm with morphine. As Bear nodded off, Dog said, "Look at his fucking arm. It's oozing with open sores."

"Clean him up and let him sleep," said Savage, wondering how much longer they would be held captive in this God awful place. That night, Dog beat on a log to accompany his chanting, while the others prayed for answers.

In the morning the Crossed Arrows gathered tar paper from the ammo cartons to rekindle the four day fire. Dark smoke once again filled the air with the stench of burning human flesh. Everyone continued to rake and shovel through this human bonfire until there was no meat left on the bones. Bear accidentally hit a swollen body with his pitch fork. It popped like a cannon, as dead flesh spewed like a cancer over him. He puked his guts out, wondering how many more souls would be collected from this battlefield.

As the men watched the fire turn into ashen embers, they could see that Bear's eyes held the look of death. His sickness brought on recurring nightmares, and Bear could no longer associate with the others. He felt his soul had been captured and kept to himself, listening to his music on his battery-operated record player. His rig and his music became his only pleasures.

As he sat listening to the Temptations, Bear complained to Ghost, "We've done every impossible mission. I feel like one of the walking dead. Most of the time we have no food or ammo, but we're still expected to take the pounding from these fucking Viet Cong. This war has no purpose. Hell, who knows if we'll ever see our world again?"

"Hey, play that James Brown record again. I really like him," requested Ghost. Bear changed the record as everyone sat back, rocking with the Godfather while Savage accompanied him on a C-ration can.

Everyone in the platoon knew this Indian group had the best dope and music around, and when one of the white men brought Bear canned peaches and pound cake, he extended an invitation to share their booty. After that, a friendlier rapport developed between the Indians and the white boys.

Early one morning as everyone sat in their foxholes smoking a joint and listening to music, Savage asked, "Anybody got a green wrapper?"

"You had a handful of that shit this morning. You better watch it, man!" said Drum.

"Yeah, man. I do my thing, you do yours!" snapped Savage, wiping a trickle of blood from his nose.

"You're frying your fucking brain. Geezus, if you keep this up, you ain't gonna have a lining left in your nose!" warned Dog.

"I like my high, and I like it fast! So up the nose she fucking goes," answered Savage, snorting another line.

"We've got to do something," stated Dog.

"Bullshit, everybody's doing their own thing, man. You either pop pills, smoke your brains out, or shoot up. What's the big deal anyway? I like horse," said Bear.

"Yeah, so do I," agreed Ghost.

"Who gives a fuck? We'll kick the habit when this war's over," said Savage as he and Bear got up to leave.

It was late night when they finally slid back in the hole. Smiling, Bear said, "Bingo!" and laid down some short barreled AK-47's.

"Where in the hell did you get these?" questioned Dog.

"Went shopping," answered Bear, tossing a few boxes of 7.62 rounds toward them.

Everyone laughed as they inspected the stolen equipment. Savage smiled, saying, "Shit, some of these guns are from that last raid."

"These be numba one pop-pop guns. I no lie to you," mimicked Bear in a lousy Vietnamese accent.

"Hell, the way you two gather things, you should have been born to the squirrel tribe," laughed Bait.

"Do you think we can confuse the enemy?" laughed Savage.

"Who cares, as long as the fucking bullets find the heart of the target? Down by the river, I spotted a Vietnamese who had taken a direct hit in the head from something. Can't believe it shattered his skull and left the skin intact. Man, that zip's scalp was stretched to the size of a watermelon."

"Fuck the dead slant-eyed, slope-headed Gook! We got the supplies they dropped yesterday. Those stupid bastards dropped them in enemy territory," added Savage.

After the sun set, the Crossed Arrows fought their way through another night of screaming tracers while trying to locate an underground depot. As they sat watching the green and orange tracers piercing the night from afar, Crow commented, "Yeah, and it looks like they're tearing the hell outta us again."

"The depot's gotta be around here somewhere. We've been looking for these sonuvabitches for days," said Bear.

"I think it's a supply house and an underground hospital," said Rat, pointing to the map.

"Hell, it's got to be here," said Ghost.

"We'll find it, and I promise we'll get inside," added Rat. While continuing their search they suddenly felt a vibration from the ground. Rat pressed his ear against the ground and shook his head affirmatively, saying, "It's there, man! In that fucking mountain."

Ghost studied an embedded stone and when he gently moved it aside, everyone heard a humming.

"Yeah, that's an old generator," replied Ghost.

"Yeah, fucking party time!" smiled Crow.

Rat, the thinnest and most agile of the group, crawled through the small hole and into the cave. While inching toward the sound, he saw the shadow of a man passing along the dimly lit wall. Stepping out of the darkness, Rat sunk his knife deep into the soldier's gut, pulling upward, ripping his way to his victim's throat. Easing the lifeless body quietly to the floor, Rat continued working his way downward. Once he saw what he needed to know, he headed back to the top to find the men were already inside.

"It's the biggie! About three stories down and half the size of a football field," whispered Rat. The men followed him, working their way into the bowels of Mother Earth. The team paused, then stepped quickly from the shadows with drawn M-16's.

"Kill'em all!" ordered Bear as they opened fire, leaving twenty men lying quietly on a blood-spattered floor. Quickly searching the entire area, they found a room that held thirty beds of wounded North Cong. The Crossed Arrows opened fire, then Bear casually walked among the beds.

"Please," begged one Vietnamese man, as he showed Bear a picture of his family.

"I ain't no social worker, buddy. This .45 is my way of life," said Bear as he held the pistol to the man's head and pulled the trigger.

The sweep was clean, and all the detonators were set as they scrambled back to the top. Everyone felt good as they watched the mountain collapse from within. As the dirt spewed upward, they all smiled knowing another secret facility was blown off the map.

They hit the trail, running back toward friendly lines. Reaching safety, they took their first rest. Some walked around to check things, while Bear leaned against a tree and tied off his arm for another shot.

Dog walked over, saying, "What's up?"

"I had a dream a while ago," answered Bear. "I saw me back at the Sundance tree, and I was spiraling down, out of control, into Mother Earth. A voice spoke to me, saying, 'Free will is at play and everything is coming apart.' God, I've got a bad feeling on this one."

"Aw, man, stop believing that shit. Have a joint. We're gonna be all right," answered Dog.

"I know I've been removed from the blanket. My connection with the land has been broken," stated Bear.

"Fuck man! Just shut the fuck up about it! You sound like that goddamn prairie nigger, Rat," growled Dog.

"You know when we lose our connection to the land, we can no longer find our way back to our people," said Savage.

"Well, talking about it ain't gonna help you keep the connection," argued Dog.

"I told you I was losing the sight of life," stated Bear.

"Try to get back your strength with Great Spirit," encouraged Savage.

"As long as he's this way, he ain't gonna try nothing," growled Dog.

Suddenly hand grenades exploded all around them, and everyone ran for cover. Bear lay wounded on the ground, and no matter their efforts, the men remained pinned down. Bear drifted toward the spirit world, only to return after seeing Granbear's burial scaffold fall and Buffalo walk from the debris saying, "Rebuild your faith, Grandson. It is not your time. Your spirit has much left to accomplish."

As the others tried to work their way toward Bear, the ground was peppered with bullets. "Those bastards are using Bear for bait! We gotta do something before he dies!" urged Dog.

"I'm going," said Snow.

"Wait! It's almost dark. Let him be!" said Rat.

"When the time is right, we'll all go," counseled Crow.

As the sun sank in the sky, Savage yelled, "Cover my ass, I'm going after him."

As Savage returned with Bear in his arms, the others hid in the underbrush. They had just enough fire power to slow down the enemy and elude them. When they could at last rest, Savage held Bear's head and felt for a heartbeat, whispering, "He's alive, but very weak."

"No mother-fucking Gook is gonna take one of us out," said Snow.

"Look through his shit," ordered Dog, hoping to find Bear's rig.

Since Drum thought like a junkie, he said, "He's got it here somewhere," and tore the covers off the speakers of Meeko's record player. "Fuck, man! Look at this shit! He's a goddamn walking drugstore," laughed Drum, filling a syringe with horse to make Bear feel less pain. Everyone took turns carrying him, and as they entered camp, Savage eased him onto a stretcher. Silently they all watched the medevac lift up into the air and head to Da Nang with Bear aboard.

Because Bear had been hit with heavy shrapnel in the right side of his body, he had to stay in the hospital near Monkey Mountain for six months before they shipped him to the Great Lakes Naval Hospital. When he was released, Meeko flew home. Having served three years and eleven months in the Marine Corps, he was declared a disabled veteran and awarded many medals along with an honorable discharge.

Meeko was nervous when he stepped from the plane in Sacramento. Jake approached smiling, but was shocked at the sight of the thin, gaunt man who wore the look of death on his face. As they approached Seven Two Charlie, Jake asked, "Wanna fly our best girl home?"

"No, not today, Jake. Still a little shaky," answered Meeko as they climbed into the cockpit. Meeko affectionately patted Seven Two Charlie's panel, feeling good, knowing he was finally back in the world he loved.

American Indian Movement

Jake circled the field just above the rooftops to show Meeko the many new structures at the fixed base operation. He glanced over, and seeing that Meeko was nervous, took care to land smoothly. As he chopped the engine a crowd rushed toward the plane to greet them.

Meeko looked out and was surprised to see many old friends waiting anxiously for them to deplane. Jake tried to help Meeko from the plane, but was gently pushed away. Meeko felt uneasy using a cane, and sensing Jake's pity, was too proud to accept his friend's support. Meeko's eyes filled with tears as longtime friends embraced him, joyfully welcoming him home. Meeko smiled shyly when he saw the huge "Welcome Home" banner strung above the hangar doors with food and drinks waiting inside.

The party lasted long into the night. Meeko drank heavily to boost his confidence and compensate for his insecurity. After many drinks, he fell to the floor in a stupor. Jake and two old friends carried him up to his old bedroom, lay him across the bed and covered him with a blanket, then left quietly.

It was late morning when Meeko awakened, hungover and in need of his medication. He took his pills and gave himself a shot to calm his nerves, then sat on the edge of the bed and lit a cigarette. Jake entered with a pot of coffee and breakfast. Jake felt awkward as he gently told Meeko that Manfred had died a peaceful death from old age. Slowly the tension between them melted and they talked at great length about the past four years, laughing about many fond memories.

"Meeko, I want you to live here until you are well enough to continue your flight training. Eventually I would like for you to consider becoming a partner in the business."

Meeko had prayed for this day and was grateful for the offer, although he feared his ill health might prevent him from fulfilling his obligation. As they walked through the facility, he noticed a lot of new planes and equipment. Their walk ended at the flight-line and both men smiled at the sight of Seven Two Charlie. There she was, sitting proudly in her old tie-down spot. Both agreed there would never be another plane like good old Seven Two Charlie.

When they returned to the hangar, Jake said, "I've got to leave. I'm flying tomorrow." Meeko watched the Jeep disappear into a cloud of dust, leaving him with an empty feeling. As he walked back to his sleeping quarters alone, a deep sadness engulfed him as he mourned the regrettable death of Manfred. It seemed strange that the airport no longer had a mascot.

Meeko struggled up to his room wondering if he would fit in with all of these new changes. He saw a simple room filled with many memories and felt safe. His old ballcap still hung from the back of the chair and some of his paintings were pinned to the walls still waiting to be framed. He picked up his old sketchpad and flipped through pages of childlike drawings. Meeko wondered if he could ever become the artist Granbear had envisioned, and questioned whether his experiences with war and drugs had left him too disillusioned. He felt the severe head pain caused by his injuries return and took a handful of pills before falling into a deep, troubled sleep.

The airport noise jolted Meeko awake early the following morning, taking him immediately back to the hell of Vietnam. Feeling a desperate need to escape, he gave himself a shot, grabbed his cane and headed for the stairs. He gripped the rail tightly, hobbled down to the pilot's lounge and limped around the airport to rekindle old friendships. He felt like an outsider and spent the rest of the afternoon exchanging small talk with the pilots.

By twilight the day had ended for everyone but Meeko who found himself alone at the airport. He went outside to Seven Two Charlie and took a seat under her struts to watch the sun dim its light on another day. As a few stars began to appear in the sky, he dreaded the oncoming darkness, wondering if it would force another confrontation with his unexplained fears. He felt isolated in this strange world and nausea gripped his stomach as another panic attack began. "Oh fuck! Here it comes," groaned Meeko as he tried to gain control over his mind. Again feeling helpless and unable to combat his situation, he downed more pills in an attempt to escape another onslaught of terror.

Meeko used his cane to struggle to his feet and walked slowly down the runway. He fought against the excruciating pain that crippled his body as he tried to forget his horrible memories of Vietnam. Once again, bombs were exploding all around as he frantically crawled to where he did not know. He could see the Viet Cong moving in as he dug himself into the ground and gasping for air, lay screaming for help. Many of the men Meeko had killed in Vietnam hovered near, ripping open old scars as they continued to march toward him, filling his mind with the stench of death as they whispered about his inadequacies as a Marine.

Meeko heaved his cane aside in anguish and crawled on his hands and knees to escape his demons. Mired in the hopelessness of his situation, he spiraled into an uncontrollable fit of rage and began to cry. Something rose from deep within his gut and he heard a demonic howl cursing *Wakan Tanka*. Shadowed voices stalked him for hours as he lay paralyzed and wailing. He could see a future filled with failure if his body did not heal, but what terrorized him most was the warning from his doctors that his mind might be forever crippled by his experiences in Vietnam.

Meeko lay at the end of the runway until almost daybreak, then forced himself to crawl on his belly until he could reach his cane, and with great determination got back on his feet and hobbled to the hangar. The crew was gathered in front of the building, and rather than face more rejection or pity, he took the back steps to his room, relieved that no one had seen him in this condition.

Meeko recognized that his health problems could easily destroy his life and decided to learn to walk without his cane. Consequently every night after the crew left, he forced himself, despite extreme pain, to walk miles around the dark airport grounds. Although he fell many times, each step brought him closer to his goal.

Night after night, his body ached with cuts and bruises as he used his hatred to muster his strength to fight his lonely crusade to become whole again. Meeko more than doubled his medication in order to keep to his rigid training schedule. Surprisingly, within three months he was walking without so much as a limp. After six months he was running with the wind, and except for the pounding headaches, it seemed his life was returning to normal.

On this day, Meeko smiled as he entered the terminal and collapsed on the overstuffed sofa. He felt good about having just made his first five mile run, and invited Jake to dinner. After that many invitations came his way and, once again Meeko began to spend time with his old friends.

However the relentless headaches caused by the blood vessels in his back that had collapsed from the shrapnel wounds, forced him to routinely return to the Veterans Administration Hospital for medication and examinations. The doctor prescribed a stronger drug to help him deal with the pain. It made Meeko feel strange to such a degree that there were times when he would see himself sitting across the room staring back at himself.

One evening while at dinner with Jake, Meeko started shaking uncontrollably and fell to the floor, incapacitated. Jake was horrified as he watched Meeko's right eye bulge from its socket, his head drawn tightly against his shoulder. Jake rushed him to the hospital where the doctor on call looked at his contorted face and quickly gave him a shot of methadone, causing the attack to subside. Since the doctor was unable to diagnose Meeko's condition, he had him spend the next month undergoing extensive tests. When he was released, still without a diagnosis, he was put on a new medication designed to minimize the attacks.

Meeko soon found that drinking alcohol along with his street drugs and the prescribed pills gave him some relief, and later discovered that the best pain relief came from pressing an empty coke bottle hard into his shoulder blade. If even this drastic approach failed, Meeko would cry out to *Wakan Tanka* for mercy, promising if he could be free of pain, he would return to the reservation and find a medicine person to heal him. But once the attack ceased, his promise would be forgotten in the fog of his drug and alcohol abuse.

Meeko convinced himself he was functioning well under these conditions and continued his ground school training. Soon he felt ready to climb back into the cockpit, but each time he scheduled a checkout flight, the unbearable pain in his head would flare up and he would have to cancel. Week after week Jake reviewed Meeko's flight book, only to find he had failed to log any air time. He had long suspected that Meeko had a psychological problem connected with Vietnam and felt it was time for his young friend to face reality.

One day he found Meeko on the floor in his darkened room, reeking of alcohol and writhing in pain. "Fighting with those goddamn ghosts again, huh? If you would sober up and get off of those fucking pills, you might get well!" bellowed Jake, picking up the now empty prescription bottle. "It's time we get to the bottom of this shit."

But Meeko, still in a state of denial and accustomed to blaming others, cried, "It's not my fucking fault they can't fix what's wrong with me. If I don't stay drunk or doped out of my head, I can't stand the fucking pain. Jake, I'm losing my mind."

"Bullshit, Meeko! Face it! You're afraid to fly!"

"You don't know what you're talking about. You've changed! You've become nothing but a robot, chasing the almighty dollar. You say you're my friend, but you're not. You're too filled with greed and self-importance to see that I'm a desperate, sick man!"

"Meeko, it's not me who has changed! You dumb sonuvabitch, can't you see I love you like a son? You're using this illness to manipulate me and avoid facing your fears. You're hooked on drugs and too fucking afraid to admit it. Otherwise, why won't you climb back into the cockpit?" Jake's voice was accusing and he knew the repercussions of his words would be profound. He received no response from Meeko and stomped out of the room, angry that Meeko was not willing to help himself.

Jake's accusations shocked Meeko into a moment of sobriety. He got off the floor, opened the drapes, lit a cigarette and paced angrily around the room. He hated the vile drugs that were sucking the life from him, but did not know how to break the grip they had on his soul. Feeling helpless and disappointed in himself, Meeko crawled into the bottle for the next few weeks. Each time he tried to sober up, his fear triggered another panic attack, followed by a drunken blackout. Jake would find him lying in his own vomit and would take care of him.

Things got progressively worse until one night Jake received a phone call informing him that Meeko had been arrested during a drunken brawl and needed to be bailed out of jail. Jake arrived at the jail, furious that Meeko had become a danger not only to himself, but also to others. "You are no longer functioning in reality. You can't fight this battle alone. You've got to go back to the hospital!"

Tears filled Meeko's eyes and he hung his head in shame, nodding in agreement.

After securing Meeko's release from jail, Jake drove him to the hospital, where the emergency room doctor ordered a strong sedative and admitted him to the psychiatric ward. For the next few weeks Meeko, even though heavily sedated, remained tormented by memories of Vietnam. Every time he closed his eyes he was fighting the Viet Cong—smelling the stench of burning flesh as he ran through rotting jungles, dodging bullets and fighting for his life. These horrendous nightmares gained such power over him that he became convinced the staff members were Viet Cong soldiers and he was a prisoner of war locked in a cage deep in the jungle. He no longer spoke English, but reverted back to speaking the enemy's tongue.

As weeks passed, Meeko began to grasp the fact that he was in a VA hospital in the United States. During one of his mandatory group sessions, he violently attacked an attendant and took him hostage. After hours of negotiation, Meeko was placed in restraints and moved to the lockdown ward.

Day and night demons haunted Meeko's soul as the hallways echoed with his anguished screams of terror. For weeks his personality vacillated between that of a docile zombie and a raging maniac. Many mornings the staff would find he had broken free of his restraints and was lying in a fetal position under his bed, crying like a baby. The doctor, hoping to stabilize these mood swings, prescribed a variety of medications, all to no avail.

When four more Vietnam veterans came to the hospital with the same symptoms, the doctor saw there was a pattern and isolated the group for observation. After further diagnostic study, he concluded these men all suffered from post-traumatic stress disorder, and prescribed each the appropriate medications.

Once Meeko's mood swings were identified, the doctor arranged for the government to give him full disability and health benefits. Meeko agreed to return each month to pick up his medication and submit to further tests. When Jake picked him up, Meeko was thankful for his friend's support during such trying times.

Following Meeko's release from the hospital, Jake gave him menial jobs around the airport to occupy his time, and Meeko felt secure knowing he would never be without food or shelter. Upon receiving his first disability check, he discovered he also qualified for government funds to continue his education just as Granbear had wanted him to do.

Although Meeko's condition during daylight hours improved, at night his mind still raged with demons. He changed his work schedule to nights hoping to avoid them. At the start of an episode, he would walk the runway, distraught, asking the moon birds to protect his soul and provide him with the knowledge to heal himself. Hearing thunder, he would beg Lightning Man to let the rain spirits purify his soul. Other times, when his feelings of depression and futility became overwhelming, he would plead with Breathmaker to take away the gift of air and stop the sorrow that held him in bondage.

Many times the demons' voices mocked him with laughter, and Meeko felt as if he was falling through the crevasses of time. He watched many sunrises through tearful eyes, fearing he was losing his mind. When life became unbearable, Meeko didn't hesitate to use up his month's supply of pain medication in just a few days, knowing he would always be able to find a dealer on the street eager to sell him enough to last until the end of the month.

And yet, despite his desperation, Meeko still longed for the courage to once again climb back into the cockpit of Seven Two Charlie. He considered his erratic behavior and worried that he was going insane. He also wondered why he could not find the courage to renew his flying career rather than give in to the invisible war that raged inside himself. Since life was eternal, he thought, why shouldn't he just end his pain through death? But then he would remember *Wanbli Gle'ska* and pray that Eagle would come to his aid.

One night as Meeko walked the flight line, he could feel Seven Two Charlie beckoning him to climb aboard. He climbed into the cockpit and reached for the starter switch with trembling hands, but could not bring himself to touch it. Wailing with grief, he finally accepted how much he feared death. Meeko felt an unknown hand touch his shoulder, and began to relive his experiences with Seven Two Charlie and what Jake had taught him about being a fearless warrior of the sky. Meeko lit a joint, remembering it was Jake who had shown him how to land a plane on a dirt strip or country road. He recalled that Jake had taught him how to feel his gut when flying by the seat of his pants.

His mind flashed back to a dark night in the high country when they had been caught in a blinding snowstorm. They did not know whether the plane was flying toward the sky or the earth. Meeko opened the side window and pretended to catch a cloud to mask his fear of death. That night, it had seemed forever before Jake had pierced the final cloud cover, exposing the distant lights of a small Idaho town on the horizon. Yeah, Charlie and Jake were cool-headed dudes. As he patted Charlie's panel, Meeko wondered why life couldn't be that simple again. As he stepped out of the plane, he knew it was time to make some changes.

Early the next morning he went directly to the pilot's lounge for his morning coffee. He dropped his last bit of crystal meth into the cup, then sat back and waited for his hair to stand on end. Smiling, he calmly picked up his clipboard and the keys to Seven Two Charlie, and walked toward the plane. After pre-flighting her, he climbed into the cockpit, hands shaking slightly as he strapped himself into the seat and yelled, "Clear!" He eased out the throttle and set the trim as he began to taxi toward the runway. Determined to fly or die, he pressed the mike button, saying, "This is Seven Two Charlie ready for takeoff."

"You okay?" Jake's voice boomed back.

"Never felt better. It's time to get back in the air."

"Hold up and I'll go with you, little buddy."

"Not this time, my friend. I gotta do this one alone."

Jake silently held the microphone for a moment before answering, "You're right, my friend. Active runway, one-eight. Have a good flight."

Meeko clicked the mike button twice to acknowledge the message, then added power and lifted off, pressing ever so lightly on the right rudder to adjust for the heavy crosswinds. He heard a loud boom in his head and was instantly back in Vietnam watching a helicopter being blown to bits. Sharp pains ripped through his head, as his body broke out in a cold sweat and he began to lose control of the plane.

"Meeko! Pull her up! Pull that fucking plane up, you goddamn dumb blanket ass Indian!" thundered Jake.

Instantly, Meeko snapped back to his senses. "Everything's okay with this fucking blanket ass, my friend. So don't worry about me, just worry whether the insurance is paid up on this bucket of bolts," chuckled Meeko, climbing out and leaving the flight pattern.

As the city faded into patches of plowed fields, and for the first time since his return home, Meeko felt free and once again able to appreciate the wide open countryside. Easing Charlie's nose down, Meeko leveled off fifty feet above the ground. The excitement of the moment fired his passions so he decided to do some hedgehopping. Pulling back into the sky, Meeko felt alive again. Not too shabby for a reservation Indian who thought he had lost it all and now was back in the air to stay.

Spotting a shepherd's camp off the left strut, Meeko flew low, rocked his wings and watched as the shepherd waved back. His gas gauge was low and Meeko decided to stop for gas and food at a small town in the distance. A lump rose in his throat as he proudly touched down and taxied to the gas truck. "Thank you, *Wakan Tanka*, for helping me find the courage to live," he prayed humbly as he shut down the engine.

In the coffee shop, Meeko watched a cute blonde in a tight blue uniform slink toward his table. "Did anyone ever tell you that your body is as beautiful as a P-51?" he asked flirtatiously.

"Yes, everyone that comes in here," she answered coyly with a wink, setting down a glass of water and taking his order.

"Well, did they ever tell you what beautiful controls you have?" he inquired.

"All the time. Wanna test them out someday?" she asked, giggling as she strolled away.

Meeko ate his sandwich, knowing the waitress was fascinated that he was Indian. As he paid for his food, he said he would return sometime soon and wanted to see her.

"I'll be waiting," she answered.

It was long after dark when he arrived back at the airport. Jake was waiting as Meeko stepped from the plane, reporting that the flight was good.

"I told you. All you needed was to get back in the air. Planes heal natural born sky children," replied Jake, confident that Meeko would become his old self again.

For the first time in years, Meeko slept until morning without a nightmare. After awakening he asked Jake to let him fly regularly again. Following many checkout flights, Jake scheduled him back on the flight line, and before long Meeko was feeling free and happy again.

After picking up his first paycheck, he flew back to visit the blonde waitress, Barbara, a sweet sixteen-year-old. She was happy to see him, and for the next two months they went on movie dates, to picnics, hikes along the mountain trails, and out to dinner as a romance developed between them.

One day, Meeko arrived to discover that they were going to see Barbara's parents. As he sat nervously across the table under their scrutinizing glares, he sensed this meeting was prompted by more than mere curiosity about his heritage, salary and age. Hesitantly, he answered their questions, relieved when Barbara finally suggested they take a ride in the country.

As they stopped at a roadside inn for a drink, Barbara started to cry, saying, "Oh, Meeko, you must help me. I'm pregnant, and my dad is threatening to send me away to have the baby and put it up for adoption. I told my parents that you were the father and we are going to be married."

Unable to believe what he was hearing, Meeko answered, "How could you do this, Barbara? We've never been together. You know it's not my child."

"I didn't know what else to do. If you'll marry me, I promise when the baby is born we'll get a divorce, and I'll ask you for nothing," she sniffled.

"I'm in no position to handle this kind of responsibility. You're a sixteen-year-old kid, and neither of us is ready for a committed relationship. I need to be established financially before I can consider a family. We're friends, but there's no love between us. Marry the baby's father," Meeko answered, getting up to leave.

"He refuses to marry me. You are my only chance. If you help me, I could return to school after the child is born and get a good job. Who knows, maybe the baby would be a joy for the both of us," she begged.

By late evening the alcohol, drugs and Barbara's tears had persuaded Meeko to fly to a nearby town to marry her. The next morning he woke up with a new bride and they immediately left for the airport. Once they had landed, he nervously tried to explain the situation to Jake whose silent stare expressed resentment over his stupidity.

Meeko rented a small house in a middle class neighborhood and he and Barbara began a marriage based on lies. Their life consisted of shopping for the baby, visiting Barbara's parents, and going out for dinner and a movie. In time, they began to fit more comfortably into the neighborhood, socializing with the neighbors at cookouts and other community events.

Surprisingly, Meeko began to believe in the American dream. He enjoyed working with neighbors on various projects and answering questions from the children who were fascinated by the Indian who flew a plane. However, upon his return home after dark, Barbara was often angry about the time he had spent telling the children about Indian culture.

When summer was over and school began, Barbara was pleased that she no longer had to share her husband's attention with the children, but soon other issues caused tension. Barbara had terrible morning sickness and became very lazy. After working all day, Meeko would come home to a dirty house and have to clean up after Barbara and her friends. Then too, she complained about everything particularly the flying business, which required Meeko to work on the weekends and leave town frequently. Yet as winter approached and business slowed down, allowing Meeko more time at home, Barbara began having temper tantrums when she had been drinking heavily.

Meeko had not attended his group therapy for weeks and consequently was back on heavy painkillers. In addition, he felt increasingly resentful toward Barbara because she had never told him about the child's father. One day Meeko found his pain medicine missing. During a fight with Barbara in which he accused her of stealing his drugs, he lost his temper and beat her, giving her a black eye and a split lip.

Appalled at what he had done, he spoke to Jake about it. After a long discussion with his friend, Meeko took the rest of the day off. He picked up Barbara's favorite Chinese food and a dozen long-stemmed red roses, and went home. As he walked into the bedroom, roses in hand, he stared in horror at his wife in bed with a seventeen-year-old neighborhood boy. He left the house without a word, never to return.

Meeko moved back to his room at the airport and filed for a divorce. He enrolled in college and worked long hours to keep his mind off his problems. Six months later, he was back on a regular schedule and feeling happier. One day as he approached the front office, Barbara appeared and blocked his passage, saying, "Lost the house, because I couldn't pay the rent. The baby was a boy, but it was born dead. Probably from that beating you gave me." Meeko listened stoically, but when she asked for money, he got angry and walked away.

Later in the pilot's lounge, he saw the newspaper headline, "Indian Uprising at Wounded Knee." He read further, unable to believe what was happening on the reservation. He tossed the paper aside. "Did you read this?" he asked a pilot named Joe. "It fucking pisses me off! It's just another ploy of the goddamn government to fuck the Indian over one more time! When does this thing called democracy apply to the Indian? Whatever the government wants, it takes. Fuck, what has happened to justice in this country? Fuck, man! I fought for this country, and nobody cared if I was an Indian when those bullets were flying at me."

"Easy, Meeko! There's nothing you can do," Joe replied.

"I will do something!" barked Meeko, as he grabbed the newspaper and headed for his room to pack. On his way back down the hall with his belongings, Meeko tapped on Jake's door and entered. He threw the newspaper on Jake's desk, saying, "Read today's headline?"

"Yeah," Jake nodded. "Fucking shame."

"I'll be gone a few days! I'm going home to check on things."

Jake walked him to the plane, saying, "You be careful, call if you need me. Who knows what you might be walking into up there."

As he lifted off, Meeko was deep in reverie about the reservation people. He remembered hearing the old people speak of the three hundred eighty-five broken treaties with the whites and knew how hard it was to cut a trail into white society. His heart filled with anger as he recalled the Big Foot massacre on December 29, 1890. The United States had been fighting its longest undeclared battle against the Indian people when the Seventh Cavalry, in a cold winter blizzard, gunned down three hundred men, women and children while they carried a white flag of truce.

He thought about the battle of Wounded Knee and wondered why, after a hundred years, history was repeating itself. Was there going to be another slaughter? God, if people would read their history, they would find the pages packed with white lies! They would see how the government shrouded its greed in a tinseled glory of bullshit, while ripping off the Red Man's land and his way of life.

The American people needed to understand more about their ancestors. Maybe now they would be willing to look at the Red Man's mistreatment and see the Indian again hunted down and slaughtered like an animal. Maybe the white people would understand the real purpose behind the slaughter of all the buffalo. It was time to expose the government's plan to continue the extermination of the Red Man. He could still hear Shadowhawk saying, "Reservation. Isolation. Annihilation. Extermination. That is the future of the Red Man."

The great white father was indeed a very clever coyote. When the government developed the relocation program for the Indian, it was just another ploy to take their land and rid the world of the Red Race. Indians had been given the option to relocate to a white city, or stay on the reservation and be cut off from government support. Those who did leave to follow their dreams soon found that without a job or schooling, they were forced to live in the ghettos outside mainstream society.

Meeko was jolted back to reality as he flew over the Badlands. God, it felt good to be back in Indian country. As the plains widened, becoming a sea of long swaying grass, he observed the outskirts of the reservation and saw nothing had changed. Circling down over Wounded Knee, he studied the old run-down buildings that leaned together. He passed over the little white church that was standing in a field of overgrown weeds graced with headstones. He felt the heartaches of his ancestors and wondered if the gift of the horse had really helped the Indian, or had instead become a tool for the white man to break the Indian nation's back?

He spotted an isolated field, landed, then hid the plane in a large grove of trees. During his long walk to town, he passed among familiar trees and bushes. It felt good to once again bathe himself in the rawness of nature. He slipped down a ravine and grabbed a sage bush to break his fall. Catching the odor of sage in his hand, he filled his lungs, remembering the gift of protection given by this green thing. He could almost hear Granbear saying, "Everything has a purpose. *Wakan Tanka* would never create useless things—he leaves that job to the stupidity of humankind."

Smiling to himself, Meeko climbed to the top of the hill and let his eyes feast upon the simplicity of reservation beauty. The wind touched his hair and he felt love for the land coursing through his veins. As far as the eye could see, sage and sweetgrass adorned Mother Earth's body.

He looked from his heart, knowing that life was not always what it seemed. He sat down for a moment, staring over the land, watching the spirit that moves in all things. Even the sage held its secrets deep within its silver-green leaves. He watched the grass bend under the warm gusting winds and realized it too played its part in the reproduction of life. Meeko watched the clouds and knew that very soon the crackling voice of *Wakinyan* would bring another Dakota rainstorm. He remembered how quickly prairie storms could arrive and immediately continued his journey. Surely there would come a day when all people will understand the strength in the gentle silence of *Wakan Tanka*'s work.

Meeko wove his way through more underbrush and crossed the river as the wind picked up. He felt the old ones join with its voice to welcome him home. Eagle called from overhead, reminding him of another time and place, "How high do you dare fly, Little Sparrow?"

Meeko stepped onto the road to see an old truck approaching him and hitched a ride into Wounded Knee. The old man fought through his busted gears and said, "I wouldn't go near that place. Too much trouble. The place is crawling with Feds and the Goon Squad."

"I'm heading to Shadowhawk's—just outside of town."

"Uh huh," the old man answered. And as Indian protocol requires there was no more conversation for the rest of the trip, until they pulled to a stop in front of Shadowhawk's place. "Welcome home, Grandson. I'll see you in the sweats tonight," said the old man as he drove away.

Meeko, happy to be once again interacting with the ways of the old people, chuckled as he watched the truck fade into the distance. He walked toward the house, followed by two suspicious, growling dogs. Shadowhawk was waiting on the porch to greet him. The two brought each other up-to-date over a warm meal, then prepared the fire for the evening sweat.

Shadowhawk stacked the wood and lit the flame, saying, "There seems to be a sickness in many of the men who have returned from Vietnam. They are ashamed of themselves and angry with the government. Some are still fighting the demons from that war. Others are getting an education to help them battle the government. Once they have their sheepskins, our men will pick up their weapons and be ready to fight the white man in his own language, just as Granbear always dreamed. Yes, it's good to see our men coming back to the blanket. Grandson, we've got to have a hot sweat tonight to clean the white man's war off of you. We certainly don't need any evil alien spirits walking around stripping away your life," said Shadowhawk, handing Meeko a cup of coffee.

While they sat watching the fire, Meeko asked, "What's going on in Wounded Knee?"

"I will speak to you, but my words will not be said quickly," answered Shadowhawk. "It's time for change. These young men returning from Vietnam are carrying a strong voice with the people. The old Tomahawks call them a radical group but I, as well as others, understand their views as a good thing. We're tired of living with broken promises of hospitals and schools. We want good doctors, and we want to return to our old beliefs without interference from churches and government. The Indian Movement is speaking up for all of these rights, and its supporters are striving to bring back the old ways.

"Since its inception, the United States political forces have tried to stop this new movement. God forbid the Indian people ever unite in a common cause. The difference between these two cultures is that they march to different drums. The people are listening to these new leaders, and their words are breathing life back into them.

"The government keeps forgetting the Sioux have never ceased fighting. We have had Indian activities as far back as 1944. It was called the National Congress of American Indians. Another spurt of recognition happened for us when Ira Hayes helped raise the flag on Iwo Jima. In 1953, that's when the "No Indians Allowed" signs came down from entrance doors in Rapid City, South Dakota. Then in 1961, the

National Youth Council helped establish American Indian studies on the college campuses. In 1969, Alcatraz was held by the Indian and another battle followed for game and fishing rights. And just look at what they have done to *Paha Sapa*, the Black Hills! You call that art? I call it mockery!

"Grandson, the American Indian Movement is becoming the muscle and the mouth to push our people forward. The breeds and the bloods are coming together to help fight a battle for freedom. Consider our history. When the white foreigners arrived in our country, they would have died during the first winter if it had not been for the Indians and their knowledge of the land. They called this place a wilderness and tried to tame it. We called it our mother and tried to take care of her. Their hearts were filled with greed, they took our gifts and in turn destroyed the land, our culture and our way of life. The people are beginning to remember their forefathers, and the American Indian Movement is bringing pride back to the people.

"Of course, the government doesn't approve of the new organization, and therefore the national media is forbidden to cover our story. Yet a single act of violence associated with us finds its way to the major networks. We are tired of being stereotyped as Redskins who paint pretty pictures and wear ribbon shirts and Billy Jack hats. We're tired of watching our young people give up on their future and turn to drinking, sniffing glue or committing suicide in their teens. The average American would have a hard time believing that their government not only condones what happens to the Indian, but participates in our destruction.

"This war of words is over, and we're not going to take any more broken treaties. We're finished with empty promises, and the people are raising their voices in anger. Everyone is tired of listening to a few token Indians who do the dirty work for the United States Government. We're not going to sit back and listen anymore. The old people are beginning to unseal their lips, and they too are speaking out about what whitey has done. It was the white system who created this monster, and the old people are saying it's time for it to turn and eat them. It's time for the government to deal with our country, which is within their country. Indians need to unite as one nation and let the public know about all the government's unfulfilled promises.

"The Red Man came back from Vietnam and was recognized by our people as warriors. They knew their people wanted their voices heard. They wanted the public to learn of the harsh treatment of the Indian. The public needs to know that we are considered wards of the federal government, but we're not going to stay hidden among a stack of papers for another hundred years. In fact, the Bureau of Indian Affairs is just another token organization of the United States Government.

"We are like a bunch of sheep going to slaughter, herded around to listen to the 'I-don't-know-people' tell us nothing except to sign another government form! We're tired of this. Last week, I had to sign another five-year lease on my land. I'm tired of turning my property over every year to a local white farmer for three dollars an acre and then having to watch the government pay him eleven dollars an acre not to grow anything on it! Yes, the time has come for the public to learn about this bungling bureaucracy and its inefficient civil servants who run the reservations. It's time Washington recognizes that Indian is not merely a word, but a race of people. I'm tired of suffering these brutal wrongs. There have been too many years of hunger, cold winters, no money and no jobs on this reservation."

Meeko shared Shadowhawk's anger and asked, "Are we getting ready to fight Old Yellow Hair again?"

"Yeah, could be 1876 all over again, Grandson," answered Shadowhawk with a smile.

The following morning, Shadowhawk and Meeko drove to town. They got out of the truck and as they walked around, they could hear the place buzzing with angry words. They walked to the general store and sat down on a wooden bench next to some elders listening to their soft guarded voices speaking of trouble. Men, women, children, why even the old people, were grumbling about the Feds, the BIA and the Goon Squad all working together.

Meeko grew angry when he learned of the drive-by shootings, the beatings and the arrests of innocent people. One young girl had been shot, another had lost her sight in one eye, while two others had been raped by federal agents. Many homes had been destroyed while being ransacked for valuable ceremonial articles, most of which had found their way into the pockets of the agents.

Suddenly Meeko heard the words, "Hey, Bear, when did you get back in town?" It was Savage, his old Vietnam brother.

Meeko shook his hand, saying, "Got in yesterday."

"Come to help, or just sightseeing?"

"Don't know. Thought I'd look around," answered Meeko.

"Wanna take a walk? I'll fill you in."

As they fell in step, both crossed the road and headed toward the river. They sat smoking a joint as they discussed the situation until long after dark. Both were particularly upset over the invaders who were looking hard to find the leaders of this new Indian movement. "Last week, we had a *Yuwipi*, and the spirits told us you were coming. Guess they thought we needed a pilot," laughed Savage, as they sat in silent agreement under a moonless night while listening to the crickets sing.

Abruptly, the cold muzzle of a rifle nudged Meeko's temple. "Move, and you're a dead man," said a threatening voice from the dark. "Now get to your feet!" Meeko recognized the Goon Squad member, but remained silent as he and Savage were taken to the FBI field office. Once their interrogators were satisfied with what they had to say, they were released.

Meeko and Savage crossed the road and entered the back entrance of the little white church. Meeko smiled, thinking his brothers had chosen the perfect place to do battle since they had an excellent view from all sides. Dog lowered his rifle, asking, "What brings you home, bro'? Did you hear the call of the drums, or have you learned to read smoke signals?" he teased, handing his old friend a cup of hot coffee. They spoke angry words among themselves as Meeko listened to why it was necessary to fight. "We may not rewrite the history books, but we're gonna add a new goddamn chapter," laughed Dog.

"Our function is to become the voice of the people," said Savage. "We no longer want to follow old whitey's beliefs. We got our own, and we don't hold them in front of us for others to inspect. They're in our hearts and you have to feel them. Our younger generations have no future unless they return to the old ways or assimilate into whitey's world of confusion. This breeds suspicion among our people. Shit, even when we returned from Vietnam, many of our own people viewed us as the enemy. Hell, without a good education, how can we function in that society? Who can blame us for being pissed? We carry deep scars from the wrongs done to our people. Look at the scalping of Mother Earth and the filth in Father Sky. The water is contaminated. In fact, there's little room for the animal or even the plant life anymore. Shit, they've taken it all without realizing they're killing off any future for their own race."

"They know, but they don't give a damn," replied Dog, passing a large piece of cedar bark to Meeko to smoke himself off. Meeko took it and prayed, guiding the smoke over his head four times. As he passed it along, he recognized the elderly white priest sitting quietly over in a corner.

Meeko asked coldly, "Why in the hell are we discussing these things in front of him? And what the fuck is he doing here, anyway?"

"Hell," laughed Dog, "we throw him out and he just crawls back. Seems he wants to help us."

"Yeah, but gossip has it we're holding him hostage," said Savage.

Father Hanby listened to what they were saying. "Men, I have known each of you since you were children. I believe in what you are doing, and all I am trying to do is help!"

"I don't trust you, and I resent your presence around me. You're an outsider and will always be an outsider. To me, you're just another one of those do-gooders who keeps a firm hand on us children," scowled Meeko.

"Hey, c'mon, Meeko. Leave him alone, he's just an old man. We need to talk about things that are important. We need supplies," said Savage.

"Listen, I was talking to a weed about this problem the other day. It said you can spray us with chemicals or pull us up by the roots, but in time, my friend, we will always grow back to aggravate the fuck out of you," laughed Dog.

"You've got a good point there, Dog," chuckled Meeko.

"Hell man, we've got to stand together, just like we did in Nam. We already know we're the bad guys, no matter what we do," chortled Dog.

"Everyone listen up. We've got enough food for two more days, then we're dead in the water," interjected Savage.

Everyone looked toward Meeko who smiled, saying, "Hey, let the winged ones take care of that shit."

"Good. Like old times, we're in business," answered Savage as everyone dispersed to handle their personal missions.

At sundown the following evening, Meeko, Savage and Dog left on the first of many flights to and from Wounded Knee. As these three Vietnam veterans slipped out the back of the little church and down the hill, they knew the moonless night was a good sign. Dog joked and complained as usual, particularly when he had to assist in bringing Charlie out from under the trees. But everyone understood it was part and parcel of the brotherhood that rested between them.

As they climbed into the plane, Meeko revved the engine, hopeful this adventure was going to heighten their warrior spirits. Smiling as they left the ground, they climbed skyward knowing something good was manifesting for the future. Each man listened quietly as the wind spoke in non-verbal demands, telling them it was time to return to their roots and feed the cause of the people.

Meeko reflected on the reservation's jobless situation and felt sad to think that over ninety percent of the people were unemployed, barely surviving off their government issued commodities. "I hate what they call a job around here. Hell, most live on a salary well below the poverty line. You know, it would be good if we could regain total control over our land. We could develop strong education and work programs to entice the young people to stay on the reservation."

After their initial flight, the men continued their runs, each flight consisting of moving people and bringing in food, supplies and ammunition. After the first month, Dicky Bird with his Goon Squad and the FBI heard of Seven Two Charlie's flights. Soon other leaks surfaced, giving rise to suspicion of treason within the Indian movement. The activists knew there was a snitch among them, but just as in Vietnam, with the passage of time it became increasingly difficult to distinguish enemies from allies. Many drive-by shootings were still happening, so the group decided to send men to different locations throughout the reservation. Meeko, Dog and Savage chose to move into the interior where only a trusted few knew their whereabouts.

One afternoon a runner showed up at their site, saying, "You've got to make a flight. Things are getting worse at camp, and we need more ammunition. A guy will meet you in Minneapolis with money and guns."

Although the men felt apprehensive, they decided to leave immediately. They arrived at a privately owned airport during a thundering rainstorm and waited until after midnight before locating their passenger. They loaded the supplies into Seven Two Charlie and sat socked in at the end of the runway as the rains remained steady, creating less than fifty yards of visibility. Meeko knew his payload was too heavy and he would need the complete runway to lift off safely. Taking a chance, he lifted Seven Two Charlie into the soup, keeping low until they finally hit clear weather and a full moon popped into view, giving them good visibility. Everyone breathed a sigh of relief, but apprehension still rode heavy with each man as they approached the reservation.

When they saw the little fires burning at both ends of the landing field, they started to relax, feeling everything was okay. Meeko circled over the drop area, and Savage opened the door to push the supplies from the plane. Everyone watched them fall and Meeko cautiously studied the area again before landing. Seeing nothing, he dropped Charlie's nose down for a straight in approach. The moment the wheels touched down, the field lit up like the Fourth of July. Huge spotlights were directed at the plane as gunfire scattered across the entire area.

"Hang on," yelled Meeko as he poured on the coal and lifted Charlie back into the air. But it was too late. Seven Two Charlie had taken some rounds and oil was streaking across the windshield. "Goddamnit! I can't see! Brace yourself! Got to shut her down. C'mon baby," coaxed Meeko as he skimmed the top of the trees and bounced her back onto the field. Charlie's left wing clipped a tree and she spun, falling to her side.

"Run! Get the fuck outta here! Try and reach the river! We'll meet you there if we make it," yelled Savage.

Dog and the passenger left the plane, but Meeko and Savage stayed with Charlie. Old Dicky Bird's Goon Squad, along with the FBI, were already yelling into bullhorns while advancing with high powered machine guns. "What do you wanna do?" whispered Savage as they crouched near the plane. Meeko watched the trucks and the four wheel drive vehicles emerge from their hiding places, while blinding lights from an overhead helicopter swept the grounds. It was Vietnam all over again.

"Look at that goddamn bastard who's heading up the posse. That sonuvabitchin' Sioux traitor is one of our members!" growled Savage.

"Yeah, I know. Think we need a diversion," shouted Meeko as he moved toward the plane.

The Goon Squad leader spotted them and fired off several rounds, throwing a cloud of dust around their feet. Meeko said goodbye to Seven Two Charlie as he dropped a lighted match into the running gasoline. "Run! She's gonna blow," signaled Meeko as Seven Two Charlie was consumed in flames. As they dropped to the ground, a loud explosion filled the air with flying debris. Dicky Bird and some of his Goon members advanced, as Meeko and Savage stood with their hands high in the air.

"You Sonuvabitch! Do something! Just give me a fucking excuse to blow off your commie heads," yelled Dicky Bird.

"Where in the hell is the media when you need it?" asked Savage.

"Forget the fucking media. Just spread 'em, and shut the fuck up before I blow your stinking guts into next week. You fucking people ain't getting no messages out to those goddamn bleeding hearts," snarled Dicky Bird. All the men were rounded up, and when Meeko saw Dog stretched out like a hide drying on the ground, he knew it was over. "All you fuckers are going to prison and you'll be there until you're old and gray," smirked Dicky Bird.

"Fuck you, man! You won't live to see that happen," spat Meeko.

Bull rage registered on the puffy-faced Goon leader as he smashed Meeko in the face with his rifle butt, leaving an open gash across his left cheek. Meeko staggered toward him as another hit him from behind. His knees buckled and he fell to the ground. "Hey, I know him! That's the fucking pilot," yelled an agent. "Get up, you mother fucker," he yelled, grabbing Meeko by the hair and dragging him along the ground. By the time they had reached the trucks, all the prisoners were bleeding from this senseless, brutal attack. They were handcuffed and thrown into the waiting trucks to be transported to jail.

Rumor had it that the movement had negotiated a surrender and the second war at Wounded Knee had ended. Meeko felt good knowing they, as a people, had held the little white church for seventy-one days. It was the first time he had felt free on the reservation. As they were booked and placed in cells, an angry crowd grew in front of the jail. Guns were fired, signs were carried, bottles were thrown, mace was sprayed, sticks became weapons and blood spewed from both sides of this war. And for days many people were arrested, and so the people who lived on the reservation continued to suffer.

For months, the men sat in small cells awaiting trial and reflecting on their future. Their back-and-forth bantering about their dilemma helped them accept their unknown fate. One thing everyone agreed upon was the movement had stirred the souls of all the people, regardless of color.

Shadowhawk quietly gathered a few elders together and made a plan. They contacted many friends that were rich, generous and sympathetic to their cause. Sunny Beam was one of those people. They spoke of mutual friends and relatives before he explained the reason for contacting her. After Shadowhawk hung up the phone, he said that Sunny would become a heavy supporter and put forth an effort to contact many influential people who would donate their time and financial support for the cause.

Meeko, Dog and Savage sat around playing cards thinking over their situation. Meeko spoke of what Granbear had once predicted. "It's going to be education that frees the people. Someday we'll see Indian doctors and attorneys. Hey, who knows, maybe a brother will sit in the White House as president," chuckled Meeko.

"Yeah, I can see it now. The First Lady serving fry bread, beans and dog meat to a foreign diplomat," laughed Dog.

"Remember, we're a nuisance and considered shit disturbers by the government. Don't you realize we're an embarrassment to this country? Shit, most whites think of us as a lazy bunch of drunks and druggies," stated Savage.

"Yeah, but the most amusing thing about us misfits is, we are! Hey, they've tried to educate us, cut our hair and change our name to Billy, Bob or Jack. Well, I haven't seen one damn Indian turn white yet. Hell, the United States has always had a plan and it doesn't include the Indian. We have a big brother, and that big brother knows what's best for us. They want every goddamn one of us dead or sitting in the pages of a history book, explaining how brave we were in our death. You know they'll bury the truth again and rewrite this story to protect themselves," chuckled Dog.

"Then what is the plight of the Indian?" asked Savage.

"Shit, if this keeps up we'll be an endangered species, like the eagles. Who knows? We'll probably end up in a place like a zoo to be gawked at on Sunday afternoons along with the screaming monkeys sitting in the next cage," laughed Dog. Everyone looked at him in disgust. Dog squirmed but continued, "Hell, will you two get real!

We all know there are less than one million of us left, including the breeds. Isn't that what happens with all the rare specimens of the world?"

The following night the word went down that Shadowhawk and Jake were coming to the jail. Everyone was excited and Meeko was hoping Jake could post bond, but while waiting for the paperwork to be processed, they were suddenly shipped to another facility and were soon lost in the system.

After three and a half months there was still no arraignment date. Meeko was visited once by a court-appointed attorney and never saw him again until they sat together in the courtroom. When he heard the charges were bank robbery and gunrunning, he could not believe his ears.

The jury trial was set and within a month, Meeko faced sentencing. That day, he dressed neatly and tied a white bandanna around his head. As he stood in handcuffs, his feet and waist shackled by chains, he studied the judge's cold eyes which peered steadily over his glasses. Then turning to survey the all white jury, Meeko knew he would be serving time. And indeed, the jury deliberated only ten minutes before returning a verdict of guilty.

When the judge told him to stand for sentencing, Meeko said, "I am innocent of this charge. I have not robbed a bank. If I am to go to prison, then sentence me for what I am guilty of. Am I guilty for helping my people? If helping my people is a crime, then I stand guilty. Your prison means nothing to me. It may hold my flesh, but Great Spirit holds my soul."

"That's enough!" yelled the judge, bringing his gavel down hard. "You are sentenced to fifteen years in the Atlanta Federal Prison."

The judge's words echoed in Meeko's head and he shot his fist toward Father Sky, knowing he would be back to fight another day. As the guards led him from the courtroom, Meeko promised himself that he would continue his education and return to fight the justice system in the future. With patience and time, he knew he could break the enemy's back. And so the seeds were sown that day for future generations to continue the battle. As the mole comes up again and again, anytime and anywhere, so will the Indian continue to fight the battle of freedom for the people.

Prison Life

It was early fall when the van stopped at the gates of the Atlanta Federal Prison, better known as the "garbage dump," because it housed only the most hardened criminals. Cresting high above its aging walls were four towers strategically placed at each of the corners. Meeko glanced upward to see shadowy figures peering from behind dark, slanted windows as they entered the sally port. He noticed armed guards with readied rifles parading the catwalks that marked the facility's circumference. Scrutinizing the cold watchful eyes peering from anesthetized faces gave Meeko a foretaste of what his next fifteen years might be like.

As they slowed down a guard jumped aboard and handed the driver a clipboard. "I see you got a new bunch of fish this morning. Where did you get the Indian?"

"Picked him up at county this morning," the driver answered, handing back the signed forms as he departed.

Two more guards came aboard and removed the shackles and handcuffs from the prisoners. "Get out and walk single file through that steel door and wait for me," ordered one of the guards.

The men did as instructed and within twenty minutes they had entered the receiving area where they sat on long wooden benches lining the walls to wait until their names were called. When his turn came, Meeko stepped to the counter and turned over all of his personal possessions to be tagged and was handed a prison rule book to read.

The group entered another room and the prison processing continued. Meeko was surprised to discover it was mandatory for everyone to complete a past health history. Pictures were taken detailing all scars and tattoos, then their race and religion was documented. The new arrivals showered and shaved in preparation for their dental and physical examinations. Past records on time served in juvenile hall, county jail or prison were collected and placed in a file, referred to as the inmate's jacket. The prisoners were given an identification number which was stamped on everything that pertained to them. By noon Meeko had been tagged, bagged, numbered and processed out of his identity and given a new one that met the standards of the United States Penal System. His next challenge would be to learn two systems—the prison rules and the more daunting ones of the inmates.

That afternoon the newly arrived inmates were taken to the orientation room and handed a folded gray blanket, bar of soap, toothpaste, deodorant, razor, toilet paper, wash cloth, two changes of clothing, one pillowcase and two white sheets. As they were marched through the last steel door, it slammed behind them with a loud bang of futility.

Meeko's heart sank as he saw a crowded, open-domed wire cage called a holding tank, growing like a sinister mushroom in the center of the room. Each man was assigned a cot as the guard bellowed, "You'll stay held here until we've completed processing your files and assign you permanent living quarters. In the meantime, get used to following a clock and taking a shit in front of the world, boys." The guard smiled maliciously as he turned the key in the lock—a sound Meeko would never forget.

Meeko walked to his assigned cot and methodically made it up, placing the rest of his things underneath. He lit a cigarette and sat stoically on his cot reflecting on how the prison system had just stripped him of his human rights. As if that was not bad enough, there was no space or solitude in this small overcrowded existence. Although tempted to scream like a captured animal, Meeko knew if he was to stay alive, he could not allow his emotions to show outwardly or demonstrate any reaction.

By the end of the second day Meeko realized there was a time to eat, shit, bathe, work and sleep—but no time to think. He watched the ignorant and poor try to jockey themselves into positions of power within this aggressive atmosphere, and came to the realization that a man in prison was either predator or prey. Instinctively Meeko viewed the prison system as a deliberate plan to destroy man and his spirit. He had to change his paradigm quickly if he were to survive in this barbaric, raging community. He understood it was only a matter of time before he too would have to prove himself a man.

To keep from going insane, he forced himself to see the humor in this quandary and decided to view the prison as a mental institution. Surely the great white father would find the error of his ways and bring in the cavalry to rescue him. To amuse himself, he observed the power plays among the Blacks, Whites, Hispanics and Indians who had their own games. This conglomeration of cultures, education and religion brought forth extreme displays of personalities, from machismo to blatant homosexuality. Each group had a selected leader and every member responded according to his place and rank within that particular hierarchy.

The old inmates arrived like a pack of hungry wolves, surrounding the cage to size up the new prey, and the wheeling and dealing began. Meeko watched with contempt as new inmates were brazenly selected from the meat rack to become their potential fuck boys. He watched through all this pandemonium as many straight men succumbed to the role of sexual victims, being forced to partake in homosexual relationships. All the muscle daddies pursued the young, pretty, small-framed men, while the ugly ones were quickly tossed aside like human waste.

Meeko was intrigued by the large number of habitual criminals among the group. These "old-timers" knew the ropes and easily slipped back into following the unwritten rules that would re-establish them among the inmate leaders. By this time Meeko had come to the conclusion there were two sides in prison—Them and Us!

A guard motioned Meeko to him. As he approached the guard smiled, exposing a mouthful of scattered yellow teeth. In a heavy southern drawl, he asked, "Hey Chief, are you a reservation Indian?"

"Yeah, Sioux."

"Well, you ain't gonna find no fry bread in this part of the country," the man snickered.

"That right?" Meeko shrugged his shoulders as if it didn't matter.

"Yep, I've been watching you. You know what's going down. This is a tough place, boy, and I'm gonna give you some advice. If you wanna leave here alive, you gotta keep your nose clean. I'm only telling you this because we're both Indian. My great-grandmother was a Cherokee."

Meeko remained composed, biting the inside of his cheek to contain his laughter. Oh God, he thought, not another Cherokee princess story. Why in the hell does every southerner tell the same goddamn story?

Sure enough, the guard began, "My Pappy always bragged about us being part Indian. You see, my great-grandmother was a Cherokee Indian princess."

Meeko listened stoically, answering in his most serious voice, "Yeah, you're Indian all right. You've got those high cheekbones."

The guard smiled proudly. "Why, thank you. I'm glad you recognized that. Since we're both Indian, maybe we can become friends. Just remember we house tough criminals in this place, and I don't want you to get in trouble. Make sure you watch out for those fucking dagos and those dumb Alabama boys. They got a lot of clout here. They've got their own deal in this joint. Now as far as the rest of 'em, fuck 'em. By the way, I've heard some talk about that long, pretty black hair of yours. You gotta watch your ass, boy." Meeko remained expressionless as the guard walked away, running his billy club along the wire cage as a personal threat to those watching.

Meeko noticed five Indians walking his way. The oldest approached first, saying, "*Hau*, Grandson. I'm Larry Blackbear, Oglala from Pine Ridge. We heard you were here. Just came to welcome you. Right now there is nothing we can do but share information. We've gotten you assigned to our block. You'll be moving tomorrow."

"What difference does it make? We're all in the same fucking prison," answered Meeko. The four brothers locked a hard gaze on Meeko, silently challenging him for showing disrespect to a man of medicine. Meeko made a mental note of this challenge for future reference.

"Remember we are brothers, Grandson. We'll talk tomorrow after you've moved in," said Blackbear as the group walked away.

Early the next morning two guards approached, saying, "Okay Indian, roll 'em up." Meeko picked up his things and followed them as they silently escorted him through many steel doors, moving him deep into the bowels of the prison system. He noted all the security systems and knew they would stop any adventurous soul who had any fantasies of escaping. They arrived on the third tier and Meeko felt the urge to run when he saw that a ten-by-twenty-foot cell in C Block housed six men. "In you go, Indian. Take that bunk and locker."

Meeko stepped inside, glad to see his bed was near the outside wall. One inmate was sitting on the open toilet, while four others ignored him. As the door rolled shut, Meeko wondered how he would handle living in such a small space for the next fifteen years. He deliberately took his time placing his things in the locker, then unrolled his mattress onto the metal bed and made it up. Meeko, feeling hostility from one of his cellies, decided to remain aloof and casually stretched out across his metal bed. As he thought over his situation, he noticed a reflective light coming from the far end of the corridor. He got up and walked to the bars. As he stood there, a bear-shaped Indian named Rudy who looked about thirty-eight years old walked over and handed him a cup of black coffee. The two men stood looking through the cold steel bars as they silently drank their coffee.

"C Block has the most deranged sonuvabitchin' guards in this prison," Rudy began. "See that rail? That's one helluva fall if you accidentally slip on a banana peel. I've seen a couple of men trip and fall over that rail with a little bit of help. Man, there was blood, guts and smashed bones splattered all over that bottom floor. Took a whole day to clean that shit up. Wouldn't think about jumping, unless you had wings."

Meeko saw the rail was about six feet high with a mesh wire surrounding it.

"In here, *Kola*, you're going to need friends. Prison teaches you that your life is like a small candle flame burning in a strong wind. We Indians need each other. It keeps our soul lights burning." Climbing into his bunk, he added, "Blackbear asked me to bring you to our group meeting."

Meeko liked this gentle man and sensed they would become good friends. He finished his coffee and returned the cup to Rudy, thanking him with a nonverbal gesture as he sat back down on the side of his bed. He thought of all that he had gone through to this day and wondered what had happened to his all-American dream of a good job, wife and kids. Why wasn't it possible to be like the family on "Father Knows Best?"

Meeko feared he would become just another stupid, dirty, drunken Indian destined to spend his life behind bars. He then reflected back on himself as an eleven-year-old child and saw his jail cell in a new light as a warm bed and three square meals a day. He could see the building blocks that had prepared him to become a guest of the United States Federal Penal System—the orphanage, Renna, Granbear, Shadowhawk, the Marines, Vietnam, his bad marriage, drugs and alcohol. It revolted him to know that he had fucked up big time! Disgusted with himself, he rolled toward the dimly lit hall to get some sleep.

Long before daybreak the next morning Meeko was awakened by the earsplitting sound of a buzzer. Guards immediately swarmed the area and ordered everyone from their cells for a head count, saying someone was missing. The inmates were pissed when they found the poor bastard had been locked in the shower, another apparent victim of gang rape. Once head count was completed, Meeko and Rudy went to the chow line for breakfast and joined the Indian group. After eating, they all followed Blackbear outside to the learning tree where the Indian inmates always gathered to focus on their heritage. Meeko and Rudy joined the men sitting in a circle.

"We welcome a new member to our group. We Sioux know many things. Some of our people have accepted the French word 'Sioux' as our name, but I sometimes wonder if they know it means enemy, or cutthroat," said Blackbear, smiling. "We accept that people are related to all life. Meeko, while in prison, we need to set aside our prejudices toward other tribes and clans and support one another." Meeko understood, but doubted if he could accept this thinking, particularly since two Navajo brothers were looking at him with smirks on their faces.

When the group finished Meeko went directly to the Navajo brothers to speak about the problem. The conversation was brief, and when he walked away he was satisfied that he had just insulted another bunch of "prairie niggers."

"Those dog eating Sioux will never learn! Arrogant sonuvabitches!" they complained, stomping off in the opposite direction.

That afternoon Meeko passed the recreational area and saw the two Navajos playing cards. He was good at cards, and wanting to count coup on these two, he asked to join them in a few hands. In prison cigarettes equaled money and he was proud when he won two cartons, enough to keep him going until he found someone on the outside who would send money to put in his account on the prison books. Day after day he continued to gamble until he had established a good reputation among all the prison gamblers.

As time passed Meeko began to investigate the possibility of making his voice heard in the larger prison population. Some days he would spend hours in the library, researching prisoners' rights. Others, he would go to the outdoor recreation area, hoping to find another card game. He occasionally visited the recreation room, but hated the incessant noise from the television and radios that competed with the bickering of the card players. Meeko, bothered by all this chaos, would leave and go to the yard to pump some iron. Many times the area was so filled with the smell of reeking bodies that he would just leave rather than take the chance that the stink might damage his sensitive smell. Meeko was beginning to realize that no matter where he went, there were people, people and more people, allowing him no place to be by himself. Fuck this place! I can't stand the constant noise. In anger, he would return to his cell, hoping to escape into the solitude of books.

Meeko's nights were as restless as his days, as he continued his search for peace and quiet. One morning he awakened to a slow, drizzling rain and a sky blanketed with dark clouds. Another gray day in the Atlanta Big House. Meeko left the building and joined the Indian group sitting under the learning tree in the bone-chilling rain. Shivering from the dampness, he listened to Blackbear's wise words.

By the time the group broke up for the day, the sun was shining and Meeko headed for the outdoor track determined to start a running program. No matter the circumstances, he would not allow another day in prison to control his life. After his first lap around the track, he began to feel at peace. After his last round he smiled as he watched the sun fight its battle to pierce the dreary morning clouds. He showered and changed clothes then checked on a job posted by the Education Department.

Upon his return Meeko joined his Indian brothers outside at the learning tree because it was the only place where there was any peace and quiet. Blackbear glanced up with a smile, then continued his lesson. "It's important to understand how your mind works. Clarity helps us broaden our concepts, and we must have clarity if we are to develop stronger beliefs in the old ways. Before we can return to the blanket we must remove all of our harmful thoughts about others.

"To better understand this, remember that the world is the sacred home of all Creator's children. Think back when you were children being cherished by your caring relatives. Think of how they kept peace and harmony within all things. We gave up this beauty when we were placed in prison where every aspect of our lives is controlled. Now *Wakan Tanka* asks us to regain control of our minds and find a space to have good, sacred thoughts."

Blackbear went on to speak of the white man's Garden of Eden theory. Meeko had heard these words a thousand times and each time they made his pseudo-logical mind explode. The discovery of a race of so-called civilized people was completely illogical, and he strongly believed that whitey had not come here with peace and love for the people. He had come to steal and destroy the red race while reshaping Mother Earth to fit the European way. What was there to understand in the words of Blackbear's so-called wisdom?

Later that afternoon Meeko sought out Blackbear and emphatically told him that his teachings seemed too idealistic. Blackbear grabbed him brutally and yelled, "First, never question a man that has the power to do a *Yuwipi* ceremony! Second, if you don't like what I say, then stay the fuck away from me!" It was the first time Meeko had seen his quick temper, and now he knew why Blackbear was serving life for murder and raping a child. He calmly apologized and agreed to consider Blackbear's theories.

As they sat down together, Meeko handed him a cigarette which meant silently pray for me. Blackbear took it and said, "I teach to soften the hearts of the men. I want them to spiritually free their minds from their long hatred toward all life. This will help keep down the fights and may even prevent the killing of one of our Indian brothers. Maybe someday the world will understand the Indian's point of view."

Hearing the truth in these words, Meeko apologized for his short-sightedness. He parted with a much stronger appreciation for Blackbear's sincere teaching methods.

That night in bed Meeko thought of their conversation and decided to help this *Yuwipi* man by writing a program that might help Indians to fit into the prison educational system. He would use the format of other rehabilitation programs, but develop his own from the Indian's point of view. His program would take into consideration the lack of education among most Indian convicts, and he would be sure to schedule the classes so they fit in the prison's rigid time frame.

Since it was mandatory for all inmates in USP Atlanta to work from seven-thirty to three-thirty and meet the lockdown head count, Meeko began to determine all possible hours available for them to get an education. His program would be available to all races, in hopes this would stop the tensions among the men. He went to the library and researched all available material. When his program was finally completed, he considered the possibility of selling it in hopes that it would re-introduce the concept of the Indian in the system. He proudly submitted it to the Education Department, but it was rejected without even being read. Disappointed and feeling that his efforts had been useless, Meeko knew there was no understanding of what the Indian in prison needed.

He left the office and returned to his cell where he took stock of where he was in the system. How had he ended up in a place that was nothing but a closed society of murderers, rapists and robbers? Why did the prison openly allow so many killings, beatings, gang rapes and ongoing homosexual activity? How could anyone ignore the shit smell that crept through the corridors every night?

Frustrated with his situation, Meeko needed to clear his mind. He went to the office and signed out, then headed for the track. His angry thoughts drove him faster and faster around the track. Prisoners were treated like cattle herded through a turnstile, and no one gave a fuck about their welfare. Prison was a money-making business. Prisoners were cheap labor, and each year the head of prisons received big money for each of them. Why should the prison system consider the dignity of a human? Why not humiliate and degrade a person by forcing him to sit on a fucking open toilet for everyone to watch him take a shit? Picturing himself in these situations, Meeko recalled the time Rudy had told him to use a quick courtesy flush when taking a shit to reduce the odor. God, how could anyone live with such ineptitude and disrespect for bodily functions?

Yet God forbid if you were stupid enough to risk infringing upon a staff member in any way. Why do they even choose to work in this tomb of human waste? This place might control his body, but it would never control his mind. With that resolved, he decided to take on the system and make it work for him.

Using everything Granbear and Shadowhawk had taught him about controlling his senses, he decided to travel to Shadow World as often as possible to escape his environment, letting his mind find peace in swirling colors and potent energy in the shapes of squares, triangles, circles and vortices. In a matter of weeks, he was less aggravated with prison life and felt more positive about his future.

Soon Meeko was adept at freeing his mind anywhere, anytime, regardless of circumstances. For him, time in this hell-hole existed only in relation to people, places or things. One night while stretched out on his bed, he struggled to reconcile this limited perception of linear time with *Wakan Tanka*'s gift of the four seasons to mark natural time. If it took one year for the earth to circle the sun, and if one turn of the earth represented a year of his life, then why, he wondered, was he letting his life slip away? He opened his eyes and again thought over the problems behind these prison walls. He contemplated the violence he had seen, and realized it was compounded by the fact that there were no air conditioners to alleviate the sweltering summer heat and no adequate heating to ward off the winter cold. He was convinced that this discomfort provoked gang fights and killings among the inmates. Meeko tossed and turned most of the night, thinking about how he might contribute to prison reform during his incarceration.

Early the next morning he awakened with a blinding headache. Fearing one of his attacks, he skipped the chow line and went directly to the infirmary for medication. By the time a staff employee found his records and his medication was approved by the doctor, Meeko was in the throes of a full-blown attack. Seeing his distorted face, the doctor gave him a shot, handed him some pills and sent him back to his house to rest. But instead, Meeko sought solitude out at the learning tree. Desperate with pain, he drifted in and out of consciousness as he lay on the cool ground and begged *Wakan Tanka* for help.

An hour later the Indian group found him battling his illness and encircled him. Blackbear prayed, pulling invisible things from Meeko's head, and passed the pipe around for everyone to smoke. When Blackbear saw that the ceremony was having a curative effect, he sat with his back against the tree, his eyes half closed, and explained his role as a healer. "All people emit energies, and a person of medicine must collect this energy, directing it to a specific point to heal another. A person can only experience a true healing by understanding that we are all connected to the totality of creation. Negativity, on the other hand, causes illness, which turns us into useless generators. When anyone loses control of his emotions, it takes a person like me to bring in the spirit helpers. So you see, our greatest source of energy is *Wakan Tanka*. As Indian, it is our duty to follow the sacred medicine ways and honor our ancient teachings. We Sioux regard *Paha Sapa*, the Black Hills, as the center of all that is. It was once a place for our sacred ceremonies, but sadly, the white man has turned it into a three ring circus and has resorted to hawking trinkets from the history of the Red Man."

Blackbear then handed each man a round stone. "These are from *Paha Sapa*." Everyone sat quietly studying his stone, rolling it gently between his thumb and forefinger. "Let these stones speak to you so you can learn from them. Let them take you to your needs. If you listen patiently to their voices, they will tell you of your oldest histories. When you pray with your stone, you should acknowledge its power as it helps you experience all the sacred miracles of life."

By now Meeko was feeling better. Remembering that scientific research could not rule out the existence of unusual occurrences in Indian rituals, he asked Blackbear, "If the mind continuously produces pure energy from the deeper mind, does the thought process continue to generate this energy when you speak to a spirit in the dream state?"

"The mind has many levels and functions," replied Blackbear. "It is not a coincidence that the old ones taught us to raise our hands and reach to Great Spirit with our hearts and minds.

"Although you cannot touch Spirit physically to prove its existence, you can sense it. I think of myself as a message bearer. I'm not a *Wichasha Wakan*, holy man, but I can teach you to blow the eagle bone war whistle so that you can grasp the understanding of *Hoka Hey*, the battle cry for one's soul!

"Just as birds cover their hatchlings with protective wings to ensure the future of their species, so do we use our spiritual wings to protect our younger generations so they will be strong in their walk on Mother Earth. It is the old teachings that keep the Red Race springing forth like blades of tall grass on the plains. We must see that sacred medicine circles are kept in a manner that embraces all things.

"My brothers, if we are to win any battle in life we must prepare ourselves before committing to it. If we are to survive behind these prison walls, we must look at what brought us here in the first place. Maybe we needed to be placed behind these walls to serve *Wakan Tanka*. I know I will be here for the rest of my life. Before your time here is up, I want you to know *Tunka'shila* and keep him always in your heart. Remember, *Wakan Tanka* did not make you bad, it is you who has given yourself shame. It was your lack of honor that brought you here. If you have shown inconsideration to another in life, then know you are not worthy of the gift of consideration. All of your bitter hurts only prove you hold a grave sadness in your heart. Do not cheat yourself out of these good principles when you can bring back a good life. Honor yourself and protect your truths as you commit to do good things while you are serving time. It is your responsibility to become a good person. Life has always demanded that you follow your beliefs and honor your life's journey so that you can stay connected to the force which moves in all things."

When Blackbear had completed the session with a closing prayer, each man left with a deeper understanding of *Wakan Tanka's* universe. Meeko returned to his house and was lying across the bed reminiscing on Granbear's long ago words, when Rudy approached him saying, "Blackbear tells us he's heard of your great-grandfather. Says he was Medicine."

"Granbear, my great-grandfather, told me that long ago the people spoke directly to the Great Spirit. We talked about the future of the reservations and how the government regulations would someday take the people away. Well, that has happened. The government with its relocation program has shipped many of the people away to live in white ghettos. He often spoke about the mixed marriages that would produce breeds, and wondered what kind of people would emerge from these two different cultures."

"Yeah, I think a lot about what's going to happen to the Indian. Will breeds fit in to the scheme of things, or be destroyed?" pondered Rudy, with an unexplainable sorrow for all breeds. With tears pressed against his eyelids, Rudy said, "I'm a breed, and most times I'm not accepted by the white or the Red Race."

"Rudy, look at the increase of white births. Soon the land will run out and they will cross into the reservations."

"Then where will we go?"

"I've come to the conclusion that intelligence can only be guided by wisdom. Granbear told me that education was going to be our weapon of the future. Rudy, I was taught that ignorance kills the spirit, and I think it's time to prepare ourselves to stop the encroachments on our land, mineral rights, beliefs and culture."

"Meeko, I only know reservation life. I don't understand the dealings of white society."

"Geezus H. Christ, Rudy! When are you ever going to listen? The white folks are here, and they ain't going away. As a nation, we're going to have to fight this fucking system and you've gotta understand the system to do it!"

"Aw, fuck it, man! I don't care what the rest of you do, I'm not getting involved."

"Okay, fine, Rudy! Just listen! I'm starting college next semester. I've checked it out and I know our schedule. We start our day at five o'clock. Breakfast at six, work until noon, then an hour for lunch and back to work until three-thirty. After dinner we are free by six o'clock and we don't have to be back in our cells until nine-twenty for the last lockdown head count of the day. All we do on weekends is piss away our free time watching sports or shitty movies, so why don't we enroll in some college courses?"

"That's true, Meeko. But I don't want to get a white education. It means constant pressure. Life in here's enough without taxing my mind."

Exasperated, Meeko said, "I don't know about you, Rudy, but I'm walking out of here with a degree in my hand. It's hard, I know, but you can do this. I know you didn't finish high school and don't understand the procedure. I promise I'll fill out all your paperwork and help you get your GED."

"Okay, if you promise. I don't want to look like a fool."

"Hey, Bro', we're one. Now listen to me. I've found that the classes start at six and finish at nine. That'll give us plenty of time to get back to our cells before lockdown. I figure if I can keep up with the reading assignments and papers during the day, then I can help you at night and on the weekends."

"If you'll do that, I'll keep up with the medicine studies with Blackbear. Meeko, try not to push away his spiritual teachings just to accumulate money. Remember, money don't buy happiness."

"Goddamnit, Rudy, I know my greatest enemy is myself, so stop talking about it. This prison may control my body, but I'll never let it rule my mind. My great-grandfather taught me that all power comes from *Wakan Tanka*. I promise I will continue my studies with Blackbear and use what I know to repair my spiritual bond with *Tunka'shila*. Let me share something with you. Long ago I promised Granbear that I would get an education so I would know how to fight the white world. I know I'm guilty for not using what I already know, but I'll keep my word to him."

Rudy hung his head wondering if he could accomplish what Meeko was asking of him.

"Rudy, don't worry. I would never let book learning take me away from my spiritual beliefs. As far as I'm concerned we all need to follow the old ways, but education is the power tool we need to survive. Money in itself is hollow, and a person who would base his life upon it is a fool. Of course it won't buy happiness, but it will give me material comforts. I know someday we both want to have a good wife and a family. Well, damn it man, you have to have money to support them."

By the end of the day Meeko had proposed his ideas to other Indian inmates as well, some of whom wondered if he was challenging Blackbear's position on the white man's education. Nevertheless, he worked long hours to pass his entrance exam and decided to pursue psychology as his major since the workings of the mind intrigued him. Within two years, he had received his BA and Rudy, along with other inmates Meeko had tutored, had graduated from high school.

Upon receiving his degree, Meeko obtained permission to establish a therapy group. Not only had he excelled in such courses as Transactional Analysis and Guides To Better Living, but he had learned everything he could about white history and religion. He believed it would help him understand white thought processes so he could walk in both worlds unscathed. Armed with this new knowledge, Meeko felt capable of conveying his viewpoints to all races. He knew Granbear would be proud of his efforts. His insatiable appetite for knowledge continued. When he heard of the Mensa group, an organization that represented the top two percent of the world's mental giants, he passed their test and became a member of this elite group.

Meeko took advantage of every situation that arose, and eventually his name was brought to the attention of the Department of Education. He was given the position of secretary to the superintendent of all educational programs in the prison system. Meeko loved the job, and his prison jacket quickly expanded with glowing reports of his performance. An eloquent speaker, he was adept at winning people's trust. Moreover, he continued to educate himself and learned to follow business protocols, all the while manipulating the paper trail in the federal system.

When he was denied parole at his first hearing, Meeko researched the issues and filed an appeal. Meanwhile, other inmates lined up to ask him to handle their prison grievances and gradually he became the best jailhouse attorney in the prison.

Determined to get paroled and convinced he was being denied it on the basis of his affiliation with the American Indian Movement, he consulted with Jake, who hired an attorney. Three months and four days later Attorney Don Griffen sat waiting in the visitors room. The attorney looked over Meeko's files and agreed to take his case, reminding him that his status as a prisoner was viewed critical. He concurred with Meeko that people in high places did not like how he was using his education to manipulate the system and advised him to stop filing appeals for his fellow inmates and, in short, keep a low profile. "If I file for another hearing and we lose, your sentence could be extended. What you are asking me to do is a gamble, but the decision is yours. I'm sure when you think this through, you will see my point," said Don.

Meeko left the visiting room disappointed, but suspected the attorney was right. He sought Blackbear's advice and was told to maintain his integrity and patience with the system. "The old people predicted the black skies would come. They said the stars would not assist those who have abused their bodies and Mother Earth, but would help those who live by the laws of the land. This is what the white man does not understand. He wants to control the land and steal from the people. Someday he will destroy everything along with this planet.

"Many years ago when the foreigners came to our reservations, they used their bibles as bullets to fight against our old ways. They told us that God had given them the Bible to reform the Red Man and clean the land for his chosen white people. Many of our brothers and sisters accepted these teachings, believing they came from Creator. But today we know those people fed us the lying ways of the maggot. Whitey will never be satisfied until the Red Race is wiped off Mother Earth."

Late one afternoon during his daily run, Meeko picked up speed and stopped fighting the natural rhythms of his body, releasing a barrage of unanswered questions. What is this message I carry in life? Why does life not flow for me? What is in my past that still controls me? Meeko knew he was far too stubborn to give up on himself and decided to integrate his intellect with his instincts. As his mind finely broke free, the wind swirled around him, touching his heart with soft whispers that said, "Run Indian, run for your freedom!" Meeko was smiling as he came off the track and walked briskly to the shower, knowing there was wisdom in following his attorney's advice.

After his shower Meeko saw four guards threatening a well-known snitch, and he went immediately to Blackbear to inform him of the situation. In response, Blackbear told the Indian group that evening, "I've heard some rumors about what's going to happen to a certain stoolie. They're threatening to burn him tonight." Pointing toward Meeko and Rudy, he added, "He lives in the cell next to you and they'll be moving his cellmates out. I want you to stay in your house this evening. It's best we mind our own business. Remember, we're in prison. As Indians, we do not take sides with other races. This allows us to freely associate with everyone."

"Hell, what difference if a whitey gets fried? He's just another piece of useless garbage being removed from Mother Earth," smirked Meeko. All the others adamantly agreed with him.

"Stop your judgments! That's all I have to say."

Everyone left the track and returned to their cells. That night C Block held an eerie silence. Meeko read until the lights dimmed at ten-twenty, then placed his mirror so as to get the reflective light from the end of the corridor to continue reading.

Rudy whispered, "The fire goes down after midnight." Meeko nodded.

"Say, Chief, will you keep your mirror handy tonight so we can know what's happening?" whispered a white cellie.

"Sure," answered Meeko, pulling his blanket over him and rolling over to face the outside wall.

Silence filled the cell as the men lay awake waiting for the planned accident. Around midnight they heard the iron door in the cell next door open. Something fell, then the door slammed shut with a bang. Everyone knew the rumble had gone down. Meeko grabbed his mirror and saw two dark figures running down the corridor just as a ghastly scream rang out. As the screaming intensified and the smell of burning flesh started to filter through C Block, everyone heard the rush of footsteps.

Still watching, Meeko said, "Guards coming. They're trying to get the door open."

The heat was so excruciating that in spite of the effort of the guards, the door could not be opened. The fire continued to intensify, forcing the inmates to the far sides of their cells as they yelled and banged on the walls for help. Horrified, the men listened to the pleading screams of the stoolie being burned alive, witnessing a hideous way to die.

Due to the unbearable heat, the guards opened the doors to all the cells and demanded that everyone stand in line for another head count. When the prison Fire Department arrived, they could tell someone had thrown a homemade fire bomb into the cell. The door was still burning hot and they were forced to stand aside. As the screams inside slowly subsided, the fire crew broke open the door and brought out a charred black mass that no longer resembled a human being.

It was four o'clock by the time the final cleanup crew finished, and even though the smell lingered, the walls were still steaming from the heat as everyone returned to their cells. Once again silence reigned throughout the prison. The lights dimmed and the inmates waited anxiously for daybreak so they could escape the stench of death.

The smell of burning flesh triggered old memories in Meeko, hurling him back to the fighting lines in Vietnam. His soul engulfed with hatred and anger, he rose from his bed like a rabid animal, cursing as he destroyed everything in the cell. All Meeko could see were the Viet Cong trying to capture him as armed guards rushed in using billy clubs and mace until they had him shackled like a pig going to slaughter. They dragged him from the cell, and by the time he was hauled into the infirmary, Meeko was well into a full-blown attack. The guards held him down on the examining table as the night nurse gave him a sedative. Meeko was badly hurt and needed many stitches from his massive beating.

He was kept in isolation and heavily sedated for the next few days. As he drifted in and out of consciousness he watched images of his life spiraling around in many colors as his soul traveled to other dimensions, at last finding peace in a beautiful world. Granbear's face appeared, but as Meeko begged his grandfather to remove him from this hell on earth, Granbear's image changed into a large female grizzly welcoming Meeko to the land of the sacred bear. The bear gently took him by the hand and led him to a stream, where she placed him in the warm waters and sang a medicine song while bathing his sick body. Then, picking him up in her arms, she set him on a soft bed of grass. As he lay there basking in the warm sun, Bear whispered, "We are a society of many medicines. We teach those who come in the right way, but we use many disguises to protect the powers of our sacred medicines."

Bear then handed Meeko a fine powder from a pulverized leaf and blew her hot breath over it while chanting. She poured sacred waters into his hand, and stirred the mixture with one of her claws, then handed him a rounded bowl with wide sides. "Grandson, drink this. Let it consume your spirit." Meeko drank as directed. "Follow my breath, and learn how to release the healing powers of this special herb." A foam rose up and out of his hand until it covered his entire body. Bear whispered, "Never divulge the name of this plant or let anyone see you perform this ceremony." She looked deep into Meeko's eyes as she took his hand and led him back to middle world. He felt her claws rake down his cheeks, leaving wide open gashes. "Before you go, memorize everything that you see. This will help you find your way back to this place. It is never wise to let another know of its existence unless they come as a true seeker of medicine."

When Meeko opened his eyes, he was back in the infirmary. A doctor was standing over his bed saying, "You've been in a coma for two days. When you are stronger, I want you to tell me who you were talking to."

Blackbear stepped toward the bed with a twinkle in his eye, knowing that *Mato* had come to visit, and asked if they could have a prayer smoke. The doctor agreed and stood back, watching with curiosity. Blackbear prayed in the old language to keep his onlooker from knowing that Bear had come from the spirit world to heal an Indian in trouble. After the ceremony Blackbear slipped a bear claw into Meeko's hand. Meeko knew Bear was with him and that something inside him had changed.

Arriving back at his cell two weeks later, Meeko found everyone talking about a hooded Indian who had been delivered to the prison in chains. He smiled, guessing that Dog had been transferred to United States Federal Prison Atlanta. Meeko waited until the administrative staff had left for the day then took the key from the executive desk and located the information on Dog's whereabouts. Dog, described as a rabble-rouser capable of inciting riots, was slated for thirty days in isolation.

Within the week the Indian group had manipulated Dog's paperwork, changing his assignment to C Block, and delivered the message to him. A week later Dog unrolled his mattress in Meeko's cell, then headed for the yard to find his old friend.

"Hey, shit disturber. See you've come here to get us all killed." Meeko touched his shoulder in greeting.

"Yeah! Heard you needed me. Understand you've become an educated man. I told the big shots I needed to come here and get your ass organized before one of those southern boys grabs it." Both felt good they were together again and they offered a silent prayer of thanksgiving.

During the next few months everyone came to understand the seriousness behind Dog's sense of humor. Meanwhile, he rapidly unearthed the hidden secrets of who controlled the real power in USP Atlanta.

One muggy summer day Meeko and Dog walked across the yard and, finding a rare moment of privacy, smoked as they reminisced about their time spent in the Rapid City jail. "Hell, there must've been sixteen of us packed in that little cell. We were like sardines in a can," joked Dog.

"Yeah, and whose idea was it to refuse to let the cops take our fucking fingerprints? Man, they beat the shit out of us. After that, I knew I was too good-looking to let any guard ruin my pretty face again. That's why I decided to submit to the great white father's wishes."

"Yeah, that was a bad decision. I still carry a few scars from that episode. You know, I've thought a lot about those days. Remember when we were surrounded by the feds in that field with the plane burning? Hell, I nearly shit my pants when I heard those M-16's go off."

"Hey, those .30-.30's and AR-15's weren't doing too bad either. Kinda reminded me of the time when you used that Thompson in Nam."

"Shit, I don't remember that. I just remember that damn pair of .357 Mags that chicken shit FBI man carried around in his double shoulder holsters. I bet those sonuvabitches had never been fired."

No sooner were the words out of his mouth than Dog got up and slipped Meeko a shank, saying, "Gotta go. Take good care of this."

"What the fuck are you doing? Are you crazy? Goddamnit Dog, you're gonna get us both thrown into the hole."

"Hey, man, don't get shook. The best place to stash it is in the Education Department's fucking library. You're the only one that has full access, so go do it, Bro.'" Dog grinned at Meeko as he left to join his card game.

Meeko headed for the library, cursing every step of the way. He made a flimsy excuse about needing to check out some research regarding another proposal for the superintendent and stepped into the library looking for the perfect place to hide the knife. He spotted a small hole between the top shelf and the ceiling in the far corner. Stepping up on a chair, he slipped the weapon in then slid a volume of *War and Peace* in front and went back to work.

Early that afternoon Dog and two other Indians stopped by the Education Department and asked Meeko to sign their passes for the library. Meeko signed his initials and followed the men in, whispering to Dog, "If you find it, it's yours."

Both smiled as Dog circled the room for about five minutes, then stood on the same chair and pulled out *War and Peace* saying, "I know you, Brother. You've got a mind for words." Satisfied the shank was safely hidden within the system walls, everyone relaxed and met in the mess hall. "Meeko, I was shook down about twenty minutes ago," whispered Dog. "Cover your ass. They're searching for that shank and some other contraband. Pass the word along." Then he picked up his tray and left.

Returning to his cell, Meeko found three suited up guards in nasty moods tearing everything up. Rudy's head was bleeding and Meeko asked, "What's going on?"

"Get against the fucking wall, Chief, and strip down," demanded the tallest one.

"Why man? C'mon, there's nothing going on here."

The guard slammed him against the wall, tearing his shirt off in the process. "I said strip, Chief, or I'll do it for you!" Knowing he meant business, Meeko calmly removed his shoes and dropped his pants.

"You have no reason to be on my case."

"I've got every reason to be on your case. Maybe I'm doing this because I hate Indians. But you can bet your sweet ass that you're gonna do what I want you to, no matter how I treat you! Now spreadum, Chief! Pull those cheeks apart so I can see the light of day," the tall lanky guard demanded, pulling on a rubber glove and sticking his finger into Meeko's ass to begin his cavity search.

Humiliated, Meeko shouted, "Fuck you, you sons of bitches!" As the words left his mouth, he was struck from behind, and with blood trickling from his head the guards forced him, naked, down the corridor.

In anger, one said, "You're going to pull thirty days in the fucking hole, boy. Maybe that will teach you not to be so mouthy with your superiors. Haven't you Sioux bastards learned yet that you don't talk back to us white boys? I'm looking forward to seeing just how brave a fucking Indian is. I'll see you when you come out in thirty days. Believe me, by then you'll either be dead or a sniveling punk!"

Everyone knew Meeko was going to the basement where, according to rumors, crazy Big Mike raped or killed most inmates who did time there. This six-foot-tall black man, who had allegedly murdered twelve members of his family, was the guards' supreme threat to the inmates. And sure enough, there he stood naked in his cell, beckoning the guards to bring Meeko near his cage. The guards teased him until he was riled up, then tossed Meeko into the darkened eight-by-eight cell alongside Big Mike's.

Before the door slammed shut creating total darkness, Meeko saw the cell was solid concrete. There was a hole in the middle of the floor for a toilet and a slit at the bottom of the door for receiving food and water. Time passed painfully slow for the next week. There was no day or night, only the sound of guards coming and going. At times Big Mike raged while playing with his feces, emitting a horrendous odor that filtered into Meeko's cell. He felt sorry for this mentally ill man who rightfully belonged in an institution for the criminally insane.

The second week, the guards brought in a high-powered fire hose to bathe Big Mike and wash down his cell. But when they got too close, Big Mike attacked and the two guards had to beat him into a corner. When Meeko protested against their brutality, he was given the same ruthless treatment. Knocked to the floor by the water's force, he heard the guard say, "Hey, Chief, we're doing this because you're a dirty Indian. We know it's you who's stinking up this basement." After the brutal bathing, both Big Mike and Meeko lay in fetal positions for the rest of the night, shivering from the cold.

Another week passed, and Meeko counted the lines on the wall that he had scratched to mark his time in the hole. He sensed an evil closing in on him, driving his mind to the edge of time and space. He felt hundreds of gnarled hands reaching out from the walls to capture his soul and saw disemboweled and disfigured vulture-like forms eating at his flesh. Meeko intermittently laughed and prayed as he fought these demons, unaware that the madness growing within him was grafting onto his face an inhuman mask of hate.

Meeko envisioned his birth from the Sea of Souls. He knew someone had given him seven years to add to his mortal life. He saw himself trade them to a young soul and felt that soul coming toward him to collect this debt. A doorway opened and he could see horrible worlds which he recognized as his past lives. "Why are you here? It's too soon," Meeko stammered.

"You are wrong. I've been coming in and out of your life since Vietnam. My access to you first opened with your drug and alcohol indulgence," answered the young soul.

All day Meeko fought him, wailing in prayer. He felt the gentle touch of a spider as it crawled onto his hand from the darkness. "*Hau, Iktomi Unci*, Grandmother Spider, thank you for coming. It is you who weaves the worlds together and creates nature's wondrous colors that make this world beautiful. I know you teach artists to paint and writers to write. I am ready to paint. I beg you to ride on my brushes and implore you to disempower this cruel, evil one who is destroying the goodness of my soul by feeding on me like a deadly insect. *Hau, Iktomi*, spin me a strong web for protection. Share your powers with me," pleaded Meeko.

He felt a tiny bite followed by extreme nausea. A voice softly hummed, "It is I, Brown Recluse, who has come to your rescue. I teach the powers of silence, but first you must learn my posturing gestures. Learn my body language so we can communicate without words. If you do as I ask, you may walk the darkness on my silken threads—providing that I allow you to continue life as a mortal."

"*Unci*, let me live and when I leave this place I will use your gifts to paint."

"Grandson, I will spin a place on my web for you as long as you walk within my spirals. If you do this, I will let my power glisten on the morning dew as your paintings are spread across the world."

Meeko felt a sun-like warmth on his skin and began to chant until he knew Brown Recluse lived in his heart. A very clear picture of the snakes he had seen in Vietnam flashed through his mind, and he saw himself sitting in the insect and snake world. "I ask my snake and insect brothers to share in their powers. Come, my creepy-crawly brothers, escort the spirits of the dead to dance with this Indian," he entreated, reeling deeper and deeper into the underworld. Meeko fell with exhaustion as he lay listening to the moans of the hovering gray figures that now approached him. As these smoke-like masses flew out of his cell and across the basement, he knew they would appear throughout the prison.

Meeko repeated the lesson of the spider for the next two days, prompting a variety of inexplicable happenings. Big Mike watched the unusual ceremony and became mesmerized, which caused the guards to believe Meeko had some kind of control over him. Then the guards became too afraid to work. One swore he had been shoved down by invisible hands, while another heard eerie moans echoing throughout the basement day and night. The guards huddled together as far from Meeko's cell as possible, observing his demonic face each time he screamed with lunatic laughter. Soon Meeko was projecting evil outward with such force that it filled the floors, walls and ceilings with writhing snakes—diabolical creations also seen by a fearful Big Mike.

Days later, Meeko's door swung open and the blinding light forced him to the floor. When he raised his head, the three guards saw his evilness and backed off. Meeko stepped proudly out of his cell and shook Big Mike's hand, acknowledging the beauty of his soul. Then he silently thanked *Iktomi Unci* for his new ability to read another's thoughts.

The guards took Meeko to shower, gave him clean clothing and released him back into the general prison population. As he walked into the sunlight, he accepted the fact that this thirty day experience might force him to serve his full sentence.

Within two weeks Meeko had read the file about his stay in the hole, where reports indicated that he was insolent, had an unstable personality and should not be trusted within the general population. His Indian brothers, more than anyone else, noticed significant changes in his personality. At times he was hard and cruel, other times sweet and gentle. Mostly he kept to himself, working to maintain the balance of his new power.

While picking up his mail one day, Meeko found three official-looking brown envelopes—one containing a degree from his pharmaceutical course, another a certification as counselor for a children's drug abuse program, and a third document declaring him an ordained minister in the state of Ohio. Immediately he filed a petition to open a United Apostolic Church where the congregation could practice a newly founded religion based on caring for Mother Earth and teaching her children how to live in peace and harmony. Meeko was pleased with his accomplishments in the academic world, and even more delighted when a few days later a Mercer University professor helped him re-enroll so he could work toward a doctorate before leaving prison.

One morning as Meeko and Dog shared a doobie, Dog spoke of an unusual murder. "During your lockdown, the guards busted the big man on a drug deal. Apparently another inmate didn't know how to handle a shank and fell on the blade. Since his fingerprints were all over the handle, his family was informed that he had committed suicide. Can you believe the good prison system letting a dumb sonuvabitch like that play with a knife? I understand his partner hopped the rail the following day. I guess he thought he was Superman and tried to fly outta here. Hell, he ended up splattered all over the bottom floor."

"Shit, you're just a walking newspaper today. Maybe you should consider writing a fucking gossip column for some big newspaper," teased Meeko.

"Yeah, well, what the fuck! It beats the hell out of sitting in the hole for thirty days. I hear tell that a bunch of moaning spooks and crawling snakes moved into the basement."

"Must've been the dampness."

"That sounds reasonable to me."

It was ten-twenty when the lights dimmed. As usual, Meeko maneuvered his mirror toward the corridor lights to continue his reading.

"Put that goddamn book away, boy, or do you want some more time in the hole? Hell, it's written in English anyway. We both know a goddamn Indian can't read our language," snapped the guard who had busted him before. Meeko smiled, closed the book and pondered on *Title Twenty-Five* which he referred to as the Indian bible since it dealt only with the laws pertaining to Indians.

The next day Meeko decided he needed connections within the inmates' power system. He went to visit the Dixie Mafia who were the most dominant power in the prison.

"Hey, Chief, been looking for you. I need to talk with you, good buddy. I've got some minor problems at home and need you to fill out some legal papers," said their leader.

"Sure, no problem. I need cigarettes, toiletries and a few items from the commissary." As they walked to the commissary, Meeko suggested they stop in the legal library to start on the case. Meeko knew it was time to make some money and he felt good that his first client agreed to pay money for services rendered. Within two weeks he had won his first legal battle against the system and had a deposit put on the books.

Word got around quickly. Since everyone knew Meeko had no visitors and received no mail from the opposite sex, another indebted inmate went to Meeko, asking, "Hey, Chief, need to ask you a question. Do you have any girlfriends or a family?"

"No!"

Taking a photograph from his pocket, the inmate asked, "See this cute little thing? Her father's stay of execution was denied, and they transferred him to Reidsville this morning. Here are some things he asked me to give you."

Meeko opened the package and found cigarettes, socks and an old electric coffee pot along with a note which read, "By the time you get this, I will be gone. I've spoken to my family, who would like to have a visit with you to thank you for helping me through a bad time. They are simple people. Sign these visiting papers, and be my good messenger."

After Meeko finished reading the note, the inmate said, "I'm his cousin. And since we Southerners don't like owing anybody, I added this cute little thing to your visiting list. If you'll sign the papers, she can visit you next week." Meeko smiled, signed the papers, and thought about what he could say to the man's family. He also considered the possibilities of meeting a woman and wondered if she would show him kindness.

A week later, Meeko was given a pass to the visitors room. Dressed in his best, he entered the visitation area, where he spent an interesting day with an older couple and two young girls, one of whom was the cute fourteen-year-old in the photograph. It was four-thirty and visiting hours were almost over when they invited Meeko to live with them once he was out of prison. Although he declined, he enjoyed his first visit with people from the outside world.

On the way back to his house, he encountered Dog, who said, "Where in the fuck have you been? I've been looking for you everywhere! This is important, man! Here, read this!"

Meeko read the paper. "What kinda scam have you been running?"

"Man, I've been running ads in magazine lovelorn columns and using your pictures. I'm trying to help you. A woman in New York answered and I wrote back telling her I was an artist. I sent some photos of your art work. She's interested in representing you when you get out, and she sent me this contract in duplicate. You were in the hole, so I signed your name to them and mailed one back to her."

Meeko read the contract. Sure enough, Dog had forged his name. "Some fucking letter work, buddy. My signature looks very realistic," Meeko smiled. "But don't you think I can sign my own damn name to a contract if I want representation?"

"Yeah, but I cut us a good deal. You should be thanking me. It's steady money coming in each month, and all we gotta do is tell this broad you'll send her enough paintings for an art show. It don't mean you gotta do it. Just tell her anything to keep those monthly checks coming in," added Dog as he escorted Meeko to the Accounting Department.

Meeko was shocked to see two thousand dollars had been posted to his account. Thinking this scam wouldn't last longer than a few weeks, Meeko and Dog went to the commissary where they purchased food, toiletries, cigarettes, a fancy radio with dual speakers and headphones, and ordered a TV to be delivered in a week. Following their shopping spree, Meeko listened frequently to his favorite blues station.

Three days later, his radio was missing. When he inquired around, one of the inmates offered, "I hear that new black dude was in your house looking at it, and somebody told me he saw your radio walking down the corridor. Might ask that dude over there."

Meeko grabbed the inmate's shirt and slammed him against the wall, saying in a calm voice, "Well, Score, I want my goddamn radio. So pass the word, man!" Turning him loose, Meeko went to his cell, threw back his mattress, twisted open the rail on the bottom of his bed and pulled out a leg shank. He knew it was time for him to establish himself as a man if he expected to stay alive in this prison. He carried the shank openly to make sure this registered heavily on all those he passed and walked directly into the black group's house and said, "No mother fucking nigger is going to take anything from me! Who do I have to kill to get my goddamn radio back?"

Shock, then anger, registered on the men's faces as they stood to counter his bold confrontation. But instead, they offered subservient apologies. "Hey, man, we don't want no trouble. We'll take care of it, Chief. Don't worry, that radio will be in your house before lights out tonight," said the leader, extending a hand to show it was a done deal. Meeko did not understand their sudden change of attitude until he turned and saw over fifty inmates gathered behind him in support—including his Indian brothers, the Dixie Mafia, and other friends. Within the hour, the black leader had placed his radio by his bed, along with a carton of cigarettes and a blues tape. Meeko accepted the gifts as an apology and they went about their separate ways.

After breakfast the following morning he went to the yard to smoke and listen to his radio. He felt a strange buzz and knew Dog had loaded acid in his joint. Soon a small drip from a leaky pipe became a rainbow, then a bouquet of wildflowers, and finally the river that ran behind Shadowhawk's place. Suddenly Meeko began to relive many of his childhood memories. He recalled kneeling once at the water's edge and hearing the water speak to him. Now he could feel its flowing body and hear the water spirit say, "Scoop me up in your hands, open your fingers and watch me vanish. Doesn't the dampness prove you have been in the presence of Father River? Seek perception, not distortion. Never lose sight of a real life. Life is perfection when you do not let yourself become absorbed into another's dream." Next, Meeko saw images of himself, young and free. Then abruptly, these images turned into animated flashes of his tortured existence. To get away from them, he began digging a hole in the ground.

Dog came to his rescue. "Easy, man! You're tripping. C'mon, look at what you're doing, fool! You're digging a fucking hole to hell. Stop it before the goddamn guards see us," said Dog, frantically trying to refill the hole.

"Hey, Brother, I became one with that water, and I owe you," Meeko finally remarked. "The trip was great. What fucked me over was when I saw my past lives reflecting on the river's surface and realized my destiny is in my hands. I saw a dark haired woman with blue-green eyes coming into my life. I know I'm going to meet her."

Later, still unable to dismiss the dream woman from his mind, Meeko went to his house, pulled out a canvas and paints, and began to paint her. For days he visited Shadow World as though he and the woman were together. He continued to paint her until one afternoon, thinking his paintings were not good enough, he threw them away.

Dog saw an opportunity in this waste. The prison art show was due to open in two weeks and forging Meeko's signature on the application forms, he entered his buddy's paintings in the show. Upon acceptance, Dog wrote to all the women who had answered his ads, inviting them to attend the exhibit. Amused by Dog's antics, Meeko painted feverishly day and night until he had twelve pieces ready for the show.

On the Sunday morning of the show, Dog helped Meeko set up their display and conversed with the guests as they arrived. By the end of the day Meeko was amazed that he had sold every painting. Dog, considering himself Meeko's agent, took half of the proceeds, saying, "I earned this! You'd have had nothing without me." Meeko was impressed by Dog's cleverness and felt he might make a name for himself in the art world. Following this venture, Dog spent entire days learning promotion skills, while Meeko continued to paint. Meanwhile, his list of women sponsors grew to include a few who ordered special portraits of themselves.

Several weeks later, a very upset Dog arrived at the Department of Education and pulled Meeko aside. "Hey, man. We gotta talk. Our check didn't arrive from that New York art dealer and it's my fault. I've been too busy and forgot to write her. We gotta get a letter in the mail today if we expect to keep her money coming in. Since I'm your manager, sign this fucking thing so I can get it in the mail." Meeko took his time reading what Dog had written. "Just sign the fucking thing. I gotta go, man."

Meeko calmly handed it back, saying, "Sign it yourself. You write my signature better than I do." Dog snorted and stormed out of the office, leaving Meeko laughing over his buddy's latest quandary.

Prison life slowly returned to its normal schedule. One day as Meeko sat at his desk typing another boring report, a guard approached him, saying, "You have a visitor."

Meeko didn't have the slightest idea who it could be. As he entered the visiting room he was surprised to see Cute Little Thing walk brazenly toward him. She planted a passionate kiss on his lips, at the same time passing a balloon filled with pot into his mouth, saying, "Swallow," then handed him a coke to wash it down.

It was a difficult moment for Meeko as he tried to swallow the balloon without drawing any attention from the guards. After his second coke, he told Cute Little Thing he needed to cut the visit short. Extracting a promise for her to return, Meeko said goodbye, concluding that he would definitely enjoy more visits.

Upon his return to his cell, he told Dog of their windfall. Dog handed him a large glass of salt water, and within a short time Meeko was sitting on the toilet. Dog reminded him not to give a courtesy flush until another inmate had dug through the shit and retrieved the balloon. That afternoon Dog had rolled the contraband into pin joints and sold them all, splitting the profit fifty-fifty with Meeko.

Cute Little Thing continued to visit once a week, each time bringing a balloon filled with pot. As Dog and Meeko's business grew, they needed to find an accomplice connected to the outside world, someone who would convert their cash into funds that could be posted to their accounts. Meeko chose the Cherokee guard for this role, offering him a small percentage of the take. The guard agreed to remove the money from the premises and mail it back in the form of a postal money order. This arrangement worked so well that Dog soon decided to begin selling speed to expand their market. This enabled them to enjoy the comforts of life, particularly special foods from the kitchen.

Meeko's and Dog's new business added to his prison education which was far different from the schooling he'd had on the reservation, on the street or in Vietnam. He learned to intimidate others with his large vocabulary and eloquent speech. Proud to have earned so many degrees and pleased with the power he could now wield over others, he began to think of himself as an educated and polished Indian. As a result of his power trip, he began to indulge increasingly in his old recreational drug habits. Dog watched his friend's drug dependency grow and was concerned about his well-being. He used his connections to stop Meeko's interactions with both Cute Little Thing and the prison drug dealers until Meeko was cut off from all suppliers. Once again Meeko went through withdrawals, assisted this time by his faithful friend, Dog.

One morning Meeko stepped into the yard and saw the sun fighting with a few scattered clouds. He sat down and thought of the beauty of life that Granbear had shared with him. Overhead he saw the yellow chest and black wings of a meadowlark. Fascinated by its flight pattern, Meeko knew a joyful inner journey awaited him if he could surrender to the song of Meadowlark. Recalling that Meadowlark lived in the South Door of the Medicine Wheel, he decided to start playing his flute again to connect to this winged messenger.

Meeko saw Dog approaching with a can of pop. Extending it to him, Dog said, "Peace, Brother. Hey, man, sorry about shutting you down, but something had to be done about your habit."

Meeko looked at him, nodded his head and popped the tab off the can, letting the foamy liquid spew over him. Dog smiled, then said, "Seems like it was a little anxious to get out of the can."

"Yeah," answered Meeko, "particularly if you shook the fuck out of it before you handed it to me." Both laughed, knowing their friendship was still intact. "Made that five mile run last night. Clocked in my best time yet. I had a weird dream. Saw a strange man walking on my dreams. Wish we could do a Peyote ceremony to check out its meaning."

"Yeah, the only strange man around here is you. Besides, you gotta be careful what roadman you allow to control your mind. I remember taking seven buttons once. Boy, that scared the shit outta me, but it was one helluva world I went to. You know, if I could understand the existence of the seven worlds, maybe I would know the purpose behind what's coming to me in my dreams. I wonder if humanity is going to make it through another catastrophe. Meeko, the knowledge is always there for those who can let go of their egos. If you expect to achieve immortality, you've got to know the difference between old wisdom and foolishness. As long as the grass grows and the waters run, we will remain as one with Mother Earth.

"Yeah tell that to the fucking system that is destroying our people with their bullshit. How many years and how much patience will it take for whitey to follow the natural laws of Mother Earth? I learned from my thirty-two days in the hole that education doesn't always prove equality."

"Meeko, how can an Indian with your education go through life and never learn truth? You know if an Indian breaks manmade laws, he can accept his punishment and do his time without shame. But with the old ways, we know our punishment comes when we break *Wakan Tanka's* law and I call that higher education. I don't break spiritual laws, but feel I can do what I want about conforming to this fucking system. All I know is I hate the bullshit and the crooked laws of the government."

"Okay, you're right! But not all whiteys are shit. Remember Jake—that white man who took me under his wing and taught me how to fly the skies like an eagle and make money at the same time? Education is an intriguing weapon when you look at the bigger picture. In ten years there'll be millions more people born in the United States, and our reservations will be the only undeveloped land. Think of what could happen if all five hundred twenty-two Indian nations united as one and developed our resources, built gaming casinos, and promoted band concerts on the reservations? We could support all of our people, build schools and hospitals and become the world's most powerful nation within a nation!"

"Yeah, I see what you're saying, but you're the dreamer, I'm the realist. I also think it's important to maintain our old ways. As long as my hair is wrapped in braids, I'll always remember who I am. I think my hair sends a message to help whitey remember what he has done to my people."

Meeko smiled, thinking that the reservation was like a federal prison without visible bars. Like the people, he too still dreamed of the return of the buffalo. "Well, I've gotten the degrees, and I shook the hand that gave me the weapon to fight the governmental structure."

"Maybe, my friend. I've found loopholes in *Title Twenty-Five*. When we get out, we ought to test these laws that rule our land," proposed Dog.

"Hey, Bro, who knows? Maybe I'll stand with you in that courtroom someday as an attorney. After all, the law is based on interpretation."

"Meeko, follow your fate, my friend. You may play the role, but remember you're one of the original people, even if you did take those tests to get those goddamn diplomas. Damn, what honor is there in reading their books and then being tested to see if you lied? Now, where in the hell is the honor in a system where you gotta prove you read their fucking books? I'm a good human and I remember when a foxhole was our home. Shit, look at the fame we got from Wounded Knee. Here, take this signed contract and let this white broad make you a rich and famous asshole Indian," chuckled Dog.

Meeko looked at his contract with Dog and saw that it had been terminated. He read further to see that his paintings were financially unencumbered. Dog had negotiated a contract with a well established art dealer in New York without any strings. Meeko put it back in the envelope, not knowing how to say thank you. Looking at Dog, he said, "When we're both free again and I have money, I'll fly us back home. I can show you things that would turn a sparrow into an eagle."

"Yeah, Meeko, since we're dreaming, let's spend about a year along the river banks with a fishing pole in our hands. Can't you see the great bald eagle flying over and stealing the fish from the line?"

"Hell no! I'd grab his ass and take a few feathers, then eat the sucker."

Dog smiled and replied, "It's good to have a *Kola*." As the day ended both stood as one along with their other brothers in prayer at the learning tree.

The following morning Dog stopped by the Education Department to discuss the upcoming Atlanta quarter horse show with Meeko and both agreed it would be nice to ride a pony again. That night as they continued the discussion, childhood memories of animals on the reservation, especially dogs, were triggered within Meeko. Suddenly he pulled out a fresh canvas and began a composite painting of several dogs from his past. One had died of old age, another had been shot, and his favorite had been eaten during a naming ceremony. He and Dog laughed as they recalled sleeping with dogs at night to stave off the freezing nights on the plains. "When it got down below zero, we measured the cold by how many dogs we had in the bed. Sometimes it was a three dog night, and that was better than sleeping with a skinny woman," chuckled Dog.

Early the next morning Meeko began to paint feverishly, and by lunch he had attracted an audience of men interested in his endeavor. Gradually the painting evolved to portray a dog with a fat little body, short legs, an elongated wrinkled face, drooping ears and sad eyes like a basset hound's. By the time the painting was finished, it had inspired a game of interpretation among the inmates. Some thought that the dog had a haughty attitude, while others swore it was a street smart pup with a professional con's mind. To add a dimension related to their present experience, Meeko painted a ball and chain around the dog's left foreleg, dressed him in a black and white striped shirt with the number 97986 1/2 across the front, and a pillbox hat cocked to the side of his head. Meeko named the arrogant pup Manfred, the Snooping Hound.

From that day on, Meeko was accorded more respect and inmates frequently inquired about Manfred's welfare. For fun, Meeko decided to treat Manfred as a regular inmate, and he began answering with remarks such as, "Manfred's not too well. Somebody dropped bad drugs on him yesterday. And another thing! He's pissed off over the shit and fart smells down the corridor every night, says he can't sleep."

Dog would often chime in with something like, "Yeah, when I took him for his walk last night, man, he told me why he's in prison. He committed no crime but was railroaded into the Big House. He smelled something like tainted meat and went into a butcher shop to check it out. He found this hindquarter of beef lying on a chopping block in the sun and felt it was his duty, being the considerate dog he is, to move it out of the sun. Well, the fucking butcher caught him and called the dog pound, and the rest is history."

"Now, where is the justice in that kind of bullshit? Hell, man, that's the fucking cops for you," added another inmate.

As the mythic life of Manfred continued to unfold, the inmates decided he needed a female companion to help him through his depression.

"Hell, he's not depressed, he's bored. It seems everyone has a picture of a naked female except Manfred," remarked Dog.

"Well, let's get him a pinup of a classy looking dog," said Meeko.

Soon all the inmates were busily writing to friends and family to help them search for a poster of a foxy lady dog. Within weeks the prison post office had received stacks of letters containing pictures of canine beauties.

Finally, when nothing seemed to be good enough for Manfred, the Cherokee guard stopped by Meeko's house, and proudly handed him a poster. Meeko looked at it closely and with a shocked look on his face said, "Manfred's no punk! Don't you know that Lassie is a fucking male dog?"

"Oh shit, are you sure?" asked the guard.

"Don't sweat it," chirped Rudy. "I know that's a Lassie look-alike. Hey, I can prove to you it's a girl dog. Do you see a dick anywhere?" he continued, adamantly pointing to the crotch with his finger. Once everyone agreed this was the perfect pinup, Meeko hung it on the side of his locker next to the painting of Manfred.

Meeko's painting of the jailhouse hound soon became a listening post where the inmates came to express their opinions, solve their problems, vent their grievances or voice their dreams. The Indian brothers invented so many stories about Manfred that some believed the picture could actually talk, and one even reported that Manfred had spoken to him in dreams. Sometimes Manfred's dilemmas reflected the inmates' concerns.

One day when asked about Manfred's prison status, Meeko replied, "Oh hell, he's pissed off again. It seems his records are fucked up. His file has him listed as a beagle and if we don't get this straightened out, he'll never make parole."

"Well, fuck, man. You're the jailhouse lawyer. Draft him a writ," answered an inmate.

"Yeah, I could, but this is an emergency. He can't get into the yard to take a piss until the paperwork is done," countered Meeko. The inmate went to the library to begin the paperwork. Soon the documents had been filed officially establishing Manfred's presence at Atlanta Federal Prison.

Often Manfred's psychic abilities protected the inmates. One morning while walking through an isolated area, Meeko saw an inmate cupping a joint and to have some fun, he whispered, "Manfred said to stash that man, there's a guard coming."

"No shit," answered the inmate, swallowing the half-lit joint. Hours later he told Meeko, "Thank Manfred for the warning. Tell him I owe him one." Before long, Manfred was not only safeguarding the inmates, but also giving predictions on romance, drug deals and release dates.

One day Meeko unexpectedly received notice that his attorney, Don Griffen, was coming for a visit. Upon his arrival Don seemed excited, saying, "I finally obtained copies of the bank's video tapes. They clearly show the two men who robbed the bank, and neither one is you. In fact, they are serving time in another prison. I've worked a deal for them, and they've admitted to the robbery. Here is a copy of the documents. As soon as the governor signs them you will be a free man."

Three weeks later Meeko was moved to the minimum-security area. One morning he saw three black cars pull through the front gate and was informed that an investigating team from Washington had arrived to correct the prison system's blunders. It wasn't long before first offenders were being transferred out, while others were being released on early parole. Meeko contacted his attorney for his official date of release and was told they always wait until the last possible moment to let inmates know. While he waited for the paperwork to arrive, there were days when Meeko felt his nerves were on a runaway train. Finally he was informed his release date would be posted within two weeks. That was the day he told Dog the good news.

Dog was happy for Meeko, but depressed about the twenty years he had left to serve with no chance of parole for being framed of killing a man. The two prepared for Meeko's imminent release by reviewing the correspondence from the New York art dealer. They spent hours reading and discussing the paperwork and the best way to continue business with her. They phoned her and by the end of their conversation, Meeko felt confident that if she had the influence she appeared to have, he would be set for life. Filled with a sense of promise, he spent the next three days getting his paintings packed and shipped to New York.

As his release drew closer, Meeko separated what he would take from what he would give to other inmates. The painting of the jailhouse dog posed a minor problem until Meeko decided to release Manfred through a fire ceremony. On the following Sunday morning at sunrise, Manfred stood poised to accept the purity of fire. As the heat of the flames began to curl the corners of the painting, Meeko said, "Today we release a good friend. May your soul return to the spirit world. Come often to visit those of us who wish to see you." Touched by the ceremony, the inmates walked away with solemn faces.

Early one April morning Meeko was told, "Roll it up, Chief, you're outta here."

Having waited five long years to hear these words, Meeko walked excitedly to the gate. From there he was driven to the release house, where he was handed new clothes. After dressing, he braided and wrapped his hair in strips of red cloth. Putting on his jeans and black ribbon shirt, Meeko slipped into his boots, then put on a new leather vest. He smiled at his reflection in the mirror and when he placed his Billy Jack hat back on his head, he knew he was looking fine.

It was nine o'clock when Meeko finally stepped onto the street as a free man. He thought about Dog and hoped his friend would be okay. He wondered how many stories Dog would tell about the crazy Indian and his dog, Manfred, who did five years in Atlanta Federal Prison. Meeko called a cab and stepped inside saying, "Take me to the airport." Atlanta Federal was now a thing of the past…

Meeko Meets Sunny

Five long years had passed since Meeko had lived in the "real world." Feeling thankful for his freedom but extremely insecure, he boarded the plane, promising himself that he would never spend another day behind prison bars. He took a seat by the window and began reading the *New York Times* to learn about Manhattan, his future home. Astonished at the high cost of everything from clothing to housing, he realized he would have to make major adjustments financially and emotionally to function in this society.

As he looked out the window at the simple beauty of Mother Earth, he was grateful for the sustenance and sense of continuity the land had given him, despite the changing social conditions. He silently offered a prayer of thanks to *Tunka'shila* for his freedom and his heritage.

After lunch Meeko looked at his watch, realizing that soon the brothers back at the prison would be meeting under the learning tree. He could almost hear Blackbear, saying, "Do not look outside of yourself for anything. Give respect to yourself as you look inside for your answers." He thought of his good friend Dog and the twenty years he still had to serve without possibility of parole and wondered if he would ever see him again.

As the plane prepared to land, Meeko couldn't believe he was in New York about to meet the art agent who had arranged a show of his work. He realized with great joy that he now had an opportunity to be what Granbear had foreseen—an artist.

At the gate he waited for his agent, Joanna James, amazed at the large noisy crowd moving swiftly around him. Out of the blue an articulate voice called out, "Over here, Meeko," and a smiling, well-groomed lady stepped from the crowd and shook his hand in a businesslike manner.

"Come, let's go," she said as they walked briskly toward the exit.

"I thank you for this wonderful opportunity to show my work and for the clothes and the ticket to New York. You can deduct those expenses from the proceeds of the art show, which I hope will make us money," offered Meeko.

"You're very welcome. Call me Joanna," she added while hailing down a cab and climbing into the back seat. "Having the artist at the opening usually guarantees its success. For your convenience, I've rented a suite within walking distance of the gallery. Tonight is the press party and the guest list includes the most influential New Yorkers. I drafted a contract for you to sign, and for future sales I have established distributors across the country who will sell signed prints of your best work, doubling our profit. If we work together, you will be well established in the art world," remarked Joanna as she patted his hand.

Happy at the thought of becoming an established artist yet somewhat uncomfortable with Joanna's aggressiveness, Meeko slowly moved his hand away while smiling at her. He felt overwhelmed by the dense traffic and tall buildings that surrounded him. This chaos seemed to accentuate the aggressive attitudes of the people jamming the sidewalks. When the two arrived at their destination, Joanna said goodbye to Meeko, with a reminder that she would meet him in the hotel lobby at seven o'clock.

A uniformed man guided Meeko first to the desk, then up to his fifth floor suite. Elated to be alone for the first time in five years, Meeko tested the comfort of the king size bed, then turned on the large television and went to the stocked bar to mix a drink, discovering a tray filled with a variety of cold cuts, cheeses and nuts. Thrilled with these luxuries, Meeko went to the window to view the busy city below. A lonely pigeon sat on the window ledge staring at him. Meeko smiled at the little messenger, taking it as a sign to call Jake.

After a long conversation about the details of his release and his new career as an artist, Meeko expressed a need for legal counsel to negotiate his contract with Joanna, so Jake gave him the number of a good New York attorney. As he hung up, Meeko felt confident about his future as an artist.

Further exploring the luxurious suite, he was astonished to find the closets and drawers filled with men's clothing. He noticed a note pinned to one of the jackets and read, "Enjoy! You will find more in the front closet, along with canvasses, brushes and paints. Sincerely, Joanna." He tried on everything, thinking this must be a magnificent dream and that Dog had given Joanna enough information to ensure the fit.

After filling the tub with hot water, Meeko took a luxurious bath. Feeling totally relaxed, he glanced into the mirror admiring his muscular frame, then wrapped himself in a soft towel and lay across the bed. After falling into a deep sleep he awakened, hearing the elevator stop as footsteps approached. He immediately jumped up thinking it was a guard and as they passed his door he chuckled, knowing his prison patterns were going to be hard to break. Finding it impossible to get back to sleep, Meeko mixed himself another drink and turned on the television. Still restless, he dressed early and went to the lobby to wait for Joanna.

When she arrived, she said, "My, you look wonderful," taking his arm and escorting him down the street to the gallery. As they entered, she added, "Come, I want to introduce you to some of your important guests." For the next hour, Meeko played the gracious host, answering dozens of probing questions about his heritage, creativity and artwork.

Later, he watched a beautiful catlike woman walk through the crowd and was magnetically drawn to her. Fascinated by this mysterious lady, Meeko kept his eyes on her as she wove her way through the crowd. Moving next to Joanna, he asked, "Who is that woman?"

"Her name is Sunny Beam. Let me introduce you. She will be a good contact if she likes your work." As they approached, Sunny turned and looked at them. Electric currents raced through Meeko's body when he discovered he was staring into the gray-green eyes of the lady he had tried to paint so many times in prison. He knew without a doubt this was the woman Granbear had spoken about.

She extended her hand, smiling. "It is nice to meet you. Your work has certainly created an excitement in this town," Sunny added, then turned and excused herself.

Stunned by her raw strength and beauty, Meeko muttered a trivial response while he watched her glide back into the crowd, knowing Sunny Beam was the woman he wanted in his life. He followed her closely, listening to her gentle laughter and congenial conversation with those gathered around her. When she vanished into the night, Meeko felt a deep longing and vowed he would get to know this mystifying lady.

The opening was a great success and as Meeko walked back to his hotel, he wondered what kind of spell Sunny Beam had cast upon him.

To fulfill Joanna's request, Meeko rose early the following morning and went to the gallery dressed in his traditional Indian attire. While Joanna was busy telling a workman how to hang his newly arrived paintings, Meeko wondered if the public was ready for these depictions of Indian history and if he had truly captured the sensitivity of his long ago people. Looking out onto the busy street, he recalled the many painstaking hours he had spent in his dimly lit prison cell painting these works, and prayed the public would understand the meaning of his art.

A cutting squall whipped at the windows, reminding Meeko of Granbear's words about the wind's formless hands always pushing him forward or backward in life. He felt a kinship with the wind, and like this force of nature which lives everywhere, he too had no address yet knew his presence would be felt in the world. Meeko realized if he was to be successful, he must not accept life as a balmy summer day but rather ride to his dreams on the raw power of the ever changing winds.

He slipped his medicine bag from around his neck and idly traced the time-worn designs with his finger. Time had separated the red from the blue colors in the painted circle, leaving a faded, childlike five-pointed star. Meeko had never appreciated how much time he had taken to understand the powers that lived inside this sacred pouch. He remembered when Granbear had taught him the meanings of each symbol and contemplated his words. "Life is as free and impartial as the wind. It matters little if it rips open old scars or caresses you with new ability. Enjoy each movement of the wind as it creates necessary changes for you to stand in your own self-will. Be Creator's tool, and serve the people while enjoying the strength gained on life's journeys. Remove self-importance, and remember that flattery leads to false friendships. Fame and fortune can strip you of honor just as a sandstorm can strip the desert floor."

Meeko was jerked back to reality by the loud, intense voices of people who were discussing his art. He placed his medicine bag back around his neck and quickly hid it beneath his shirt. After the fifth painting had been sold, he knew New Yorkers liked his work and he would be treated well. Then around three o'clock, Meeko was astounded to see Sunny Beam walk into the gallery. He rushed to help her close the door, causing her to smile as she brushed her long hair from her face. "Thank you. I love the wind, even when it's angry. It makes me feel alive," she said, her eyes sparkling.

"Please let me give you a personal tour," suggested Meeko, blushing as he took her arm and graciously escorted her around the gallery. This time, he took every opportunity to extend the precious moments with her by explaining his work in detail. Sunny knew he was a Sioux, since most of his work illustrated their traditional ways. Seeing a painting titled *Wolf Trail*, she stopped to study it more closely, then remarked, "I love wolves, and this painting seems to have captured the very essence of Wolf's soul. I know this animal well. I was raised Wolf Clan by my medicine grandmother. My real name is *Ezonzon Wi Cha Nah He*, Sunlit Soul."

"You're Indian?" gasped Meeko, surprised.

"A breed."

"Do you follow the old ways?"

"Yes."

"Which reservation are you from, maybe I know some of your people," he asked arrogantly.

Sunny felt old resentments surface as she thought that once again a blood was questioning her heritage. "My father is a blood and my mother is a breed, and both are drunken blanket asses just like most of you insecure bloods. I owe you no explanations of who I am, and if you think you can use me as a bleeding heart to sell your art, then get real brother, because you have just met your worst nightmare!"

Alarmed at her reaction, Meeko smiled charmingly and said, "I wasn't trying to insult you. Just thought we might have something in common. Let me apologize and buy you lunch."

"You have a lot of nerve! First you insult me, then you ask me for a date. I don't date Indians! I find you rude and a little too unpolished to even consider as a friend. So stay away from me, otherwise I will suck you up like a soda and use you as a token Indian toy boy !" yelled Sunny, as she stormed out of the gallery.

Meeko followed her onto the street saying apologetically, "I'm very sorry. I was just hoping we could get to know each other better."

"Oh, please! I thank *Wakan Tanka* every day for making me different. At least I can survive in either culture, and I certainly don't need to parade my heritage by dressing in leather, bones and beads like you do! Did you fall out of the pages of a history book or are you just trying to prove who you are?" she snapped as he continued to trail after her.

Meeko wrote down his phone number and quickly handed it to her, saying, "Please call me and let me take you to dinner to make amends."

"Bullshit," replied Sunny, wadding up the number and sticking it into her coat pocket. "Don't hold your breath waiting for the phone to ring. May *Wakan Tanka* allow you to continue to live in your glorious style," she snarled, getting into a cab.

Meeko was dumbfounded. Although he had never liked breeds, he wondered why he had been arrogant, especially since he was interested in dating her. He admired her strong spirit—an uncommon trait since he was used to breeds trying to please bloods. Yes, Sunny Beam is a beautiful, sensuous woman with arrogant dog eating Sioux pride to match. He was infatuated with her and accepted her challenge, knowing it would take another arrogant dog eating Sioux to capture this woman. "Let the battle begin," he said forcefully, walking back into the gallery.

That afternoon, while sitting over a late lunch with Joanna, Meeko remarked, "Sunny Beam is impossible, yet exciting, spitfire Sioux beauty."

Joanna laughed at Meeko's plight and his characterization of Sunny, remarking, "Yes, I heard the two of you this afternoon and you did not handle it well. But I think she was intrigued with your work, so maybe she will forgive you."

After they returned to the gallery, Meeko removed the wolf painting from the wall despite Joanna's protests, telling her with a childlike sweetness, "Don't worry, I'll have a better one in its place by tomorrow. I want to give this one to that free spirit to fix the damage I've caused. After all, we need Sunny Beam to help sell these paintings."

Wanting to keep this powerful artist as a client, Joanna accepted his reasoning. Then she asked, "Shall we have dinner to celebrate your success?" Detecting his lack of interest, she added, "I thought we'd catch Sunny's show after dinner."

"You know her that well?" questioned Meeko, while wrapping the wolf painting.

"Well enough to get you backstage," she said intriguingly.

"Did you know she was Indian?"

"Yes. It's what makes her an especially interesting woman."

That evening after dinner they had front row seats at Sunny's show. Throughout her performance Meeko was in awe of her confidence and elegance. Sunny's inner beauty equaled her talent, and admiring her command over the audience, he knew she was expressing her identity with Sioux pride. As the curtain fell on the final act, he tucked the painting under his arm and followed Joanna backstage.

Finally reaching Sunny's crowded dressing room, Joanna cooed with outstretched arms, "You were wonderful. You remember Meeko, the Indian artist, don't you?"

Sunny offered her hand to him saying, "How could I ever forget your token Indian visiting New York? Did you enjoy the show?"

"Very much," mumbled Meeko, shocked to see this powerful stage performer barefoot and dressed in an oversized white terry cloth robe. "You project yourself ten feet tall on stage, yet you are a small woman."

"Oh, please! Just have a seat," she said, stepping behind a screen to change into her street clothes. When she returned to her dressing table, Meeko watched her hairdresser brush her hair as he dabbed at the sweat running down her face. He remained silent while watching others bend to serve Ms. Sunny Beam and bit his lip to stop a possible snicker.

Meeko knew the visit was over and handed her the painting, saying, "This is for you. I hope you will forgive my ignorance and accept this small gift in the spirit it is given."

As Sunny tore the wrapping off and saw the painting of the wolves, her warm smile convinced Meeko that he was indeed forgiven. Then she kissed him on the cheek and whispered, "Thank you. I will cherish it always—but you're still an asshole."

In frustration, Meeko stepped close and whispered, "I know you're tired, but would you consider joining me for a drink or possibly a late dinner?"

Hesitating for a moment, Sunny finally answered, "You're right, I am tired. Rather than go out, why not stop by my place and I'll send out for something. Maybe we can talk instead of fight." Shocked at her acceptance, Joanna politely excused herself, explaining that she had an early morning appointment.

Sunny led Meeko out of the theater and into a waiting cab, which sped toward New York's Upper East Side. He was surprised when they eventually stepped out of an elevator into a spacious penthouse decorated in soft pastels with elegant Indian artifacts reminiscent of ages past. Sunny opened the drapes, exposing a huge garden and a magnificent night view of the city, saying, "Make yourself comfortable while I change." The lights dimmed and soft music filtered into the room as Sunny reappeared wearing pajamas, her hair wrapped in a towel. Making herself a drink, she asked what Meeko wanted.

"Rum and coke—strong," he answered.

Sunny ordered Chinese food before sitting down on the sofa. For a moment Meeko nervously sipped his drink, then offered, "Let me hang the painting for you."

"I envision it somewhere on that wall," she said, pointing to an empty spot facing the door. "It will be the first thing people see when they enter," she smiled, handing Meeko a hammer and a picture hanger. Sunny sank back among the pillows on the sofa and watched him hang her new painting.

The doorbell rang and Sunny went to collect the food. By the time she returned, Meeko had the painting placed and both stood back to admire it. As he reached to adjust the corner of the painting, Sunny saw a rose tattoo between his left thumb and forefinger and gasped. "Oh no! This couldn't be the man my grandmother predicted so long ago," she thought, suddenly excited but uneasy at the same time. Gently touching the tattoo and feeling a mysterious presence, she asked as casually as possible, "Why this?"

"I got it when I was twelve years old and lived on the Rosebud Reservation."

Sunny nervously lit candles and placed the food on the table. They ate looking out over the city, both feeling awkward and wondering what to say.

"Have you been around many reservations?" questioned Meeko.

"Raised on them," answered Sunny, thinking Meeko was rather handsome and wondering if his touch would match the gentleness of his voice. Then feeling uncomfortable with her thoughts, Sunny shifted her focus.

"I invited you here to explain why your gift is important to me. Since I'm Wolf and Wind Clan, I relate very strongly to the simplicity of your style. My grandmother taught me that Wolf is our earth teacher, and it was this animal that helped me understand discipline, loyalty and family unity. Following Wolf's ways has taught me how to build a quality life and accept my multi-faceted personalities. Wolf demands I live in the moment which is my total reality."

"I'm glad you think my work reflects our Indian Heritage." Suddenly Meeko heard a sniffing sound and asked, "What's that noise?"

Laughing, Sunny pushed a door open, answering, "It's ShaTonga, my wolf. She helps me see the world through different eyes." A wolf walked into the room, acting apprehensive about having a stranger in the house. As ShaTonga lay down close to her feet, Sunny continued, "She was a gift from my father, who raises wolves. She won't hurt you unless she thinks I'm in trouble. If you ignore her, she'll eventually approach you."

"Lady, you're definitely full of surprises," answered Meeko, ignoring her warning and reaching out to pet the wolf. ShaTonga let out a low growl and bared her teeth as the hair on her back bristled. Meeko withdrew his hand, mumbling an apology. Sunny laughed at his predicament and reminded him that he had been warned.

"I understand you served five years in prison for Indian activities?"

"Yes. Unfortunately, I did not foresee time behind bars as the price for helping my people. As you know, there are no jobs on the reservations, and I was tired of seeing my people live below poverty standards. It seems the reservations are a third world country surrounded by the luxuries of the American dream. Someday, I'd like to see my people return to the old ways."

"Really? When is the last time you took a close look at reservation life? What about the physical and mental abuse? The hunger, the ravages of alcohol? The killings, beatings, suicides, rapes, incest and spiritual illness? I don't know anyone who has ever lived on a reservation and escaped these miseries. We have the highest suicide rate in the world among our Indian teenagers. What happened to the honor and integrity of the people who say they follow the old ways?" snapped Sunny.

"These problems do exist, but consider the government agencies' role in causing the conditions that gave rise to them. First they destroyed the buffalo, which in turn destroyed the Indian. Then they placed the survivors on reservations, gave them alcohol, and let the Indian do the rest."

Sunny sighed at the futility of it all. "I suppose the government pours the booze down every drunken Indian's throat? I believe the standard speech goes, reservation, isolation, annihilation, and someday the buffalo will return!

Sensing her disgust, Meeko voiced his political views with more caution.

"Sunny, before the white man came, we considered ourselves the caretakers of Mother Earth. We, as a people, were connected to the land and treated everything in a sacred manner. Sometimes my mind explodes with these so-called logical, civilized ways. Look at my paintings. Most of them were born from resentment, hatred and anger over how our elders were treated. I believe that someday people will respect the old ways and see the beauty of our truth then learn why we incorporate all life forces into the true principles of life. I know our history proves our truth, and I hate the way white society still sees us as uncivilized heathens."

"Maybe it's hard for you bloods to follow the old ways, but it's even harder for us breeds—the whites don't want us and neither do the Reds! I've always had a love-hate relationship with both races, so I will continue to practice my medicine unaffected by either one."

Feeling it best not to discuss his political views any further until they got to know each other better, Meeko excused himself so he could work on the painting he had promised to deliver to the gallery by the next afternoon.

As Sunny walked him to the door, Meeko hesitated for a moment, then put his arms around her. "Thank you for a beautiful evening. Promise me that I can see you again. I want the opportunity to drink in more of your beauty," he whispered, running his forefinger gently down the side of her face. Seeing that she accepted his touch, he kissed her gently on her lips, adding, "I'll see you tomorrow."

"Maybe, that is if you can find me in the park," Sunny answered, smiling flirtatiously before closing the door. Her cryptic challenge appealed to the warrior in Meeko, who hailed a cab and crossed town with a happy heart.

Back in his room he ordered a large pot of black coffee, then set up his easel. As he considered what to paint, his thoughts of Sunny and their verbal sparring about traditions made him wonder who would survive the battle if they ever had a serious dispute. He thought of the Dog Soldiers and their connection to Wolf and soon his brush was moving across the canvas in brisk strokes and by late midafternoon the painting was finished.

He walked to the gallery and when Joanna saw the painting, she smiled ecstatically knowing Meeko had created another winner. She took the painting to the storeroom, saying, "I'll let this dry, then I want to get two thousand signed prints made before we sell the original." Meeko nodded his approval and left to get some much needed rest.

Early the next morning Meeko headed to Central Park, trusting that if Sunny were the woman he had dreamed of, the rose tattoo would lead him to her. Allowing the rose to guide him, Meeko saw her as he turned onto a jogging path and called out. Sunny stopped, then grinned knowingly as he raced toward her. When she had finished her run they sat on the grass while Sunny casually tossed peanuts to the squirrels. Taking Meeko's hand, she idly traced the rose tattoo with her finger saying, "Tell me more about this."

"When I was a child my friend tattooed this rose on my hand. I guess I have a vivid imagination, because I've always dreamed about a woman and her connection to the rose. I learned it represented love and happiness, that's when my interest grew stronger and stronger in the power of the rose. I use this tattoo in many ways, and sometimes it helps me find things. In fact, it was through this rose that I've learned to control my emotions. It helps me see beauty, and sometimes I use it to gather my strength. I call it the rose that blooms forever. Sometimes it guides me to my next painting."

Thinking over his words, Sunny responded "Roses are important but have different associations for me. I know the sweetness of the rose, but I also know the sharpness of its thorns. Often, roses remind me that beauty can disappear in a careless moment and that many aspects of life have a dark side. Whenever I receive roses as a performer, I try to understand the reason underlying the gift.

"Before my grandmother's death, she made me promise that I would never allow anyone or anything to redirect my destiny. It was her fertile teachings that prepared me for my life in show business and taught me that I had the beauty of a wild rose. She also taught me that I was a warrioress, and should have thorns like a rose to fend off enemies. Like the rose, if you try to take my flowers, I take your blood.

"After my grandmother's death, my life changed drastically. I was forced to live with my father, whom I did not know, and under his harshness, I wilted. We were dirt poor, and I could no longer respond to life as a beautiful flower. However, my father did teach me to survive in a world rampant with violence, alcoholism and hunger. I learned that life is not always fair and that I had to fight to the death like a rabid animal for my beliefs and my existence."

Meeko heard her truth and thanked her for sharing this personal aspect of her life. In great admiration, he remarked. "Sunny, when I saw you on stage, I watched you move people like a flowing river."

"Sometimes, but my strong opinions often get me in trouble. I love the theater because it allows me to share my emotions openly without the possibility of being hurt. I love beauty in everything. It's what makes me happy."

"I hope that someday I can let the sun smile in my heart like you," said Meeko standing up and extending his hand to Sunny. "Would you consider having lunch with me, so we can continue chasing life's rainbows?"

Sunny agreed and took him to her favorite outdoor cafe. After they had ordered, Meeko took her hand saying, "Sunny, you've been my every thought since we met. Your wit and strength fascinate me. I believe you've somehow captured me in a magical spell and I beg you to either release my soul from this misery, or consider spending more time with me."

Remembering she had a few days off, Sunny answered, "I'll think about releasing you if you have the courage to take a two day trip to the mountains with me." The following morning Meeko, Sunny and ShaTonga cruised down the freeway, exhilarated and eager to spend a few days alone in nature. By early afternoon, they arrived at a hotel in the Catskill Mountains. After checking in to adjoining suites and unpacking, Meeko opened the door to Sunny's suite and asked if she would like a snack before dinner. Within fifteen minutes, room service had set up a beautiful table with some finger foods and a bottle of wine on the terrace overlooking the wooded area.

After the bottle was empty, they strolled through the woods as though some mystic hand from the past was leading them toward a thicket of tall pine trees. Sun rays were filtering through branches casting streaks of light across their pathway, letting the beauty of the moment embrace their souls. Meeko picked some needles from a spruce tree and began chewing them with a devilish twinkle in his eyes. As Sunny gave him an inquiring look, he said, "Once when I was very young, I thought I was in love. I went to a medicine woman we call Wicahmunga, and she told me that if I chewed spruce needles and rubbed the juice into the hair of the one I loved, she would be in love with me forever."

Then as Meeko spit into his hands, Sunny took off running and as he caught her he growled like an old bear. "You'll never get away from me. You are mine forever." He wrestled her to the ground and rubbed the spruce spittle into her hair. Over the next hour, their play developed into a romantic teasing which sparked passion.

In the light of the full moon, they walked hand in hand back to the hotel listening to a distant cry of a lonely wolf which enhanced their romantic mood. Sunny fearing these new emotions, became apprehensive as she realized Meeko might possibly be the man her grandmother had predicted long ago who would bring her great love but also much pain.

It was an awkward moment, so Meeko suggested that they change clothes and meet in the dining room. Arriving first, Meeko made sure everything was perfect for their first romantic interlude. As Sunny approached, he gently kissed her on the cheek and, in awe of her grace and beauty, he helped her with her chair.

After lingering over a glass of fine wine, they ordered a seafood entrée and sat quietly listening to the soft music of the orchestra both reflecting on their unspoken feelings. Then without a word, Meeko pulled Sunny from her chair and led her onto the dance floor, where their bodies melted together to the rhythm of the music. Feeling Sunny's desire, Meeko let his lips brush gently against her neck and whispered, "I know you. You are the woman of the rose. I can see beyond your flesh to the real beauty that shines through your being like the stars in the sky."

Once again remembering Cheering Woman's words, Sunny gently pushed him away. They returned to the table, where they finished dinner caught up in a magic far removed from this world. Feeling her hesitation, Meeko leaned over and whispered, "I'd wrestle a bear for your love."

Old memories mingled with the present as they returned to their rooms and sat on the patio talking. Meeko lit two cigarettes and handed one to Sunny. "Since we've met, I seem to stumble over my words. Your strength feeds me with such an inspiration to live. In return for this wonderful gift, I offer you this red rose."

Meeko placed his left hand into Sunny's, exposing the tattoo. "I realize it is not the most lavish of gifts, but this special rose holds a certain magic. Its petals will wrap you in a promise of protection and it will never die. If you let its beauty inspire you, we can reach beyond our greatest desires. Please accept this rose. The only care it will need is for you to share an honest love that may someday rest between us."

For a moment their hearts beat as one, but feeling uncomfortable with his persistence, Sunny excused herself and retired for the night. As she lay in bed thinking about the evening, Sunny heard the gentle trill of a flute and longed for a love she had never known.

A short time later Meeko entered her room, moving through the darkness like a cougar. He brazenly undressed and crawled into her bed. Two hungry animals ravenously reached for each other and as their eyes locked, Meeko slowly licked his fingers and walked them between her breasts, sliding his tongue down her body and piercing her like a summer sunrise breaking on the horizon.

The following morning Meeko awakened to find a note pinned to Sunny's pillow and read, "I have taken ShaTonga for a walk. Find me if you can."

Eagerly anticipating another romantic encounter, he called down to the kitchen and asked the cook to pack a picnic lunch. As he strolled along a trail through the woods in search of Sunny, he had no doubt that he was deeply in love. He also knew that if he was to capture this woman, he must remain as humble as Rabbit yet as brave as Bear.

Suddenly Sunny jumped out from the trees, screaming like a mountain lion and attacked him. Startled, Meeko clutched his chest then grabbed her, saying, "Woman, are you trying to give me a heart attack?"

"I'm just trying to see if you have a heart," giggled Sunny.

"I do, Sweetheart," he answered, taking her hand and leading her through the woods. "Your wolf spooks me. She's not very friendly."

"I told you, to win her friendship you must allow her to make the first move. Let's run with her—she feels free in the woods."

Spotting a beautiful lake surrounded by huge boulders, they ran with ShaTonga to the water's edge. Then, finding the water shallow, they waded to a small island in the center of the lake for a picnic. There, Sunny climbed to the top of a knoll and removed her blouse before lying down to bask in the warm sun. Meeko took off his shirt in a mock challenge, then spread their picnic lunch on a blanket and poured two glasses of wine. As Sunny raised her glass in a toast, he kissed her lightly on the lips, but ShaTonga, asserting her territorial rights, nosed her way between them. To appease her, Meeko pulled a bone out of the picnic basket and offered it as a bribe. They giggled as she immediately relinquished her territory and moved away with her prize.

On a whim, Meeko removed the medicine bag from around his neck and gently slipped it over Sunny's head.

"What are you doing? You know better than to share a personal medicine bag with anyone."

"Sunny, look to the future and trust that I share my medicine power with you," answered Meeko. She quickly removed it, hinting that someday they might become that close.

It was late afternoon when they finally returned to the city. Sunny dropped Meeko off at his hotel, promising to call him soon. As she drove home, she acknowledged that she liked him, but still feared the consequences predicted by her grandmother.

Soon after arriving at her apartment, she fell into a deep sleep in which a Three-legged White Wolf walked in her dreams, foretelling an upcoming death. She awoke gripped with panic. The bedroom walls seemed to swirl before her, and she saw Sam's face floating in the center of the purple orchid on her nightstand. Unable to go back to sleep, she headed for the terrace with the mail, hoping to divert her thoughts. But a letter from Auntie Rose had her running to the phone to see what was wrong with Sam.

"He's in the hospital. They suspect it's cancer," answered Auntie Rose.

Stunned with grief at the news, Sunny took ShaTonga and drove out of the city to sort out her feelings. "Oh, *Wakan Tanka*! Please don't let Sam die," she prayed. Still feeling restless, she turned the radio dial to a country-western station where she heard Sam's favorite song and a wild freedom touched her heart. Her mind filled with memories of the times she, Sam and the dogs had spent together in the mountains, Sunny regretted that she had not been home in five years. Tears rolled down her cheeks as she recalled the warm sunny days they had spent together by the mountain's cold singing rivers. How she had loved sitting with her feet in the water, listening to Father River's voice as the rushing waters flowed over the stones.

This contemplation of her past, caused her to wonder who she really was. How had she drifted so far away from that simple life to become a slick, veneered woman hiding behind many masks? And in becoming this pseudo-glamorous celebrity, had she stripped herself of her true identity?"

Exiting at Cooperstown, she headed for the charming twenty-room motel she had purchased five years ago in the Wyantha Mountains. Sleepy Hollow had served as her sanctuary, and she was saddened at the prospect of having to sell the place for tax purposes. She dreaded having to tell Shung' and Eddie that once it was sold they may have to move back to the reservation.

Shung' greeted Sunny and walked with her around the grounds. Sunny admired the improvements they had made and reluctantly told Shung' of the impending sale. They stepped into the restaurant and joined Eddie for a leisurely breakfast, then spent the rest of the morning preparing the books for the accountant. The ledgers showed a large profit margin and they celebrated with a piece of Shung's hot, homemade apple pie.

Late that afternoon Sunny took ShaTonga for a long walk up Wyantha Mountain. As they sat in the apple orchard watching the deer eat the last of the apples, Sunny remembered when a mother deer had once allowed her to pet her new fawn—a powerful moment of simple beauty that contrasted sharply with her experiences as a celebrity, and vowed never again to stray from *Wakan Tanka's* creations. When the sun began to drop over the mountain, she reluctantly returned to the motel.

At breakfast the following morning, Eddie gave Sunny a more complete update on the motel's activities and the status of her horse, Paddy. "Been working Paddy. He's got the makings of a top trotter, but it's going to take more training to keep him from breaking stride. Sometimes I think he's as stubborn as you are, but yesterday he ran his last quarter mile in twenty-three seconds."

"Great! Let's go see him." Sunny led the way to the pasture where she saw her sixteen-hand black beauty grazing in the far corner and whistled for him. Paddy arrogantly tossed his head, then playfully ran at her. Sunny stood her ground, knowing Paddy would turn away at the last moment. When she tried to place the halter around his neck, he refused. But in keeping with their established routine, as Sunny moved toward the barn, Paddy followed, nudging her in the back. She took a handful of grained molasses and fed him while Eddie harnessed him to the sulky.

Everything seemed peaceful until Paddy began to fight against the blinders. Sunny took a firm grip on his bridle and commanded him to settle down, then asked Eddie if it was okay for her to work with him.

"Sure, he's your horse."

As she eased onto the seat Paddy reared without warning, then stumbled as he came crashing down onto the sulky. Sunny was thrown to the side as Paddy lay still on the ground.

Everything happened in the blink of an eye. Stunned, Sunny jumped to her feet and helped Eddie examine Paddy for possible injuries.

"He's okay! Just a little shook. It's those damn blinders, they spook him. I should've known better than to use them since you wanted to work with him. Are you okay?" asked Eddie, pulling Paddy to his feet.

"Hey, don't worry, Eddie. It's that skittish sonuvabitch I'm worried about. Shit, this pisses me off! He's just cost us another five hundred dollars. Look at this mess," she grumbled, picking up the broken pieces of the sulky and tossing them aside.

"Don't worry about the damn sulky. I've got a friend who needs to get rid of one. Right now, I'll hitch him to the old one so you can work him past this morning's bad experience."

Eddie brought it from the barn and he and Sunny hitched Paddy up again. Sunny climbed into the seat as Eddie led them onto the track. She moved him smoothly through the first quarter. Eddie smiled as he heard her threatening Paddy while snapping the whip close to his ear. On the second time around, Sunny had him down to business. On the third trip around the track, Eddie signaled to bring him in and Sunny slowed him down to a hot walk before returning him to the barn. Eddie unhitched the sulky and left the grooming to Sunny since he had work to do back at the motel.

It was a beautiful day, and since Eddie was not around to stop her from riding Paddy, Sunny placed a saddle onto his back, cinched him tight and swung her body into the saddle. She leaned forward leaving the reins loose as Paddy raced across the field. At her urging, he jumped a wide ditch and as they sailed over the barrier, both felt an exhilarating moment of freedom. She took the reins and pulled Paddy back under control, trotting him toward the base of the mountain. As they climbed the narrow trail up the mountain, Sunny noticed it was covered with tall, overgrown bushes and trees. She leaned forward to pull aside the branches covering their pathway. Unfortunately one slipped from her hand and smacked Paddy hard in the face.

"Oops, sorry, baby," apologized Sunny, as Paddy slowly turned his head, giving her a look as if to remind her that she too had a responsibility to make this journey safe.

A beautiful green meadow opened before them as they reached the top. Sunny took a moment to embrace the view of the valley nesting far below. Riding to the middle of the field, she dismounted near a tree and spread a blanket on the ground using her saddle as a pillow. Paddy grazed nearby as she lay watching the billowy clouds drift above, and every so often he would come close and nuzzle her. She thought of the days when Paddy was just a colt and of the many jacket pockets he had ripped with his nose, trying to get at their hidden treats. She realized that although he would always have a special place in her heart, it was time for her to sell him and for them to complete their separate destinies.

It was near sundown when they arrived back at the barn. Sunny spent time grooming Paddy before returning to the darkened motel. A beautiful tray of food was waiting in her room. As she nibbled, she picked up the phone and dialed Meeko who anxiously asked where she was. Sunny explained her situation, promising to see him when she returned to the city.

Sunny slept peacefully that night. The following morning before the crack of dawn, she and Eddie sat on the split rail fence having their morning coffee as they watched Paddy run and play in the pasture. He tossed his long mane and fanned his tail out like a proud peacock. Sunny laughed at his antics. "Look at that confident bastard. Isn't he a beauty?"

"Yeah, he's a champ. Someday he'll make big bucks for someone."

"I know. I hate to sell him, but it's time. I've spoken to the woman that's buying him. She has agreed that if she ever sells him, I have first right of refusal," said Sunny, trying to hide her sadness. By ten o'clock she had signed all the papers and given Shung' the details of what must be done and was headed back to the city.

At her apartment the next day, Sunny called Auntie Rose to ask about Sam.

"Sam is terminal, and I'm afraid it's time for you to come home," whimpered Auntie Rose.

"I'll catch the next plane," answered Sunny, hanging up and immediately dialing Kate to book her a flight.

"You can't go anywhere! You're booked solid! The road tour starts at the end of this month, and you have rehearsals. Have you forgotten that filming date in California? Sunny, these are play or pay contracts! There's no way you can cancel these engagements without losing a fortune," argued Kate.

"I said Sam is dying and I'm going home!" Sunny screamed defiantly. "Cancel every fucking contract I have, and don't book me anywhere until I tell you to!"

Kate, becoming more sympathetic, said she would take care of everything and would call Meeko to let him know what had happened.

Sunny was packed and waiting as Kate arrived.

"I'm glad I caught you. I couldn't get reservations with the airlines, so I called your old friend, Ken, and he's waiting at the airport to fly you home." Sunny kissed her goodbye, told her to take care of ShaTonga then placed her bags into the cab, promising she would call when she arrived.

The flight to Tennessee was long, and Sunny was anxious to see Sam. Irritation showed on her face as she stepped from the plane into a large crowd of fans seeking her autograph. The pilot saw her frustration and offered his arm to protect her as they pushed their way through the mob. Sunny found Auntie Rose at last and took her arm. "Goddammit, Auntie! How many times must I tell you not to talk to the press? Oh, never mind—just get me to the hospital," she whispered through clenched teeth.

"I'm sorry, honey. The paper called, and I told them you were coming home because Sam was very ill. I didn't think they would invade your privacy under the circumstances." As they drove to the hospital, Auntie Rose continued, "The doctor says Sam's body is filled with cancer and they can't operate. All we can do is make him comfortable."

A fearful Sunny walked down the long, sterile corridor. She quietly pushed the door open and stopped when she saw Sam lying on the bed with his eyes closed. Fighting back tears, she approached the bed and touched his arm.

Sam opened his eyes and smiled weakly. "Hi, Sissy. It's been years."

"I had some free time and decided to let you take me hunting."

"That's good. But we'll have to wait until I get off these goddamn drugs."

"Auntie Rose tells me you've been sick." Sunny tried to keep her voice cheerful.

"Oh bullshit! You know how she is! It's her fault I'm on this fucking medication. I'm just a little under the weather. I'll be fine in a couple of weeks."

At that moment, a nurse stuck her head in the door and told Sunny to make her visit short as Sam needed his rest.

Angry over the nurse's bossy manner, Sam struggled to raise himself up on his elbows. "You stay the fuck outta here. I'm visiting with my daughter!" Turning to Sunny, he added, "Don't listen to these fucking people! They're all nuts. They think they know everything, and believe me, they don't know jack shit about me!"

"Well, well, listen to you. Maybe you're better than they think."

"You're damn right!" Sam declared, trying to catch his breath. "Hey, I want you to see my new pups. They come from Old Blue's bloodline. One of them took first in the last national field trials. Maybe while you're home we can go to the mountains for a couple of weeks—if you can remember anything about dogs, that is."

"I'd like that, Sam."

"What have you been doing?"

"Oh, lots of traveling, trying to build a career."

"Let's see, since the last time you were home we buried your brother. Hazel is still fretting over the way the government shipped his body back home in a fucking bag. We all miss him."

Tears welled up in Sunny's eyes. "It's still hard to accept that such a good person had to die so young."

"Hell, don't you know Creator always takes the good people and leaves the mean ones here to run this goddamn place? You know, Sissy, he wasn't like you. He was kind and gentle, but you've got that killer instinct. You're a born fighter. You've always wanted everything from life, while your brother wanted to watch life." Sam stared off into space with tears in his eyes, then looked closely at Sunny.

"What's that shit all over your face? You look like one of those goddamn painted Kewpie dolls!" He rubbed the makeup from the side of her cheek and wiped his finger on the corner of his sheet. "Goddamn, Sissy, get in there and take that crap off of your face before your skin falls from your bones."

"You're right, Sam. My face needs a few days without any makeup," she agreed and sat down on the edge of his bed.

Fearful that a moment of intimacy might develop, Sam yelled, "Get a fucking chair, girl! There ain't enough room on this bed for me, let alone you."

With a knowing smile, Sunny pulled a chair close to him. "Sam, you're just a mean, nasty old man." She handed him three beautifully wrapped gifts. His eyes twinkled like a child on Christmas morning as he carefully unwrapped them to find a hand-painted buffalo hide, a carved bear-bone hunting knife, and Sunny's Rope of Hope, made so long ago. Sam turned his face to the wall, his body shaking with silent sobs.

Respecting his feelings, Sunny got up to leave saying, "I'll see you tomorrow," then closed the door behind her crying as though her heart would break.

In the car, Auntie Rose told her what the doctor was doing for Sam. "Sunny, the doctor has him on strong pain medication, but you know Sam. He waited too long, and his body is eaten up with cancer. The doctor says he's probably got two months at most, but he could die at anytime. I told him you'd want a second opinion and he agreed. This doctor has known us a long time and you know he loves Sam. He told me that whatever you decide is what he'll do."

As Auntie Rose pulled up to Sam and Hazel's house, Sunny was stunned by the transformation that had taken place. It was now a big white-framed farmhouse, and hanging on its wraparound porch was her grandmother's old swing. Out in the back stood a gigantic barn with a newly painted rental sign that said 'See Rock City.' Sunny laughed, knowing Sam had bartered the space to have his barn painted for free. Sam's new red pickup truck sat next to the dog pens which were occupied by his prized coon hounds. Sunny smiled when she noticed the front yard was actually growing grass.

"I invested every penny you sent us in this big, comfortable place and put it in your name to make sure that Sam couldn't lose it in a dice game."

Still laughing at her Auntie's trickery, Sunny joined Hazel in the living room. She noticed a framed black-and-white promotion photograph of herself displayed above the new television set and made a mental note to replace it with a more personal picture. As they sat drinking coffee, Hazel caught Sunny up on family happenings. "Sam still stays as drunk as a skunk and terrorizes the town every weekend. But Auntie Rose threatened not to give him another cent of your money if he didn't stop beating the family. I'm glad she did that, cause he hasn't hit anyone since."

"That's good, Hazel." Sunny did not want to remember those days.

"Sunny, you're so much like Sam, with your temper and all. I'm afraid of what will happen if he dies."

"Well, Hazel, if I remember correctly, Sam has always kept his word, and like Sam, I'll do the same. But since I can see you're afraid, I'll give you a paper saying I'll pay your bills as long as they are reasonable. Will that be enough security for you?"

Hazel heaved a sigh of relief and handed Sunny an envelope filled with bills. Sunny took them and stuffed them into her pocket.

"Come, let me show you what Auntie Rose let me buy with the money you sent. Sunny followed her through the house, finding it had a new stove, washer and dryer as well as four bedrooms and three full bathrooms. Each bedroom had a closet, bed and a dresser. It was a far cry from the days of pallets and cardboard boxes. In fact, she suspected Hazel had probably forgotten how to use an outdoor privy.

After the grand tour, Hazel informed Sunny that her cousin Ruth had married a white man and they had twin boys. Cousin Louise was living with a married man, and Auntie Violet had been placed in an insane asylum. Uncle Carl had sold the grocery store. A tractor had turned over on Uncle Titus and he was now paralyzed. Cousin George was in prison for murder. Cousin Tim had been killed in a motorcycle wreck. Cousin Bob had died in a knife fight and his half sister had run away, but they had found her in a halfway house in California.

Sunny only half listened as other family members stopped by to ask for money to solve their problems. She agreed to most of their requests, considering the hours of entertainment they provided as payment in full from this crazy family.

"Hazel, I'm very tired. Where do I sleep?"

"We don't have a spare bed, but you can sleep on my new sofa," she answered, handing her a quilt and pillow. Sunny lay curled up on the sofa thinking, "God, I have but one identity with these people and that's money! Yet even with money, nothing really changes. Hell, I built and furnished this fucking house and still don't have a place to sleep." She pulled the covers over her head to drown out the barking of the dogs and promised herself she would have a bed in the house by tomorrow evening.

The following morning, dressed in jeans and cowboy boots, Sunny joined everyone for breakfast before leaving for the hospital. Taking Sam's truck, she stopped at a roadside stand to buy him some fruit and his favorite treats. Although the locals recognized her, Sunny new they still considered her the Indian kid from the wrong side of the tracks.

As she walked down the corridor to Sam's hospital room, Sunny heard him thundering, "Get the fuck out of here, you pinheaded fool, and give me back my fucking tobacco!"

Seeing Sunny, the nurse explained, "He's impossible. The doctor gave him strict orders not to smoke, but somehow he's gotten hold of more tobacco."

"Give it to him," demanded Sunny, snatching it from her hands.

"But the doctor said..."

"I don't give a fuck what the doctor said! Now go and tell the doctor I want to see him." Sunny rolled Sam a cigarette, lit it and handed it to him, saying, "Here! I'll get you a carton! Just be quiet until I talk with the doctor."

When the doctor arrived, she arranged for Sam to order in his food and have round-the-clock private nurses. Sam was to be provided with every comfort and his every whim satisfied.

From that moment on Sam truly enjoyed his hospital stay. He was given twenty-four hour visitation rights, and his old cronies were now allowed back into the hospital. Sunny rented him the largest color television in the hospital and, as usual, Sam invited all the other patients to watch their favorite programs with him. But Sam, being a realistic man, used his new power to manipulate people and situations. When Sunny found out he was charging them they had a serious talk. Sam decided they could watch for free but only if it was the show he wanted to watch.

Each day he was dressed in soft, new pajamas. His bedside chest held cartons of cigarettes and when he disliked the hospital menu, he was allowed to order his food from the better restaurants. He loved his new position of power, and even the doctor agreed he seemed in better spirits. One day, Sunny was surprised to see her father looking through a huge leather-bound scrapbook of write-ups and pictures pertaining to her career. She was shocked that he cared enough to keep clippings.

"What's it like being a star?"

"How'd you get these things?"

"I made a collect call to your manager, Kate, and told her I was your father. I asked her to send me a copy of everything. She sent me this scrapbook and each month, I got copies of all your pictures and press releases. Now, I want you to tell me all about this scrapbook!"

"Why, you clever old coyote. Kate never told me."

"I know! I told her if she did, I'd get her fired."

Glad for his interest in her career, Sunny opened the first page in Sam's book and launched into the story of her first days in New York City.

"After Auntie Rose left, I continued my studies then eventually landed a part in an off-Broadway show where I worked until it closed due to lack of funding. Rather than beat the streets for a job, I approached a modeling agency and was turned away. I felt your blood coursing through my veins and thought about what you would do under the circumstances.

"The next morning I returned to the agency's arrogant, fat receptionist with a beehive hairdo and strolled past her despite her protests. Opening a big black polished door, I walked in on a fat, cigar-smoking man sitting behind a desk and said, 'I have a good body and I need a job.' The man looked me over and gave me my first magazine cover."

"Well, you finally learned what I was trying to teach you," said Sam, smiling in satisfaction. "Why modeling? I thought you wanted to dance, sing and act?"

"It was the quickest way to get money for the family. After that first contract, I retained a management group, and they taught me the difference between show and business. Then I cut a few records and broke into live performances, movies and television."

"It seems strange that they'd pay you all that money for doing nothing."

Sunny laughed. "Damned if I know why, but the more my face got plastered on magazines covers, the more money I made, and the rest is history."

Sam closed the book and lit another cigarette. After a long, pensive draw, he asked, "Are you still a good girl?"

"If you're asking me if I sleep around for money, the answer is no. Sam, a whore sells her body, I sell my talents. As far as wanting a man to take care of me, I don't need it. I do that job very well myself."

"I told those bastards you were no whore."

"Geezus, Sam, what in the hell are you saying? Stop listening to that bullshit. I work my ass off, not screw it off! I'm too fucking independent to ever be a whore! Probably could be a damn good Madam, though."

"Watch your fucking mouth, Girl! I don't want anyone thinking my daughter is bad."

"Now, if you're asking me if I date any particular gentleman, the answer is yes."

"Think you'll get married?"

"Hell no! Not in this lifetime."

"Now, Sissy, every woman needs a man to take care of her."

"Well, I don't."

"Then who's this man you're dating? I suppose he's thinking of marrying you?"

"I think he wants to ask me."

"Well, there must be something wrong if you don't know for sure."

"Nothing is wrong, Sam. He's a very nice person who paints pictures for a living."

"In other words, the sonuvabitch is a struggling artist who wants to marry you so you can take care of him."

"No, Sam, but he is Indian."

"So what? Does he make enough money to take care of you?"

"Oh, for God's sake, Sam. He takes care of himself. Shit! I have enough people to support already. I don't need another responsibility in my life."

Sam bristled at her remark. "Oh, so that's how you feel about this family. We're a fucking responsibility, huh? I'll get out of this damn bed and show you who takes care of who! You can take back your fucking house and keep that goddamn truck you bought me, too."

"Sam! Shut your mouth! Your bullshit doesn't frighten me anymore. Just who in the hell do you think you are? If you say one more word, I just might knock you on your ass!"

Sam's mouth flew open in rage. Then, with gritted teeth his voice accelerated. "No one has ever talked to me like that and lived! You're not getting away with this! I'll get out of this bed and beat your ass," yelled Sam, struggling to get up.

At that moment a nurse rushed in, asking if anything was wrong.

"No. It's just a little father-daughter conflict, and Sam's upset because he's losing."

The nurse smiled, rolled her eyes, then left. Sam turned to face the window and pouted while Sunny moved around the room humming a song as she picked up his things. Finding a fresh deck of cards, she broke the seal and shuffled the deck.

"Wanna play some poker?"

"Hell no, and don't you talk to me!"

As if she hadn't heard, Sunny dealt a hand of five card stud and pulled out two hundred dollars, challenging, "Got any money?"

"None of your business!"

"Think you can take this two hundred dollars from me?"

"All day long."

Sam sat up in bed, lit a cigarette and reshuffled the cards. By two o'clock that afternoon, he had her two hundred dollars and Sunny was in debt another three hundred. Sam took great delight in bragging about his winnings to the staff, his visiting cronies and old girlfriends. In between sending for sandwiches and drinks for his friends, he was happy to tell all of his visitors that his daughter not only lost two hundred dollars but also owed him three hundred more.

The following day Sam challenged her with, "Wanna go double or nothing?"

"Sure."

Sam dealt and at the end of the game Sunny dug deep into her pocket for six hundred dollars. He smiled and stuffed the money into his pajama pocket. "Next time you'll know better than to go up against your old man."

Sunny leaned over and kissed him on the forehead, whispering lovingly, "Good night, asshole."

As she left the hospital, Sunny stopped by the nurses' station to warn the doctor to stop playing poker with Sam since he had a rather large amount of cash on hand. The doctor laughed and thanked her, telling her he had already lost about four hundred dollars the night before.

On the drive home, the winds came up and the sound seemed to comfort Sunny. When she entered the house, she was thankful that Hazel had prepared dinner, but was not happy that she seemed rather anxious to spend time with her.

"Like my new mugs? I got them at a garage sale with the money you sent for my birthday." Sunny smiled as she endured two hours of idle chatter, before crawling into the new bed which had been set up in the living room. When Hazel asked if she could keep the bed after she left, Sunny sighed with disgust, then turned out the lights and went to sleep.

Sunny remembered her promise to Sam and went to the dog pen the following morning to see his favorite pup. She called to it and as it came near, she reached down to scratch its ears. "Yeah, boy, you do look exactly like Old Blue."

She went to the side of the barn to check on the newly stretched hides, and noticed an old fruit jar lying on the ground. Picking it up, she went to the faucet and was washing it when Hazel came out and asked, "What are you doing?" She watched Sunny fill the jar with Sam's special hundred and ninety proof 'medicine.' "You're not going to do what I think you are, are you?" Sunny gave her a stern look and Hazel went back in the house where she watched from the kitchen window until Sunny left for the hospital.

At the nurse's station Sunny learned that Sam had experienced a bad night, so she went directly to his bedside. The doctor was still there. He told her that Sam had a rough night, and his medication had been increased so that he would not suffer that kind of pain again. After the doctor left, Sunny fluffed Sam's pillows to make him more comfortable.

"Bad night, Sissy, but the shots make me feel better."

"I've brought you something that'll make you feel even better," said Sunny mischievously, pulling the fruit jar from her purse. Sam grinned like a disobedient child and stashed it behind his cigarettes. "Now, that's what I call medicine. Throughout the rest of the day, Sam continually took swigs from his jar, feeling no pain which kept a gentle smile on his face.

"Why do you keep a place in New York when you have a home in Los Angeles?"

Sunny could not believe how much Sam knew about her business. "Since my work keeps me on both coasts, I bought an old Spanish style house in L.A. with pegged wooden floors and a red tile roof. The rooms are big and have high ceilings. The living room fireplace stands over nine feet tall. I bought it at an estate sale and since it needed work, I got it for a good price. It's located up in the hills overlooking Griffith Park. It's a wonderful place and it gives me a feeling of belonging to something. Whenever I'm in California, I spend my time remodeling it and walking through the hills.

"There's a four car garage and maid's quarters that I use for an art studio. The yards have terraced gardens covered with ivy and colorful flowers. I enclosed three patios and hung big Spanish pots filled with hanging plants from the ceilings. I have a large rose garden off the dining room and when I open those windows the smell is intoxicating. Why, even the eucalyptus trees house a few owls. Sam, you'd love it. When you get well, you'll have to come for a visit."

"Nope, don't like it! All those trees are nothing but a home for ticks. Those blood suckers will kill my dogs. Are those owls stiginneys?"

"No, they're horned owls. I know you'd like the tall pine tree that reaches up to the second floor. When the wind moves through its branches, it makes a sound that rocks you to sleep. An old blue jay lives in that tree. One day I left a piece of chocolate cake sitting on the patio and when I returned, he had eaten it. Now whenever I'm in California, I keep a chocolate cake around just for him. If I don't put a piece outside, he pecks on the bedroom window. Sometimes he even lets me touch him. I also feed a lizard who lives in the stones around the pool.

"But my funniest story with this house happened during a heavy rain storm. Everything around me was flooded so a mother skunk moved into my patio with her four babies. Needless to say, when I became aware of their presence I respectfully gave them plenty of room. Once the rains stopped, she took her little family back to the park, and with a thank you of skunk shit, she gave back my patio."

Just then the phone rang and Sam picked it up. He frowned when the caller identified himself. "Meeko who?"

Sunny reached for the phone but Sam waved her away. "I've been wanting to talk to you. Oh, yeah? Well, if you want to talk to me about that, you'll come here so we can talk eye to eye." A moment later, Sam hung up the phone.

"Sam, I wanted to speak with him! And I don't want him here."

"Well, it's too fucking late. He'll be coming here tomorrow to speak with me, not you! I told him you'd pick him up at three."

Sunny left the hospital, feeling mixed emotions over Meeko's arrival. But the next day when she saw him deplane, she knew this was the man she was going to marry. Both smiled as they embraced, but said nothing until they reached the car.

"Just where in the hell is this place anyway?"

"Oh, about two inches off the map," laughed Sunny.

When they entered Sam's room, he was awake and waiting to meet Meeko. After she introduced them, Meeko offered Sam a filled clay pipe and tobacco wrapped in a red cloth.

While examining the gifts, Sam asked bluntly, "You know how to use these things?"

"Yes," answered Meeko, sitting quietly yet uncomfortably stiff knowing the day was going to be a very trying one.

Sunny got up to leave so the two men could get acquainted. She leaned over and kissed Meeko on the cheek whispering, "Good luck," and walked out of the room.

Both men sat quietly for some time until Sam reached behind his cigarettes and pulled out his fruit jar offering Meeko a drink. Meeko smiled as he remembered Sunny mentioning his home run whiskey. As Meeko took his first swig, his eyes watered then he went into a coughing frenzy.

Sam laughed saying, "That'll put hair on your chest. Hundred ninety proof, boy. My own recipe."

"You're probably right. But if it does, I'll be the first Indian to grow hair on his chest," answered Meeko, wiping his nose and taking another swig.

"Yeah, if you grew hair that would be something worthwhile for the scientists to figure out. You know anything about huntin' dogs?"

"A little."

"I know you paint pictures, but can you do anything that's manly?"

Ignoring his comment, Meeko self-consciously cleared his throat and began to tell Sam his life story. Sam snickered inwardly, knowing he had just counted coup on his future son-in-law. "Sunny told me about you. So what do you have to say about my daughter?"

"Sir, I am in love with her, and I want to ask for her hand in marriage. I know she would like your approval, and that's why I'm here."

"It doesn't matter what I say—my daughter does what she damn well pleases. She's as stubborn as a mule and as untrainable as a mustang. She's smart, but she carries a mean streak like her daddy. She trusts nothing and is bitter. You might want to wait until you experience one of her temper tantrums before you talk further about the idea of marriage."

"I've experienced her temper, but I love her more than life itself. I know we can be happy together."

"Maybe you can, maybe you can't. From what she tells me, you're not only a struggling artist, but you're a shit disturber and an ex-con, which makes me wonder just how you plan to support her. I do know Sunny makes a bad enemy, and if you ever hurt her, I'll probably kill you, that is if she don't do it first."

Meeko understood Sam was going to demand his patience and total protocol. After several more drinks, they decided to drop the subject and spent their time discussing mutual acquaintances they had on the reservation.

Sunny returned some time later and jokingly asked, "Is everyone still alive?"

"Hi, Sissy! I think I've made a pretty good deal. I sold you for two mules, ten ponies and a twelve pack of beer," smiled Sam with devilish eyes.

"Is that all? I'm worth much more than that!"

"Hell, I thought it was a damn good deal. After all, you're no spring chicken."

As Sunny smacked him in jest, Auntie Rose arrived just in time to stop the playful fight. Sunny spent the rest of the evening pampering Sam while everyone talked.

Sunny and Meeko left the hospital at eight o'clock. The ride home was rather awkward, but when they pulled into the yard, Meeko stepped out of the truck and asked, "Would you mind showing me Sam's dogs?"

Sunny took him to see the pups while they talked over his visit with Sam. As they entered the house, Hazel greeted Meeko with a warm welcome and they all sat down at the kitchen table. She served them plates of warm food and after informing Sunny the front bedroom was prepared for Meeko, Hazel took his bags to the room.

Sunny felt happy as stillness settled over the house. It was a moonlit night and she invited Meeko to sit with her on the porch in her grandmother's swing.

"Meeko, my family is very plain, but they are good people in their own way."

Meeko took her hand, saying, "Believe me, it's you who has my complete attention, not your family. Don't you know I'd wrestle a bear for your hand in marriage?"

Sunny laughed, countering, "I think you already did that when you met Sam."

"Sam's okay, but you are an experience. There are still times when I'm unsure of how to express my feelings around you. And most times, I can't find the words to express the love I feel for you. Have patience and let me speak what's in my heart. We've known each other for only a short time, but surely you know the Great Spirit brought us together for a good reason. You are the major piece that is missing from my life, and I'll have no future if I'm not with you. Sunny, my happiness is the smile on your face. Why, even your words give meaning to my life. I feel we must have been together since the beginning of time.

"You are that which warms my soul, just as the sun touches each flower to fulfill its need for warmth. You've shown me the true meaning of dancing in oneness within the sacred circle of a relationship. Think of it as two people possibly sharing in the joy of a perfect love. My love for you is not just an emotion, it's much more. It's two people willing to share a splendor beyond this world. If you'll share this kind of love with me, surely you can understand that this is what makes me whole. My lovely, lovely lady, you must allow this man to show you how much he's capable of loving one woman."

"Meeko, your words weave a beautiful web. I too feel a strange tug on my heart, but perhaps our need to be loved has become so desperate that it may be impossible to satisfy either of us. I think it's too early to speak about it."

"My love, I have chased you from life to life, but this time I will not let you slip away from me. You must stand by my side as my wife," said Meeko, dropping to his knee and slipping an engagement ring on her finger. "If you say yes to this man, then you may do with me as you wish. You must marry me quickly before you are convicted of breaking my heart. I want this marriage. Your father wants this marriage. Why not have the wedding at the hospital so your father can give his daughter away?"

Moved by her feelings that they did indeed belong together, Sunny whispered, "Yes."

And as the trailing edge of night rolled over the quietness of the land, they awakened in each other's arms to find everyone had gone. After a fast shower and a quick breakfast, Sunny drove to the hospital to find Auntie Rose and Hazel crying in the hallway. "Go to your father. I will take Meeko and Hazel for coffee," said Auntie Rose.

Sunny entered the room and quietly walked to the side of Sam's bed. She saw his clear gray eyes were filled with tears.

"Daughter, I saw your grandmother last night. She tells me I'll join her soon."

"Grandmother was here? That should make you happy, not sad."

"Sunny, I'm not sad to leave this world, I'm afraid of what I'm about to tell you," he said, taking her hand.

"And what might that be?"

Sam looked away, staring at the ceiling. "Long before you were born, there was a young girl that I grew up with and even as children we were in love. We shared our dreams and hopes for our future, and when I became a young man, I promised her I would help fulfill her dreams. But as teenagers, we were careless and she got pregnant. We both wanted her dreams to come true and tried to abort you, but it didn't work. Your grandmother feared what we'd done and promised that if we'd go ahead and have the baby, she'd raise the child. It was agreed that your mother would stay out of your life, and I promised not to tell you until I was ready to return to the spirit world. I've kept that promise. I want your word that you'll never try to contact your mother. I want you to just continue your life and let her stay in peace."

Stunned, Sunny asked, "Sam, are you saying that child was me? How in the fuck could this be kept from me all these years? Who else knows this shit?"

"Goddamnit, Sunny, shut up and listen and I'll tell you!"

"Hazel had a stillbirth three days before you arrived on my doorstep. Since no one knew of the loss of her baby, we just didn't tell anyone. I gave you to your grandmother as promised. Sunny, I still love your mother, and it's like no other love I've ever known. Promise me that you'll never contact her."

"I thought my mother was dead. Are you telling me that she's still alive and has never wanted to see me? Sam, that's bullshit! What kind of woman gives away her own flesh and blood?" screamed Sunny.

"Goddamnit, Sunny, shut up and listen! She couldn't be married or admit to having a child out of wedlock and still have a career. Today she's famous. We've stayed in touch, and she's helped you in many ways. Where'd you think the money for all those dance lessons and that fancy school in New York came from? When your grandmother died, I thought I could make a home for you, but I couldn't because you reminded me too much of your mother. I punished you for the loss I felt."

"What kind of a woman would throw away a man that loved her and her child for a fucking career? My God! Why didn't anyone tell me about this?"

"Don't blame her—it was just the times," answered Sam weakly as he drifted in and out of sleep.

Sunny left the hospital in a daze. Back at Hazel's, she spent the rest of the day walking though the woods with Sam's dogs. She tried to understand her jumbled feelings about Sam's confession, wondering which family members had known her story and never told her. She felt sure that Auntie Rose and Shung' must have known.

Sunny's emotions bounced back and forth from rage to sorrow, as she mourned the mother she had never known. This nameless, faceless woman haunted her thoughts, diverting her attention from the shell of a man who lay dying in the hospital.

At five-thirty the following morning, Sunny arrived back at the hospital hoping to get more answers. Sam looked like a little boy wrapped in a loving embrace. He sat up with a gentle smile on his face and stretched his arms toward the foot of his bed. "Mama, you're here." With these words, Sam lay back on his pillow and expelled his last breath.

Sunny saw Sam's spirit intertwine with Cheering Woman's and watched the two spirits drift up and out of the room. As gentle tears rolled down her face Sunny said her goodbyes to her father and grandmother. She walked into the hall to tell everyone the sad news. As they rushed into the room wailing, Sunny left the hospital to mourn her loss alone.

At the funeral parlor, family and friends of many different races came to pay their last respects to Sam the Dog Man. But not until she arrived at the gravesite and watched the last shovel of dirt cover his casket, did Sunny feel the deep pain of the realization that it was over between her and Sam. She looked up to see a small-framed, veiled woman standing like a shadow under a distant tree. Was this Sam's mystery woman? Sunny approached her, but the woman in black turned and hurried to her waiting limousine.

Sunny began to run. "Wait! Talk to me!" The sound of her voice was drowned out by the screech of tires.

Meeko caught up to Sunny and wrapped his arms around her while she cried openly. Two days later, Meeko returned to New York while Sunny stayed behind to make financial arrangements for the family.

Desperately needing to be alone, Sunny loaded the dogs into Sam's truck and drove to the mountains. It was almost dark when she arrived at the lake campsite where she and Sam had spent so much time together. She turned the dogs loose, then built a slow burning fire and put on Sam's old coffee pot. Once she had set up the tent and unpacked the camping gear, she poured herself a cup of coffee and went to sit under Sam's favorite tree watching the rain fall in small, steady drops.

Within an hour she noticed dark clouds were beginning to blanket the sky and feeling chilled, she put on her hunting jacket. A knife fell from the pocket, and as Sunny bent over to pick it up, she remembered it was the first gift Sam had ever given her. Wailing in grief at the sight of the knife, Sunny removed it from its sheath and began to cut her hair. After sitting in mournful prayer for hours, she cut into the flesh of her arms and legs.

The intensity of the ceremony prompted her to relive her life with Sam, all the while obsessing over his mystery lady who had given birth to her. She questioned Sam's love and devotion toward this woman. These thoughts ate hungrily at Sunny's mind, her emotions erupting until she could no longer pursue another thought. It seemed the still air and the slow, drizzling rain kept her locked in the prison of yesterday's sorrows. The dogs returned and lay quietly at her feet as though they too understood her many losses.

Daylight broke on another gray morning as Sunny and the dogs went to the lake. She sat on the same log where she and Sam had discussed her wish to go to New York. Was death a balance to life, and if so, who benefited from it? Was the transition itself painful? Were people mere bags of chemicals and water collecting information through sensory stimulation? If the purpose of life was to gain wisdom, where did this wisdom go when life ended? Frustrated with her lack of understanding, she tossed a stone into the water and watched the ripples form a wide circle as the waves moved back toward shore. The ripples reminded her that even though she was an individual, she was still part of the whole and therefore affected everything within that whole.

When Blue's new pup ventured out on the log, she scratched his ears, remembering a poem she had written as a child:

Blue tick hounds, mountain high,
White school, scary time, oh my,
Unpainted shacks, dirt poor, outdoor toilets,
broken down fences, barns galore,
Dried up swamps and snakes were the day,
Tire swing hanging from the tree, and no yards to play,
Sawmill running, long into the night
Buzzards hovering as hunger makes another strike,
Mountains, dogs, and whiskey stills,
Oh, Grandmother, I come and still ask,
how can I ever climb this impossible hill?

"Sam, you sonuvabitch! I wanted things to be different between us! I needed you to live, not die!" she wailed.

Sunny heard Sam's dogs baying in the distance, but knew that what she heard could not be true, since they were lying at her feet. She took this as a sign that Sam's spirit was still with her, and it made her feel safe during this dark hour. That afternoon she hiked the trails she had once walked with Sam. As night fell, she and the dogs lay watching the stars melt into balls of soft light as an owl hooted three times. Sunny knew the owl was confirming Sam's death and predicting three more days of bad weather.

The following morning, Sunny was awakened by the familiar sounds of the woods filled with the sparse beauty of chirping birds. After a farewell cup of coffee with Sam, she packed up and loaded the dogs into the truck then headed down the mountain. Auntie Rose was waiting anxiously and insisted that she drive Sunny to the airport.

As Sunny boarded the plane, she knew she could no longer deny her heritage. It was time to return to the reservation—time to reclaim her roots.

Sunny Returns to the Reservation

Sunny arrived in Billings, Montana, early on a Friday morning. Before catching a private plane to the Fort Peck Indian Reservation, she called Shung' to let her know she would be arriving soon, eager to learn whatever she could about Sam's mystery woman. When she landed, much to her dismay Shung' was not there. However, other relatives and friends were there waiting with her cousin Willie to welcome her home.

Sunny smiled when she saw some of the old people sitting on a wooden bench pressed against the back of the cab of Willie's truck, while the children were jammed in the remaining space of the truck bed. Sunny climbed onto the tailgate and since it was customary for visitors to bring food or gifts, she directed Willie to stop at the grocery store. She was surprised to see it was now a chain supermarket stocked with hundreds of handmade Indian items including blankets, quilts and shawls, as well as tobacco, sweetgrass and herbal medicines.

Sunny told everyone that they could shop freely, so the people stuffed five shopping carts to capacity. Seeing everyone was in a festive mood as they headed home, Sunny smiled at the sight of the old people and the children digging into the bags to retrieve their candies and bubble gum. Within minutes, their mouths were filled as they sat quietly chewing on their favorites treats. The joy Sunny saw in the people over such trinkets caused her to reflect on the time when she too had been like one of those children.

As they pulled into the yard of Sunny's childhood home, Shung' greeted her warmly. When she saw all the bags of food, she smiled knowingly and pushed Sunny aside to take charge of the groceries. Sunny watched her organize everything in her small kitchen and when storage space ran out, Shung' instructed that all the canned goods be arranged in an orderly fashion under the beds in both bedrooms. When this was completed to her satisfaction, Shung' told Sunny to place her bags in Cheering Woman's old bedroom.

Many of Cheering Woman's things were still where she had left them and Sunny immediately connected to her past. It felt strange being back in her grandmother's room, and when she saw a large white box sitting on the new star quilt covering the bed, she became curious. Shung' entered and smiled then pointed with her chin, indicating that Sunny should open it. Sunny lifted the lid from the box to find the beautiful white doeskin ceremonial wedding dress her grandmother had worn long ago. She caressed it close to her body, crying tears of joy as she thought of the countless painstaking days it must have taken her grandmother to bead this dress.

"Your grandmother asked me to keep this for your wedding day, Sunny." Taking it, Shung' placed it back into the box and continued, "I'm glad you're here. We have much to discuss. When the new owners took over the motel, Eddie started drinking and I decided to move back home. After the giveaway tonight, we'll talk about this man you want to marry and discuss your responsibilities to Medicine."

Sunny was happy to see that the money she had sent Shung' was being used to repair Cheering Woman's house. She felt good that Shung' had also taken her advice to buy a new truck. She knew that Shung' could help her deal with Sam's death but felt apprehensive in talking about her upcoming marriage. Sunny tossed her high heeled shoes in the corner and dug into her bags to find a pair of jeans, a jacket and her cowboy boots. She pulled her hair into a ponytail, donned an old baseball cap and glanced into the cracked mirror where she saw a face filled with great sadness.

Upon entering the kitchen and finding no place to sit, she went to the stove, grabbed a piece of stew meat from one of the dented pots and sat in the living room with Willie who was sucking on a beer.

Feeling there was not enough room in the house to think, Sunny took Willie up on his earlier offer to take a ride around the reservation to see what was happening. Shung' overheard their conversation and asked them to take some of the groceries to Gramma Spottedhorse and to remind her to be ready around three o'clock when someone would come by to pick her up for the giveaway. Sunny and Willie arrived at Gramma's and visited for awhile before driving around the old familiar countryside.

A cold wind whistled through the broken truck window and Sunny tucked her head deep into her turtleneck sweater to escape the chill. From time to time, they picked up hitchhikers along the road and before long a caravan of vehicles was following them from house to house, joining in her homecoming while she visited old friends. It had been a long time since she had lived this way, and Sunny loved the bond that still existed between her and the people.

"Heard you were thinking about getting married," mentioned Willie.

"Yeah. He's a very nice guy."

"Doubt it. Hear he's Assiniboine. Personally, I think it's dumb to get married. They never work out. Did you know Shung' chased Eddie away a couple of months ago?"

"Yeah, she mentioned it."

"Heard he was living over on Rocky Boy Rez. If you buy the gas, I'll take you over if you want to see him."

"Maybe. But first let me see what Shung' has planned." Even though Sunny knew that Shung' was always busy taking care of the people, teaching and running healing sweats, she hoped to get some time with her to talk about the marriage ceremony.

"Before you marry this guy, hadn't you better tell him how you think? You should hang around here for a while so you can see how the Uncle Tomahawks are kissing the government peoples' asses. Hell, most of those official bastards have never been on a reservation, but they sure know how to fuck up our miserable lives. We're not like you, Sunny. We can't just leave the reservation and let the government take everything from us. With your power and money, you should stay and help us fight for our rights. I hope someday you'll take the time to learn how to manipulate that Self Determination Act. I know you've got the education and connections to battle everyone's bullshit words. Instead of getting married, maybe you should consider being the warrioress they say you are. The people need jobs, hospitals and educational programs. Hell, I'm sick of writing fucking proposals that get turned down again and again. But then maybe you don't want to help," needled Willie, trying to guilt Sunny into remaining on the reservation.

"Hey, wait a minute, Bro'! Yes, I've assimilated into mainstream society. If anyone wants to bring back the old ways, then let that be an individual choice. Take a look at yourself! How wonderful are your noble traditions when it's blatantly apparent that you've become an alcoholic? I stand up for the people in my own way by sending money to help alleviate the hunger and poverty!"

"Well, big shot, I can't do that! But I can be a staunch supporter of our Red Nation that is forced to live within the laws made by our great white father," argued Willie, angry at Sunny for referring to his obvious drinking problem.

"Willie, do whatcha gotta do! If you're really that concerned, get yourself an education so you can legally fight this shit in court without using violence. The old people want us to defend our nation peacefully and return to the unity of family ways, and I try to obey them."

Willie saw her old temper flare and spoke more gently, "Look around you, can't you see the alcohol abuse and all the children born with fetal alcohol syndrome? By freeing them from this disease, you are helping to give birth to our struggling nation. I'm afraid if you get married you will no longer feel the lightning running through your blood for the people. Everyday, I spend a lot of time with Shung' and Joe LittleDog discussing reservation politics, but nothing ever gets done. Don't be mad, I just fear losing your support if you get married."

"Don't worry, Willie, I stand with the people, married or single."

Sunny punched him hard in the arm to make amends for the exchange of harsh words between them. Somewhere deep inside, she knew she would someday return to live on the reservation. Silence rested between them as Sunny stared out the window at all the brightly painted houses. Her anger rose as she remembered how her grandmother had been forced to use the brightly colored paint supplied by the government. On the reservation everyone had to paint their homes with whatever color was available; no matter if it was red, orange or purple, the paint was supposed to be considered a gift.

She thought of her position as a breed and wondered if it was a curse or a blessing. God, which side of the street do I walk on? The Red or the white? Or do I run down the middle of the freeway and get run over by both societies? Why is there such bitter hatred among both races against us breeds? One after another of these thoughts raced through Sunny's mind.

Willie sensed her pensive mood and said, "Hey, Cuz, I'm sorry. I didn't mean to put a damper on your homecoming. I know when the time comes, you'll pick up the medicine bundle and do your real work."

Sunny nodded, fearing the responsibility of returning to the reservation to continue her medicine training. Suddenly feeling very cold, she asked Willie to drive her home.

"I'll bet coming home makes you appreciate the comforts of city life," chuckled Willie as they drove into the driveway. Sunny was surprised to find so many people had already arrived for the giveaway. Inside, everyone had their plates piled high as the wonderful smell of beans and fry bread filtered into the living room from the kitchen. Sunny felt safe in this familiar, loving atmosphere filled with teasing and shared fun.

During the giveaway, which was for an elderly couple, several people volunteered to do the repairs on their house and drive them wherever they needed to go. Another promised to take them to the doctor and do their shopping. Sunny offered money to take care of some of their expenses. Before the night was over, Shung' made sure all of the couple's needs had been met. As the last guest departed, Sunny curled up in a blanket and stretched out in front of the pot bellied stove to watch the last of the flickering embers turn to ashes before falling asleep.

It was long before daybreak when Sunny felt a gentle nudge on her foot. She rolled over to see Shung' standing nearby motioning for her to join her for breakfast. Sunny crawled out from underneath the warm blanket, grumbling quietly to herself when she saw the clock read four-thirty.

Sitting at Cheering Woman's kitchen table, Sunny sipped her morning coffee as she waited for Shung' to speak.

"It's been awhile since we've spent time together. It's good to have you home. I've always known that someday when the time was right you'd return. We'll spend some good times together and try to find the things you seek. First, I want to correct that big mouth, Willie. I know he told you about my personal life. People just can't mind their own business. Eddie and I have our own kind of marriage. We come together, and we go apart. And that's all I have to say.

"You've come here to find many answers. I'm ready to speak about your past. When you called and asked me about the mystery lady, I told you I'd tell you the truth about your father and mother when you got here. To do this right, I must go back to the beginning, so that you can understand why so many things were done in a certain way while you were a little child.

"You were born out of wedlock, but never removed from the blanket. Your mother, Anna, was a beautiful girl and Sam was a very handsome young man. There was much talk when they found out she was pregnant and had gone to a white doctor for an abortion. But it didn't work, and when they came to speak to your grandmother, they agreed to have the baby and let her raise it in the old way. Although your mother left the reservation to search for a career in the movies right after you were born, she came to visit you until you were three years old. She and Sam continued seeing each other throughout the years, and their love for each other never died.

"In fact, the old people always said that their kind of love could never be broken or tarnished. Sam always had trouble being around you because you looked too much like your mother. Your mother knew the family was dirt poor and helped support Sam, Hazel and you. She also paid for your grandmother's house and established your scholarship. It's clear that those two people loved each other and you very much."

"What does my mother look like?"

"Like you."

"Who were her relatives?"

"They say her father was one of the white cowhands over on the Lars ranch and her mother was one of the young "Left Hand" girls from the Rocky Boy Reservation. As a youngster, your mother stayed around your grandmother a lot. When she got pregnant, she went to work for a white couple until you were born, then moved to California."

"Why didn't she let me know her, or at least contact me after Grandmother died?"

"Because your Grandmother felt it best for your paths never to cross. She hoped you would be independent, capable of walking in both worlds and she wanted you to become Medicine."

"Are you really related to me?"

Seeing Sunny's pain, Shung' lovingly answered, "Yes. I am much younger than your grandmother, but we had the same father."

"Damn it, Shung', I hate all this secrecy! I want to find my mother and hear her side of the story!" declared Sunny, determined to know more about her roots.

"I will not allow you to go against your grandmother's decision! Cheering Woman said that was the way it was, and that is what we will do! That's all I have to say!"

Upset by Shung's words, Sunny slammed her fist on the table and stormed out of the house to sit under the old apple tree.

An hour later, Shung' went out to comfort her. She placed her arms around Sunny who lay her head in Shung's lap sobbing hysterically. Shung' stroked her hair soothingly. "Sunny, I know you want information about your past, but are you strong enough to forgive and love them enough to complete the circle with your parents? Your grandmother worked hard to provide you with a loving environment so that you could someday have an honorable relationship with a loving man.

"Your spirit is one with your parents, and this connection will merge with the loving relationship you have with Meeko. Your grandmother wanted you to find a man who would love you enough to break the bondage of abandonment that lives in your heart. She always knew Sam's death would bring you home to get married. She told me that when this happened I was to tell you the complete story of your early life."

Shung' took a letter from her pocket and handed it to Sunny along with Cheering Woman's pipe.

"Before you open this, listen to my words. Life is powerful and its demands are simple. A loving attitude opens the creative force that transforms desires into realities. Let this letter become the sun that will always shine through every dark cloud that comes into your life. Don't let the truth about Sam and your mother become your downfall."

Her hands shaking, a tearful Sunny opened the letter and read:

My Dearest Child,

I am watching you through the kitchen window as you practice with your Rope of Hope. By the time you read this letter you will have your Rope of Hope well established between your lovely ears. Sam is happy and with me, and I know as you sit with my trusted sister, you are considering marriage. I want you to finish your medicine training with Shung'. Once she has released you from this training, take the knowledge and share it with the world. Only then can you pick up my medicine pipe. Granddaughter, join her upon my blanket so both of you can smile at the beauty of life as a bonded family. Listen to her wise words, and let her answers resolve your question about this marriage you are considering. Pick an apple from that old tree and we will celebrate your life's progress. I love you, Sunlit Soul, and I am with you always.

Your loving Grandmother

When Sunny finished reading the letter, she held it close to her heart, tears streaming from her eyes. "Oh, Shung', I promise I'll complete my medicine training with you if you can forgive me for my insanity."

"Cheering Woman loved and protected you like no other. She kept your illegitimate birth hidden because she didn't want you to be exposed to an unforgiving society."

"I can understand my grandmother's actions, but I still don't understand why my real mother would abandon me. Who is she?"

"Her name is Anna Archer."

Sunny's eyes widened in disbelief that this famous woman was half Indian. "How can this be?"

"What difference does it make? You can't prove anything. That's why my name is on your birth certificate even though you're not my daughter."

Sunny pulled away from Shung' in disgust. One stupid secret had created such turmoil in her life! In frustration, she paced around the apple tree, trying to diffuse her anger.

"With all that success, she could at least have gotten in touch with me. Shung', I will find her, and I'll make damn sure she knows who I am."

"Stop this drama! Save it for the stage, where you can get paid for it. You're not going to do anything of the sort. Now, sit down and shut your mouth until I finish my story."

Sunny sat, her face still openly defiant. But she remained silent, knowing if she said one word, she would be told to leave without learning the rest of the story. Shung' relaxed, then continued.

"Cheering Woman never attended a white school, but in her thirteenth winter she became the wife of a white school teacher. During their marriage, they had eleven children, and after his death she never remarried or mentioned his name again. Subsequently, her children left the reservation to live in the white world never to return or recognize their Indian heritage. For many years my sister was destroyed by this heartache.

"Sam was still a baby when your grandmother decided to pick up her medicine pipe and become a Sundancer. From that day forward on every summer solstice she danced to the rhythm of the Sundance drums. In time, the sound of her voice was like a melodic flute that carried truth. Cheering Woman devoted her life to serving *Wakan Tanka*, and people today still speak of her medicine achievements.

"I admired my older sister, but in my youth had no interest in her ways. Even so, when I fell in love, I asked her for a potion to keep Eddie's love forever. She gave me some elk hoof powder and told me to sprinkle it over his food. Anyway, Eddie is still around, and now I'm going to give you the powder so you can scatter it over your man's food." Shung' playfully handed her an old leather pouch. Sunny looked skeptically at the gift, although she was delighted to have any potion from Cheering Woman.

Seeing Sunny was more receptive, Shung' probed deeper into her intentions toward Meeko. "Sunny, I hope you have considered what you want from this man and what you have to share with him. Every relationship is a challenge that brings difficulties. Ask yourself if you want this relationship bad enough to trust it during troubled times and if you are loving enough to rebuild your marriage should it fall. Question why you might be looking for someone outside of yourself to fulfill your needs. Never think that marriage to this man is going to be a bed of roses. Remember, all roses have thorns."

"He's the opposite of Sam. I like his gentleness and sensitivity. He's very intelligent and we can communicate on most things. I know he loves me, and wants me as his wife."

"It sounds like you are needy, Sunny. If you expect this man to fulfill your needs, you will be destroyed. Search further within before making this decision. Also search above for messages from the winged ones, the sun, the moon and the stars. Go back. Reclaim the seeds of integrity your grandmother planted long ago. Let her words take root in your mind and grow with the strength of your soul's inner beauty before you demand a birthing from those seedlings. Happiness can never grow from a soul filled with anger and hate.

"Your grandmother always said that we are like sparkling jewels made from spiritual energy. She believed that everyone should walk in honor and appreciate the gifts given by *Wakan Tanka*. She taught you that Mother Earth was created through beauty, harmony and balance. She dreamed that you would train the children of tomorrow, and I see no way for you to escape this destiny."

"I think you are wrong! Grandmother knew I couldn't be involved with both medicine and a career."

"That so? Sunny, you remind me of your grandmother's walking cane—beautiful yet so rigid. Try instead to understand the power that comes from the bending willow tree. Let the sun warm your heart so that your soul can reflect its real beauty. I won't allow you to escape into this marriage before freeing yourself from the anger of your past."

"I've worked hard to get where I am, and I will not give up my career to become a medicine woman."

"You can't do anything in life if you continue to let hate and fear rule you! You must accept your past experiences as a useful lesson, rather than seeing yourself as a victim of life. In reality, nobody gives a shit. I believe your maneuvering between the red and white races is causing a conflict of principles. Remember, the woman who rocked your cradle made you a courageous warrioress, giving you strength, self-respect and self-confidence. Your grandmother's love made you who you are today. I suggest you mend your crippled emotions so you can avoid destroying your future.

"Sunny, reflect on the illusionary pictures of you that have appeared on billboards and try to see how you feed the masses with your deceptive masks! That woman of false power is not the woman who stands before me. You have never run from a battle before, so why are you running from Medicine now?"

"Shung' you know nothing about the price I've paid for my lifestyle! When I went on the road with my show, my lonely hours were filled with hard-bodied men. I would pick one up and use him for sex and romance. When it was time for me to return to work, I wouldn't even remember his name. Shung', I was never a hooker, but I was spoiled by rich men. The game was simple—they wanted a beautiful woman on their arm to impress their cronies. I've been engaged to several men at one time. I even had a black velvet box filled with engagements rings each tagged by their names. But now I want to marry for love. I truly believe I'll be happy with Meeko."

"I know more than you think. You don't know how to love anyone. You've punished every man that has ever come into your life because of Sam. You're like a coyote! Your romantic charm tricks them into your trap and sex keeps them at your beck and call. And you don't give a damn who you hurt.

"You make me so angry when I think of the good life your loving grandmother gave you. But all you ever do is throw it away. Just remember, it was my sister who made you see the beauty in all things, and it was she who wove you from a blanket of beauty. I won't allow you to dishonor any of her efforts with your stupid lifestyle! So, trust what you were taught and learn to walk your talk!"

Sunny knew she had crossed Shung's boundaries. "Shung', I don't want to fight with you. I just want to live my life without your interference. I'm not good enough to be Medicine."

"With your low morals and bad attitude, I agree that you are not worthy of being Medicine. Sometimes I feel a contempt toward you that is just about equal to the scorn you hold for yourself. But we both know that Cheering Woman saw no value in judging another. I say you've got to get back to your spiritual traditions before you can even learn Medicine. Now, get yourself ready for a sweat. Maybe the sincerity in your prayers will release the demons of distrust clawing at your heart."

Silent but furious, Sunny hated what Shung' was putting her through and went for a walk to think of a way to remove the veil that now separated them. She kicked a stone in exasperation and thought of leaving, never to return. Instead she went to the apple tree to relive the moments when Cheering Woman had come to console her after her death and the numerous times she had saved her from Shung's wrath. Sunny knew that Shung' had spoke the truth but feared that she would demand her to study Medicine and postpone the marriage. What she hoped for was to marry Meeko and pursue Medicine without conflict.

Sunny returned late, stripped off her clothes and bent down to enter the *Inipi*. Shung' smiled as she knelt and pressed her face in the dirt, praying for understanding before crawling in on all fours. As the hot stones were placed one by one in the altar, Sunny immediately saw spirit faces in them.

After the third round, Shung' whispered, "I see the night sun is starting to warm your heart. Sunny, this sweat must heal whatever has come between us. Your anger and confusion come from the sadness of Sam's death and the heartbreaking ways of your past." Shung' motioned for the Fire Chief to drop the flap on the last round. Then darkness bathed them with a certain peace as Sunny listened to Shung's ongoing prayers and chants.

Sunny fervently begged *Tunka'shila* to purify her thoughts. "Oh, *Wakan Tanka*, let your breath of steam rid me of this confusion," she prayed as Shung' poured dipper after dipper of water over the stones. Sunny inhaled deeply and felt the heat melt through the shield of her closed mind. "Oh, *Tunka'shila*, I fear that I can no longer respond to life without your help. Great Spirit, I fear losing myself. Give me the strength to understand this strange emotion called love."

When the flap was lifted on the final round, Shung' and Sunny sat for a long time in the *Inipi* quietly talking. "Shung', I saw Cougar in the glowing stones during every round. She is the one that has walked with me since I was a child. I need to talk with you about my latest experience with this cat."

"Yes, I saw her. She's telling you to detach from your emotional guilt and accept all that you are."

"After Sam's funeral, I went to the mountains to gain a better understanding of why his death affected me so much. I was sitting by the campfire drumming and chanting, when I traveled to another world and found that Black Cougar was still walking with me. It was she who gave me the power of solitude. It was Cougar who taught me to build my mental strength and kill off my inner enemies. Over the years I've become too comfortable with her, and now I no longer feel deep emotion for anyone but Meeko.

"But that night on the mountain, she stayed far away in the beginning and paced around the outer rim of the campsite. Slowly she moved in closer, instructing me to hold a gold chain that was hanging around her neck. She told me not to look at her. At first she purred loudly, then let out a bloodcurdling scream and lunged onto my back. Her claws penetrated my lower spine in slow motion, leaving large puncture marks. She gently licked my wounds and we merged as one into a white cougar.

"I found myself standing on a narrow pathway looking up at a vibrating mountain of energy that supported a huge gold-white mansion with a bright blue roof. A voice spoke, saying, 'You have awakened upon a difficult path. The climb will be dangerous. It will take great courage to accomplish your earthly mission. If you accept this brave undertaking you will walk along the edges of the abyss. You will learn the epitome of a mortal life, bringing you one step closer to your release from the never-ending cycle of life and death.' Shung', Grandmother once told me that someday I would know Cougar. It seems that cat always walks on my mind when I'm in trouble and stays with me until the experience comes to an end."

"Well, well, Granddaughter, it seems you've been blessed with a very complicated gift. It is a great honor to be touched by her power. Cougar demands that you have commitment and control over your emotions before she will let you walk with her on the Medicine pathway."

"Shung', I'm not capable of doing that. I fear if I try and screw up, I could lose my mind."

"If this insane fear is your quest, so be it. Why don't you devote the time to developing your ability to join the spirit of Cougar and let her speak through your actions? Granddaughter, always listen to Cougar. Whether your feelings are bad or good, let her know that you are willing to control your emotions to gain the heart of Cougar." Shung' reached over and patted Sunny's hand. "I'll help you understand that which cannot be explained by the spoken word. Someday Cougar will purr from deep inside of you, then you'll see the importance of shape-shifting."

As they left the *Inipi*, Shung's face held a worried look. She was concerned about what Sunny was going through, but at the same time she was happy that a peace now rested between them. Hand in hand they walked to the house, feeling happy over their shared experience. Shung' made coffee and both sat at the kitchen table with steaming mugs in hand, ready to begin a teacher-student relationship.

"Shung', can you shape-shift?"

Appalled, Shung' answered coldly, "Never ask me such a thing again! You know if I answer you, I could lose my power." Quickly changing the subject, she added, "Let's talk about the building blocks of a shape-shifter. They must see everything as a box with many mirrored sides so they will not get lost in a cube of their own destructive reflections, never to return."

"What do you mean by boxes, cubes and mirrors?"

"My word, girl! You can't be that simpleminded! If you become captured by a problem and cannot make the proper decision to fix it, then you're in a box and have no space to grow. To get out of the box, or problem, you must climb onto the line of infinity which travels upward from the center of all things! Take any problem that needs to be resolved between two people and see it as an upside down triangle. Place the problem on the top. That is the line of negotiation. Place yourself on one of the lines going down and the other person on the other line. With integrity, you both can then walk toward the connecting point of the triangle to resolve the problem. Just like we did in the *Inipi*."

"Shung', I'm not following you."

Aggravated with Sunny's lack of knowledge, Shung' grabbed three sticks and formed an inverted triangle on the table. "Look at the space in the center. Space equals width, length and height in our three-dimensional world. Look at the top of the triangle as the East-West Door. See how the two lines come together in a point? If we look at the completed triangle, we have one in three, or three in one. Now consider the space inside the triangle again. It directs everything toward a common goal and that is the completion. That's how you work out a problem between two people."

"I see. If two people can negotiate without emotional harshness across the top line, then they can agree to walk toward a common goal. Is that your triangle?"

"Yes," Shung' replied. "What is above is below, and everything is birthed from sacred mathematics. Cougar says to disconnect from all your emotions and never allow another to use your feelings of insecurity to manipulate and harm you. For example, if I wanted to experience a heartfelt love but allowed someone to use this love selfishly against me, then eventually my love for them would be destroyed."

"Are you telling me I need to go back and learn time, space, matter, dimension and measure again?"

"Yes, but before I agree to train you as an apprentice, you must know who you are and bring me your pipe properly filled along with tobacco, sage, cedar and sweetgrass. Only then will I consider becoming your *Unci*."

"Shung', I will do that. I want you to know that I accept you as a strong medicine woman and I would like to become an apprentice under you."

"Sunny, women are very powerful. The reason I hesitate in teaching them medicine is because they are too squirrelly and can turn into bad medicine. If I accept you as my pupil, know I will always ask more from you than you are willing to give. I'll challenge you beyond your wildest imagination. But if you get good enough to step onto the Medicine pathway with me and do not complete your journey, I'll dismiss you and allow you to destroy yourself. Are you sure you still want to become an apprentice of mine?"

Threatened by the challenge in Shung's words, Sunny answered, "Yes. I want to become an apprentice and I hope someday to become equal to your power."

"Humph! That'll be a cold day. I've forgotten more than your pea brain will ever know. You've been away from the old ways a long time. What you're asking from me will be very difficult to accomplish. It irritates me that you've allowed your mind to become lazy. By now, I would've expected you to have mastered your cougar vision. With all the training that your grandmother gave you about Cougar, why do you continue to use the bad side of its power? That big cat doesn't lay around in a tree all day sleeping. It kills, eats, lives, dies and has perfect timing. She shows no emotion and never justifies her actions. Cougars see what they want and take it!"

Sunny knew and accepted that Shung' would force-feed her until she accepted the old traditional teachings. Listening to her heart, she went to her room, returned with her filled pipe and sat submissively before Shung'.

"*Unci*, I want to return to the old ways. I promise to do as you ask."

"Sunny, I've always dreaded this day. I would rather have you as part of my family than a student. I'm not sure I want to give up as much time that will be needed to train you. Before I smoke your pipe, tell me, can you still run with Wolf?" Shung' lit a piece of sage to clean the vibrations before listening to Sunny's response.

"Sometimes, but mostly Wolf comes with bared teeth to warn me of trouble. The last time I ran as Wolf was six months ago. I awakened one morning in my hotel room and saw what I at first thought was a dog standing next to my bed. I called the front desk to have it removed, but when I opened the door to let the bellman in, it vanished. I offered some feeble excuse about dreaming, but I was not dreaming! Wolf was there!"

"Is that the only time Wolf came?" questioned Shung' with uneasiness.

"No. Two years ago, a pilot friend dropped me off in Canada so I could spend some time alone. I rented a cabin near the wilderness and spent most of my time roaming through the woods. One day I noticed a black timber wolf following me at a distance. I began leaving food along the trail until I got her to follow me back to the cabin. Eventually she came inside, and within a few days she let me touch her. What amazed me most was how she sensed that I was going to be leaving. The day before I left she vanished, and I never saw her again.

"That wolf still walks in my dreams. Sometimes she warns me of danger and other times we run and play. She taught me to dig the mandrake root and told me it was used to shape-shift. I ate it and became Wolf. I loved the strength I felt as I hunted with the pack and the taste of warm blood after a kill. Lately she's been coming into my dreams and ripping out the throat of a short, fat, balding man. I join her in the kill, and we eat from his chest cavity. I can hear the sound of bones crushing. This frightens me to the point where I can't sleep for weeks."

"Well, Little Rabbit, it seems Wolf is teaching you to kill your fears. Fear is self-destructive, which makes me ask, are you the predator or the prey in your life?" questioned Shung' with grave concern.

"I believe I'm becoming a predator, but I really don't know. While I was in the mountains after Sam's death, I had a scary vision. I became a member of a pack of seven wolves and three puppies. I heard wolves howling all around us and we hurried into a den. As I transformed back into human, I heard a loud blast and felt a searing heat coming from the walls of the den. I crawled to the entrance and saw the air was on fire and everything was dying from suffocation. I saw animals running blindly, their flesh falling from their bodies as though they were being burned from the inside out. Then their bodies exploded, leaving only skeletons.

In terror, I crawled deep inside the cave with the pack. The leader placed three puppies under my stomach and told me I was to raise them as a means of rebuilding the wolf race. Then I heard a voice say, 'You are watching things to come.' The voice promised to keep me safe if I would eat from the mandrake plant and the tannis root."

"Sunny, Cheering Woman often spoke of these plants. Mandrake is a hypnotic plant and tannis root restores general health and prolongs life. It was once used for embalming the dead. Some medicine people still use these plants to cast spells and to gain sexual favors. If mixed properly they will open the mind, but if mixed incorrectly they will kill you.

"Oh, Sunny, the spirits are talking too loud for us to ignore them. I too have seen a great earth war and the return of the star people," added Shung' reluctantly. She picked up Sunny's pipe, asking, "Did you load this pipe for the marriage or was it for learning?"

"Both." Sunny's voice was pleading.

Shung' went to the Sundance Circle to smoke the pipe. Sunny followed, knowing Shung' was asking the spirit world for validation of her dreams. She believed in Shung's medicine, but disliked her strict demands. Shung' was very impatient and Sunny knew it would be difficult to accept her as a medicine teacher without comparing her to Cheering Woman.

After two more days of intense questioning, Shung' accepted Sunny as an apprentice and agreed to perform the marriage ceremony.

Sunny felt she could now communicate her intimate concerns to Shung' and told her about her female problems. "When I went to live with Sam he beat me badly, causing internal injuries. I've hesitated to get married because I can't have children. But I haven't told Meeko."

Shung' motioned Sunny to follow her to the fire pit, where she asked her to stand naked over the low flames. Then as they discussed the problem further, she placed many herbs in the fire which created much healing smoke. With her bare hands, Shung' reached into the fire and picked up a live coal. "What do you see in this coal?"

Sunny took it hesitantly and bounced it in her hand. "I don't see anything." She quickly dropped the coal and checked her palm for a burn mark.

Shung' angrily put the hot coal into her mouth and held it there for a moment, then spit it into Sunny's hand. "Why do you always expect others to give you your answers? It's you who believes in confusion and fear, not me! Get out of your head and into your heart long enough to read the coal. Didn't my sister promise that love would come to you and the man would look from behind prison bars before you ever met him? You've always known this soul, and you should know he doesn't want children. He's here on the pretense of helping you with your birth purpose, but in reality he lives his life to benefit himself."

"You're wrong. He loves me like no other, and will always place me first in his life. Shung', I know he doesn't have a selfish bone in his body."

"That so? Are you telling me this is his truth, or your illusion? Sunny, I hate your stupidity. You, my dear one, wear a magnificent crown of total idiocy. Maybe someday you will relinquish this crown of wolf shit and have the sense to pass it on to your successor. The Red Road is long and narrow, but it is your choice to turn right or left at any fork. You don't have to walk off a cliff just because it's there! Now, stop walking in blindness and listening with deaf ears!"

"Why is it that no matter what I say, you must find something wrong?" shot back Sunny.

"Because you're walking proof that you are an arrogant, stupid, helpless female. Why can't you feel your festering inner fears? Why not embrace the rain, and like the little blue mountain flower, know when it is spring and time to grow again from the life-giving soil of experience? The gift of life is for women too, not just for men, and many women have not had children or wanted them. These times demand that we women walk to a different drumbeat.

"Look around you. Where is the person who will give you the opportunity to have a good life? Look at the old people who live a life of poverty. See the children who are in need of food, clothing and a place to live. Look at the throwaway fetal alcohol babies that are born every year and all the teenagers who commit suicide or spend their lives going in and out of detox centers. Look at all the failed marriages on this reservation and the high number of our people leaving for the cement jungles of the city.

"Sunny, we are becoming an invisible race. Without our braids and buckskins, our songs will soon be dead, along with the elders. The Indian's hell is beyond whitey's imagination. Don't you realize there is no place to go in this country and be an Indian?

"I remember as a child, there was great love among our people, but today that sense of kinship is less evident. Sometimes the jealousies Indians have for their own brothers and sisters reminds me of crabs. If you put one in a bucket, it'll get out. But if you put two in a bucket, one will crawl to the top while the other will inevitably pull it back down. Sometimes I wonder if we've lost so much of our own language that we actually believe English words express a truth. If we continue following the white man's ways, we'll live alone with no families because we too will be afraid to touch life.

"I worry that the system is making you a wizard of bullshit. Taking responsibility for your life demands courage. You will find it in silence and solitude. You are so headstrong, sometimes I think Creator kissed you with a lightning bolt. I pray the day will come that you can harness this energy and use it to fulfill your life's destiny."

Overwhelmed by Shung's words, Sunny's eyes filled with tears. "Stop feeling sorry for yourself! Learn to fly, *Sku'ya*, and your magic will take you far from all the clouds of doubt. We humans gather our true identity from our souls. Turn to the fire within and learn to warm yourself so your power can be shared with others. Open your eyes, and touch the magic in all things. When you venture to other worlds, you must spiral upward with Eagle to infinity. Ride with the wind, and take its messages to your heart. Become your own best friend. Never suppress who you are and let *Wakan Tanka* guide you to accomplish your birth purpose.

"Do you remember Cheering Woman always said there is no such thing as loneliness if a person has the courage to accept the strength that comes from having close family ties. Such courage is what once made warriors and warrioresses. They knew that loneliness would make them weak and they could not fight an honorable battle with loneliness as their weapon.

"You must be very careful, *Sku'ya*, not to let the cities capture you with their false gifts of money and fame. Many who have gone to search for these gifts have lost their hearts to alcohol and drugs. Tomorrow you will join me in an important meeting. Now, let's go to bed."

The following morning Shung' and Sunny went to the tribal council meeting. Sunny was surprised to see a woman as head of council and asked, "When did this happen?"

"You'd better learn the power of being a woman, or you'll turn into a squawking Magpie," said Shung', chuckling. "Humph, you've lived with white people far too long. You've forgotten how to think like a Sioux woman. A woman must become a powerful warrioress. When an obstacle is put in her path, she must take a good look at herself and her lack of knowledge. It takes a strong woman to be a leader, and we Sioux train our women to become leaders. As an *Eyeska*, breed, you can slip through enemy lines without anyone knowing, and walk comfortably between cultures. Creator made you with lighter skin and hazel eyes so you could serve all races."

That afternoon on their way to the airport to pick up Meeko, Shung' lit a cigar and puffed contentedly.

"Sunny, we women need to join as one sisterhood to fight the corruption thrown on the pathway of our younger generations. I have long known, and many others have dreamed, that someday you would return to become a strong warrioress and help our people open doors. Through your career you can get us media exposure so all the races will hear our story and support our rights."

"I can't promise I'll be able to do that, but I'm willing to offer my support if I am kept informed of your goals."

At the airport terminal, Shung' knocked ashes from her cigar as she watched Meeko embrace Sunny and give her a warm kiss. Shung' hung back suspiciously as Meeko picked up his bags.

"And this must be Shung'?" he asked.

Shung' nodded curtly and continued to ignore him. After lunch they dropped him off at Shadowhawk's with the promise he would join them for dinner.

"Don't like him. I've heard of his people," grumbled Shung' as they shopped for the evening meal.

"Oh, Shung', you've just met him. I promise, he's not like you think," answered Sunny, hoping that in time Shung' would accept Meeko.

Shung' bought her special sweets and was in a better mood as they drove home. She built a fire in the wood stove and cooked the evening meal while Sunny set the table. A knock sounded at the door and Shung' opened it. She grunted as Meeko submissively entered and handed Sunny a freshly picked bouquet of wildflowers.

"Humph, where'd you get the posies?"

"Oh, I stopped by a friend's, and picked them from his field." Taking no notice of Shung's sarcasm, Meeko smiled and handed her a beautifully carved statue of a wolf.

Shung' grunted a feeble thank you and motioned with her chin toward the place where he was to sit at her dinner table. After the blessing was given for the food and the day, Sunny fixed a plate of food for Shung', placed it in front of her and waited for Medicine to take the first bite.

Shung' made a clockwise circle around her plate with her hand, saying, "Body take what you need and get rid of the rest." Shung' remained quiet during the meal and upon finishing, lit her happy pipe and leaned back in her seat with a cup of coffee to study Meeko. At last she spoke.

"You, being Nakota, came to marry a Dakota woman. We Dakota believe love is life, and to understand its meaning, we believe love is best expressed through another's spiritual growth. Love rests in every life force whether it be a stone, flower, tree, animal or star."

"I totally agree. I want to walk by her side and support all of her endeavors. *Unci*, I love this woman more than life itself. I feel honored that she has accepted my proposal and happy that you are willing to marry us in the old way. I promise I will always honor this as a sacred marriage."

"We'll see, Grandson, we'll see. We are Dakota, which means 'friend' to some and 'enemy' to others. We sometimes recognize the sign of Snake in another, and I think you have Snake power. What do you do with a snake, Nakota man?"

Meeko shrugged his shoulders, not knowing what Shung' was getting at.

"Well, we bite off its head and eat it, then use its skin for a belt. I suggest you keep in mind my granddaughter will continue her work without any interference from you or this marriage. Sunny is a breed, trained to serve. That is our way!"

"What can I do to assure you that I will honor her and her work, along with our marriage?"

"Only time has those answers. We'll speak again at sunrise tomorrow." Shung' motioned Sunny to her room as she escorted Meeko to the door.

Early the next morning in the *Inipi*, Sunny and Meeko expressed their beliefs in answer to Shung's questions. She wove each one into a web of sharing and spoke long about the possibilities of the relationship unraveling.

After the sweat, Shung' sent Sunny and Meeko on a long walk to discuss the possibilities of a failed marriage. When they returned, both felt confident that their marriage would last and would be an example for others to follow.

When Sunny awoke the following morning, she still believed that Meeko was the man she wanted to share her life with. Exhilarated by the crisp coolness of the morning air, she went in search of Shung', who was leaning over an open fire pit stirring a large pot of boiled meat and potatoes. Sunny's smile was bright as she greeted Shung'.

"I see your relationship with this man has rekindled your soul. There is a sparkle in your eyes that shouts happiness. Hold this dream inside and embrace its beauty. Now, join me in welcoming the morning sun while we listen to nature create the tone of another beautiful day. Listen well, *Sku'ya*. Make sure you can hear the subtle notes of *Maka Ina's* song."

"Are you saying musical notes help form my feelings?"

"Like the crystal clarity of a mountain stream." Shung' smiled warmly, handing her a bowl filled with water. "Use this as a mirror to look inside yourself and see your future. Ask yourself if you have the courage to face the upcoming changes that are about to enter your life. If you see something you don't like, then don't give it room in this new marriage. Hold passion in your heart for what you want changed and let this passion mold your future."

Sunny sat under the old apple tree with the bowl, smiling as she saw the sun's rays turn the water into sparkling rainbow-colored diamonds. She looked at her engagement ring and recalled Cheering Woman's scolding words when, as a child, she had dropped a gunnysack filled with coal and it had ripped open.

"Granddaughter! What have you done? Do you realize that you have spilled precious potential diamonds all over the ground? Don't you know that it takes much time for coal to become what it is? It starts its life as a leaf on a tree, and once the leaf dies, it lays still for eons, packed into the bowels of Mother Earth. That poor dying leaf had to learn about time, pressure and heat before it could be transformed into coal. Think of the miracles that transpired as it waited hidden in the ground until all of its relatives meshed together as one hard stone. Then many more eons of time, heat, cutting and polishing made this beauty into a sparkling stone.

"Someday, Granddaughter, you will happily recognize this piece of coal when your love places it on your finger. Everyone will call it a diamond, but we both know that it's just a wise piece of coal. Remember, everything including a diamond, has a spirit and will gladly supply you with the tools to find answers. As the diamond, life takes time, pressure and polish for a human soul to shine as bright. When you learn the depth of all things in life, you will know truth without struggle."

Sunny knew in time she would find many answers in this simple bowl of water. She considered whether her carefree lifestyle would change in marriage and concluded it would not. Then with apprehension she thought about how she might be confined by the conformities of marriage, and wondered if Meeko felt the same.

Sunny left the comfort of the apple tree and found Meeko who had just arrived and joined a study group under the arbor waiting for Shung's arrival. Shung' sat down with her coffee in hand and began.

"We're going to discuss how to redirect sexual energy. Abstaining from sex is a great opportunity to learn self-discipline. I laugh at you insecure women who fear your sisters will sexually steal your man, knowing all along that he is controlled by his little pee-pee. Women, you can enjoy sex but your spiritual growth is far more important than allowing the three inches of limp skin hanging between his legs to rule you. Personally, I find younger men easier to train and they have better stay power.

"To me, going without sex is a choice that lets you redirect that energy to higher spiritual powers. At times everyone should learn how to harness their sexual drive and use its energy to build power over their physical needs. This kind of control stops fears and depression which are usually created by an unhealthy relationship with yourself.

This gift to Self allows you to focus on empowering your spirit and stops sexual energy from controlling your life. When you learn to control your sexual drive, instead of letting it control you, this intense primitive energy can be diverted to its purest form. When this energy is transformed and used only by the mind to control your emotions and physical body, you can connect to a higher spiritual growth.

"Pure energy washes the spirit clean, and only then can you erase the bondage of sexual entrapments. I believe in crushing all harmful actions into dust and letting them settle elsewhere. Let Great Spirit weave your lives beyond your animal needs. Find a spider web and study the builder. Grandmother Spider teaches the sacred language, but she also kills and eats the male after mating. Tonight I call upon her to weave my words into your fate and establish the laws of sexual energy that hold most of your lives together." Shung' closed the lesson with a prayer.

After the lesson, Meeko and Sunny followed Shung' into the house, hoping to discuss their upcoming marriage ceremony. Sunny fixed Shung' a plate of food, then sat quietly waiting for her to finish her meal. When Shung lit her happy pipe, Sunny knew she was ready to speak about their marriage.

"Both of you want this wedding, but you also fear it like an animal with its foot already caught in a steel trap. Your fear of commitment is the trap and it has been created from your past disappointments at others breaking their trust with you. Such thinking has stopped your spirits from soaring free. Both of you have roamed through life sharing in many relationships without accepting responsibility for those relationships. I suggest you take apart all these traps and learn the value of a lifelong commitment.

"Meeko, I know you love this woman, but I also believe you are in love with her abilities. Both of you should understand that few women are able to fully use medicine power. Like Sunny, some refuse to recognize it exists. My sister taught Sunny the freedom of woman power from childhood. If you truly love Sunny, you will encourage her to complete her training in Medicine before the marriage, for then you will know if you can stand by such a strong woman. The power I'm speaking of can never be controlled by another, but it can be shared if there is an understanding of what it takes to become a medicine woman. Meeko, if you do this my way, both of your spirits will remain free and someday your souls will merge into one."

Meeko felt intimidated by the presence of this powerful woman. "I believe you, Shung'. I know you require all your women to develop their power. I know this is important to a marriage because a woman is the foundation for a man. Woman is the life-giver, as is Mother Earth. I would be appalled if Sunny did not stand up to me and demand her rights as a woman. In fact, how could I love a woman that would give up her power to become the property of a man? In this marriage, Sunny and I will be equal. Shung', I want no other by my side."

Shung studied Meeko closely before responding cautiously.

"Meeko, your boyish charms do not blind this old woman. Remember, once I perform this spiritual ceremony, it will be for life. I believe when two people come together to make one relationship, there are many things to consider. Marriage is a learning process, but as I've said before, real love means the spiritual growth of another. Learning to love another is our hardest lesson in life. No matter what you feel at this moment, there will be times when you will cause each other great sorrow. I fear such times could overwhelm both of you. The oneness of a relationship creates goodness for all concerned and it cannot be based on deception and confusion, if it is to work.

"If you step upon this pathway without these considerations, you will surely walk the Black Road of misery and destruction. Look beyond yourselves and asked yourself if you have examined this relationship close enough to build the beauty that is demanded in a good marriage. The gift of a spiritual marriage ceremony must serve the relationship with dignity. I ask you to look at this marriage through spirit eyes before you make your final decision.

"During a terrible thunderstorm while I was young and stupid, I went to speak with a medicine man to make me a perfect marriage. When I got there, he was too busy to see me, and I waited in the pouring rain for hours before he invited me in, asking, 'Why did you stand in the rain when you could have taken shelter under a tree? Did you not hear the silence of the birds' voices as the Thunderbeings began to speak of the coming downpour? Did you not hear the warning of the winds just before the rains began to fall? Aren't these sounds the many voices of *Wakan Tanka*? Being one of his children, did you not know you would get wet in the rain?' Smiling, he handed me a towel and said, 'Use this, you're getting my floor wet,' then offered me a seat.

"Realizing my excitement had overruled my common sense, I lowered my head in embarrassment for getting his floor wet. Here I was, brazenly speaking to this knowledgeable man without considering anything except myself. Now I ask, are you two standing in the rain, or are you thinking that you can take shelter in the love that you are offering to each other?

"My children, you speak of love, yet neither of you know anything about the music of your own body's harmony. Are your spirits in tune with this marriage? Think of the drum and the flute. Are they not proof that we all have a personal sound that expresses our life? So, what is this music that rests between the two of you? Is the harmony strong enough to keep you from flying away from each other in times of trouble? Also consider this. If love is a gift created from shared feelings, then why does a bad marriage become as heavy as an overfilled backpack during a hard day of mountain climbing? I hope you both can adjust to the extra emotional baggage that each of you are bringing to this joining."

"That's not the way I feel, Shung'. I think of love as a flowing river. If we go with the flow instead of swimming upstream, then we will never tire of each other," rebutted Meeko, fearful that Shung' would separate them like a fork in a river.

"I don't care what you think, Meeko. Remember, I know your people. I remember when you were about three years old and pissed on my friend's best dress. Is that what you mean when you say go with the flow? Personally, I think I'd be happier sitting on the shore, watching all you Nakotas float by just in case some of you still couldn't control your bladders!"

Meeko's face reddened with embarrassment, knowing it was useless to banter with this old woman. It was beneath his warrior spirit and he'd be damned before he would let her make a spectacle of him.

"Meeko, when you find me no longer irritating but instead amusing, you will have learned to read people rather than listening to their disguised words. When you become as old as I am, I hope you'll be smart enough to understand the impact of a Coyote's clever words. I enjoy battling your arrogance because I know you couldn't find your way through a snowstorm in your own back yard," chuckled Shung'.

"Meeko, I'll play your game. How does Wolf, Cougar or Bear kill a deer?" asked Shung'. But before he could answer, she added, "Think of the weakness of the victim, asshole. Now, what animal should you have known before trying to persuade my feelings to fold under your control?"

Wanting to say more, but knowing Shung' would never back down from her challenge, Meeko quickly apologized for his bad manners.

Shung' smiled, then leaned back in her chair knowing she had won another round. "Little boy, separate love and games; otherwise you will give yourself only emptiness and never have room to hold a joyous moment in your life. Your mind is a wonderful thing if you use it wisely as a storehouse of information. Quit trying to outsmart me, and learn where to place your feet in my presence. Express the truth that is inside of you, not all this snake oil bullshit. I already know about your life. I still say both of you should break this engagement that is made out of need and fear. If you pick up a stone and go into it, then you and the stone will have made a connection. A true marriage is the same as with the stone, communicating without words.

"Love is not shown in words it is shown in actions. Love lives in every life force. Love can never be confused when it comes from the heart. Love can speak through a tree, flower or stone. You both must free yourselves from the past griefs that are still buried deep inside of you, otherwise, this marriage will become all the pain and sorrow gathered from those yesteryears."

"But I have fixed all my problems," bragged Meeko.

"Meeko, please, you're talking to Medicine," begged Sunny, embarrassed by his bravado.

"Oh, shush, Sunny. The two of you remind me of the time I watched a little worm turn into a caterpillar, then spin a cocoon to finally appear as a beautiful butterfly. When it emerged its wings were wet, but the butterfly knew if it was to live, it must keep its wings moving in the air until they were dry.

"The beginning of any relationship is as fragile as the wings of a butterfly. There is nothing more beautiful than watching a butterfly dance gracefully from flower to flower. It tells me that life can be a wonderful experience. I see marriage as a butterfly. Surely you know to expect changes in your life when you get married, but that does not mean those changes have to be traumatic. Marriage or butterfly, they both must weather many stages in life but the butterfly also says not to take things too seriously. I want you both to take time to think of this marriage as the life of a butterfly before we discuss this any further," said Shung'. Turning to Meeko she signaled that it was time for him to leave.

Sunny mumbled a quick good night to Meeko and hurriedly went to Shung's bedroom, only to find the door closed. Reluctantly she went to her room and crawled into bed, and there she lay replaying the hurtful sparring match between her medicine teacher and her future husband.

Before sunrise the following morning, Sunny went to Cheering Woman's grave to smoke her pipe. As the sun broke on the horizon, she put her pipe away knowing that whether or not the marriage took place was going to be her decision. Sunny knew Shung' was against the marriage, but she didn't appreciate her exposing Meeko's weaknesses. She was concerned that Shung' might still refuse to perform the marriage ceremony if she did not pick up the medicine bundle and fulfill her obligation to her grandmother. She left the graveside, knowing there was still much to consider. By the times she reached home, Sunny had come to the conclusion that it would be best to humor Shung'.

She saw Meeko and Shung' preparing a morning sweat and hoped they were going to make peace with each other. Grabbing her towel, she asked permission to join them in the *Inipi*. Harmony reigned during the first three rounds of the sweat. During the fourth round, Sunny heard spirit voices falling upon her soul like stars falling from the skies as she prayed humbly for the strength to pick up Cheering Woman's medicine bundle.

"Oh, *Wakan Tanka*, bless this upcoming marriage," prayed Shung', and Sunny cried with gratitude as the steam rose off the Stone People with *Tunka'shila's* breath of life.

Wolf emerged from a shapeless mass of brilliant light that spiraled upward from the stones. Everything seemed to shape-shift into another time and space as a man stood in their presence, saying, "All the great cycles are coming into full force. Even the stars will begin to shine as suns from many worlds. Observe the power that makes the world in which you live. Life is never an empty space to be filled only with illusion."

It was no surprise when everyone felt the *Inipi* shaking as Sunny spun into a violent storm crossing the plains. A voice from above spoke to Sunny's soul, "I know of the wolf bundle, and as spirit, I can see it is of much concern to you. I will come when you are ready. In time you will know me, and then I will help you fulfill your promise of long ago. I have things to teach you if you will reach beyond your three-dimensional world. Gather your balance and become one with your grandmother's bundle. Feel Great Spirit's love, so you can find the trail back to your destiny."

Sunny felt the impact of the spirit's words pulling at her soul and whimpered helplessly as she was taken to another reality. She heard soft musical tones, indicating that her learning journey with Shung' would mark the beginning of extraordinary events to come.

Embracing their personal messages from the spirit world, the three left the sweat with peace in their hearts.

After the sweat Meeko willingly gave Shung' the respect due a medicine woman. She, in return, provided him with support for the next three weeks as preparations for the wedding ceremony were completed. At one point she told him, "To cause worry in another is an inconsiderate act of manipulation that fuels resentment. When either of you has doubt, know it will eventually destroy both spirits unless you remove yourselves from the situation. In this marriage, I wonder who will become the predator and who will become the prey!"

"Shung', I consider any mental abuse incomprehensible in my relationship with Sunny. To build our relationship in a caring manner, Sunny and I must have guidelines so we will never abuse each other."

"You must keep each other informed and share all major decisions. This will give each the freedom to evaluate and solve any problem that arises. Fighting, on the other hand, brings sorrow like a shadow covering the day, and soon love becomes a lost memory.

"You know around here when our men meet a female breed with a good job, they expect her to support them. The question is, since Sunny is well to do and a breed, are you going to become a financial burden to her?"

"Shung', I don't care what she is. When we marry I expect us to share in everything. Even if she is a breed, why should I treat her any differently? I know she has a bad temper and I realize any abuse toward her will destroy the relationship. Believe me, I just want our love to grow and blossom."

"Meeko, don't go hearts and flowers on me. I want you to accept the possibility that bad things can happen. If they do, would you be able to soften the blows in the heat of battle?"

"Yes, I would! Is not the cup of sweetness stronger and safer in the hand of a trusted love? When we first joined lips, it brought happiness. I know love must be cradled in the arms of warmth and protected as a newborn soul."

"Meeko, I know you want this love to sing forever in your heart. I am asking you to shelter this joining in the arms of patience. This can only be accomplished when you understand the importance in bonding your two souls in the marriage blanket ceremony. My worry is over those things that are not fixed. I hate to see this marriage turn into agonizing pain as you struggle to survive the bitterness that you two have suffered in your young lives."

"Shung', I know you have doubts about me, but do not withdraw your permission for this marriage. We want to hold each other for life and develop fond memories to look back on in our old age.

Shung' then asked Sunny to join them.

"I want a promise from you both that your painful past will not interfere with this marriage. I want you to promise me that you'll surrender to devotion during the bad times. I want assurance that when you grow older you'll still be able to walk together in the winter snows and sit by the fires of yesterday's memories holding hands while listening to one another with an open heart. I want this marriage to birth a faith in time as your vows are renewed each spring. I want balance and sensitivity shared equally as you hear the melting snow run off the mountaintops and feed the babbling brooks below. I want you to roam the hills and valleys of your minds and share in these new thoughts. I want the warmth of summer to grow in your hearts. And when fall arrives, I want to see the harvest fill your lives with the endless fruits of your labor.

"I want to know regardless of your age, you will still run and play with the wind and let it nourish your souls. I want each of you to feed the other's soul flame with the light that shines from your eyes. And when the winters of life come, I want your joined souls to announce that you have arrived at another place still bonded in marriage as one."

"Oh, *Unci*, we both want an eternal love that sings our prayers to the stars even in our later years," affirmed Sunny, smiling radiantly.

"Shung', I promise during the bad times I will remind Sunny that we are spirit, not flesh. I will always remember your words in our twilight years when we dwell as children beneath Father Sky and give thanks to Mother Earth for the wisdom that they have shared with us," added Meeko.

"You both speak beautiful words, but as a seer, I have already seen this marriage bringing devastation to you and have warned you. That is all I have to say. We will have the ceremony as soon as things can be arranged," said Shung', hugging them both.

Early the following morning, Meeko met Sunny in the parking lot at the Bureau of Indian Affairs in Poplar, Montana to investigate the housing situation. Before heading in different directions, they agreed to meet at the café in Wolf Point around two."

When Sunny arrived at Wolf Point, the real estate agent showed her many houses for sale, but each was in a neighborhood known for its prejudice against Indians. By late afternoon, having looked at all the available properties without success, Sunny felt discouraged and waited for Meeko at the motel. When he arrived, she told him, "I've spent the whole day being rejected. I will not put up with this kind of prejudice! The better homes are owned by whites who refuse to sell to Indians. I was told the only viable options were in the Indian neighborhoods."

"Well, Sweetheart, I've found that most of my four thousand acres of Indian property is leased to the local ranchers and oil companies. The BIA superintendent and the tribal council informed me that I couldn't build on allotted land without the consent of all the allotees. And of course, such a request must also be approved by the Department of the Interior."

"We can't build on our own land, and we can't buy a house in a white neighborhood, but I heard of a place off the reservation, about a two hour drive from here. It's a two story house with ten rooms on twenty acres. It has a barn, a pool that could be enclosed and a guesthouse that could be turned into an art studio, but it's been vacant for over a year and needs remodeling. And as you know, the summers up here are short and the winters hard and long, with temperatures well below zero most of the winter."

"Well, we could spend the winters in front of a big roaring fire until summer returned," offered Meeko.

"Or we could spend the winters at the beach in California," proposed Sunny.

Discouraged, they went to speak with Shung', but she was not home. Deciding to wait for her, they took a blanket and a copy of *Title Twenty-Five*, then sat under the trees in the backyard. Using this Indian book of law they researched a way to release their reservation land. Looking closer at the Self Determination Act, both decided it would be fun to go to Washington and test its potential for freeing up Indian land.

When Shung' arrived, she suggested using a portion of her property deep in the interior of the reservation.

The next day, Sunny drove out to see the land. Almost instantly a feeling of doom crept over her, intensifying her apprehension. Glancing constantly in her rearview mirror, she suddenly saw the form of a man running close behind the car. Although she pressed the gas pedal to the floor, the figure accelerated right along with her. As she eased off the gas, it unexpectedly slammed into the rear of the car.

Sunny turned to see the silhouette of a man dressed in a trench coat, with a wide-brimmed hat pulled low over his face hovering over the trunk. She screamed with fright at the horrible sight. She drove at high speed down the lonely one-lane road trying to escape. As a huge gust of wind hit the car, it raised the brim of the demon's hat allowing her to see his face pressed against the rear window. Two red eyes glared at her from a charred face. Terror gripped her heart as she recognized the demon *Gnaski* who had possessed Sam so long ago.

Sunny screamed hysterically and fought to stay on the road while a burning heat from the demon's red eyes filled the car. She felt him crawling into her mind and knew if she was to survive she had to get to Shung'. Crying and praying as she drove at breakneck speeds, she jumped a ditch, crossed an open field and finally pulled into the yard. Once inside, she collapsed in Shung's arms, shrieking incoherently. "I saw the demon! He chased me for miles."

Shung' held her for a moment, then roughly told her, "Go smudge yourself and do not leave this house." Shung' called Meeko as Sunny's shaking hands tried to light the smudge bowl.

Meeko raced to the house and attempted to soothe Sunny, but to no avail.

"It's the same demon that Cheering Woman released from Sam long ago. I sensed something was wrong as soon as I turned onto the old highway. Then I felt something attack me when I passed the last farmhouse."

"That's where the old snow fence used to be—the old people call it the doorway to the evil world, because it's the spot where the demon disappears when he's being chased. He has never been caught, but his tracks have been found, proving his physical existence. Sunny, somehow you have gotten his attention, and he's after your soul," said Shung' with great concern.

"Oh, my God, Shung', are you sure? He walked on my mind and I saw him open his arms wide in a welcoming gesture. Then he called out, 'Welcome, my child. You belong to me!'"

"Yes, that proves he's touched you. Whenever he's seen by someone on the reservation, a horrible death will occur or a large fire will burn down a dwelling. We must find the right people and do a strong ceremony to free you. If it doesn't work, I want you to leave this reservation and never return." Shung' motioned Meeko and Sunny to follow her to the car.

At Gramma Spottedhorse's house, Shung' explained everything and then asked Sunny to repeat her experience. Gramma listened carefully, then said,

"This is very bad. The demon does not attack unless someone has made a deal with him. It sounds like someone very close to you has done so and offered you up as payment. What surprises me is that he generally finds his victims around bars. He loves dancing with drunk women, and I've heard that many of them have given birth to his soulless children."

"My father was once possessed by this demon," cried Sunny.

Gramma looked up and shook her head in despair as tears of sorrow slowly rolled down her cheeks, dripping from her wrinkled chin.

"No way in hell will I let him steal her soul!" shouted Shung'. "Grandson, go bring Shadowhawk to me. You'll find him down on D Street visiting relatives!" Meeko left quickly without question.

After moments of silence, Gramma said, "What you are about to do is good, Shung'. You have made a wise decision. Perhaps the two of you can save the soul the demon is trying to capture. We should've stopped them from performing that Sun Dance over in Frazer seventy years ago. I clearly remember four people died after that summer solstice ceremony. The old ones should have stopped that stupid medicine man. He's the one that left that evil door open. Because of his ignorance, we must all suffer while the demon continues to grow stronger. He gets his power by feeding on weak souls and is already so strong he can take a physical form. Shung', I'm afraid he's already too powerful for any mortal to fight. I fear that evil door will never be closed. Look at how he controls our people through their need for alcohol and drugs. He's the reason we had to build those detox centers."

Meeko returned minutes later, the crunch of his tires bringing their conversation to an abrupt halt. Shadowhawk entered and sat in front of Sunny, saying, "Don't worry, I know about this demon, but what I can't understand is why he's attacking you."

"He's coming through either Meeko or Sam," answered a sullen-faced Shung'.

Everyone starred at Meeko in disbelief as Shadowhawk said, "Listen very carefully, Meeko. This demon has attempted to destroy you many times. Are you tempting your fate in any way?"

"If you're asking, am I drinking again, the answer is no. If you're asking, am I taking drugs, the answer is yes—but only as prescribed and in the proper doses."

"I understand. But we must protect Sunny," insisted Shadowhawk.

Shung' shook her head. "There's much work to be done. We need to get the sweats going. Get all the old Sundancers to gather the things we need."

"Shung', if you are considering taking Sunny to the Valley of the Living Dead, remember it is very dangerous. She could lose her soul," advised Gramma Spottedhorse.

"Yes, Gramma, don't worry. Shadowhawk and I will run the ceremony. It'll take a couple of days to gather what we need," said Shung' reassuringly.

Gramma Spottedhorse took Meeko's and Sunny's hands in hers. "I'll pray hard for both of you. My children, please walk cautiously and trust in Shung' and Shadowhawk. This ceremony will take much courage and I beg you to become the breath of *Tunka'shila*. I know Shung' and Shadowhawk will see the two of you will not be cheated out of life. Once this ceremony is completed, be very careful and always listen to the sacred voice of *Wakan Tanka*."

Solemnly they began preparing for the *Yuwipi* ceremony which would be after sundown the following night. Many sweats were run to build power. Certain people were asked to gather special wood for the fire, while other trusted souls were asked to find powerful herbs to be used in the *Inipi* to prepare for the spirit calling ceremony.

That night Shadowhawk and Meeko left with a hunting party to search for a certain deer. When they returned with it, Sunny noticed that both had blood on their faces and knew the deer had been taken in the proper manner. Everyone helped skin it and cut the meat in the accustomed manner for cooking. Many others heard of Sunny's need and brought special foods and blankets to be used in the ceremony.

The depth of the preparations told Sunny she was in great danger. Why had she returned to the reservation anyway? She went for a walk to get away from the nightmare of her thoughts. Slowly the fog began to lift from her mind and she returned and sat quietly listening to the stones in the Old Man Four Generations fire pit.

When they were ready, she turned her back letting her clothes fall to the ground, then placed a towel around herself before entering the *Inipi*. Once everyone was seated inside, seven stones were brought through the doorway and placed in a circle in the fire altar. Shadowhawk used the new deer antlers to work them into place, then with a prayer he sprinkled different herbs on each one. As the blessed water was added to the stones, the *Inipi* filled with steam. Everyone sat in silence as Shadowhawk explained the importance of the upcoming *Yuwipi*. Many prayers and chants began while a calming strength filled the people as they inhaled the fragrance of the sacred herbs.

"My strong *Hunka* medicine brothers," began Shadowhawk. "We shall leave this world and go to the spirit realm to help our sister. Today we stand as a loyal family to this woman." Within moments, the spirit of Wolf covered the stones. Shadowhawk pointed, saying, "Wolf spirit is joining us in battle to help this woman make good decisions. As Sundancers, we are one with the wolf pack, and must approach this situation as Dog Soldiers. And that is good.

"She will soon become one with the Bear Clan family, and we need to help protect her from a demon. Sunny, I know you have control over a strong spirit called *Round Face Man*. He has the power to do your bidding," remarked Shadowhawk as he poured water over the hot stones and began to pray. One by one the Sundance brothers prayed for assistance in the upcoming healing ceremony. When the closing prayer of that round returned to Shadowhawk, he told Sunny to ask her special spirit to come and fight the demon.

Shadowhawk poured more water over the stones, releasing *Tunka'shila's* breath wrapping everyone in a dense cloud of blistering darkness. The hotter the *Inipi* became, the stronger and louder were their prayers. Again, Shadowhawk addressed Sunny. "What I'm asking involves a heavy responsibility. I know this mission can be dangerous. This strong spirit builds its power from your energy and shortens your life each time you call upon him to do your request. Make sure you give exact instructions on what you need. We both know if necessary this spirit will destroy everything in his pathway to achieve your goal."

Sunny nodded in agreement, then took a moment to honor the gift her grandmother had bestowed upon her before starting her prayers. Suddenly she saw many balls of blue light flashing and moving around in the *Inipi*. A crackling sound reverberated throughout followed by brilliant streaks of light. *Round Face Man* appeared bellowing. "What is it you want?" Sunny spoke in detail of her needs asking in reverence for him to go and do her bidding against this evil demon. Humbled by this powerful experience, Shadowhawk and the men mumbled their appreciation and respect for this spirit's powerful presence.

Silence spoke loud as everyone sat quietly, then Shadowhawk prayed. "*Hau, Wakan Tanka*. Thank you for allowing this powerful spirit to come and help us." The brothers echoed his words. "*Hau, Mitakuye Oyasin,*" concluded Shadowhawk touching the door to signal the end of the ceremony.

When the people came out of the sweat they embraced the power of another beautiful moonlit night. Meeko handed Sunny a towel, apologizing for not attending the sweat, explaining that he did not feel qualified under the current circumstances. Sunny was hurt but said nothing.

Shadowhawk called to Sunny, "I need to speak with you. Come, join me in the Sundance Circle." Sunny quickly dressed, and together they walked to the Tree of Life. After many promises on the Sundance Tree, they walked in a sunwise direction around the full circle. "Shung' tells me you are returning to the medicine way. I know you've had many experiences with the spirit world, and I respect and hold great honor in my heart for your ability. I know of your work and I trust and honor Shung's decision to teach you. I thank you for trusting yourself to me."

"Shadowhawk, I feel a great trust in you as a medicine man," answered Sunny as they left the circle to join Meeko and Shung'.

The following morning, Sunny left to go into town to shop for the items needed for the night ceremony. She purchased one yard each of unbleached muslin, red, yellow, black and green cloth, a bag of *kinnikinnik* and two beautiful handmade star quilts.

Following her return, she made a plate of food for Grampa Old Raven Crow. Finding this eighty-four-year-old medicine man sitting under a tree, she placed the food beside him and waited for him to acknowledge her presence.

Grampa set his work aside and smiled at Sunny. "Let's see what you have there that looks good to eat."

Sunny handed him his food and waited in silence until he had finished his meal, then took his empty plate to the kitchen. She returned with a gift of a brain-tanned buffalo hide on which she had painted his life story. Grampa's eyes twinkled with pleasure as he examined each drawing and praised Sunny for its accuracy. Then laying it aside he asked her to bring his knife, telling her it was stuck in the wall by the side of the back door.

As Sunny ran to get the knife she passed through the kitchen where the women were preparing for the evening ceremony. Old Woman, Grampa's wife, insisted Sunny taste one of her dishes then shoved a spoonful into her mouth. Sunny tasted a bland, watery substance and frowned. Seeing her puckered mouth, Old Woman picked up a box of cornstarch and added several large spoonfuls to the watery flour mixture. Old Woman stirred it until it thickened, then held out a second spoonful for Sunny to taste. Fearful of being fed the whole pot, Sunny swallowed with an approving smile then grabbed the knife and ran out the door back to the safety of Grampa. She sat close to his feet, watching him rip the last of the unbleached muslin into tiny squares. Sunny handed him his knife and watched as he cut a length of string then filled each tiny square with a pinch of tobacco, twisting each prayer tie onto the string.

Once the blessed tobacco ties were completed, he wrapped them around a block of wood and handed them to her. "I remember when you were very young and first came to me for tobacco ties. I tried to teach you how to make them, but Shung' tells me you still haven't mastered the art. So, I want you to promise never to embarrass me by telling anyone that it was me who taught you how. I will always make them for you. That is my gift to you." Sunny nodded, knowing it was his way of thanking her for the buffalo hide.

As darkness crept over the sky and the last sweat was completed, they drove to Auntie Lizzie's for the ceremony. Sunny noticed the house was in need of repair and wondered why Meeko had not taken care of this problem. As they entered the barren room, she noticed the windows and doors were covered with heavy blankets and a few pillows had been placed on the floor around the room for the old people to sit on. Everyone spoke in soft whispers about the seriousness of the ceremony as Sunny and Meeko waited in the far corner of the room for Shadowhawk and Shung' to begin.

In the center of the room five coffee cans held flags of different colors. Two powerful helpers stood by Shadowhawk, while two more stood by Shung'. In unison, they quickly bound the feet and hands of both medicine people, wrapping and tying their blanket-covered bodies in front of the altar. As the lights went out, rhythmic drumbeats and singers opened the ceremony. Muffled prayers came from both medicine people as the ceremony slowly built to a frenzied pitch. After two women led Sunny to the altar, the room filled with flashing blue streaks of light announcing *Round Face Man's* appearance. Pale blue lights flickered around Sunny's body leaving tiny burn marks across her face. Each time this happened, Sunny cried out in pain.

With only the glow of their decorated moccasins visible, many spirits danced toward Sunny. The jingle of bells was heard as she was forced to dance with each of them. First two, then four, then six, then eight. Sunny felt herself floating upward as hundreds of hands touched her, gently at first, becoming more intense until they became harsh blows. As she brought her hands up to protect herself the glowing blue lights rolled through the room like a molten wave and the hands melted into the walls.

Shung' spoke in the old language as Shadowhawk commanded the demon to come and stand in front of them. A black form instantly appeared, emitting streaks of brilliant red, orange and yellow energy that shot in monumental proportions toward the two medicine people. Hot winds blew across the room accompanied by unearthly moans coming from the Valley of the Dead. As the dead floated throughout the room, the people cried, screamed and prayed for help.

Suddenly, the room was filled with the sound of things breaking, and Sunny was hit on the head and fell to the floor. She felt as if she were being thrown from a cliff into molten lava, but just before she hit the boiling mass a spirit transported her to the doorway of the demon's home.

Lights flashed and thunder crackled as Sunny stepped over to the Other Side. Then a voice boomed, "I have come to help you capture this demon. I am wise and very old. I dislike serving a puny human. Now that I am here to obey your wishes, know that if you try and use me wrongly, I will free myself and when you die, your soul will be mine!"

"I call upon you to free me from this demon. I wish you no harm," answered Sunny.

"Then let it be so," thundered the voice of *Round Face Man*. More lights flashed and a cold north wind began to blow hard, causing screams of terror from a space beyond time. Outside, large hailstones beat against the windows until broken glass covered the floor. Suddenly, a deadly silence filled the room. The lights came on to reveal Shung' and Shadowhawk sitting stoically at the altar, their quilts folded and their ropes coiled neatly on top of them.

The people gasped when they saw Sunny lying unconscious in front of the altar. Shung' stroked her face and spoke softly as Shadowhawk stood over them, feathering Sunny off and praying for her to return.

Sunny opened her eyes and whispered, "I went through the doorway, and have brought you a gift of proof." Smiling, she let a red-hot coal roll from her left hand onto the floor. "I saw flames burning from both sides of my hand, yet felt no pain. I cannot explain what happened, but I knew I had to bring proof that I was there."

Noticing a large circular burn in the palm of Sunny's hand, Shung' poured a red powder over the wound, then Shadowhawk sucked out the poison. At that instant, beams of light shot out from Sunny's hand. Shung' picked up the coal and saw it had turned into a shiny piece of obsidian. Everyone smiled, knowing a strong battle had been fought and won.

As dawn arrived there were few people left in the room and Shung' knew much gossip was already spreading over the reservation about this ceremony. She asked the Sundance brothers to pack up the food and take it to the needy. When the room had been brought back to order, Sunny and Meeko were left wondering if the demon was really gone from the reservation.

Later that day many of Meeko's relatives came to announce that Red Feather, Chief of the Assiniboine tribe, was formally adopting Sunny into the tribe as a daughter. Sunny and Shung' both saw this as an attempt by the Nakota people to raise Sunny's stature, since she was only 'a lowly Dakota woman.'

Within a week, both families came together to celebrate and acknowledge the adoption. As Meeko's family walked by her extending their hands in friendship, Sunny felt their warmth.

"You have created a strong place for yourself among us. I'm proud to have you as a daughter and offer myself as Fire Chief for your marriage ceremony," said Shadowhawk. Sunny nodded with deep appreciation.

Following the adoption ceremony, Shung' whispered, "Sunny, no matter how many adoptions you are given, I know you'll always remain a good Dakota woman. It's that Dakota blood that gives you all your strength and courage. We women work hard and are willing to do our part during the good and bad times. We speak with demanding words and have always had a strong place among our people. Now we have once again proved we can protect our own."

Shadowhawk smiled. "*Hau*, Shung'. You have always been my sister, even if you are one of those Dakota women."

On the day of the wedding, Shung' and Shadowhawk led the couple into the *Inipi* to begin the sacred ceremony of their joining. Sunny and Meeko knew if they were not spiritually ready, Shung' could still refuse to perform the marriage ceremony. Shung' took the couple to the *Inipi* where they smoked her black pipe. Then they waited for the first stone to be brought in and placed in the center of the altar. At the beginning of each round Shadowhawk filled the two black pipes and handed one into Shung' while smoking the other outside the door of the *Inipi*. Each time she offered it up to Wakan Tanka she asked that the marriage would be born from the sacred *Inipi*. During the first three rounds, there was much talk about the marriage vows, the duties expected and the faith owed to one another. After the fourth round Shung' informed the couple that the ceremony would take place and that she would perform the Crossing of the Two Black Pipes. At the end of the fourth round, Shung' told Sunny and Meeko to dress and fill their red clay pipes to share with each others' families during the ceremony.

Feeling thankful that everything had gone well, Meeko reached over and squeezed Sunny's hand before they went their separate ways to dress for the ceremony. Upon their return, Meeko was dressed in his handsome smoke-tanned beaded leathers while Sunny wore her grandmother's white doeskin marriage dress. The couple's relatives began to gather on opposite sides of the circle to represent the joining of Sunny and Meeko.

Sunny and Meeko were acutely aware that a family member could at any time stop the marriage by refusing to smoke their pipe. As the couple shared their pipes with the families, Meeko spotted Wicahmunga standing with his relatives and broke into a cold sweat. Wicahmunga smiled wickedly at him and shook her finger in warning. Fearing she would not smoke with Sunny, he breathed a sigh of relief as she took Sunny's pipe and sanctioned the ceremony.

Seeing Meeko's distraction and wanting to respect Shung's black medicine pipes, Shadowhawk directed him to immediately place a sacred circle of sage and four chokecherry branches in each of the four directions on the outside of the marriage circle. Still following Shadowhawk's instructions, Meeko took a red flag and placed it at the West Door. To the North, he placed a blue flag, to the East a yellow flag and, to the South a white flag.

Shadowhawk then shaped the chokecherry branches into an eight-foot marriage tree, as Shung' told Sunny and Meeko to place their tobacco ties and flags among its branches then invited the family members and friends to do the same. When the colorful flags began to fly as the breath of the winds touched them, Shung' placed a buffalo skull at the West Door, then stepped forward and opened the ceremony in prayer. "*Hau, Wakan Tanka*, we offer these prayer flags and tobacco ties up to you to sanction this marriage."

As the ceremony began, Meeko offered up his wealth to Sunny's relatives, signifying he would be a good provider. After looking around for any disapproval and seeing that everyone remained quiet, Shung' felt satisfied that both families sanctioned the marriage.

"The Crossing of the Pipes is a very old ceremony that goes back to the beginning of the original people," said Shung'. Both medicine people and all the relatives and friends felt this eternal bonding as the pipes were brought forth and offered up in prayer by Shung' to *Wakan Tanka* for permission to light them.

Shung' decreed: "The fire must match the sun if it is to give a good birth to your marriage."

Shadowhawk announced: "These chokecherry branches I have gathered are to recognize you, as a man, and you, as a woman. They represent the provider and the life-giver. Each of you must maintain these responsibilities if you are to live together in a good way."

Shung' handed Shadowhawk one of her black pipes, and they filled the pipes with all the green things then invited all the two legs, four legs and no legs, along with all the directions to join them in the crossing of the pipes ceremony.

Sunny and Meeko stood solemnly at the marriage altar as Shung' and Shadowhawk lit the black pipes and shared them with the couple. Once they were smoked, everyone knew the union would now be witnessed by *Wakan Tanka*. When this was completed Shung' and Shadowhawk cleaned the pipes and offered the ashes to the wind, both smiling as the wind simultaneously swooped down taking the ashes toward the South Door.

Shung' stepped forward and motioned for the couple to face the West Door. In prayer, Shung' acknowledged the four directions with her pipe as the couple moved in a clockwise manner to follow the sacred black pipe. When Shung' lit the pipe, she smoked it with the couple, instructing Shadowhawk to wrap them in a buffalo robe, symbolizing the strength of this spiritual marriage. Shung' blessed the marriage then lit certain herbs, using her eagle wing to smoke off the couple as she prayed to all the powers for their eternal bonding.

Sunny stood proudly and could almost hear her grandmother speaking of the power in a binding love as the drummers and singers began to play the couple's honoring song, captivating everyone with their enchanting high-pitched voices. The families and the couple were now bonded in the old traditional way, and a great beauty was reborn among the people.

In lieu of wedding presents, there was a public giveaway. After everyone expressed their heartfelt wishes to the couple, the oldest of the grandmothers took the gifts that were given by Sunny and Meeko and wisely picked the proper ones to give to the most needy families.

Meeko and Sunny stood in the place of honor next to the elders feeling good to be back on the blanket of family unity. They promised *Wakan Tanka* on the black pipes that the sacred vows that now rested between them would always be honored. As the giveaway ended, food was served.

Late that afternoon Meeko casually asked Sunny, "How can we prove to the white system that we are married?"

"We have a traditional marriage—the strongest bond possible. It was witnessed by the people, and that's all the proof we need."

"Yes, among our people that's true, but we need the proper bureaucratic paperwork to make it 'legal.' That way we please both cultures."

"You Apple! Why don't you get off the fence and decide whether you are a Red Man or a White Man?" teased Sunny as the families joined in their playful bantering.

That evening after all the guests departed, Shung' and Shadowhawk took Sunny and Meeko to the marriage altar to complete their ceremony. Shadowhawk built a perfect fire, dismantled the altar, and offered each piece up to the spirits, asking support for this sacred marriage. When he had taken down the last flag, he gathered every bit of sage, all the chokecherry branches and all the ashes left from the pipes then gave them to Shung' which she offered all these sacred articles to the fire in prayer.

Shung' stood next to Sunny and said, "This is the final act of purifying this marriage. You are now bonded to your sacred vows from life to life for eternity. *Tunka'shila* has joined the love that you hold for each other, a love like no other has been sent as a sacred message on the smoke to *Wakan Tanka*."

As they watched the flames become dying embers, Shung' said, "Sunny, Medicine is strong in you. You will never escape this responsibility. As you travel back to the white man's world, you will see *Wakinyan* racing across the sky and feel an excitement in his presence, yet there will be no rain. This will be the thunder spirits letting you know the importance of your destiny. Another sign will come in the form of a man that looks like a wolf. His presence will remind you to call on the power of Wolf as you live in the white world as a married woman."

Sunny and Meeko slept little that night. Long before dawn the next day, they bid their goodbyes and as they drove away, Sunny waved farewell to Shung' until she became a mere shadow in the doorway.

Honeymoon

As they left for their long drive to the airport with Willie, Sunny and Meeko were grateful for the seeds of Medicine that had been planted to inspire visions of their future together. They felt that in time, their love would harvest and feed their hungered souls as they grew old together.

To reassure himself of Sunny's lasting love, Meeko said, "Sweetheart, I know we were meant to be together and share in a perfect life. I pray that I never awaken to find that you've been only a dream."

"We were born to share in this life as one. I saw it written in the stars," Sunny answered softly as Meeko snuggled close feeling bolstered by her tender words.

Their trip was uneventful until they crossed into Colorado and noticed many dark clouds forming overhead and lightning boldly flashing across the sky without a sound from *Wakinyan*. "There's a bad storm brewing," observed Meeko with concern.

"Yeah, kinda spooky. The winds are too still," said Willie pulling into a large truck stop. Meeko and Sunny went inside to fill their thermos with coffee, while Willie got gas. He joined them at the cash register, where a man with wolflike features was asking Sunny for directions to Denver. Shocked by the man's appearance, she mumbled a quick reply then hurried with Willie and Meeko to the truck. "Did you see that guy? He scared the shit out of me. He looked exactly like what Shung' had predicted."

"Yeah, he gave me the creeps," answered Meeko as Willie nodded his agreement.

As they drove on, the three became aware of other unusual things happening. Birds deliberately flew toward the windshield, then veered off at the last second. They saw animals eating from road kills that were not part of their normal diet. When three coyotes stood in the middle of the road refusing to move, they became very unsettled.

"I don't fucking like this. There are three of them and three of us. Who's tricking who?" Willie lay on the horn, cursing and shaking his fist through the open window of the truck. He was forced onto the shoulder of the road to get around them, but when he looked back in his side view mirror he found they had mysteriously disappeared.

Suddenly the thick, dark clouds dropped lower and lower to the ground. Willie was horrified when he saw the wolflike stranger standing on the side of the road with his thumb out.

"No way am I gonna give him a ride! We're getting the hell outta here," yelled Willie as he pressed the gas pedal to the floor.

Sunny gasped. "Do you think that could be Shung' or Shadowhawk shape-shifting? Or maybe it's the demon from the reservation chasing us?"

Filled with apprehension, they drove the rest of the trip in silence, and everyone was relieved when Willie pulled into the airport terminal. As Meeko retrieved their luggage, Sunny leaned over and kissed Willie fondly on the cheek.

"I'll miss you, Bro."

"Hey, me too" he answered shyly.

Sunny and Meeko stood for a moment watching Willie's taillights fade into traffic, both hoping he would be safe on his return home.

After they had picked up their tickets to Miami, Meeko suggested they stop in the lounge for a drink. Taking a seat near the window they sipped their drinks in silence, Meeko watching the busy planes, Sunny observing the happy couples passing and wondering how many were going on their honeymoons.

"Meeko, why do people have the need to get married?"

"I don't know, maybe they love each other," he answered indifferently, wondering what was causing her pensive mood.

"Do you think people choose to fall in love, or do you think they're destined to love a particular person?"

"Sweetheart, you do have an unusual way with words. I treasure the way you ponder life's mysteries, but sometimes you analyze things too much. I think you should rest that beautiful brain and just accept that our marriage is our only reality. We're together because it's written in our hearts. Someday I'll prove to you that we belong together. Don't you know that I'm going to be the most wonderful, loving and devoted husband that has ever lived?"

"I know, but sometimes people come together to fulfill their own selfish needs. They chase dreams, not reality," said Sunny, still pensive.

"Sunny, my inquisitive little eccentric, that may be true for others, but not for us. No matter how you try to explain it, we're together because we want to be. Why can't you just accept that our marriage is different?" Then hoping to lighten her mood, Meeko added, "Remember back in New York when a group of your posh lady friends came to visit? I loved their shocked expressions when I served them that piss-elegant tray of gourmet foods wearing only a towel for a loincloth and your underpants for a war bonnet."

"You were an ass. That was really embarrassing, but also funny. Did you ever figure out where underpants are really worn on the female anatomy?" she teased.

"Well, they do look better on you. Besides, your panties would be too small to cover my butt."

At that moment they heard their boarding call. They found their seats and Meeko put their carry-on luggage in the overhead compartment before continuing, "But if I could wear them, I bet I'd look adorable."

Refusing to allow Meeko to have the final word, Sunny replied, "I may be small, but I can fit into your pants any day."

"Well, if that's so, I would have to walk behind you to hold them up."

Again, Sunny persisted. "Okay, funnyman, tell me why we are on this plane heading for Miami."

"No-o-o! I can't tell you that! It's a surprise," he answered, secretly hoping Sunny would prod him with more questions. The trip was long and no matter what she tried, Meeko remained tightlipped until they landed. He led Sunny through the airport and hailed a cab, giving the driver instructions to their destination.

When they arrived at a boat dock in Fort Lauderdale, Meeko insisted she wear a blindfold as he led her along the dock. Sunny thought the game was ridiculous, but she humored Meeko by acting confused and playing along with him. "Just a little farther. You're going to love your surprise," he said as he removed her blindfold. She whooped with delight when she saw the beautiful sixty-foot boat.

"Sweetheart, this is going to be our home for the next month."

Robert, the Captain, welcomed them aboard as a crew member took their bags. Then without warning, Meeko swung Sunny over his shoulder, saying, "My lovely bride, I want this to be an adventure you'll never forget."

"You crazy fool! Put me down," yelled Sunny, laughing and fighting playfully to get free as Meeko carried her aboard the boat. Upon learning the captain was one of Meeko's prison buddies, Sunny was a little uncomfortable, but after being served a sumptuous lunch of fresh seafood and fine wines she felt reassured that he was a gentleman.

As the boat pulled away from the dock, Sunny and Meeko stood at the bow enjoying the wonderful breeze of the open sea as Meeko encircled her in his arms.

"My beautiful lady, do you like my surprise? We're going to see many of the Caribbean islands on this trip. Do you realize that I don't have to share you with anyone for a whole month? No phones, no managers and no family. I want this honeymoon to surpass all your dreams. Let's create a world from our childhood fantasies, then live the fairy tale together."

"Oh, Meeko, this is a dream come true. I never thought such things were possible except in the movies. It's the perfect way to begin our life together. I love the romantic mood you've created. You're the most extraordinary man I've ever known. Every day we spend together, I feel my love for you is greater than it was the day before and wonder how that's possible."

"Sunny, you are the woman of my dreams. I've always believed in your existence and knew you only had to be found. I knew from the moment we first met that you were my reason for living. Your touch creates such warmth in my heart. I thank Creator for sending you to me, and I want to spend my life making you happy. I never want either of us to go to bed angry, and I never want to make you cry unless it's from happiness. Let's promise if we ever argue, we won't rest until it's resolved. I want to always know that the smile on your face was put there by me. I never knew a love like this could exist between a man and a woman—we are one mind and soul. My Sweetheart, let's not join the crew for dinner; instead, let's go to the cabin and make wild, crazy love!" Meeko pressed his body hard against hers and for the moment both felt safe, wrapped in their dream.

Several minutes later Robert yelled, "Hey, look portside." Meeko and Sunny saw a huge tan sea turtle floating in the water. "It's got to be at least six feet wide!" Meeko hurriedly snapped pictures of *Keya* before she disappeared into the darkness of deeper waters.

"That's a good sign! It proves our marriage will live to see old age. Sunny, did you know the grandmothers take the umbilical cord of a newborn and place it in a little leather bag shaped in the form of a turtle? They pin it to the baby to guarantee the child will live a long and healthy life."

"Who doesn't know that? I wore mine pinned under my shirt until I was almost five years old. In fact, I still have it.

"Did you know that Mother Earth was once called Turtle Island? I think the turtle came to remind us to live a long and healthy life together," said Meeko, trying to impress Sunny with his knowledge.

"Hey, is that another old Indian saying, or is it your imagination acting up again?"

"Well, since I'm the only old Indian I know, it must be true."

"Now let me tell you an old Indian story," grinned Sunny.

"And what might that be?"

"See those seagulls flying overhead? The old people say they are masters at practicing the laws of gravity." No sooner had the words left her mouth than a large bird dropping fell near Meeko.

"Laws of gravity, huh?" He swept his hand across the deck and pretending to pick it up as if it were something of great value, he studied it very carefully. "Sweetheart, I thought it was a raindrop, but it's not. It's a gift from the flying ones," Meeko playfully wiped his hand on Sunny's blouse. This air of carefree playfulness continued throughout the afternoon as they watched the land slowly fade from view.

As night approached and the sun completed another journey across the sky, both reflected on the first day of their honeymoon. Meeko gently said, "I pray there will be no darkened shadows born between us during this marriage. And as the fall of our lives approaches, I want the essence of our experiences to linger beyond our deaths as wilting petals of a rose. I want the core of all that we are to take root from this relationship so we can rebirth again and again to express a never-ending love for the rest of our incarnations."

A soft breeze touched their faces as they stood listening to the waves caress the sides of the boat. Sunny reached up and removed the tie wrappings from Meeko's braids. She watched the wind play with his hair, then brushed the lose strands from his face. "You're a beautiful man, but it's your words that soothe me just like a prairie wind dancing across the plains."

As the moon slowly appeared, creating dancing shadows across the waters, both felt the magic of their ocean mother.

"Woman, look how the moon is exposing our pagan souls. I give her mysterious reflections to you and wherever I go, you will know I am with you." Meeko caressed

Sunny as he led her toward their cabin. The air was filled with romantic music and beside their bed was a beautifully decorated table decked with gourmet dishes, candles and a bottle of champagne.

Meeko toasted Sunny saying, "You are mine and will always be mine." Deliberately, he spilled a few drops of champagne on Sunny's hand, then sensuously licked her fingers dry, saying, "The food looks wonderful, but the only thing that will satisfy my delicate taste buds is your body. The animal in me wants to devour all of you. To lose you, my lovely bride, would be like losing the sun. I ask you to always be there to warm me as a sunrise. Sunny, let our love bloom like none other and flow from your body to mine. I pray the rose will bind our marriage together with a soft strength."

Meeko slowly undressed her. Then dipping a long-stemmed red rosebud into his champagne glass, he slowly painted her body with it. Sunny undulated sensuously under his touch.

"Oh, Sunny, as I experience the pleasures of your body, I beg you to give me your soul. If you grant me this precious gift, I will never hurt you and will remain as humble as the rabbit."

"Meeko, when our eyes first met I knew my search for love was over. I've always known that the flame between us would become a blazing fire. I trust this love. I want it to be like Christmas every day, and when the night comes and we lie in each other's arms, I want it to be the Fourth of July with fireworks."

Spellbound by her soft skin, Meeko covered her body with provocative kisses, pursuing her with an animalistic lust. Sunny responded like a slow-burning fire as he lifted her from the sofa and took her to the bedroom where he pulled back the covers to reveal a bed filled with red rose petals. Placing her aroused body among them, he joined her, whispering, "Let me crawl deep inside of you and discover you over and over so that I will never forget this night."

Meeko moved down her body creating sensations that caused her to shake uncontrollably in sheer pleasure. Sunny arched in an unwavering moment of ravenous passion, driving both into a frenzied dance of lustful, burning sex.

Exhausted, they lay intertwined amongst the crushed rose petals, embraced by their aroma. Meeko watched the moonlight weave dancing patterns across Sunny's body and with the lightest touch of his finger, he traced them not wanting to break the enchanted spell. Sliding his lips gently across her face, he whispered, "I love you," and showered rose petals over her body as both experienced a serenity like they had never known. A peace rested between them as they watched the first streaks of light appear on the horizon.

It was late afternoon when Sunny awakened to find a single rose lying on Meeko's pillow, with a note that read: "My love! My life! Last night, I awakened many times to assure myself that I was not dreaming and that you were really there. My beautiful bride, please come to me and let's play in the sun." Sunny smiled and let Meeko's words touch her heart before joining him on the deck. Hoping the day would be as magical as the night, they sat holding hands enjoying the sounds of the gently flapping sails. They spent a lazy day swimming in the warm Caribbean waters and learning the art of sailing. As another blissful day ended, the night awakened the animalistic hunger of their erotic passion.

The second morning they awakened to the sound of the anchor dropping. Robert told them that he and the crew would be staying overnight with old friends on a nearby island. Once the dinghy had been lowered, Meeko and Sunny waved goodbye. Excited by the promise of solitude, they made preparations to explore the closest deserted island. After packing supplies in a waterproof bag, they swam toward a white sandy beach where Meeko carried Sunny ashore. Enthusiastically he climbed the nearest palm tree and hung the bag high above, out of the reach of any creepy crawlies.

Sunny commented teasingly, "Love, we're not in bear country. As far as I can tell, everything around here either swims, crawls or flies."

"I know, but I want to impress My Sweetheart with my talents," Meeko answered.

As they strolled along the shimmering beach, Sunny stopped to examine a large conch shell. "I want to keep this. It looks exactly like the one a medicine man used during a sunrise ceremony when I was in Central America."

"Great, I want you to teach me about the Mayan count." Walking further, Meeko picked up several pieces of driftwood. In need of a way to carry their bounty, he stripped naked, using his clothing to bundle everything together. Laughing, Sunny removed her clothing as well, and they played lightheartedly together until lunch time.

After eating, they dressed and headed up the beach astounded by the untouched beauty of the island. They could feel a nomadic freedom coming from the land that had been left long ago by an ancient people. As they climbed to the summit of the jagged, sheer cliffs, they saw the unspoiled land extending like a shelf over the thrashing ocean waters far below. It was obvious this plateau had been carved over thousands of years from the tremendous forces of the ocean tides. While making their way down the cliffside, they were amazed at the many magnificent caves along the way.

"I wonder if the people who once lived here used the North Star as their compass? I've been told that a golden-haired people once visited these islands," said Sunny.

Meeko stepped on a loose stone, tumbling downward. He broke his fall by grabbing an outcropping of stones. Sunny rushed to him, saying, "That was real smart! Don't you know you're supposed to test a stone before you place your full weight on it?"

"Absolutely! But it's not my fault. You have completely captured my mind," reasoned Meeko as he offered Sunny his hand.

"No, thanks. I have enough scars to prove I know how to climb down a cliff." As they continued working their way around the narrow ledges, they spotted a small hidden beach below and decided it would be exciting to investigate. Wandering in and out of many caves along the way, Sunny found one that contained many old drawings and called out to Meeko, "Come, see what I've found!" Upon closer examination of the carvings on the walls, they saw many had been erased by the tides and both agreed this had to be the ancient history left by the islanders.

They sat in companionable silence, hoping to hear the voices of these long ago people. "What do you think was once here?" Meeko asked.

"I believe there were many hills and valleys covered with ancient cities. I know the people were simple and worshipped *Wakan Tanka* in the most sacred way."

"So you think the oldest of life's mysteries still exist in the land, but it's the language that keeps us in the dark wondering about these old ways?"

"I feel the presence of those ancient people in the land. It seems all we can hope for is a slight acquaintance with their spirits."

Peaceful silence rested between them until they reached the narrow beach, where they sat watching the waves growing stronger and stronger as they crashed on the shore. To break the spell, Meeko raced alongside the surf and wrote, "Sunny, I Love You" in big letters in the wet sand. And just as quickly a wave erased his message, causing them both to contemplate how vulnerable the sacred gift of love can be.

Venturing into another cavern, they found several carved statues of different sizes throughout the cave. They climbed up for a better view and both agreed there was an eerie vibration emanating from the these figures as they danced like shadows across the ceiling. Mesmerized, they lost track of time and didn't notice that the tide had risen, causing high raging waves to fill the cave. Jolted back to reality, they saw the possible danger that was moving toward them. Hanging tightly to the jutting stone images, they climbed higher to escape the rising water that was dangerously close to filling the cave.

Aroused by the element of danger as they were buffeted by rising water, their excitement began to build and both were willing to risk their lives in a game of sexual pleasure. Meeko savagely penetrated Sunny and ravished her in fevered passion. She matched his intense passions as the pounding waves tossed and turned their coupled bodies. Their unquenchable sexual hunger conquered them as they reached a simultaneous climax.

As their frenzy subsided, both realized their heads were underwater and they were trapped by vicious undercurrents. They found themselves exhilarated by this daring adventure as they fought desperately to find a way out of the cave. When their heads finally broke the surface, they gasped for air in frightened laughter. Fighting the strong currents, they made their way through the turbulent waters and finally collapsed happily on a nearby beach. Hearts pounding, feeling safe, they lay in silence smiling in approval at the other's willingness to experience another wild sexual triumph.

"Geezus," sighed Meeko, "that got my adrenaline flowing. I'm sure glad you're a strong swimmer."

"It's the edge that always excites me. You can thank Sam for my daredevil personality."

They stood up and started the long climb back to the top of the cliff. Winded, both sat down for a moment to rest and watch the red ball of the sun fade away on another beautiful day.

As the night air became chilly, they raced back to gather their treasures before swimming back to the dimly lit boat. Chilled to the bone, they climbed aboard and quickly wrapped themselves in blankets. Meeko made hot rum drinks and as they sipped, both reveled in the other's daring, spirited soul.

When the night grew late, Meeko prepared their evening meal. They pondered the delicately embroidered details of the beauty of the night skies as they ate. Meeko gathered more blankets, suggesting they sleep under the sky quilt and study the mysteries of the galaxies. As they cuddled in each others' arms, they felt *Hanwi's* silvery beams gently touch them and penetrate their joined souls. They could almost hear a whispered invitation coming from each star as its glow wove together the magnificence of another extraordinary night. Wondrous peace enveloped them as they fell under the spell of the incomprehensible mysteries of all life. This allowed them to venture toward another time and space, seeking more of what they had experienced earlier that day.

"When I think of expressing life to the fullest with you, it's almost like reaching up and plucking a star from the sky. What kind of spell have you woven around me? Is this real or is it one of my fantasies trying to capture the impossible?" whispered Meeko.

"Meeko, I am just another you. I pray that someday we'll have the ability to touch a total trust within each other. Surely you know our souls want to experience a love that will be equaled only by the splendor of the sun, the moon and the stars. To share in such loveliness demands we build a strong belief in each other."

"Sunny, sometimes I resent having such a short lifetime to share in this splendor, and I too pray that our hearts will always beat as one. Woman, don't you know that you are my heart?" Time had become meaningless to them and sleep was their only separation. Meeko snuggled close. "So, My Sweetheart, if I say goodnight, you must promise me that you'll be by my side when the dawn breaks tomorrow morning." Knowing this woman was like no other, he drifted off in slumber ending another hair-raising, yet incredibly romantic day.

Meeko was awakened by the brightness of the sun, and somewhere in the distance, he could hear the sound of the dinghy approaching. He nudged Sunny and they dressed quickly then hurried off to the galley to make coffee and breakfast. As the crew boarded, it was quite obvious they were all suffering from a long night of heavy partying. After politely taking their coffee, they quickly excused themselves to get some well needed rest, leaving Sunny and Meeko alone to spend a quiet day swimming and basking in the sun. Late that afternoon, Robert announced they were leaving for Kingston, Jamaica.

On their fourth day at sea the boat docked at Kingston Harbor, amidst throngs of local people selling their wares. The air of excitement was enhanced by the music that flowed continuously from the steel drums and island singers. Robert explained that the island had become his home since his release from prison. He took them to his favorite restaurant, where the chefs spun their magic into a array of Creole dishes that spurred their taste buds beyond bodily capacity accompanied by tropical rum drinks that ate into their souls. It was late evening when the party ended and everyone stumbled back to the ship.

The sun rose on another lazy island day, Meeko and Sunny decided to shop for colorful clothing and gifts to send home to their friends. That evening they had dinner at one of the finest hotels, eating on an open verandah overlooking the sea.

When the flaming red sun sank into the horizon they could see the silhouettes of two ships sailing toward each other. Slowly they came together as one, meeting in the middle of the sinking sun then separated, reminding Sunny of when the planet Sirius had once met the sun and was joined as one for a moment in time. This awesome memory caused chills to run through her as the last rays of the sun sank into the black waters off the Jamaican coastline.

Darkness crept across the island as they strolled along the beach listening to the steel drums accompany the singers and dancers. The sound of the gentle ocean waves breaking against the shore provided a background rhythm that created a trance-like mood on this magical island. Captured by these sounds, Meeko and Sunny embraced the mystery that brought the island experience alive. Feeling the magic course through their veins, Meeko joked that the island seemed to be stealing their souls.

The night winds picked up beckoning them to join in the mysteries of the darkness, wrapping them in a Jamaican mystery as they chased each other along the shore. Arm in arm they watched as the wind's breath lifted the waters from the ocean bed and quickly washed away their footprints from the wet sand. They walked down the beach and visited with local families who were eating, singing and dancing in celebration of life.

One day the following week, Meeko went with Robert and the crew on an overnight deep sea fishing trip. Sunny rented a suite in town hoping to pursue more information about island philosophies. A few days earlier she and Meeko had stopped to watch people remove melted wax from the church steps, so she decided to buy some candles and go there to pray. She purchased the candles and a voodoo doll at a quaint little shop. While there, she inquired about Ashna, a Vudan priestess she had heard about from the locals on the beach. The shopkeeper told her that if she went to a certain church in the center of town that evening, she could meet Ashna.

At ten o'clock Sunny arrived at the church. A crowd had gathered and thousands of candles burned on the entrance steps. She lit her candle and placed it alongside the others then sat down to pray. Once her prayers were completed, she looked around and was surprised to see many familiar faces from the local shops. She did not meet the priestess until after midnight and was very disappointed by her abrasive manner. Sunny decided to talk to Robert before pursuing this endeavor any further.

The following morning Sunny sat at an outside cafe pondering the power of this mysterious woman when she saw Robert's boat coming into the harbor. She called for her check and as she handed the waiter her money, he hesitated, then blurted out, "There is a Tomburrie tomorrow evening. Would you and your friends like to come?" Sunny enthusiastically accepted the invitation and left to meet the boat.

As the boat neared the dock Meeko tossed Sunny the line, then the crew jumped out and moored the boat. The men were excited about having caught two swordfish and insisted on having their pictures taken with them. After Robert gave the swordfish to friends to prepare for the evening's festivities, Sunny told him they had been invited to a Tomburrie ceremony and she wanted to attend.

"You bet we'll go. I never miss any of the island traditions. This particular ceremony comes from the old slave days. It's been forbidden for years, but the local politicians don't dare interfere with a Vudan priestess."

"Why forbidden?" asked Meeko.

"Years ago, the Tomburrie ceremony was performed by the slaves while they were working in the fields. It is considered one of the most sexual dances ever performed. When the slave owners saw that plantation productivity was going to hell, they passed a law to stop this primal lovemaking. It seems they wanted less dancing and more work. I've heard there are drummers who can empty a field in less than ten minutes. They create a certain rhythm that seems to drive the people between the rows and into a prone position. Oh yes, you two will love the Tomburrie."

That night as they neared the narrow crowded streets on the outskirts of town, the sound of the steel drums touched their souls, changing their moods to match the heartfelt rhythm. Cautiously they moved through the mass of black faces, trying to approach the home of the Priestess Ashna. As they worked their way along the vine covered walkway, Sunny saw Ashna in the center spirit-calling circle, shrouded by the dim red glow of lights.

Robert spotted some wooden benches and suggested that they sit as high up as possible to see everything. From their seats, they watched the dancers below. A large black man, naked from the waist up, suddenly appeared in front of Sunny and maneuvered her to the center of the yard. Dancing in a very sensual manner, he grabbed her by the cheeks of her ass, forcing her to match his every movement. In bewilderment, Sunny looked to Meeko for help. Robert, seeing her dilemma, walked over and tapped the man on the shoulder, dancing her to the safety of Meeko's arms.

"I told you this dance was sexual as hell. They mean no harm, but these people live, work, pray and make love to the rhythm of the drums. It's in their blood. For them, the beat of a drum sets the pace for Mother Earth's on-going dance of fertility."

Just then, a large black woman grabbed Robert and pulled him into the dancing crowd. He grabbed the woman's ass and directed her every movement with his body pressed hard against her. Meeko and Sunny watched in amazement. Robert was definitely experienced in the sensuous dance of the Tomburrie!

Sunny smiled at Meeko and both kicked off their shoes, joining in the wildness of the fertility dance. The hypnotic, suggestive drumbeat went on and on for hours. Robert watched Sunny and Meeko from afar, then approached them suggesting they take a break and join him in a bottle of rum while waiting for Ashna to acknowledge their presence.

At last Ashna, wearing a red satin dress and smoking a large cigar, sidled near. Staring directly into Sunny's eyes, she thrust a half-filled whiskey bottle with a live snake swirling around inside at Sunny. "Drink, fine lady. Let the spirits enter your body." She moved closer, again demanding that Sunny drink as she forced the bottle into her face.

Sunny firmly pushed the bottle away, yelling, "No!"

Angercd by this strong rejection, the Grand Priestess challenged, "Why not, fine lady? Are you afraid of this Hoodoo woman?"

"I wouldn't say I'm afraid of you, but I'd like to know more about you and the ceremony before I ask you for some training."

"Ah, Indio, I see. Then watch us and learn about truth, faith and fortitude."

Ashna clapped her hands together, signaling for a frenzied drumbeat to call to the peoples' spirits. Dancers dressed in white garments adorned with many magnificent bright colors, entered the sacred area spinning and twirling frantically. Their eyes took on a glazed look and many collapsed to the ground their mouths frothing. Others stayed on their feet but shook out of control, their eyes rolling back in their heads. It seemed the beat of the drum was driving everyone into a state of madness. Spirits took over the dancers' bodies and spoke of inconceivable things. Many of the onlookers recognized the voices of their departed kin and offered gifts to them while listening intently to their wise words.

Sunny watched in amazement as the priestess cured many people during the ceremony. One man pierced both sides of his chest with metal meat hooks. He calmly tied two ropes to these hooks and was pulled high into a tree. There he hung for hours before they let him down. When his feet touched the ground, there was no blood coming from his wounds and Sunny watched with astonishment as his puncture holes closed, leaving no marks to prove his chest had ever been pierced.

At exactly eleven o'clock, everyone left without a word for the beach. Sunny and Meeko were surprised to see crowds of people sitting along the shoreline with gifts ready to give to the spirits. As the sound of drums filled the air, Ashna and her apprentices opened the ceremony. Her Vudan followers sang and danced around the sacred fire.

Sunny felt the drums match her heartbeat and when the universe opened to her, Robert and Meeko watched in amazement as she fell into a trance-like state, moving into the fire circle to experience the Vudan spirit world. Suddenly, she was falling and seeing a world that she had never known. Planets were spinning, star worlds were enfolding over each other as they brought purity to the impure world of Mother Earth. Within the hour, Sunny was back on her feet, walking with Ashna and speaking of her experience.

In unison, the Vudan people lit their torches and candles and walked to the water in a hushed silence. At the stroke of midnight, they heard a huge wave rolling toward them. The people prayed and placed their gifts along the shoreline. The wave crashed onto the shore, taking the gifts, torches and candles the people had offered. At this instant, darkness seemed to freeze time and hold the people in reverent song and prayer. Sunny knew she had been in the presence of many powerful spirits.

As the people prepared to leave, Ashna approached Sunny, saying, "Tomorrow, Robert will bring you to me." Then she silently vanished into the night.

Before sunrise the following morning, Robert drove Sunny to Ashna's house. She was surprised to see even at this early hour a large crowd of people was already waiting to see Mother Ashna, the most powerful woman on the island. As they walked to her gated door, Robert said, "I'm not allowed to go any further. I'll wait for you in the car. Just walk in, she'll be waiting for you."

A young girl dressed in white greeted Sunny with a smile and said, "She is waiting," then vanished.

As Sunny entered a sparsely furnished room Ashna motioned for her to sit on an old sofa, then ignored her. With bowed head, another young girl brought in a tray filled with freshly picked leaves, cleaned roots and an ornate pot of boiling water. The girl set the tray in front of Ashna, who chose certain leaves, then poured the hot water over them, stirring them carefully with a wooden spoon. She offered Sunny a cup, saying, "Robert tells me you are interested in learning our spirit ways."

"Yes. Your ways appear to be very similar to ours," answered Sunny politely.

"Our ceremonies come from the original people, long before there was an Africa. We strongly believe in the power of all spirits. Last night you saw the spirits calling people to ceremony. Those people have the power to groan or spin in spirits who use their bodies and minds to do spirits' work. There is a duality in my work. I can either drive away bad spirits or charm them into helping me do my bidding, good or bad. I come from the gourd and use its knowledge by stamping the ground to frighten away an evil spirit. But when the gourd rides another too strong, I find it necessary to take it into myself to rid the person from their misery.

"Indio, don't judge me harshly. I work with all spirits. Power is power and it does not matter whether it's good or bad. It's a person's choice to do harm or good for another. My life has always been dedicated to ceremonies for both life and death. You are here because you want me to keep your marriage safe."

Sunny was surprised that Ashna knew this, and wondered if she knew the truth about her past fears.

"Your confusion about my power is amusing. You're here to have your marriage protected and to remove the destruction from your many past lives together. You fear this marriage because you think the demon is connected to your husband's soul. You need me to rid you of your doubts and to remind you to follow what you already know." Ashna cocked her head to one side as if she was listening to someone.

"Cheering Woman is here with us. She says she is your grandmother and she is the one who taught you to believe in the plant people. She says to give you these leaves for Meeko's ulcerated stomach," continued Ashna as she handed them to Sunny.

Although shocked by this information, Sunny could not deny the proof. The leaves confirmed that her grandmother was with them.

"Now that you know I am real, give your husband this powdered root and within three days he will be cured. You are spiritually healthy because you have always talked to the spirits. This is why you have the attention of the snake. She has blessed you with the power of charm. A man, your father, stripped you of these powers by your fear of him. The day you and your father were out hunting food and you killed a snake, you took back your power. Your father knew this, and took its bones and placed them in a gourd that you now call Gourd Man. The snake still waits for you to join her.

She will help you destroy all the deceptive people that try to enslave you with fear and hate. Your grandmother says to find your truth and develop your healing powers."

Sunny gasped, "How do you know these things?"

"When I need to prove things to a non-believer, I speak to a spirit called Old Black Slave. He tells me everything. He says that you need to find the powers of the golden snake. She cannot come to you because of your raging anger. You must heal your worldly illusions so you can receive the powers of the seven golden rings. I will help you, if you will do as I ask.

"Indio, I understand hate and anger. My people were slaves and forced to work in the fields to serve their Portuguese owners. Our women birthed many breeds and as black women, we were servants and nannies in their homes. We taught our ways to our masters' children and took back our woman power in the next generation. Our women understand that you can do little with your life until you fix what is broken inside of you.

"The snake is waiting. It is up to you to have enough courage to draw out the poisons that have entered your life. Take these red and black soils and mix each into a paste. Paint half of your face with red and the other with black, then sit with the full moon. This will remove the sting of the scorpion from your soul." Ashna pointed toward two cotton bags.

Sunny was horrified and afraid to move when she saw two snakes coiled on top of each bag. Ashna laughed, then took the snakes off the bags before handing them to Sunny.

"When you are ready, call on your grandmother. She will show you how to use the power of Snake."

"Ashna, how do you know these things about me?" Sunny nervously fumbled with the bags on her lap.

"As a Vudan priestess, I must know these things, just as you will someday. Listen, Indio, go back to the beginning of time and learn about the philosophies of your race and accept who you are as Medicine. I too had to learn my history. My grandmother's grandmother forced me to learn the richness of my forefathers. As a child, she spoke to me about my people being chained and stacked six inches from another's face in the bowels of slave boats. Those ships were never cleaned and many were forced to lie in another's vomit and shit, while shackled to the rotting dead. It was a long journey across the waters to a foreign land. My people became death-like, as they lay listening to the prayers of others, adding them to their own for stronger spiritual protection. It was the spirits that helped my people survive under these terrible conditions.

"Our ways teach us the principles of life. Your creation story is the same as mine except the names are different. There was Ollaron, who created the people from a handful of clay. There was Yamina, first woman, who gave birth to a son called Aruna. As Aruna grew older, he fell in love with his mother and lusted for her. When he became strong enough, he raped his mother. A child was conceived from this horror, bringing great shame and disgrace upon Yamina. She fled into the African jungles where she lay until she gave birth to the child of incest. This devastation caused her breasts to grow to immense size until they slowly became the never-ending streams of life which created our beautiful lakes of today."

"You speak my grandmother's words. She once told me a similar creation story that dictates all of our sacred natural laws," said Sunny timidly.

"Indio, we may know the great spirits by different names, but the spirits are all the same. We call the God of Thunder, Shango, and our River God is called Oshan. Aya is the Goddess of Gold and Health. Ogan is our War God. Arushka is our God of Agriculture and Avda is the Goddess of all the green things. You call our Goddess Yamina, *Maka Ina*, the one who nurtures and feeds all Great Spirit's children.

"So as woman, you should know we control the invisible side of life. Like your people, we also chant and drum in the spirits. We smoke off, light a candle, or cut the throat of a black chicken to let the blood heal or kill another. It is woman who is intimate with the spirit world. It is woman who sacrifices her heart for her loved ones. It is woman who personally understands the likes and dislikes of the spirits and can ask for many things. We gift the spirits that help us. Some like mirrors, rice, beans, beads, cigars, rum or combs. They will give us whatever we need as long as we respect and appreciate them. Now go! Meet me tonight at the church." Ashna turned and walked away.

"Wait!" Sunny handed her an envelope containing three crisp one hundred dollar bills. "I'll be there. Thank you for sharing with me."

Ashna took the envelope and stuck it into her blouse. Looking at Sunny with cold eyes, she added, "You did not come to me for knowledge. You came to judge me and see if I was real. I have given you what your heart asked for. You are desperate and you fear that demon will destroy your husband. So I will take your money and fight the battle that you fear to undertake."

Sunny felt shame as she walked away, knowing Ashna's words were true. She found Robert and as they drove home, she mentioned that she and Meeko would be meeting Ashna that evening at the old church.

Sunny spent the rest of the day in contemplative thought. As they arrived that night she became apprehensive when they searched through the crowd and could not find Ashna. Sunny sat down and lit her prayer candle. Suddenly a hand touched her shoulder and she turned to find herself looking directly into Ashna's eyes.

"Stay with your prayers until the candles go out, then bring the melted wax to me." As suddenly as she had appeared, Ashna vanished.

"Weird lady. Rather scary, don't you think?" asked Meeko.

"Shhh, be quiet, she knows and hears everything."

Sunny continued to sit in prayer. Within two hours the candles burned down to a mere flicker, then nothing. Sunny scraped up the wax and as she turned to speak to Meeko, Ashna was there. "Come with me." Without question, all three of them got into the car and followed her directions until they came to a long, dark, dirt road. When they reached a wide crossroad, Ashna told them to stop the car. Meeko pulled to the roadside and shut off the engine. They silently followed her on foot. For some unknown reason, Meeko began to feel extremely warm and everything around him started to glow in different colors. Even the appearance of the trees and bushes made him think he had stepped into another world.

All at once Ashna stopped, and taking a stick she drew a large circle around the couple. She placed Sunny in the North and Meeko in the South, warning, "Do not move out of this circle until I am through with the ceremony, otherwise you will die."

She took two white chickens from her black knapsack and stepped into the circle, dancing and chanting while holding them in the air. Next she danced around Sunny, placing a chicken's beak on the line of the circle behind her. She repeated this procedure with Meeko using the second chicken. Both were amazed the chickens did not move. Ashna continued to mumble words that neither understood, but they did recognize some of the animal sounds and the bird calls.

As Ashna danced around them, the Spirits began to speak through her, frightening both Meeko and Sunny. Suddenly she picked up both chickens by the neck and swung them in circles until their heads ripped from their bodies. Taking their blood, she drew unusual designs inside the circle all around the couple.

Meeko stood in silent terror. He knew this woman carried the powers of Wicahmunga and wanted desperately to run, but was too afraid.

Ashna looked his way in disgust, then explained: "These patterns will protect you as long as you walk the way of the sun. To keep this marriage, there must never be a lie between you. If either of you break this rule, the offender will become a victim of fate and will die in great suffering."

She concluded the ceremony by marking their faces with blood squeezed directly from the chickens' headless bodies. She dug into her bag and pulled out two handmade dolls and marked their faces in blood with the same designs she had made in the circle. "Keep these dolls together and with you always. Give them gifts and speak kindly to them. In time they will learn to like you and will ward off all evil spirits." As though predestined, the ceremony ended abruptly.

Meeko wondered why Ashna had chosen to use the full moon in their ceremony, but understood when he saw shadows of many tormented demon-like figures surrounding the outer rim of the circle. Sunny remarked she had heard the suffering moans of the dead as she watched the wind carry them away.

"Since you are leaving soon, I myself will return here in four days to complete the ceremony. By that time, you two will be separated," said Ashna. No one spoke during their ride to her home, but as Ashna got out of the car, she admonished, "I warn you! No secrets can be between you, otherwise the doorway to the evil world will open on you."

On the drive home both Meeko and Sunny were afraid to speak about the ceremony. As they walked along the dock to the boat, Sunny took the dolls from Meeko's hand.

"There is something very strange about these dolls."

"I know, and I also saw something very eerie around us during that ceremony," added Meeko.

"Do you think the ceremony will fend off the evil ones?"

"I don't know. It could have been real, or it could have been a power scare. She reminds me of Wicahmunga, and I know that woman could scare the fuck out of anyone."

"Oh, for God's sake, Meeko. You fear everyone that reminds you of Wicahmunga. I know this woman has power, so I'm going to follow her advice," concluded Sunny as they entered their cabin. She placed the dolls safely in a box, saying, "Because of the way you feel about Ashna, I will take care of the dolls for us."

Robert knocked at the door of their cabin to inform them that the weather was perfect and they would be leaving immediately for Miami. Sunny froze, knowing Ashna's words were beginning to come true.

Meeko pulled Sunny close and wrapped her in his arms, whispering, "Trust me, no matter what happens." Sunny tried to ask what he meant, but he covered her mouth with his hand, saying, "Please, ask me nothing. Just know that I love you, no matter what happens in the next few days."

Over the next few days Meeko became indifferent toward Sunny and slept on deck, giving her little attention. On the fourth day back at sea, she was awakened in the middle of the night by the noise of something being dragged along the deck. Arriving on the dark deck she found three men dressed in diving gear, pushing large bail-like bundles overboard. Recognizing Meeko as one of them, she tried to grab him, but he ignored her and jumped in the water as Robert quickly pulled the boat away.

"Robert, what in the hell are you doing? Those divers are miles from shore. They could die out there!" Sunny fought Robert for the wheel.

"Sunny, this is not your concern. I'm doing what I was told! Now, go below and stay there until we dock. Meeko will meet you in Los Angeles in four to five days."

Feeling helpless, Sunny went back to her cabin feeling hurt and abandoned. She paced the floor thinking of Ashna's words as she stared out the porthole until she saw the dim light of a motor boat approaching in the distance, weaving its way through heavy fog-like clouds. Realizing there was nothing she could do, she lay across the bed and cried in frustration until she fell into a troubled sleep. Waking suddenly, she looked out to see the boat was immersed in low, hanging clouds and the winds were too still. She dressed and went back on deck.

"Robert, tell me what's going on!"

"Sunny, you know I can't tell you anything. When you see Meeko, he'll answer your questions." Seeing the futility of her situation, she turned abruptly and went to her quarters to pack their things. After the boat docked in Miami and the last rope was tied into place, Robert came to her cabin and got their things, then walked her to the dock lounge without a word. Sunny angrily called a cab and went to the Miami airport. She bought a ticket to Los Angeles and checked their bags then called Kate to give her the flight number so she could be picked up.

Upon her arrival, Sunny was happy to see Kate who had a skycap waiting to collect the luggage and take it to the waiting car. On the drive from the airport, Kate saw that Sunny was withdrawn. Taking her hand Kate gently said, "I know your personal life is none of my business. I just want you to know I'm always here for you. By the way, how was the honeymoon?"

"It was wonderful at first, but disappointing in the end. Meeko was delayed. He'll join us in a few days," snapped Sunny.

Kate knew better than to ask any more questions and changed the subject to more practical matters.

"The contracts are ready for you to sign. I think you'll love the deal I've put together. I've listed your New York flat and the Los Angeles estate. The market is soft now, so it'll take time."

"Kate, if you made the deal, I know it's the best." Sunny remained lost in thought as she stared out the window.

"We're in our third week of rehearsals. Some of your favorite musicians are back, and the choreographer brought in a few of his dancers from New York. Costume fittings and promotion pictures are scheduled for Friday morning at ten o'clock. In the afternoon you'll work with your keyboard man on some new material. I called Camella, and she's at the house taking care of ShaTonga. I plan to return to New York Saturday morning, that is if you don't need me."

The driver pulled to a stop, grabbed the luggage and took it into the house. Sunny looked worried, realizing the coming year would bring major changes in her life. Seeing her troubled expression, Kate said, "Sunny, I know the coming months are going to be tough, but this tight schedule is needed to pull your finances back together. You know building a new show is very expensive, plus the marriage has cost you more money than I had anticipated. Also I've paid off Sam's hospital and funeral bills. I did try to schedule a few weeks off during the year so you could spend more time with Meeko. If you follow the itinerary I've set up, you'll be out of debt by the end of this year. We'll know more about your investments after we speak to the attorney."

"Thanks, Kate. Sorry about the attitude. You know I always pull my fat out of the fire. I just need to get back to work. Don't worry, I'll see you later."

Sunny waved goodbye and walked up the steps into Camella's outstretched arms, feeling the comfort of being home. Camella was filled with excitement and eager to hear about the honeymoon as she led Sunny to the patio, where they sat at a table filled with beautifully arranged fresh fruit. Sunny picked at the food and Camella, sensing she was not going to discuss her new marriage, quietly cleaned the table and continued her household duties.

Sunny roamed through her flower gardens and played with ShaTonga the rest of the afternoon. For the moment such distractions seemed to lessen her concern about Meeko. As night settled over the house, Sunny filled the tub, adding fresh cut herbs then climbed in for a long, relaxing soak. Dressing in a comfortable nightshirt, she went to the bedroom where she found a tray of assorted foods sitting in the middle of her bed. Knowing she could not sleep, she gathered all of her contracts from the desk and climbed into bed to read them. Picking at the food, she smiled at the brilliance of Kate's management skills and her financial wizardry. As she set the papers aside and turned off the light, her thoughts returned to her worries about Meeko. The house seemed too still, which only heightened her fears. After taking three heavy duty sleeping pills, she remembered she had an early appointment with Kate, so she set the alarm.

The alarm sounded and as Sunny fought the drowsiness, she yelled to Camella for a pot of black coffee, then stumbled into the bathroom to take two diet pills. By the time Kate arrived, Sunny was waiting on the patio with a tray of assorted foods and her manager's favorite coffee.

Time meant money to Kate and everything was business as usual. All appointments were established in hourly intervals, which took their day from breakfast to brunch and through the evening cocktail hour. By ten o'clock that night, all contracts were signed and Sunny closed the door on another business day with her manager. Badly needing to strip away the aftermath of the day's hectic pace, Sunny took a hot shower and several sleeping pills along with a glass of wine in hopes of avoiding another night filled with anxiety.

Sometime during the night the phone rang. Thinking it might be Meeko, she grabbed it, only to hear a dial tone on the other end. Fearing the worst, she lay in the dark, tossing and turning until she finally fell asleep. Late the following afternoon Sunny awoke and realized she had missed rehearsal. Filled with guilt, she drove frantically to the rehearsal hall, where she watched the dancers burn with new and exciting energy. She felt intimidated, wondering if she could keep up with the fast pace of her new show.

"Well, well, I see our star has finally graced us with her presence. Where the fuck have you been? How do you expect me to set the stage when you're not here? What's the matter, Darling? Is your marriage falling apart already?" Johnny, the choreographer, called out in his feminine, catty way.

Sunny strolled arrogantly toward the stage and shouted, "Shut the fuck up, Johnny, and don't you ever go there with me again! Remember, asshole, I pay your salary! What I do in my personal life is none of your goddamn business!"

The producer stepped from the shadows. "Cast, please take a half hour break." He turned to Sunny and Johnny. "Never let me see this kind of behavior in front of the cast again! Is that understood? All right, Sunny! This is our money you are playing with, so why in the hell are you late?"

Sunny tried to change the subject. "I can't work with this queen! I want him fired."

"You can't fire me! I have an ironclad contract. She's just a temperamental bitch who can never follow direction."

"Oh, I beg to differ with you, Johnny. If you read your contract, you'll see that she can fire you at any moment!" stated the producer. "This battle of clashing wills and overblown egos will close the show before it opens." He canceled the rehearsal and sent the cast home demanding that Sunny and Johnny return the next morning with the proper attitude or he would enforce a hundred dollar fine for every hour they were late and every uncalled for critical remark.

Sunny left the studio, knowing her producer was right, but hating his tight control on her show. At home, she told Camella not to answer the phone, then went to her bedroom to be alone. After hours of brooding and hating the loss of freedom that this contract represented, she was determined to win this battle and prove her self-worth once again.

Early the following day, Sunny made her rounds to the makeup artist, the hairdresser, the photographer, and the costume designer, then met with her music arranger to discuss the new material. By noon she stepped on stage to start rehearsing her dance routines with Johnny.

After several exhausting days of rehearsal, Sunny left the theatre and went directly home, too tired to change from her wet workout clothes. Fearing she could not keep up with Johnny's rigorous demands in the dance numbers, she called her physical trainer's answering service, saying, "Tell Teddy to come to the house as soon as you get this message. My show is too fast for me to cut, and I only have one month to get my aching body in shape."

Depressed, Sunny hung up the phone and stepped into the shower. Teddy had already arrived and was setting up the massage table when she hobbled into the room like a whipped puppy. "Oh, girlfriend! What in God's name have you done to that poor body?" Teddy giggled.

Sunny gave him the finger, dropped her robe and dramatically collapsed onto the table, saying, "Shut up, Teddy, I'm dying. Every muscle in my body is screaming in pain."

Teddy heated a special oil for her massage and teased in his usual whorish manner, "Girlfriend, just relax. Let these magic hands renew this beautiful body. Honey, within a week, I'll have you dancing circles around those little shits. I watched rehearsal the other day and let me tell you, I flipped over a couple of your hunks."

"Oh, please, Teddy. Who cares about your love life. Just fix this tired body before I die." Sunny let out the usual dramatic screams of ouches and yelps, but Teddy ignored her complaints and kept the energy flowing as he babbled on about the latest healing oils, herbs and massage techniques he had learned. By the time he was finished Sunny was completely relaxed and every muscle was free of pain. As she collapsed for the night Teddy quietly packed up and stopped by the kitchen to give Camella a shopping list of special foods, juices, vitamins and minerals, reminding her to insist that Sunny follow his prescribed regimen.

For the next two weeks, Teddy kept her muscles loose while feeding her vitamins and special drinks to bolster her mental and physical strength. Sunny felt good about what she was accomplishing without the need for sleeping pills.

Driving home in high spirits one night, Sunny was surprised to see all the lights in the house were off. Thinking Camella had retired early, she tiptoed upstairs to her bedroom, turned on the lights and screamed when she saw Meeko sitting on the edge of the bed with his arms extended. "I missed My Sweetheart."

"You bastard! Why in the hell are you sitting in the dark? You could have called out instead of scaring me half to death."

Meeko walked over apologetically and took her in his arms. "Sweetheart, you know I move within the silence of time. I wanted to surprise you."

"Don't touch me, you shit! Where in the hell have you been? Geezus Christ, you abandoned me in the middle of the fucking ocean, leaving me with a goddamn idiot while you sneaked away to who knows where! And now you show up in my bedroom and scare the fuck out of me! And you think I'm supposed to rush into your waiting arms?"

"Whoa! Easy, Baby. Listen to me! I'll tell you everything if you stop your ranting for a minute. Sweetheart, I owed Robert a big favor from our prison days and now the debt is paid. I couldn't tell you because I wanted to make sure you weren't harmed."

"Stop trying to placate me, you Blanket Ass! You could have called! After all, I am your wife and should be given some consideration!"

"Sunny, I promise, I'll never do anything like this again. My Sweetheart, let's not fight. I'm home and I need you to tell me that you love me." Meeko gently picked her up, placed her in the middle of the bed, and with soothing words began to undress her.

"Get your hands off of me and stop treating me as though I'm just a stupid woman. I know you made a dope deal and it was not just marijuana!"

"True, but what difference does it make? It's over and I won't talk about it anymore. Understand?" Sunny was livid and lunged at Meeko. He chuckled at her wild attempt to hit him and held her close to ward off her blows. "My, my, you're so tough. I think you're as cute as a spotted pup when you're angry. You know I'm not a fighter, I'm a passionate lover," Meeko teased playfully trying to kiss her.

Finding it was useless to fight against him, Sunny giggled. "Fuck it! I don't care if you get yourself killed," Then grabbing his penis, she demanded, "Give me your word that you'll never do anything like this again or I'll pull your dick off!"

Meeko begged for mercy, saying, "Okay, Ms. Sunny Beam. I give you my word." As she let go he ran his hand over her thighs and they both crawled under the sheets, Sunny melting under his touch.

During the next three weeks, their lives centered around their work except on the weekends, which were filled with rest and attempts to bring back the sensitivity in their relationship. Sunny's grueling schedule allowed Meeko the time to make a studio in the guesthouse and prepare for his upcoming art show. Both kept to their rigorous schedules while supporting the other's endeavors. Meeko sent his last painting off to New York, then prepared to accompany Sunny on her road tour opening in Las Vegas.

After arriving in Las Vegas, they settled into their new quarters. It had been almost a year since her last public appearance and feeling apprehensive about the show, Sunny went backstage to check on the sound and light boards, props and flies. Satisfied that everything was ready, she returned to her suite and dressed for the press party. At six o'clock, Sunny walked into the room on Meeko's arm looking exquisite, but her stomach was tied in knots. She graciously answered questions while the promotion team handed out press kits. Meeko soon found himself among a milling crowd of fans. A little blue-haired woman approached him, saying, "Don't you think she's wonderful?"

Meeko replied in a sweet flirtatious fashion. "You don't think I would be married to any other kind of woman, do you?" The woman, lost for words, giggled. Meeko winked at her, causing her to walk away smiling in confusion. He chuckled at his cleverness as Sunny gave him a dirty look. Sunny felt her tension building and excused herself knowing it was time to withdraw and prepare for her opening night on the Las Vegas Strip.

Sunny felt more at ease in her dressing room, and was thrilled to find it filled with flowers, gifts and telegrams. After checking her wardrobe, she said, "Well, I'm as ready as I'm gonna be." Sunny dressed for the show and could hear muffled voices filtering into her dressing room and knew she had a full house. At eight-thirty the house lights dimmed and the overture began. A melodic voice announced, "Ladies and gentleman, Ms. Sunny Beam." As the curtain slowly raised, the music came alive and colorful lights flooded the stage as Sunny stepped into the spotlight and began to weave her magical powers of illusion.

The pace of the show accelerated as Sunny changed from gown to gown, each more breathtaking than the one before. When the final curtain closed on the extravaganza, she bowed humbly to a standing ovation. After the third curtain call, she knew the show was a hit.

Meeko, watching her take a final bow, was astounded by her charisma and the control she had over the masses. As he watched his beautiful bride walk toward him, he felt proud she was his woman. Kissing her on the cheek, he said, "You were wonderful, you never cease to amaze me. I can't believe how you make those people eat out of your hand and they love you for it. I just don't understand how you can do it night after night!"

"I pray, Baby. I pray," she answered, as they worked their way through the backstage crowd and into her dressing room. Slipping into her favorite robe, she wrapped a towel around her neck to catch the sweat. As many people crowded into the dressing room to congratulate her, Meeko leaned close telling her he would order something special for their dinner to celebrate her success, then left.

To avoid the crowd, Sunny took the service elevator up to her suite and was surprised to find it filled with flowers and notes from friends. ShaTonga ran to her, tail wagging, to welcome her home. Sunny affectionately petted her before entering the living room to find Meeko pouring everyone a glass of champagne. After relaxing with their drinks everyone moved to the large balcony to enjoy a beautiful dinner overlooking the Strip.

During their meal, ShaTonga weaseled a place into the conversation by laying her head in Sunny's lap and whining. She stroked her affectionately, saying, "Ah, my wolfer puppy, without you around to remind me of who I am, I would never remember." She took a large piece of steak from her plate and gave it to ShaTonga.

Frowning, Meeko complained about feeding an animal at the table.

"Why not? She would share her food with me," joked Sunny, giving the wolf the rest of the meat. With a low growl ShaTonga warned everyone to stay away and carried if off to another room to make sure no one would steal her food.

"God, you're such a heathen," grumbled Meeko.

"I know, and this heathen is going to bed," Sunny answered, leaving the table.

Once they were settled for the night, ShaTonga crawled into Sunny's bed, placing her head on the pillow. Sunny giggled as she watched an aggravated Meeko push and shove ShaTonga to make himself a small space next to his wife.

When the curtain fell on her last show in Las Vegas, Meeko watched in amazement as the crew tore down, packed and loaded everything into the trucks within a mere two hours. Sunny and her family got in the their private bus as the musicians and dancers boarded the tour bus for a long night ride. The show's tight schedule demanded that they get rest when and where they could, so they all settled in quickly for a night's sleep as they were driven to their next performance.

A set routine developed as the tour progressed. Upon arrival the crew would meet in the showroom to prepare for the night's performance while Sunny picked up her publicity schedule from the road manager that contained the times and places for the television and radio appearances that would help push for last minute ticket sales. After her interviews, Sunny would return to the hotel for a rest. The road crew would sleep once the show was set up and when it was over they would tear down, pack up and drive to the next town.

Six months into the tour, they had worked their way across the United States and Canada. Everyone's nerves were on edge from lack of sleep as they traveled deserted highways, fighting bad weather, breakdowns and repairs on vehicles, wardrobe and equipment. The situation was taking its toll and creating constant fighting and explosive arguments among the crew.

Meeko realized that in reality the glamour of show business was an illusion and nothing but hard work. Becoming bored and disenchanted with this make-believe lifestyle, he began to spend more and more time with the road crew because they seemed more like normal people.

When Sunny found out that Meeko and most of her crew were using drugs, she voiced her fear that the show would get busted and told them if she found anyone using drugs, they would be fired on the spot. When the situation did not improve she was forced to replace trained members of her show with inexperienced help. She tightened the schedule once more to bring the show back to efficiency, but the new road crew's lack of knowledge brought about constant loss and breakage of equipment which caused everyone's morale to deteriorate.

Sunny had little time to spend with Meeko and he became resentful, taking her actions as a personal rejection. Sunny was devastated by his attitude, but no matter what she tried, he remained moody.

When they unloaded the prop trucks for a show in Dallas, Meeko found one of his paintings had been damaged and he berated her in front of the crew. Humiliated, Sunny said nothing knowing she must keep peace at all cost. Meeko felt trapped. He hated listening to all the petty grievances from the cast and began hanging out even more with the musicians and road crew.

During a rehearsal break one day, Sunny passed the musicians' dressing room and smelled pot. She was appalled when she opened the door to find drug paraphernalia lying around everywhere.

"I see we still have a problem. Your contracts state there will be no drugs around the show. Hell, look around! Can't you guys see the press is crawling all over this place? Dump this shit, right now. When I find the supplier, I'll turn his ass in! Is that understood?"

"Hey, wait minute," replied Meeko. "You turn up to fly, and smoke to turn down. Shit, even you can't keep up this ridiculous pace."

Sunny glared at Meeko, shocked that he had exposed her, but not understanding why he had become her enemy. She left the room knowing that the battle was on between them.

A short time later, Meeko returned to their room to find Sunny huddled in a fetal position in the shower, crying.

"My God, woman! What are you doing?" He helped her out and wrapped her in a towel. Laying her across the bed, he covered her shivering body as he said, "C'mon, Baby! Pull yourself together or cancel the rest of this tour. You've pushed everyone to the breaking point! The crew hates you, but they kiss your ass because they depend on you for their paychecks."

"Meeko, you know that I've done everything humanly possible for them. They're paid well but this is a tough business. Any good roadie knows what is involved before they sign on. I can't back out of this contract, otherwise I'll get sued!"

"Sweetheart, give these guys a break. We're driving straight through tonight, so get some rest and we'll talk more tomorrow," implored Meeko, handing her three sleeping pills.

Sunny threw the pills across the room in disgust. She grabbed the phone and called Kate, asking her to meet the show in Birmingham, Alabama.

By the following afternoon Kate had canceled the next two weeks of performances, re-booking them on the tail end of the tour. A new stage manager was brought in and four musicians, six dancers and all but three of the road crew were fired. Ten days later the show was back on the road with performers that understood the rules about drug abuse and being on time. The spark of life was back in the show and the pressure was minimal. For the next three months the show received rave reviews as they traveled from city to city.

Sunny was grateful when they finally arrived in the Midwest knowing the tour was almost over. There she met with Gary, the road man, and smiled in relief when she discovered the show's profits were larger than projected. Kate had paid all of the bills and there was a sizable amount in the bank.

When Sunny went to Meeko's makeshift studio to share the good news, she was horrified to see everything in disarray. His paints had been spilled and several of his canvases had been ripped. Her own portrait lay slashed and smeared with red paint.

Sunny called out to him frantically and when he did not respond, she opened the bathroom door and stared in horror. With emotions ranging from hatred to pity, she watched the blood run from a slashed, blown vein as Meeko continued to poke his arm trying to find a usable one. As he pushed the plunger in, Meeko's eyes glazed over and he ordered Sunny out of the bathroom as he nodded off and slumped to the floor. Not knowing what else to do, she began to pack his clothes.

Half an hour later, he walked into the room as if nothing had happened and when he saw his things packed, he said, "Sunny, I have no problem with you—it's your way of life."

"My God, Meeko, you knew I needed money, that's why I had to do this tour. Don't you think it's a little late to change your mind about my way of life?"

"I know, Sweetheart. But the pressure is causing my headaches to return. When I couldn't get my prescriptions filled, I went to the street and brought drugs into the show. I wanted to leave, but I couldn't without you. I thought the only way to get you off the road was to destroy your show."

Devastated and unable to speak, Sunny stared at Meeko for a long time before answering. "I never thought you were the coyote in my camp. I'll see that you leave for New York today."

Meeko shipped the undamaged paintings to Joanna, then went backstage for one last look at Sunny. She was on stage singing his favorite song, "Stormy Weather." When she glanced toward the wings and saw Meeko waving goodbye, she responded with a subtle wave as he vanished from sight. With emptiness in her heart and tears streaming down her face, she let the words of the song express her grief. Sunny left the stage after a standing ovation and went to the bus, feeling utterly abandoned and consumed by loneliness.

Despite her anger and sense of loss, Sunny continued the tour like a robot, performing in city after city. Many times she watched the sun creep through the window, ending another sleepless night. Three weeks had passed and she still had not heard from Meeko. She called Kate for information regarding his whereabouts, only to hear that he had moved into her New York flat. Filled with resentment, she dialed her New York number and asked Meeko why he was living at her place.

"I was gonna call you, but I've been busy getting my medical records transferred here and arranging my new show. I'm sorry I didn't ask if I could live here, but Kate figured it would be okay since I was short on money."

"Common decency would have demanded you ask, but since you're there and I'm here, what can I do?" Her voice was cold and unforgiving.

"Sunny, I'm sorry for fucking up. I know I can get myself together if you'll give me some time alone. I'm back on my medications, and I know things will work out. I'm doing some really good work, and after the show I'll pay you for staying here," he said, hoping to placate her.

After a long discussion, both decided the time apart could possibly help rebuild their relationship. But afterward, even though she knew the separation was necessary, Sunny felt the same old loneliness creeping back into her soul.

Many weeks later, after another hard show, an exhausted Sunny stepped into the bus hoping to get a good night's rest. She was shocked when she saw the voodoo dolls

Ashna had given her had been ripped to pieces and were strewn across the floor. She screamed in terror, knowing the significance of this destruction. A frightened ShaTonga grabbed one of the doll's heads, tucked her tail between her legs and raced to the back of the bus to hide. A hysterical Sunny picked up the pieces, then went to get the doll's head from the wolf. As she reached for it, ShaTonga snapped at her, drawing blood from her hand.

"You bitch! If you'd done this to Sam you'd be dead! There's only room for one pack leader here and that's me!"

Sunny yanked the doll head from ShaTonga, tears streaming down her face as she carefully began to examine the remains of each doll. She was filled with terror when some blood from her hand dripped onto the right cheek of the male doll. She fled to the phone and called Meeko.

"The voodoo dolls are destroyed! Do you realize what this means?"

"Sweetheart, surely you're not going to believe what that old witch told you! Hell, that crazy old woman is nothing but a spoof who preys on other people's fears. When are you going to learn there is no power outside of you? We're the ones that make the choices in our lives. ShaTonga probably tore up the dolls because she wasn't getting enough attention."

"Thanks! I really need more guilt to deal with! Meeko, I'm afraid! You were there, you heard her words and everything she told us has come true." Sunny slammed down the receiver and began to bawl.

On the road the next day she told Camella about the problem. Camella pulled her rosary beads from her pocket and prayed as Sunny wrapped the dolls in sage. When they were out of the city Sunny told the driver to pull over at the next isolated place.

Sunny got off the bus, built a fire and held a pipe ceremony to burn the dolls. She felt at peace when she returned, but continued to pray for the rest of the day. When they arrived at their next stop, a worried and superstitious Camella went immediately to a Catholic church and lit a candle. Sunny decided to keep ShaTonga in her dressing room to prevent her from getting bored and causing more destruction.

That evening Sunny stepped on the stage, hoping everything was all right, but when she missed three cues and could not remember the words to one of the songs, she panicked. Somehow she managed to finish the rest of the show before collapsing backstage. Pandemonium reigned as Gary, the road manager, sent for a physician. The doctor found her to be physically and emotionally exhausted and prescribed tranquilizers with strict instructions to rest.

By the following afternoon, there was a new itinerary established for Sunny. Fearing her reputation could be tarnished, Gary went to extreme measures to keep her image intact. He sent Camella and ShaTonga back to Los Angeles, insisting that Sunny travel by air until the tour was completed. Everything was done to make sure Sunny's needs and comforts were met. In each city on her tour, a limousine was waiting to take her to the finest hotel. Gary stayed close to her side brutally enforcing the doctor's orders.

Although Sunny somehow continued to perform up to the standards of her reputation, she was lonely and depressed. In an effort to reach out to people, she called Hazel, only to hear her stepmother needed three thousand dollars to bail out her stepbrother who was in jail again.

"Hazel, every time I talk to you it's about money! You know he's gonna run as soon as he hits the street." There was a long silence. "Fuck it. I'll wire it this afternoon. Let me speak to Peck." When he came to the phone, she said, "Hey, Cuz, I'm in a world of shit. I need four pair of your special moccasins. Maybe they'll keep me on my feet until this tour is over. At the airport you'll find a prepaid ticket to Houston. I'll meet you there."

Within five hours, Sunny was at the airport having dinner with Peck. After sharing the latest family gossip, Peck walked Sunny back to the waiting limousine. As they said goodbye, he handed her a beautifully beaded knapsack, saying, "I was kinda worried about your request, so I brought you a cozy pair of bedroom slippers to help you relax."

Sunny took it and looked inside, then roared with laughter. "Are you fucking crazy? There's at least a pound here."

"Yeah, just trying to take care of my cuz. Thought you'd appreciate some good homegrown wacky tobacky."

They both laughed and hugged affectionately as Sunny said, "Thanks, Cuz," then got into the limousine.

"Yeah, back atcha, Baby. See ya around."

Upon arriving back at her dressing room, Sunny dressed then made a strong pot of coffee. She poured herself a cup, then dipped a toothpick in the coffee and into a small vile of white powder. She casually stirred the coffee with her toothpick, then drank it, saying, "Showtime, Baby, and no more fucking problems." Sunny walked on the stage flying, knowing she was back on track.

During the following weeks, Sunny was like a machine that never shut down. Her magic potion kept her wired for days at a time. Night after night she was able to remain sharp and stable through every show.

By the time they arrived in Denver, a side musician had been hired for the evening show. He wanted to speak with Sunny, in hopes of getting a full time job. He waited for her to leave the dressing room and stepped forward blocking her pathway. "Good evening, Ms. Beam. How are you?"

She took a long hard look at him. "What the fuck do you care?" She pushed briskly past him.

After the show, the musician approached her again, saying, "Ms. Beam, you were right. I didn't care how you were. I was just kissing up to get a gig with your show."

Sunny stared in disbelief. What a gift! This was the first time anyone had been truthful with her for a very long time. She walked away smiling and called back over her shoulder, "Get packed! You're hired." Sunny changed into street clothes. When she arrived back at her room she ordered food before taking a shower. As she sat in the middle of her bed watching TV and eating, she suddenly felt lonely for Meeko and decided to call him.

"I'm glad you called. I was lying here thinking about you."

"Me too. Remember how we used to dream of developing the mineral rights on the reservation?"

"Yeah."

"Well, I've got good news. I met with an old friend who's in the oil business and we talked at great length. Since Fort Peck is so close to the Williston Basin, it caught his interest. He asked me to call and see if you would meet with him to discuss the laws that govern the rez."

Meeko was thrilled. "My God, that would be wonderful! I'll fly in tomorrow, if you can set up an appointment with him. What we need is a waiver that will allow all Indians to negotiate their own gas and oil leases instead of letting the BIA handle the bids for us. Sunny, do you remember when we spoke with Adam Steene, the superintendent? He told us if we could get a better deal, he would refuse the semi-annual gas and oil lease sale bids. You know they hold those bids at sixteen and two-thirds, up to twenty percent. We need to get a minimum of twenty-five percent to be equal with what everyone else is receiving in the oil business. I think I've found a loophole under *Title Twenty-Five* in S. 1894."

"Are you talking about the Self Determination Act?"

"You got it. I have a gut feeling it'll fly. I'll write a proposal tonight and see what we can do." Sunny was exhilarated. Meeko was flying in and they could spend some time together. The next day, they met with Murray, the owner of a large oil company, at the Denver Petroleum Club where Meeko presented his proposal.

Sunny sat watching both men quietly sizing up one another. "For Christ's sake! I brought you two together to make money and do something good for the people. So stop this nonsense and let's get down to business, gentlemen." Before their meeting ended, it was determined that a waiver was needed to expedite a joint venture contract.

On March 16, 1982, Meeko flew to Washington to address the Senate Subcommittee:

"Gentlemen, I own an Indian gas and oil leasing company. I stand here torn between what is best for my people and what is best for me. I will try to make my presentation brief, but I feel that a few necessary points must be made concerning how Bill S. 1894 might affect all the Indian landowners. Speaking first on behalf of these landowners, I must express my concern pertaining to the Bureau of Indian Affairs and the United States Geological Survey, USGS, which at the present time are not staffed to carry this additional workload.

"For example, being from the Fort Peck Indian Reservation, I personally know there are hundreds of leases that have not been reviewed. They date back to sales that took place three years ago. This is due to the excessive burdens that these two agencies are presently operating under. I have contacted each of them to make a determination of how this additional workload could be approached with more efficiency." Meeko passed out copies of his research and recommendations.

"Again, gentlemen, I have spoken at great length to the directors from the USGS and the Bureau of Indian Affairs. It was their opinions that this bill should be passed, not just considered. If you look through the portfolio dated June 23, 1976, you will find that it was originally sent to the Commissioner of Indian Affairs from the Director of the USGS.

"Please follow me closely as I quote from this document. It will help you review the inherent problems in the mediation of the oil and gas agreements. This should convince you that proper handling of these agreements will require the establishment of a separate organizational entity within either the Bureau of Indian Affairs or the USGS.

"Such an organizational entity would be designed to provide the services the Indian tribes would require for intelligent evaluation of the proposals, beginning with the preliminary stages of negotiations through the implementation of the contracts. The staff should include technical experts with supporting disciplines such as economics, contracting, legal, geological, geophysical, engineering and accounting, to ensure the proper interpretation and implementation of this agreement.

"At this time, the Geological Survey is not presently staffed or funded to assist in the arbitration to service those oil and gas agreements now being negotiated pursuant to *Title Twenty-Five S.C. 396b*. Accordingly, the proposed amendment to this agreement specifically provides and states that the supervisor is not authorized, nor empowered to monitor, account for, collect or distribute funds resulting from profit sharings contained in an oil and gas agreement; nor can they enforce these contractual provisions relating to the performance which exceeds the requirements contained in *Title Twenty-Five CFR 171* and Chapter Two of *Title Thirty* of the *Code of Federal Regulations*.

"This outlines the present situation. Now I will speak further on behalf of the landowners. I feel it is my responsibility to inform each member of this committee that we, as a People, need the protection of a special agency empowered to assist us in the monitoring of these oil and gas lease agreements. I have personally witnessed the power and shrewdness of the oil industry, and without an agency specifically established to protect the Indian's interest, I fear that we would be unleashing a pack of wolves upon a helpless herd of sheep.

"On Fort Peck alone, there are many examples of Indians having been approached in bars by oil representatives while they were completely inebriated, and offered sums as ridiculously low as two hundred dollars to sign their leases. And even though these leases are reviewed by the local agency, many times such leases have been processed and approved without the landowner's knowledge."

Meeko passed out a binder containing a set of papers and continued:

"I have gathered many opinions from conversations that I have held with major oil companies, along with numerous other independent oil companies. I have found them all to be in agreement that a bill such as this would definitely be a boon to the industry. As a member of this industry myself, I would have to agree. If my people were allowed to negotiate their own lease agreements, without an agency established to interpret and evaluate the pending contracts, the legal departments of the oil industry would have a field day using their dual meaning contractual language against my people.

"I do not mean to cast aspersions against all oil companies, but when I was faced with these contractual loopholes, it was my lack of knowledge and experience which allowed the oil companies to legally steal from me and manipulate me to their advantage.

"Now I speak as an owner of Indian land. I seek a change in these laws. We need to empower my people and give them back their legal right to negotiate the use of their own lands."

Meeko was silent for a moment, allowing them to absorb the impact of his speech. He studied each man for his sincerity and fairness toward his people, before continuing:

"Gentlemen, the land is our Mother. She has fed all those before us and will do so for the generations to come. Not only am I speaking for my people, but I am speaking for our children's children. We all know the Indian lives below the line of poverty and I think we all accept there is a great need for jobs on the reservations. But poor as we are, we will never sacrifice the bones of our ancestors to make money." Meeko sat down and waited for the committee's response.

"What you say is interesting. We will consider and discuss this issue then get back with you when we have made a determination," stated the Senate Sub-committee leader.

Meeko had a gut feeling that he would get little support from the Sub-committee members and went directly to the hotel to call Sunny about his presentation. "My Sweetheart, did I ever tell you how much I love you?" he asked, glad to hear her voice.

"How did it go?"

"You would have been very proud of me. I was nervous as hell and a couple of times I had cottonmouth so bad that my lips stuck to my gums. I was embarrassed over this and took your advice. I prayed that Great Spirit would allow the saliva to wet my mouth, and guess what? It did, and my speech was piss eloquent. If I ever rid my mind of the bitterness that hides behind my frailties, I know you can teach me the sweetness of life. If we win this one, someday they'll know the woman that made it happen."

"Oh, for Christ's sake, Meeko, tell me what happened!"

"I want you to know I held that fucking floor until I was sure I had made my point. Our problem is with the head of the Department of Interior. That sonuvabitch is adamantly against this law being changed. I know he hates Indians, but I vow to you I'll stay here until I win this battle, no matter how long it takes. They'll give me what I came here to get."

"What can I do to help?"

"Love me, but mostly pray for me. If we are to have this waiver, it will come from the spirits. I know it will help the people, yet I fear this new law could still be abused. I'm torn between these thoughts, but know I must do the right thing. If you call me and I'm not here, just leave a message. I'll be spending most of my time in the law library boning up on what they can and cannot do. I'm writing briefs to prepare my response regardless of whether they accept or reject my proposal. I must be prepared for any decision they offer. As soon as I know something, I'll call you. I love you, and remember, pray for me," said Meeko as he hung up the phone.

Sunny and Meeko spent the next few weeks in restless nights of worry. Meeko met almost daily with the assigned committee. Then late on a Friday afternoon, Meeko called Sunny with excitement in his voice. "Sweetheart, do you still have that bottle of champagne we bought long ago for a special occasion?" Sunny left the phone, opened the bottle and poured herself a glass. When she returned, he said, "Raise your glass with me, but promise you will say nothing. Just hang up the phone and go to the airport. I'll be home in three hours. Okay, My Sweetheart, are you ready?" asked Meeko.

"Ready," answered Sunny, excitedly.

"Remember when I told you the stem of the rose is covered with small swords? Well our relationship has been challenged, and we have experienced the bloodletting of the rose because we have handled our love too carelessly. Lift your glass to those beautiful lips and know we are celebrating a great victory.

"I got the Waiver!!!"

The Beginning of the End

It was a glorious moment when Meeko stepped off the plane and into Sunny's waiting arms. Handing her the signed waiver he said, "I give this to you. After all, it was you that made it happen."

Sunny smiled, knowing this was the first step toward the realization of their shared dreams. In buoyant spirits, they left the airport and spent the rest of the afternoon savoring Meeko's moment of glory in Washington where he had won another battle for the American Indian.

Early the following morning they met in Murray's office to sign all the necessary papers to open the first Indian-owned oil company on the Fort Peck Indian Reservation. They decided to wait until the spring thaw before bringing in the equipment and in the meanwhile, Meeko would open an office on the reservation to begin drafting mineral lease contracts.

After they left the meeting, Sunny called Kate to have her transfer funds into an international account, precluding the possibility of governmental control.

Thrilled to know their future was secure, Meeko and Sunny rented a suite where they spent a magical candlelit night weaving the enchantment of oneness that only two lovers could know.

But all to soon, the magic faded. When he came in late the next night, Meeko fell across the bed in a drunken stupor. Hours later, Sunny woke to the sound of running water and was shocked to see Meeko peeing on the drapes. She recalled Cheering Woman's words of warning—never awaken a sleepwalker, they can die from shock.

Furious, and not caring at that moment if he lived or died, she called out to Meeko who, embarrassed, quickly cleaned up the mess then went to sleep on the sofa. The following morning, Sunny demanded that he explain himself, but Meeko emphatically denied her accusations, refusing to discuss the subject.

After this incident, their relationship grew even more strained and Sunny decided it was time to return to the stage. She boarded the plane with tears running down her face, a gut wrenching sadness creeping into her heart. She hoped their marriage was strong enough to sustain another separation and made up her mind to courageously face whatever the future held.

Three months later, Sunny took her final bow with her production company and flew back to Los Angeles arriving home about four in the morning. She walked up the steps, her arms filled with presents as she struggled with the key to open the door.

Everything was packed for moving and a momentary sadness gripped Sunny's heart as she accepted the fact the house needed to be sold in order for them to relocate to Billings, Montana near the BIA office.

Quickly dismissing her sad thoughts, she called out excitedly like a child on Christmas morning. Camella and ShaTonga ran down the stairs, eager to receive the gifts that Sunny always provided on her return home.

After breakfast, Sunny phoned Meeko hoping he would share in her excitement about the move, only to find his schedule did not coincide with hers. She did learn, however, that he liked their new home and had already set up his art studio in the guest house. She hung up the phone in disappointment knowing she would be traveling across the country without him.

Sunny headed upstairs to take a shower and crawled into bed. As she sank blissfully under the silk comforter, she noticed some of her personal photo albums stacked on a chair. Intrigued, she grabbed the pictures and sat in the middle of the bed to look at them. When she opened the first book, several packets of pictures unexpectedly fell out. She saw they had been taken during the remodeling stages of the house. The photos stirred happy memories of when she had first purchased this home, and she hoped the new house in Billings would be as gratifying.

Sunny recalled all the lonely highways she had traveled during her early years in show business. She reflected on the memories of beautiful panoramic views under clear starry skies and the serenity of the scattered country homes nestled among mounds of fresh fallen snow.

Sunny loved the chimneys with their lazy curls of smoke drifting aloft. They had always made her feel their warmth was waiting to welcome a family member home. She had once made a promise to *Wakan Tanka* that if she was ever gifted with a home there would be a fireplace with smoke curling from the chimney and a little yellow porch light to remind all lonely travelers of the security that came from a loving family.

She smiled as she remembered the day when she had moved into this house. She had rushed to the grocery store to buy the little yellow magical light. When the clerk told her it was just a bug light, she had been devastated. But nevertheless she bought it and knew it was her special little yellow magical light that would always shine at the entrance of her home.

Sunny prayed to *Wakan Tanka*, asking him to make her Billings home as warm and inviting as this one.

Setting the pictures aside, she went to the kitchen to find the housekeeper, Camella preparing an evening snack. She kissed her playfully on the cheek while stealing a bite from the tray. Pretending to be angry, Camella scolded, "Call Miss Kate. She needs to speak with you right away."

Sunny dialed Kate, smiling when she heard her usual curt hello.

"Hey, what's up?"

"Sunny, I'm really proud of you. Financially, this tour has made you debt free. The flat sold, and I've transferred the money into your account. I'll do the same when escrow closes on the California house. The money must be reinvested within a year, so don't dilly-dally."

"Once I'm in Montana, I'll send you all the paper work on the new company. I expect to get a quick turn around on my investment."

"After you're settled, take some time to rest before we set up your next tour. In the meantime, be happy and keep me posted on how things are going."

The movers arrived early the following morning. They quickly packed the truck then headed for Montana. Within an hour Sunny, Camella and ShaTonga had begun their extensive cross-country drive. It had been a long day and by the time they reached the Rocky Mountains, Sunny was excited at the thought she and Meeko would soon be together.

As the sun sunk low in the sky a deer darted in front of the motor home. Sunny slammed on her brakes to avoid a collision, but the deer hit the windshield, shattering the glass in all directions.

After checking to make sure everyone was okay, she asked Camella to light emergency flares along the highway. Sunny thanked the Great Spirit for protecting her family, grabbed the CB mike and called for help.

The deer was still alive, and she struggled to pull its mangled body to the ground. Seeing the suffering in its beautiful eyes, Sunny knew what must be done. She retrieved her pistol and approached the deer with great sadness, asking forgiveness for what she was about to do.

She pulled the trigger. As its body went limp, Sunny's eyes filled with tears. She bent down and gently closed its eyes, offering a silent prayer to *Wakan Tanka* for its safe journey back to the spirit world.

A small crowd had gathered around them. Two of the men helped her strap the deer onto the back of the motor home and Sunny resumed the journey without a windshield. After a short distance she realized the winds were too strong to go any further. She pulled off the highway and drove on back roads to the nearest town hoping to replace the windshield, but there was no one available to do the work and she was forced to drive another fifty miles to get one installed.

The hour was late when Sunny finally climbed back behind the wheel. She knew that the Crow Reservation was getting ready for ceremony and decided to cut across their reservation and take the deer to her long time friend, Lamar, to give to the people. Determined to reach her destination as quickly as possible, Sunny stepped on the gas as dark clouds formed overhead. Within minutes *Wakinyan* was throwing bolts of lightning all around as forceful crosswinds gathered momentum to release solid sheets of heavy rain. Sunny was forced to hang her head out the window to see as she continued inching her way through the storm.

It was almost daybreak when they pulled into Lamar's yard. Finding he was not home, Sunny suggested to Camella that she make the beds in their motorhome so they could get some rest. Camella nodded, silently wondering if Sunny was possessed by the worst kind of evil demon to have made her go through such a hair raising experience.

A few moments later, Lamar pounded on the door, startling them. Sunny was happy to see him standing there with a big smile on his face. "Hey, see you got yourself a deer. Well come on in the house, I'll make you some breakfast."

Within minutes the smell of coffee filled the kitchen as everyone sat around the table discussing the accident. Lamar called a few friends and soon the yard was filled with people preparing the deer meat and loading it into Lamar's truck to take to the grandmothers for the ceremony.

When Sunny expressed her dismay at killing the animal, Lamar took her hand.

"Sunny, hitting that deer was no accident. It was a gift, and you were the vessel the Great Spirit used to answer my people's prayers. You see, it's the last day of our ceremony and we have no food for the giveaway. But I knew Creator would take care of us.

"Sunny, when are you going to stop questioning these things? We are all related and stand as one person, one pole. It's not necessary to know the reason behind *Wakan Tanka's* bigger plans. It's experiences like these that build a strong belief in the wisdom of the Great Mystery.

"Sunny, if life's lessons were easy, we wouldn't need the earth journey to grow in spirit. Just think of this as another lesson to reveal more about yourself. Don't resist knowledge, or you'll keep repeating the same lesson until you learn a bigger truth. Like that eagle flying way over there, we too can look directly into the face of any experience that Creator brings to our attention. You must learn to accept that Great Spirit works through all things. To show my appreciation, I'm going to make something very special for you out of the hide. Now let's go visit with some people who are anxious to see you again."

Sunny smiled and accepted his invitation. After visiting with many old friends Sunny, with Camella and ShaTonga in tow, left for Billings. As they drove past the large shade trees that surrounded the beautiful grounds of the Crow tribal offices, Sunny recalled the days when she and her grandmother had come here for healing ceremonies.

A couple of hours later they drove up a winding dirt road that led to Sunny's new home at the top of Emerald Hills. She had only seen the house through pictures the Realtor had sent her, and she was happily surprised by the wondrous view and the beauty of the surrounding grounds.

Once inside the house, Camella found that Meeko had stocked the kitchen with food, and was pleased to find that the furniture was set up according to the diagrams she had given the movers.

While Camella prepared dinner, Sunny and ShaTonga went to explore the ten acre plot. Taking a narrow path down the hill, they came upon an old Medicine Wheel surrounded by tall pine trees. Sunny picked sage, smoked herself off and sat in the peaceful wheel, observing the Stone People while the winds raced through the pine trees speaking in soft whispers to the flying ones about this stranger who was invading their territory. Soon many winged ones had gathered amongst the pine boughs and were loudly discussing the presence of this intruder.

Sunny looked out at the spectacular view of the city far below. She breathed in the pure air and reminisced about the time so many years ago when she had helped gather special stones like these to build her grandmother's Medicine Wheel. As the sun lowered in the sky, Sunny left the Medicine Wheel and took a shortcut up another hill where she found the guest house surrounded by a garden. Finding the door unlocked, Sunny walked in and discovered that Meeko had sketches pinned to the walls, along with three unfinished canvases that showed great promise.

All at once, Sunny's apprehension subsided and she felt comfortable with her decision to return to Indian country.

She and ShaTonga walked back to the house for dinner. After eating, she phoned Meeko at the motel. Many rings later, Meeko's cousin Ruby answered the phone. Sunny left a message that she would be arriving in Fort Peck on the morning flight and asked Ruby to have Meeko meet her at the airport.

As Sunny boarded the plane to the reservation, she saw it was filled to capacity. She took a seat next to a white man and was amazed to find him reading a copy of the new waiver, which they soon began to discuss. Other passengers overheard and many business cards were passed to her from oil representatives who wanted to do business with the Indian. Sunny arranged for several of them to meet with Meeko to discuss the potential of developing oil contracts on the reservation.

When the plane landed Sunny rushed to the small terminal excited to share this good news with Meeko.

She stopped at the door when she saw Meeko drunk, swaying back and forth as he hung onto the ticket counter for balance. He needed a shave, his clothes were filthy and his face was badly bruised. He removed his sunglasses to reveal two black eyes, and tried to mumble a welcome through his badly swollen mouth. Looking around she saw several of his buddies who were also drunk, along with a very pregnant Ruby and her husband, David.

Sunny watched in humiliation as the oil men left the terminal in disgust. Ruby struggled out of her chair and took the keys from Meeko as the motley crew climbed into the back of the truck. Still enraged, Sunny got into the front seat with Ruby.

"Ruby! What the hell's going on?"

Ruby remained quiet until she pulled out of the parking lot, at which point she let loose.

"This has been going on for a month. It's drink, fight and party all the time. Humph, I got Meeko out of jail last week for drunk and disorderly conduct. Sunny, he's so bad that me and my husband moved in with him to keep him from being beaten up or rolled every night. I told him you were flying in this morning and to get straight before you got here—but no, not him. Me, pregnant and all, I let David talk to that crazy bear.

"Well, you know Meeko won't listen, so they got in a fight and David whipped the dogshit out of him then threw him in the shower, clothes and all, and got him ready to meet you." She roared with laughter. "Hell, Sunny, I don't know what you can do with this nut. All I know is, you better do something before he gets himself killed." Ruby parked the truck in the motel lot. Meeko and his buddies headed to the truck stop to get something to eat.

"You wanna make a small wager they don't make it?" Ruby chuckled as Sunny turned and gave her a stern look. "C'mon, Sister, where's your sense of humor?"

She and David followed Sunny to Meeko's room. When Sunny opened the door, a horrible stench assaulted her, and she stood for a moment in total shock. Scattered around the room were pieces of broken furniture, take-out containers half filled with rotting food, piles of dirty clothes and several empty whiskey bottles.

"What's been going on here?"

"I don't know. He's just mean," answered Ruby, as she attempted to pick up a drape that had recently been torn from the window.

Just then, the manager stepped inside and angrily handed Sunny a bill, demanding eighteen hundred dollars to cover the damages. "I want you Indians out of my motel and don't ever come back!"

Sunny paid the bill, assuring him they would leave immediately.

Somehow she got her anger under control, and less than fifteen minutes later, she and Cousin Ruby were well into packing Meeko's things. When she found a bloody pair of women's underpants under the bed, she screamed in rage, "What the fuck is this?"

"Looks like a skinny woman's underpants, huh? I know for sure they're not mine," chuckled Ruby, rubbing her big belly.

When they had piled his things in the back of the truck, Sunny asked Ruby to drive her to the cafe where she marched directly to Meeko's table and tossed the bloody underpants into his face.

"Who's the bitch that these belong to, and why were they under your bed?"

"Probably some white honky I was fucking," drawled Meeko nonchalantly as he continued to eat his breakfast.

Sunny lost control and began to beat his face until Meeko jumped up and hurled the contents of the table at her. The owner approached them with a baseball bat, and looking directly at Meeko, yelled, "I've already called the cops! I want all of you outta here!"

Humiliated, Sunny ran from the restaurant crying hysterically.

Ruby drove Sunny to the only other motel in town where she checked, in then went to her room to change her stained clothes. Following Sunny into the room, Ruby insisted despite Meeko's bad behavior they had to find him or he would be in jail before morning. They searched numerous bars without success. In exasperation, Ruby suggested they try the Watering Hole, the gathering place for the worst reservation riffraff. They walked up and down the bar scrutinizing everyone, demanding to know Meeko's whereabouts.

Andy, six-foot-six and one of the biggest Indians on the reservation, tried to grab Sunny. "Come on Breed! I'm a better man than what you got, so let this Indian show you a good time."

As Sunny dodged him, Ruby retorted, "I guess you're too drunk to listen and I know you're too dumb to hear!" She snatched a half-empty beer bottle from the bar and broke it over his head.

Andy's face reddened with anger and he slapped Ruby hard across the face, sending her crashing to the floor. With no thought for the child she was carrying, he brutally kicked her in the stomach, causing her to scream with pain. Within seconds the room was filled with flying bottles and bar stools as the crowd rode Andy like a stubborn bucking mule to the floor.

In the midst all this chaos, the bartender helped Ruby to her feet and walked her to the back door, urging Sunny to get her to the clinic. Unnerved, Sunny helped Ruby into the truck.

The moment Ruby was seated, her water broke. After a frantic drive to the hospital, two nurses rushed her into the delivery room. Sunny waited anxiously with the sad realization that Ruby's child would be another Indian baby born with Fetal Alcohol Syndrome.

She threw her hands in the air, exasperated, with the insanity of it all. Oh yes, she was definitely back on the reservation. Welcome home Sunny!

After phoning every bar in town, Sunny finally located David and informed him that Ruby had given birth to a baby girl. On his way into the hospital, he let out a war whoop to honor the arrival of his daughter.

Exhausted, Sunny drove back to the motel. She was walking to her room when Meeko called out to her from the bar. Noting he was appropriately dressed, she sat with him, saying, "I see you've found me. Come we'll talk in my room."

"I'm not going anywhere! We'll talk here!" growled Meeko, downing his drink and demanding another.

Sunny felt a chill run through her as she recognized the red-eyed demon sitting on one of the ice cubes in his glass. When Meeko lifted the glass and drank, the fiery demon stared back at her through Meeko's eyes, and she became even more frightened. She knew it had taken control of Meeko's soul, and horrified, she went to her room.

After the bar closed Meeko picked up a key from the front desk. He opened the door of their room and immediately passed out on the floor. Sunny cried at the sight of him, knowing that if circumstances did not change their marriage would soon end.

The following morning, Meeko showered and dressed as though nothing out of the ordinary had happened. As he started to leave the room, he turned to Sunny. "Sunny, meet me in the bar at two o'clock. Some oil people will be there and you should be there too since we're signing some new contracts. I'm sorry about yesterday. I promise it won't happen again."

Sadly, Sunny dressed and waited for Shung' to drive her to Auntie Lizzie's. As they pulled into the yard, both smiled when they saw Auntie Lizzie standing excitedly at the door. "I could feel you coming," she said, as she hugged Sunny then took Shung' by the arm and walked her to the kitchen. Auntie Lizzie served black coffee and her special fry bread admidst talk of the damage the oil companies were doing to the reservation.

Finally Sunny spoke about her troubled marriage, and upon the advice of these two wise women, they drove out to Granbear's old homestead. Sunny was surprised to find that Meeko had been repairing the place. He had cleaned up the property and rebuilt the old *Inipi*. When they walked inside, however, Sunny noticed a pile of quilts folded in the corner and bottles of stale whiskey scattered around the room.

"Usually when Meeko disappears, you can find him here," said Auntie Lizzie. "Sunny, you've got to be strong during these hard times. He never talks with me about his drinking, but he's become just like Renna. I think he wants the future that Granbear predicted, but it's too much work. It's going to take many prayers and all the strength you can muster to save him."

The women cried for Meeko while they walked around the old homestead and Auntie Lizzie told Sunny about the old days when Granbear was the head of the Bear Clan. When Sunny saw 'Meeko Long Bear, 8 years old' carved on the outhouse door, she wondered what he had been like at that age.

She remembered the time when he had taken her on a picnic and they had spent hours discussing his plans to eventually rebuild the place and stock it with a herd of buffalo. Sunny could no longer see his dream. All she saw were empty fields of burnt grass and dust whipping the rotting boards from the house.

She was disheartened with her marriage and was beginning to regret getting involved with the oil business. The jobs it had created did not support families as they had intended, but rather kept ten bars flourishing in a town of three thousand people.

Upon their return to Auntie Lizzie's house, Shung' drove Sunny back to the motel. Still in deep thought, Sunny feared Meeko would never fulfill Granbear's vision. Like the rest, he now met each morning at the Bureau of Indian Affairs building to get social services, food commodities, health care and checks for the land leases, then spent the rest of the day drinking.

Why do my people tolerate the prejudice of the surrounding white farmers who lease their land through the BIA for mere pennies on the dollar? They may own the land, but the government offices make all the decisions for them.

Sadly she concluded that reservation life was a living hell that would last as long as the Indian remained a ward of the United States Government. Reservations were still among the biggest American prisons ever built—and ironically they were on the Indian's own land.

"So, how long are you going to take his bullshit? What about your life? What about your medicine training?" Shung' inquired, as Sunny got out of the truck.

"Shung', right now I can't think about my marriage or my career, much less Medicine. Give me time to sort everything out."

Upon returning to the motel, she found Meeko at the bar with three unsavory looking Indians.

"Aren't we supposed to be meeting with some oil men at two o'clock?"

"They're sitting right in front of you, Sweetheart. Say hello to my new partners, Karl, Dan and Lawrence."

Meeko slid a stack of documents in her direction. Reviewing them, Sunny saw that Meeko had given these men stock in their company as well as full rights to the use of the waiver, and the four of them had established an all-Indian drilling, seismic and dynamite company.

Setting the paperwork aside, she stated, "Before I can make a decision, I will need to send copies of these papers to Murray Oil Company and meet with our attorney in Billings."

Meeko agreed to drive to Billings with her to see the attorney.

For over an hour they drove in silence, preferring to avoid any more confrontations. Meeko lit a joint and offered it to Sunny, easing the tension between them. Soon they were talking comfortably and Meeko suggested they stop for a candlelight dinner at the Billings Petroleum Club. Sunny accepted, and before long their relationship seemed loving once again. The romantic mood continued throughout dinner, and that night they made love.

The next day Meeko received a call from Karl. After hanging up, he announced that Karl had made arrangements to meet with another oil company in Denver and wanted him to come along to explain the use of the waiver.

"Wait a minute!" cautioned Sunny. "That waiver belongs to the people, and these men are trying to steal it for themselves."

"You're too suspicious. I've been offered a piece of their oil company, and I'm going to take them up on their deal."

"You know you can't be involved in their business. It would constitute a conflict of interest. Besides, it was my contacts and my money that paid for the waiver!"

"Well, little woman, I don't care what you say! I'm leaving for Denver in the morning."

"What is this, Meeko, another Custer's Last Stand?"

"Something like that."

Sunny stomped off to the bedroom and long before daybreak, she heard Meeko's car leave the driveway, and knew he was headed to Denver.

Still angry, Sunny dialed their attorney to discuss the new, all-Indian owned company. He told her that the waiver could not be used by other oil companies until it was tested. She called Meeko in Denver, only to discover that he was not registered at the hotel where he said he would be staying.

When she still had not heard from him a week later, Sunny hesitantly called Shung', who reported that Meeko had arrived drunk at her house the night before and she had thrown him off of her property.

"When are you going to get rid of that man? He's ruining your life! And on top of that, Gramma Firsthorse is sick!"

Sunny offered to pick Shung' up and drive her back to Billings. To further appease her, Sunny volunteered to charter a plane for Gramma and make the necessary arrangements to get her checked into a hospital in the state of Washington.

When Sunny tried to use her credit cards, she found they were all charged to their limits. She called Kate and ask her to transfer ten thousand dollars into her personal account, then finalized the transport of Gramma Firsthorse.

Once this had been accomplished, she called the bank president, a personal friend of hers and made arrangements to limit all of Meeko's withdrawals on their joint account to two hundred dollars per any twenty-four hour period. She then transferred the bulk of the money back to her personal New York account.

Around six o'clock Sunny heard Meeko's car pull into the driveway and she prepared herself for a battle over the missing funds. No sooner had he entered the house than the phone rang and it was for Meeko.

"I'll be there in twenty minutes." Picking up his jacket, he said, "I'll be back in a couple of hours."

Sunny did not answer. As the car left the driveway she poured herself a glass of wine, realizing they now shared nothing but the dark clouds of deep sorrow. What had happened to the woman so full of hope who had arrived in Montana less than six months ago? Meeko's insensitivity had locked her emotions into an isolation from which she desperately wanted to escape. She called Kate and asked her to book her on another road tour in hopes that a return to her career would feed her soul in a way Meeko no longer could.

As she hung up the phone, she heard two cars pull into the driveway. Karl and Dan waited in the car as Meeko stormed into the house, demanding, "Give me five hundred dollars. The bank cards aren't working."

"I've already had to transfer ten thousand dollars into my account to cover your bounced checks, so don't ask me for another dime!"

"Well, Miss Macho, are you trying to wear the fucking pants in this family?" Meeko shoved her shoulder hard against the sofa. "Sunny, don't fuck with me! Stop meddling in my business if you know what's good for you!"

"Fuck you! Its my money and my business! And know this you bastard, you won't get another dime of my money to piss away on reservation trash! Those so-called business partners of yours don't know a damn thing about business. Look at them sitting out there in that beat-up car, waiting for you without a cent in their pockets. This is probably the first time either one of them has worn a three-piece suit, and they sure look stupid walking around with those empty dime store briefcases. Is that what you want to become?"

"Woman, I'm sick of your fucking mouth! You better shut up if you know what's good for you! My friends tell me I should just smack you around a bit, then you'd know who's the boss!"

"Don't you fucking ever threaten me! It was my mouth and my money that made all this happen. I'm not the enemy, your friends are!"

Meeko shoved Sunny against the wall. "Listen, bitch! Me and my friends have to get to Denver! If you won't give me the money, I'll take your ass to court and get it. If we're broke, then go make us some more money!"

"Take me to court, huh? Go ahead! We'll see who has the biggest balls in this family. I'll have you broke in a month if you fuck with me!"

Coldly sneering Meeko grabbed her , "You're no woman. You're a suspicious, nagging, raging, violent, unreasonable, bitchy breed. And all you breeds are insane!"

"I wouldn't take things too far if I were you, because I just might prove that statement true. And no, I'm not like most women. I've never sold myself for a meal ticket or a roof over my head. I'm a damn good enemy, so don't fuck with me. You might win a few battles along the way, but I will win the war!"

"Your stupid threats don't scare me. If I wanted to, I could rip off your head."

Sunny calmly grabbed Sam's old .22 from the wall. "You want some of this? You better think twice before you push me again, or I'll make sure you spend the rest of your life behind bars!"

"I didn't say I was going to beat you. I merely said I was advised to slap you around. Now put a lid on that anger."

Sunny laid the gun aside yelling, "You think this is anger? You better pray that I never get really angry with you! I am my own person, not just your wife! I too have a say in this marriage. What I don't understand is why my opinion no longer matters to you. It seems that I've become the bad guy in this relationship. I'm tired of being the butt of your stupid jokes. You think I challenge your manhood? Well, when you start acting like a man, I might treat you like one. Personally I think you're fooling around on me, and if I ever find that you've been with another woman, I'll make you a babbling, drugging drunk and force you to grovel for a measly handout."

"You can't hurt me, woman! I don't care how much education you have, or how smart you think you are, the business world is a man's world and there's no place in it for a woman like you. When I get back from Denver, I'm going to teach you how to appreciate a good man."

Sunny slowly approached him, her eyes filled with hatred. "Am I talking to the alcohol, or is it the drug demon that speaks so strong? Meeko, don't fuck with me unless you want to see some real demon power!"

Meeko knew by the look in her eyes that this was no idle threat. "Okay, lets talk. I'll tell the guys to take off.

When they were seated, Sunny looked at Meeko and saw a stranger, then stated flatly. "While I was at the reservation, I spent a lot of time with Shung'. She read the coals and saw very bad things happening between us. I'm worried it'll come true."

"What did the old witch tell you?"

"When I asked her about our future, she told me she saw darkness hovering over you, and reminded me that my Grandmother once described a man who would bring me many tears. She said this man would either be my greatest strength or my death. I know you are that man, and I feel a deep sadness because our love is slipping away. I told Shung' about the demon that entered your body and she warned me that it could be a dual soul or a step-in trying to take over and rule your life."

"Yeah, it's possible. Sometimes I feel like someone else has been with me since birth."

"You told me Black Bear had gotten rid of the demon. Shung' says that you've lost control of your life through drinking and drugging and if you don't stop, the demon will take over your soul, and sabotage our love, or kill us both. She says that your demon fights with me because it wants me out of your life.

"Shung' tells me that I cannot help you and asked me to encourage you to see Shadowhawk. He knows how to fight this kind of spirit. I'm sure he could heal you and help us rebuild our relationship. I beg you to see him. You're dealing with a demon whose doorways are drugs and alcohol. If you don't listen, we're both going to suffer dire consequences."

Meeko knew she was speaking the truth, and felt he was slowly losing his identity to some other being that seemed to be inhabiting his body. He saw the pain that Sunny was suffering and it hurt him.

"My Sweetheart, remember, no matter what happens, I will always love you as long as you're honest with me."

It seemed the closeness between them had been reborn, but the following morning Sunny found another needle in the wastebasket. Distraught over what Meeko was doing to himself she began to attack him, hoping to rip this drug demon from his body. Meeko tried to hold her close and apologize, but she continued to vent her anger over his drug use and the impact it had on their finances.

The fight escalated and Meeko smacked Sunny across the face open-handed.

"Yes, Miss Macho, you have given me huge amounts of money, but I deserved everything I got from you. I've paid one helluva price for being with you. Do you have any idea how much I've hated living under your control, having to kiss your ass to survive? You don't know how good it feels to take your money and throw it away.

"I've waited a long time to watch you suffer the same humiliation that I've endured throughout our marriage. I'm going to Denver, and don't you say a another word about it, or I'll break your pretty little neck."

"If your life is that bad, why don't you lodge a complaint with someone who gives a shit? Personally, I don't give a damn what you do. You can go to Denver, but I won't give you another dime."

"Well, I don't need you anymore, but for damn sure you'll always need my love and bedroom talents."

Sunny felt a coldness encircle her heart as she accused, "You've hit me, you've insulted me, and now you're saying I'm controlled by you? Meeko, I understand we each have our own needs, but I will always voice my opinion, particularly when it involves my money. I have an identity and you will never take that from me. Our marriage makes me an extension of you, as you are of me. What either of us does affects the other. We must never dishonor our vows to Creator. We must maintain our moral standards in this relationship. You must see me as who I am and respect our marriage vows. I want your love and happiness, but you need help. If you won't go see Shadowhawk, then please go to the VA hospital for counseling."

"There's nothing wrong with me! We're fighting because you never shut your fucking mouth to hear anything I say. I'm sorry I slapped you, but I'm tired of listening to your bullshit!"

"Meeko, think of what you're doing! Your aggressive attitude is driving me insane and I can't live with these drastic personality changes. You threaten to beat me, then in the next breath you say you love me. I don't know who you are anymore."

"Sunny, if you'd stop this independent woman's right to freedom crap, maybe we could have a good relationship."

"I will never be subservient to you! I'll always fight for who I am!"

"I admire your spunk, but you're a woman living in a man's world. Don't you know you women exist only to service their men?"

"Meeko, on this female planet a woman is equal to a man."

"Believe what you want, little woman." He reached over and began to stroke her hand. "Did I ever tell you that you're one helluva woman in bed?"

Sunny began to cry and Meeko gently placed his arms around her.

"Meeko can't you see that you've changed? What has happened to the sensitive, caring man of honor that I married? Our goal was to return to the reservation to help others and share our dreams, not to destroy ourselves. Where is your belief in *Wakan Tanka*?"

"Sweetheart, when you criticize me it makes me angry. It scares me when you push me too fast toward success. You take pride in success, but your drive makes it impossible to be around you very long. Sometimes I feel like I'm back in prison."

"Meeko you're like an old grizzly bear, so inconsistent, that you're consistent! I nag you because you're irresponsible and make bad choices! Stop blaming me because you can't keep your word. I hate what's happening to us. Don't you realize that you're destroying everything that we're trying to build? Somehow we've got to get beyond these walls that are keeping us apart. So tell me, what it is that you want from me?"

"Sweetheart, I'm sorry for hurting you. You know that I love you. Those walls you speak of aren't mine. If you want to prove your love to me, then trust me and stop checking on my whereabouts. And quit telling Shung' and Shadowhawk about our personal life!"

"Don't sweet talk me you fucking Coyote! You're impossible! Can't you see? You're destroying our marriage, the business is faltering and you're destroying our spiritual bond!"

Meeko looked at her coldly and said nothing. He picked up his bag and left to join his new business partners on their flight to Denver. Once again, he and Sunny had parted in anger without a goodbye.

Sunny sadly watched his car vanish over the hill, fearing the many battles yet to come. She grabbed her jacket and left for the reservation to pick up Shung' and move her back to Billings, where she wintered every year with her friend, Ida Ghost Woman.

On the drive back to Billings, Shung' asked, "Did you speak with Meeko?"

"Yes. He thinks there may be a dual soul that's controlling his life, but refuses to talk to you or Shadowhawk."

"Humph, he better speak with Shadowhawk or it's gonna be too late for him!"

"I know, but he refuses to listen. I was hoping that you'd talk to him."

"Don't hold your breath. He's not going to do anything until he's ready. I want you to get back into your medicine training."

Seeing Shung's impatience, Sunny changed the subject. By the time she dropped Shung' off at her friend's house, Sunny had convinced herself that Shung' might offer her and Meeko a healing ceremony if she returned to her studies.

Sunny felt better after her talk with Shung'. As she stepped out of the car, she saw Camella standing at the door with a suitcase under each arm. "Sunny, I must return to Mexico, my son is very ill."

Knowing there was nothing she could do to persuade Camella to stay, she drove her to the airport. On the way home, Sunny felt alone and abandoned. Once there, she and ShaTonga rambled over the property as Sunny tried to make sense of what was going on in her life. They did not return until long after dark.

Sunny checked to see if Meeko had called. Finding no messages, she phoned his hotel room in Denver and was given the number of a posh nightclub. She dialed this number and had Meeko paged.

"Hey, Sunny." It was Karl. "We're celebrating our new deal! Meeko's drunk and I don't think he can walk to the phone."

"Get him!"

"He doesn't want to talk right now. We found some honky women and we're having one helluva party. A real pretty one likes Meeko. But don't worry, I'll take care of him."

"Damn it, Karl! I swear, you're so dumb you could use a dog turd as an identification card. Now get that blanket ass to the phone!"

"Sunny, you have a good evening."

The phone went dead. Sunny slammed the phone down and made a pot of coffee, trying to control her anger. Then she sat on the sofa and stared out into the bleak night at the season's first silent snowfall. Tears rolled down her cheeks as she was engulfed by the possibility of his infidelity. Although she reassured herself that he would never cheat on her, she could not help taking into consideration the possibility of Meeko being with another woman.

She spent the night waiting by the phone, her mind in turmoil. She knew her emotions were ruled by Meeko's deceptions. Her fears had been born on gossip, but she couldn't help wondering if they were perhaps based on truth.

Karl was a shit disturber who most people on the reservation referred to as a gossipy old woman. Danny was the loudmouth and the pack leader. Lawrence was nothing more than a mere shadow. Unable to escape these crazy thoughts, Sunny grabbed her head and screamed out into the lonely night like a caged animal.

Falling to her knees in desperation, she prayed, "Oh, *Wakan Tanka*! When will this heartache stop? Why can't he see what he's doing to us? Please help him realize that his business partners are driven by greed and jealousy over the waiver and are trying to steal everything."

Unable to sleep, Sunny reminisced as she roamed the house, looking at objects that related to better times in their marriage. She picked up a pot they had bought on one of their trips to Mexico and heard something rattle inside. Reaching in, she pulled out a key and a recent hotel receipt for a Mr. and Mrs. Smith.

Her mind flashed back to the underpants she had found under Meeko's bed and all the bad checks he had written for unexplained expenses. What about his attitude and snide remarks? The woman's number she found on a matchbook cover? Still not wanting to believe he was being unfaithful, Sunny convinced herself she was reading too much into these situations. Surely he has a reasonable explanation. I've got to believe that he values this marriage. We've worked so hard to attain our dreams. He can't be sabotaging all that! Surely Meeko was not that foolish.

Still hopeful, she redialed his hotel room in Denver, and when Meeko finally mumbled a drunken hello, Sunny heaved a sigh of relief.

"Where in the hell have you been? I've been calling all night!"

"Out."

"Karl told me you were with another woman!"

"Baby, be a good wife and stop checking on me."

"It'll be a cold day in hell when you teach me anything about being a wife! Have you been with another woman?"

"No! But what I do is my business, so don't ever again question my friends about what I'm doing."

Not wanting him to hang up, Sunny changed her tack. "Meeko, you know those oil men expect certain behavior. I hope you didn't get drunk while you were with them."

"Let's just say they were nice enough to help me back to the hotel."

"Here we go again, another drunk and another deal down the drain. Don't you know those men are the scavengers of the earth and have no principles in life or in business? Why are you throwing away our future to those bums? Meeko, for once please give me the assurance that you'll stay sober until all the contracts are signed."

"What difference does it make? It's my deal! Just let me go. I'll call you tomorrow." He hung up the phone.

Enraged, Sunny dialed back.

"How dare you hang up on me?"

She heard a woman's voice in the background, saying, "Come on, hang up and let's party."

"Meeko, who is that woman?" demanded Sunny.

"Sweetheart, I can't talk now. It's a long story. I promise I'll tell you all about it when I come home."

Sunny grew afraid. "Honey, I don't mean to threaten, I just want our happiness. When I fell in love with you we cherished the same principals and freedoms. I married you because you had an honest heart. You promised me loyalty, and now you treat me like a piece of property. Meeko, I'm not asking for the impossible. I'm asking my husband to share in our relationship. I'm only guilty of loving you and I can't accept anything less than what I deserve. It seems my life with you has become one lie after another! Live today and to hell with tomorrow! I can't take anymore of this crap. If I find you've been with another woman, I'll destroy everything. Either do the job or get the fuck away from my money and let someone qualified take over. Don't test me on this, I know how to take care of business!"

"Sunny, you're one of those women who tries to act like a man. My business partners warned me I'd better cover my ass, and that's why I came to Denver. I've made sure you'll never take the company. You're too late—the contracts were signed last night and you own nothing in my company! I've already transferred and distributed seventy-five percent of the shares to my partners, and changed the waiver to keep out all white owned companies, forcing them to do business with an all Indian company. The Department of the Interior and the United States Geological Survey have sanctioned my decision. Thanks to good old Uncle Sam, as of last night, me and my partners are protected by law and you can't do anything about it."

"This is insanity, Meeko. I know the game, and you've just shown me how stupid you really are. I'll speak to our oil attorneys in the morning. I suggest that you get ready for the shit to hit the fan—and don't plan on your partners being there for you when it goes down!"

"Who gives a flying fuck? I feel good not having to deal with your kind of people anymore. Doesn't that aggravate the hell out of you?"

"Fuck your partners! Can't you see that you've lost control of both companies? Are you that ignorant?"

"I couldn't care less about what you think! It makes me happy knowing that you're losing control and I'm finally free from your fucking money. I've been your fool long enough. Isn't payback a mother fucker? I'm just a sociable person who likes to party while you're nothing but a loner looking for that almighty dollar. All I ever wanted out of you was a wife who knew her place."

Sunny was crushed. "Meeko, please let me touch your heart before it's too late."

"Never! You've already taken too much from me. Let me off of this phone! I'll talk to you when I get home."

"Meeko, are you saying that my punishment for loving you is to watch you run with lowlifes while you chase alcohol, drugs and women on my dime? The old people warned me that your new partners were greedy, lying bastards! It embarrasses me that they believe that I've married the village idiot. You'd better look at the facts. It's time to grow up! Tell your friends I'll see them in court."

"Stop your ultimatums! You've always made me feel I wasn't good enough for you. I hated your career and your high and mighty friends. Sunny, I like making you suffer through the same humiliation that I experienced during the years you supported me. I really want you to know what it feels like to depend on another for your survival. It's interesting to watch you try to cope as a helpless, dependent woman. It feels good to embarrass you in front of people. This time, your precious Kate won't be able to pull your fat out of the fire.

"Sunny, I don't care what you do. If you don't like my decisions, then file for a fucking divorce and I'll go back to my wine, women and song. Instead of nagging me, why don't you write a book about all this women's rights garbage? There are plenty of idiots out there who would buy the writings of a crazy woman. I'd rather destroy everything than see you win just to prove who wears the pants in this family! In fact, you know what really makes me feel good? I took a breed's money and wasted it."

Meeko's heartless words cut deep. Sunny had not known he felt this way about her, and asked, "Meeko, do you really hate me that much? I never knew how much you resented me. I can accept the fact that you want me destroyed but why do the same to yourself in the process? My darling, I've never let a man support me or tell me what I can do! If you think this abuse will turn me into a whimpering woman, then know, I will not let this happen to me!"

"What you're doing to me will catch up with you. Someday I'll be free again, and I'll no longer need you in my life. But right now I do need you, and I beg you to be the man I married, instead of an arrogant asshole. No matter what happens, know that I won't become your scapegoat or bend over and kiss your ass. For now, I warn you to think carefully about your business decisions because there are no friends when millions of dollars are involved. I predict your new partners will steal the company from you within six months."

Meeko took a moment to process her threats then retorted, "Goddamnit, woman, here we go again! You don't want a man, you want a god. There's no man who can live up to your fucking expectations! Are you telling me if we separate you're going to look for someone who can meet your standards?"

"My search was over when I found you. But I will not live without a man in my life."

"Sunny, don't you ever cheat on me! I love you, but your insatiable drive and demands are destroying me. When you get angry you don't care where you are or what you say to anyone. This drives me insane and sometimes the embarrassment makes me so angry that I feel like killing you!"

"What? Kill me? Why you arrogant, self-centered sonuvabitch! You know I don't fear death, so stop your scare tactics. We fight because you won't listen. Stop your drinking, drugging, and wasting money. God knows why I'm trying to reason with a drunk. I know if you were straight, you'd never try to browbeat me with this kind of macho bullshit! Don't ever think that I'll grow one submissive bone in my body and I'll die before ever again living in fear. The day will come when you get down on your hands and knees and beg me to come back."

"Ah, not so, woman. I'm telling you to shut your damn mouth! When you stop your threats and get a better attitude, then maybe I'll consider changing these supposedly bad habits you find so repulsive. But if you continue to degrade me, I won't stay around. And I promise that I will own your soul."

"In other words, there is no negotiation? It's your way or the highway. Okay get ready to fight the biggest battle you've ever encountered in this lifetime!"

Meeko heard her pain and softened his voice. "Honey, I hate to do these things to you, but you never listen unless I threaten you. You must trust everything will be all right. I'm doing what's best for us. I love you and I'll see you tomorrow. Good night, My Sweetheart."

With the phone still pressed to her ear, Sunny realized that Meeko had not properly replaced the receiver, and she heard a woman's voice, saying, "Baby, why do you put up with that kind of bullshit from a wife? What you need is a good stiff drink and a roll in the sack."

"You're absolutely right, Sweetheart," agreed Meeko. Noticing the phone was off the hook, he cautioned her to be quiet while he set it back in its cradle.

The horror of the woman's words brought on panic, laced with denial and confusion. Alone! Afraid! This is not happening to me, not me! Sunny paced the floor in hysterics, not wanting to believe what she knew to be true!

Three weeks passed before Meeko returned home. There the fights continued and Sunny's suspicions about his infidelity took a serious toll on their relationship. She spent most of her time curled in the darkness of her bedroom, fearful that she was losing her mind. So distorted were her thoughts that she began to believe their marital problems were her fault. Depression at the thought of losing everything spiraled into an emptiness beyond any she had ever known.

Meeko took her to a psychiatrist, who prescribed pills for depression. Sunny's mood swings vacillated from rage to tears to deep sadness.

He continued to come and go as he pleased, but each time he approached the door, she would beg him not to leave her alone. Meeko in turn would laugh at her fears and go about pursuing his selfish desires.

Sunny's fear of being alone intensified, triggering memories of her painful life with Sam. Many times when Meeko returned he found her in a fetal position praying for guidance.

For six months Meeko captured her mind and enjoyed keeping her in a state of confusion and uncertainty. Although he would occasionally take her out, he stayed away for long periods of time. When this happened, Sunny would phone every hospital, bar, hotel and jail, only to uncover more lies and deceit. She gradually came to believe that any kind of consideration from him was a precious gift. When she did see him, she would beg him to stay with her, but he would invariably remark, "You've become boring, ugly and fat, and you no longer have any value to me."

Although Sunny only weighed one hundred and twenty pounds, he managed to convince her that she was fat, and so she refused to eat or leave the house. Meeko enjoyed his control over her and would leave for weeks, telling her only that he was working on the reservation.

One night, as she sat crying out to the walls, she grabbed her head and screamed in pain. "I can't stand another thought to pierce my mind. I'm tired of not knowing his whereabouts! I'm tired of fighting."

Suddenly, a calmness engulfed her and she accepted there was no longer a logical explanation that could ever justify the futility of their relationship. "*Wakan Tanka*, I have forsaken all that you have given me. I am no longer capable of dealing with this terrible turmoil. Too many devastating things have happened to me, and I can no longer endure the pain. But Meeko is my life and I do not want to live without him."

After giving a departing touch to everything in the house that reminded her of their good times together, Sunny calmly loaded her pistol. Feeling alienated from the world, she stood in front of the bathroom mirror and placed the gun in her mouth, unable to relate to what she saw reflected back—an unfamiliar creature with a horrible face who seemed to be daring her to pull the trigger.

As she drew the hammer back, there was a knock at the door, and the image in the mirror transformed into a haggard version of her former self. Thinking it might be Meeko, Sunny set the gun on the countertop, and plodded like a zombie to the door.

Shung' stomped into the bathroom and unloaded the gun.

"Meeko called. Said you wouldn't answer the phone, that you were becoming suicidal and I should check on you. The next time you want to try this shit, call me and I'll load the gun for you. I see you're overdosed on pills again, so go to the kitchen and put on a pot of coffee! It's time we talk."

She pushed Sunny toward the kitchen. Sunny did as instructed while Shung' sat at the table watching her stoically. Suddenly, Sunny threw her cup against the wall and ran to Shung's arms begging for help.

"Now, now, Granddaughter, settle down and tell me how long it's been since you've eaten? Your bones are poking through your flesh."

"I'm not hungry. Besides I'm too fat."

Grabbing her by the hair, Shung' dragged Sunny into the bathroom and forced her to stand on the scale. "Fat, huh? What does the scale say?"

Sunny gasped in amazement. "Ninety-six pounds! That can't be right."

Shaking her head in disgust, Shung' ushered her back to the kitchen and set a plate of food in front of her, commanding, "Eat."

While Sunny nibbled, they talked.

"Shung', nothing in this marriage has value for Meeko anymore. As for me, I've lost control. I've started to call Kate several times to discuss returning to work, but I'm afraid to walk back on stage!"

"Over the years I've discovered at least two causes for marriage problems—a woman not telling her man when she is feeling alienated from him, and her acceptance of abuse. This disease starts in the heart. When you overlook the first snide remark to keep the peace, it quickly becomes a habit. By accepting disrespect from your man, you're telling him that it's okay to abuse you. That kills a relationship. I remember you as an independent woman, a true free spirit. How long has it been since you were happy?"

"I don't know. All I do is cry, sleep, worry and fight. I seem to just sit and watch my life tick away. I'm disgusted with myself for accepting Meeko's abuse, but I'm afraid to do anything about it. I take it because I don't want to end the relationship, yet at the same time I hate what this marriage has become. I feel like I'm building my own prison and running in circles with no way out."

Sunny raged at length, describing her pain while trying to understand the many unresolved issues between herself and Meeko. She spoke of the terrible hurt she felt when he stayed away from home, as well as the anger she experienced each time she went through his briefcase and found proof of his infidelity—phone numbers, hotel receipts and expensive dinners charged to credit cards. She told Shung' how Meeko had taken her money, destroyed their business, repeatedly came home drunk and undermined her self confidence by telling her she had no sex appeal and was ugly. She confided that whenever she tried to talk to him about a solution to their problems, he would twist the truth, making their difficulties appear to be her fault.

"Sunny, everyone wants an honest, loving relationship, but that doesn't guarantee we'll ever receive such a gift. Let's not discuss whether you will leave or stay in this marriage. Before making a decision of this magnitude, you must first get rid of the pain. You must start by showing kindness to yourself so that you can recapture your inner beauty and rekindle your fire for life. And you must seek the truth about whether you are trying to maintain or destroy this relationship."

"I'm so confused I don't even know. I do know that I'm tired of being made to feel old, ugly, and useless. I'm tired of Meeko's verbal abuse, drinking and drugging. Our unresolved issues are driving me crazy. How can anyone love what they hate? It's as though I'm trapped in a nightmare with no means of escape."

"Sunny, you were raised to be a predator, not a victim, so why are you volunteering for the job? This experience will be burned into your mind for the rest of your life if you don't take control and guide yourself through your problems like the warrioress you are! Stop blaming Meeko. You must accept that you've allowed him to treat you this way!"

"I know, but my confidence is destroyed, and I can't make good decisions. I want the marriage like it once was, but my soul is dying from all these emotional battles."

"Child, you must fight. Otherwise this relationship will hinder all your future relationships. Your soul is in trouble, and you better make the decision to heal quickly or you will die."

"Why must it be this way? I want to have an honorable and loving marriage. It was Sam who taught me that the greatest gift we possess is the ability to share ourselves with another. He taught me how to understand others by accepting their weaknesses and strengths, and always said that a good attitude will rebuild anything. Sam taught me to always speak the truth because lies sap the honor out of a person's words. But the one thing he never taught me was how to forgive a loved one who is trying to destroy you!"

"Yes, Sam had his way of teaching, but it was Cheering Woman who taught the three of us the good principles to use in all aspects of life. The question still remains, what are you going to do about your situation? You can't keep hurting your soul!

Don't you think it's time to walk your talk? Life is black and white, so why don't you get off those gray concrete fences and make a decision? Your convictions will never let you settle for less than what you've promised yourself. Sunny, you can't allow yourself to become a victim of another's circumstance by trying to make them love you in the way you understand. Look what you have created trying to do just that.

"Deceit is like a pebble that is thrown into a lake, causing ripples to race back to shore. They touch everything in their pathway, drowning us in self-imposed misery. This relationship is affecting much more than you and Meeko. It's also hurting your extended families, your business, and your mutual friends. I suggest you and Meeko have a good talk and make some very strong ground rules."

"Shung', Meeko is a liar, and I can't trust his words! I should have stopped his abuse much sooner, but I didn't. Now he thinks of me as his property, and he controls me in the name of love."

"Granddaughter, when the bond of trust between two loving people is broken, it's hard to forgive the offender. I know these experiences hurt and they are never forgotten, but in time the pain will subside. Accept this very difficult lesson and know that somewhere in the future you will become a stronger person because of it.

"Meeko is one of your better teachers in this life. He's forcing you to stand by your convictions—what I call growing in wisdom! He's a good enemy, and a good enemy teaches the best lessons. Sunny, you are the only person who will ever change anything about you. It's you who must accept your situation, and you must do so with unconditional love for yourself. The question is, what price are you willing to pay for this kind of relationship?"

"Oh, Shung'! I don't know what to do, but I do know the thought of losing Meeko to another woman is terrifying."

"Sunny, don't talk to me with ego. Instead, sort out the bad and the good in this relationship so you can see what to do. And as Sam always said, 'If you do whatcha gotta do, you'll survive.' You and Sam are like two peas in a pod—both cantankerous souls. Sam was a looker, and the women loved him. You're a looker, and any man would love you. So, Sam's daughter, be strong, no matter what the outcome."

"You're right, Shung'. It's time I work on getting this marriage back together."

"Good, and as Cheering Woman always said, 'Busy hands keep a clear mind.' Now we're going to the river for some new willow poles to rebuild your *Inipi*, and we're also going to fix what's broken inside you."

Within a week, they had built a new *Inipi*, restructured Sunny's Medicine Wheel, and canned the last of the fruits and vegetables from the garden. Each morning and evening, the two prayed together in a long sweat.

Three weeks later Sunny still hadn't heard from Meeko. Shung' remained with her, force-feeding her the old knowledge. Sunny took in the medicine teachings like a starving animal and gave her undivided attention to her studies. However, somewhere in the back of her mind, the fear of not knowing Meeko's whereabouts gnawed at her like an underfed dog devouring a bone.

One morning after their sweat, Shung' said, "If his absence bothers you that much, then go find him."

"Where would I start? He could be anywhere."

"Go beyond your mind's limited boundaries, and reach for him in the many dimensions of time. Pull down your power and ride the waves to his energy."

Sunny did as Shung' instructed, and went to Shadow World. By late afternoon she knew exactly where Meeko was staying. Shung' smiled as Sunny phoned the motel, asking to be connected to his room. When a woman answered, Sunny hung up, tears streaming down her face.

"He's with another woman!"

"A voice on the phone doesn't necessarily mean anything. Don't let your mind convict him until you have the proof. Come, we must pray."

When they reached the Grandmother lodge, Shung' tied an eagle feather into Sunny's hair, then demanded she enter properly and sit in the West Door. Shung' built a small fire at the center altar and prayed for all the winds to come. As the lodge began to groan and sway under the winds' power, the flames seemed to leap through the top.

Sunny prayed fervently, "*Wakan Tanka*, please do not let this be true!"

"Oh, *Tunka'shila*, forgive my grandchild and take pity on her. She wishes for your will to be done and not hers. We come humbly to ask for direction in this matter, not to interfere with your plans."

Sunny wept openly, thankful that Shung' was running the ceremony.

Taking two small decorated arrows and a bow from her parfleche bag, Shung' offered two prayers. At the end of each prayer, she cut two small vertical gashes on each of Sunny's shoulders, then lit the two arrows and shot it through the top of the Grandmother Lodge.

Sunny, feeling nothing at first, soon soared into many worlds. She returned knowing her mind could no longer fool her eyes or ears.

After the ceremony, Shung' retrieved both the arrows and burned them in the fire.

They were back at the house, sitting quietly at the table, when, suddenly Sunny screamed, "Meeko is having sex with another woman!"

"You still don't have any physical proof."

"Yes, I do!" Grabbing a manila envelope filled with names, phone numbers and receipts, Sunny handed it to Shung', who studied the items closely before speaking.

"I see by these dates you've had the evidence all along. This should help you make a decision."

"How can I accept that my husband is with another woman? He treated me like a bleeding heart and I became just another usable tool. The bastard only married me for money and the contacts I could give him! I've been a fool! Shung', I hate this truth."

"Wrong! You hate nothing and you're not a fool! You're a woman in love with a man who loves you in a way you can't accept."

Screaming with pain and frustration, Sunny dashed out the door and ran for miles. Stopping at the Medicine Wheel, she lay down in the center crying, "How can he do this to a person he professes to love? Am I not worthy of a real love? If his betrayal is true, I no longer want this suffering. *Wakan Tanka*, please tell me what to do."

Slowly Sunny felt herself gathering strength from her life experiences. Many flying ones came and listened to her prayers, pitying her for her sadness at being a mere human. Meanwhile the winds ever so gently whispered words of encouragement. She did not return to the house until long after dark.

Shung' set a plate of food in front of her and decreed, "It's now time to talk from the heart."

Sunny nodded and mumbled, "Please help me, Shung', I'll do whatever you say."

"Sunny, you are not an unloved person. People throughout the world love you, and their feelings are unrelated to Meeko and this other woman. You did nothing wrong, so stop your self-judgment! Accept that Meeko is with her because he wants to be. He's not rejecting you, he's rejecting himself—so get your ego and pride out of the way.

"What you fear is truth. That's what's eating your soul. He chose his own destruction, so stop blaming yourself for his actions. Start using that wonderful mind you possess and quit thinking from a heart filled with illusion. Yesterday is over! And since tomorrow has not yet arrived, you have today to fix the problem."

Sunny phoned the motel, asking the desk clerk if there was a woman registered in her husband's room. "Sunny, I'm sorry to tell you this, but they've been here for the past three weeks."

"Will you send me copies of all charges on that account?"

"I'll be happy to, and I want you to know how truly sorry I am that you are experiencing this kind of embarrassment."

Within two days Sunny received the information, including a list of Meeko's phone calls many of which were made to Cheyenne, Wyoming. She proceeded to find out who lived at that number. Taking this information to Shung', she said, "Each piece of proof I gather seems to confirm that the marriage is over. The hardest part to accept is the deception. He may have enjoyed himself with another woman, but he'll never get over this woman's scorn."

A moment later the phone rang.

"That's Meeko." Picking it up, Sunny cooed, "What a surprise. The wandering husband hasn't forgotten his home number."

"Hello, Sweetheart. I'm coming home tomorrow. Is my car still parked at the airport?"

"Yes, if that's where you left it—unless it's been towed off as an abandoned vehicle."

"Then there's no reason for you to pick me up. I'll see you in the morning."

Meeko was thrilled with Sunny's calm reaction and said to his lover, Diane, "I can take you with me to Billings and you can catch your flight to Cheyenne from there. I have some last minute things to do. Here's three hundred to buy yourself some pretty clothes."

Everyone congratulated Meeko on his cleverness. Then Karl added, "Hey, Meeko, you are good. When you get home, remember the rule: deny everything, demand proof and ask for pictures."

As Sunny hung up the phone, tears rolled from her eyes and she dropped to her knees in prayer. "Please, *Wakan Tanka*, don't make me live with my greatest fear. I don't want to become an abandoned wife."

"Pray right or don't pray at all. I am proud of you because your ego did not demand that you mention the other woman while you had him on the phone. But know this, when you ask about the affair, he will lie."

"Shung', how can I love him so deeply, yet no longer know him?"

"Love makes people act in strange ways. It will take much thought to find the answers, but you will eventually do what's best for the both of you. Since Meeko will be here in the morning, I'll go to Ida's. This will allow you to face your enemy alone, so you can rebuild in a strong way."

After watching Shung' leave, she turned on the stereo and put in a tape. Turning up the volume, she heard the words, 'the days of wine and roses, laugh and run away, like a child at play.' Just like my marriage, she thought sadly as she pondered how to go about facing Meeko.

Sunny mourned the death of her marriage and saw its ghost fade into months of lonely nights. Even the shimmering city lights that once comforted her evoked feelings of isolation in her visions of a dim future without Meeko. She sobbed as her mind traveled back through the five wasted years of their marriage. Reliving her efforts to climb the ladder of fame, she saw that show business was another illusion. She watched as faded dreams paraded ghost-like before her, and acknowledged to herself that Meeko had been unfaithful. A traditional law had been broken, and the only choice left was divorce. But although the thought of Meeko in the arms of another woman made her livid, she realized she must control her anger and remain civil during their upcoming conversation. Finally, she stilled her mind and drifted off to sleep.

When Sunny awakened at ten o'clock the next morning, Meeko still had not arrived, so she called the Flight Service Station and asked, "Did the Cessna 210 arrive from Fort Peck Indian Reservation yet?"

"Yes, Ma'am, it arrived at seven o'clock this morning," the voice answered. Sunny hung up the phone knowing that once again she had been deceived.

Minutes later the phone rang, and thinking it might be Meeko, Sunny jumped to answer it. But instead it was her friend the bank manager, saying, "I'm calling to tell you that your husband and a young girl were here at the bank and she left a bag filled with clothes that I thought she might need. Would you like me to have it dropped off at your house?"

"That would be nice. I'll see that Meeko's friend gets her clothing."

She slammed the phone down and began to pace the floor, enraged at Meeko's audacity in parading this other woman around town.

After leaving the motel, Meeko dropped Diane off at the airport. She was only seventeen, and he was sending her home to get her mother's permission for Diane to return and live with him. Glancing at his watch he knew he had to hurry if he was going to see Sunny and get back to the airport to pick Diane up by six.

When Meeko finally arrived home he looked nervous and defensive. He had a two-day growth of beard, his clothes were wrinkled, and his hair was wet, as though he had just stepped from a shower.

"Meeko, why is your hair wet?" questioned Sunny, seeing guilt written all over his face.

As his eyes darted away from her in shame, she mentally heard Shung' say, "Stay in control of your emotions. Fly with Eagle and see the bigger picture. Call on Cougar, and disconnect from all feelings so you can confront him with confidence."

Sunny's heart raced as she calmly asked, "Where have you been? There's gossip about you living with another woman. If you'll tell me the truth, I'll be reasonable. But if you lie to me, and I get the truth from someone else, I'll destroy you."

In a condescending tone, Meeko answered, "Sure, Sweetheart. What do you need to know?"

"I want to know if you're sleeping with another woman?"

"Why, no, there's no other woman. Sweetheart, I had to wait for the checks to clear at the bank before I could come home."

"Meeko, I want this relationship more than anything in the world. I pray you're being honest with me."

Realizing Sunny was too calm, Meeko grew nervous and made himself a drink before answering.

"I swear there's no other woman. Please believe that I was detained on business. We've just had a misunderstanding, but it can be resolved in time." At that moment, the phone rang and Meeko grabbed it. "It's Shung'," he said curtly, handing the receiver to Sunny.

Sunny pressed it to her ear and listened.

"Don't fight or show any facial expression regardless of what I tell you. Ida, and I were at the airport when Meeko arrived with the girl. He didn't see me, but we followed them into town. They stopped for breakfast and then went to the bank. They checked into the Highway Motel and didn't come out until eleven. He dropped her off at the airport and I assume he drove home." Shung' hung up.

Sunny now had tangible proof of Meeko's infidelity.

Fearing her calmness and shocked when his tender gaze could not touch her soul, Meeko attempted to take her hand. "Sweetheart, You know how much I love you? You know I haven't been with another woman."

"Please, Meeko, don't lie to me." Sunny, then calmly walked to the garage and brought in the bag of clothes.

"So what if a girl was with me? She's Karl's girlfriend."

"Meeko, with honesty there could be a basis for making a new beginning."

Meeko tried again to convince her of his devotion, by telling her how much he wanted to keep this relationship. Again the phone rang. Meeko pressed the button on the speaker phone and they heard Karl's voice. "Hey, Meeko, I see you finally got home. Man, you were in bad shape this morning. Did you get some hair of the dog that bit you? How's the paramour doing? Did you get to the airport in time for her to catch the plane?"

Meeko tried to cover up by saying, "My wife's sitting right here, Karl, and I don't find this funny. Stop joking! You know this will cause me big problems." He hung up as if the phone was a hot coal burning his hand.

"You're damn right it's going to cause you big problems. We both know what your partner meant. There is nothing more to be said," stated Sunny flatly. Grasping at a final shred of hope for their marriage, she asked, "Will you help me feed the animals?" Meeko picked up his jacket, and they silently walked to the barn.

When they returned, Shung was there, eager to speak with Sunny in private. Stepping outside with her, Shung' said, "I saw you two were at the barn, so when the phone rang I went into the house to answer it. A girl by the name of Diane left her phone number and a message. I told her the call would be returned within an hour."

Sunny took the note from Shung' and read, 'I will be arriving at six thirty. Call me back if you can't pick me up at the airport. I love you, Diane.'

Sunny glanced at Shung' for more detail.

"That's it," answered Shung'. "I wanted you prepared before you confront Meeko. If you need me, you know where I am."

As Sunny entered the house, she thrust the note toward Meeko.

"Who's this Diane in Cheyenne?"

The look of guilt on his face gave Sunny her answer. She pushed the button on the speaker phone and dialed the number. When a woman answered, Sunny made sure it was Diane, then sat down on the sofa to listen.

Meeko answered with a guarded hello. "Hello, my future husband," said Diane, her voice filled with excitement.

"You must have the wrong number. I'm a married man."

"Aren't you a Sioux Indian in the oil business? Don't you have scars on your chest from being pierced as a Sundancer? Don't you own a brown Cadillac? Didn't we just spend a month together on the Fort Peck Indian Reservation? Don't you dare deny who you are because I recognize your voice."

Sunny had heard enough.

"Diane, this is Meeko's wife, Sunny. You have the right man. It's quite apparent that my husband has been playing with your emotions. How did you meet?"

"We met in the bar at the hotel where he was staying. We spent the evening talking, dancing and drinking. He didn't want to be alone so we spent the night together. After we made love, he asked me to come to the reservation so we could get to know each other better. Since I'm a minor, and he had taken me across the state line, his attorney sent me back home with papers for my mother to sign, giving her approval to travel with Meeko. Maybe I'm not very smart, but my mother believed him when he said he would pay my way though college."

Sunny pressed the disconnect button.

"That kid gave me all the proof I need! So, you blanket ass bastard, what's left to say?"

"Sweetheart, I'm so sorry. I beg you to forgive me. I promise I won't see her again. You know you're the only woman I've ever loved."

Sunny looked at Meeko in disgust. "Fuck you! Don't you ever call me Sweetheart again. You don't know the first thing about marriage!"

Sunny drove to Ida's house and collapsed in Shung's arms, crying hysterically. It took her over an hour to calm down long enough to hear what Shung' had to say.

"So, now you know. Damn right you're angry and with good reason! Meeko has lied and you've proved it! I know that you feel foolish, hurt, angry, and betrayed, but the clues were there all along. There's no excuse for adultery. It's not the affair itself that's to blame, it's the deception, and you can't run from its pain. You have to accept his lies and betrayal—it's part of the healing process. Yes, what he did was horrible and shocking. You know the old relationship is dead, but you must deal with your anger and work through this to your benefit. No one can understand this kind of pain unless they've been a victim of adultery! I want you to stay with this marriage for awhile. There may be an attempt at blackmail, and I want you to remain strong and calm so you'll be prepared for anything. Now, gather your strength and go home to speak with Meeko. Try to make decisions that are good for both of you."

For days Sunny vacillated between hurt and rage, until early one morning she burst into a flaming temper tantrum accompanied by all the demons of hell.

"You dumb dishonorable bastard! I can't believe you were planning to move that white bitch into the town I live in! You're no longer the person I married. You're a lying sonuvabitch, and I'm going to kill you!"

She began to rip Meeko's shirt off his body and beat him with her fists. Catching her finger in the corner of his eye, she dug in deep with her long nails. As the blood poured down his cheek, she cackled, "I'm gonna pop that eyeball right out so you can never look at another woman!"

Then before Meeko could get away, Sunny grabbed a letter opener and slashed his face. Seeing the deep gash, she yelled, "I hope it makes a scar so I can say that I marked you for life!"

"Sunny, stop it! You're fucking crazy!" Meeko dashed to the bathroom for a towel to stop the bleeding.

Sunny followed him. "You're nothing but an apple, white on the inside and red on the outside! You can grow your hair and play Hollywood Indian if you want to, but I'm sure poor Granbear's turning over in his grave with shame at your stupidity. Meeko, before I'm through with you, I'll make you a full blood, red on both sides. Then you can tell the next whore in your life that these scars were a gift from the crazy breed you were stupid enough to marry!"

Sunny stabbed at him again and again with the letter opener.

When this attack didn't ease Sunny's pain, she got a butcher knife from the kitchen and ran toward him.

Realizing she was insane, and trying to save his life, Meeko pinned her arms to her sides.

"All right, settle down! I was wrong and I'm sorry, but you're not going to kill me and get yourself put in prison for murder over a stupid affair."

"You lying bastard! Turn me loose! I will never let a lazy blanket ass disgrace me again! This shit would never have happened if you'd listened when I told you about the pitfalls of the white system. Why should I let you live and take up space on this earth? You're stupid! You're phony! You're bullshit! You're nothing but lies and you have no fucking principles. Thank God I'm a breed and know how to live in both cultures. But not you, you're too fucking weak and stupid to live in any culture. Nobody makes a fool out of me! You owe me and I want my honor, self-respect and my money back!"

"Damn it, Sunny, I'm sorry it happened, but there's nothing I can do to change it! I promise I'll give it all back and I'll never cheat on you again."

"Meeko, I'll destroy everything and everyone that was a part of this mess and you'll never get a moment's peace. When I get off this floor, I'll make your downfall my hobby for the rest of my life. You'll learn integrity before I'm through with you! I promise you'll never stand as a leader among men again! Do you hear me? I'm going to make sure the world knows you as a fucking Indian that stands in disgrace."

An exhausted Sunny melted into tears.

Meeko held her close until he felt the fight leave her body. Then he cautiously released his grip and said, "Sunny, you're absolutely right. I do realize that it was you who opened the doors to my success, and I accept that I've dishonored everything we were together."

Sunny wiped the blood from his face and stuck her bloody finger in her mouth.

"You belong to me, and you can never pay off what you owe for selling out our marriage. Since you've altered our birth purpose, I see no reason for us to try to go further."

"Sunny, I know we can pull this back together. You could call Kate for a loan and sell the house. That will give us enough money to start over. I'm sorry I've hurt you, but I'll make it up to you if you'll forgive me."

"Hell, no! I'm hurt when you treat me like dirt in the name of love. You don't have the balls to walk in balance between cultures, but I stand strong in honor with both races. I'll become an albatross around your neck. I'll break your spirit and turn you into a groveling street bum."

For a moment Meeko listened in silence, knowing she meant what she said, then he confessed, "Sunny, for a time I forgot the purpose of my birth. I know I'll pay for this heartache. I've faced death all of my life, especially in Vietnam, but you scare the shit out of me because you embrace it as a luxury. You have a right to treat me this way, although I'd never allow anyone else to." Meeko knew he had broken a sacred law and there was no repairing the damage. He knew it was time for them to face the elders and dreaded it, knowing that an Indian marriage was sacred and should meet the needs of each other.

Once Sunny was soundly asleep in the bedroom he phoned Shung', ready to face his first elder. She came immediately. When Shung' saw his face, she cleaned and stitched the wounds, saying, "I'm glad you called. It's better we do this than have a police report written on both of you."

They talked for hours as Meeko told his side of the story.

"Shung', Sunny castrates me every waking moment. I no longer feel like a man. But without her, I have no direction in this life."

"Meeko, that isn't true. You are Indian, but you've failed to honor that identity! If you had followed the old ways you would never have dishonored this marriage. The dismantling of both souls is at stake here. It's a hard battle, and both of you have lost much. I doubt if either of you will ever recapture your shared destiny. Each of you saw a different dream, yet it was the same, and both lives have been sacrificed by careless behavior. Unless Sunny returns to the old ways, she will eventually destroy her will and lose her purpose in life.

"Both of you must stop blaming the other. This fighting is building horrible memories, and you have become dangerous enemies. I ask you, which has the greatest value, your relationship with *Wakan Tanka* or your ego? Both of you have been trained since birth to serve the people and should still do so. These bad decisions will follow each of you from life to life. Meeko, life is not just about parties, drinking, and fighting. You know how serious this is, and you also know that Sunny can be very dangerous. I think I should take Sunny with me before either of you end up in prison."

At first Meeko refused to consider this, but finally he agreed.

"Last evening I prayed for the elders to come. I know most of this is my fault. Shung', I've thought of nothing but my stupidity. I never knew I loved her this much. I'm so sorry I've hurt her, and there's nothing I can do now but pray."

"Meeko, Sunny is suffering from your bad actions, but her pain is also related to Sam. Her violence stems from him, and you're reminding her of that painful part of her life. He too loved fighting, liquor, women, and betrayal. You and Sunny have forgotten the mission that you were to accomplish in this life, something predicted by her grandmother."

At that moment, Sunny appeared in the kitchen.

"Sunny, sit down!" demanded Shung'. "Now both of you promise me that you'll stop fighting until we can make a proper decision regarding this mess."

"Shung', I won't live with this cheating liar, nor will I ever forgive him. I can't understand what I've done to deserve this kind of treatment. I'm sorry, but I can't see a future for us."

"Both of you have stepped across the line of respect. You're stuck in time and are unwilling to resolve this situation intelligently. You've both behaved badly and nothing will change until you can reach a reasonable agreement. There will be no happiness for either soul if you continue destroying each other."

"Shung', Sunny will always be my companion."

"But Sunny is the kind of woman that can burn a man to the ground."

"It's true. Sometimes I hear her prowling around the house at night like an angry Cougar, and I almost believe she's becoming one and is planning to kill me."

Shung' looked at Sunny with scorn.

"Stop using medicine in a bad way. I'm leaving, and when I return I expect the both of you to have made some good choices!"

Sunny and Meeko were silent until they heard Shung' pull out of the driveway.

"Sunny, I don't want a divorce. Let's see if we can't work through this."

"I don't give a fuck what you want! You could've honored what we've shared. At least I deserved that!"

Alienated from each other and lost in their own worlds, they both stared blankly out the window, watching the snow fall.

At last Meeko spoke. "Would you consider joining me in the family room if I built a fire and played some soft music."

"I don't like being around you. Besides, I have work to do."

"Sunny, no matter what I suggest, you refuse to let us be happy together."

"There is no more us. Our relationship is dead. I refuse to build a new one with you."

"Well, what are we going to do? I can't take this deadlock much longer. It's driving me crazy."

"Meeko, I can't accept what you've done to me. Since you were so willing to give my place to another, I no longer trust you. I feel I've been used. There's too much bad blood between us and probably always will be. Even though I still remember the beautiful moments we've shared, the thought of returning to that time makes me feel dirty and shallow."

"I've said I'm sorry. I don't know what else I can do!"

Sunny watched him head to the door and ran after him screaming. "You fucking coward, you're not going anyplace until something is settled between us! When you can tell me how to bring back the purity in our relationship, I'll straighten up."

Meeko slammed her against the wall.

"You better forget this whole affair so we can get on with our lives, because I don't know how much more of your insanity I can take!"

"You think you can't take any more? Well, I can't either. Let me tell you the cold, hard facts—you'll take nothing from this marriage, because I'll make sure we lose it all first!"

In futility, Meeko pushed his way past her and out to the car. Sunny followed. Pulling a gun from her under her blouse she said, "You're not going anywhere!" She jerked the car door open and hit him in the face with the pistol. Meeko saw there was no reasoning with her and shoved her to the ground, kicking the gun from her hand.

Smiling, Sunny stood up and wiped the blood from her mouth. "Hit me again," she screamed, ripping off her blouse. She picked up the gun. "I'm looking for an excuse to put your ass back in prison!"

Meeko jumped in the car and as he sped away, Sunny blew out his two back tires. Maneuvering along as best he could, Meeko drove directly to Ida's house to find Shung'. By the time he arrived he was driving on nothing but rims. Shung' took one look and roared with laughter.

"I told you not to mess with a Dakota Woman."

"Shung', Sunny just tried to shoot me, I've tried to reason with her, but it's useless. I'm afraid one of us is going to end up dead. No matter what I say, she'll won't forgive me. She's sworn to make me pay for the rest of my life. I know I've hurt her because of what I've done, but hell, even a convicted criminal eventually gets parole. Tell me, what to do."

"Meeko, right now she's very hurt. I think it's best you separate for a while, and in the meantime, I'll try to get her to stay with me or go back to work."

After a long discussion, Meeko agreed, and borrowed Ida's truck to the drive home. Walking inside, he found Sunny huddled in a corner, crying, still refusing to talk with him.

Sometime during the long deadly silence of the night, Meeko finally realized that he had probably lost the only woman he would ever love.

The following morning when Sunny opened her mail, she found a credit card statement for eight hundred dollars. Taking it to the family room, she threw it in Meeko's, face.

"Will this shit ever end? Why did you buy that girl clothes on my credit card? That's like putting salt in my wounds. What kind of man would put his wife in the position of paying for another woman's clothes? Meeko, you're lower than slime on a pig's belly! Fuck you! I'm going to Shung's."

She and Shung' discussed the situation over coffee.

"Shung' why don't I have the strength to leave him? Why can't I accept what has happened? I'm becoming afraid of my own thoughts! I sit for hours planning his death, and the depression has become unbearable. Sometimes Meeko tries to be kind, but it hurts when I think of what we've lost. I just can't seem to stop the pain!"

"Karl has taken over the business and Meeko's reputation on the reservation has been destroyed. Diane still calls Karl for the money he promised her for getting Meeko into bed. I now know she's not the sweet young thing she seemed to be, but a paid prostitute. And now she and her mother are threatening blackmail. Why only last week Meeko's new company bought him out for seventy-five hundred dollars. I think he's finally starting to realize the girl was a ploy to steal the waiver. Shung', everything's gone!"

"Sunny, the marriage is over but your life is not. You can still fulfill your life's purpose. Creator always gives us the space and time to heal all the wounds we receive on the battlefields of life."

"Shung', you know I believed in my marriage vows. As a couple, we gave our word to *Wakan Tanka* on the Sacred Tree of Life. We promised to support, protect, and nurture each other for the rest of our lives. What didn't Meeko understand about those vows?"

"Sunny, sometimes a greater love is born from sorrow. We live in a time when people abuse each other because they no longer understand the meaning of the word loyalty. Adultery is the outcome of uncertainty in a commitment. When one partner is unfaithful it creates emotional and financial losses, as well as lack of credibility. These things break hearts and destroy a person's mind and soul.

"In time you will heal, but Meeko will suffer far more. Most offenders don't know the difference between a loving relationship and an affair. They live in a state of irresponsibility, confusion, and guilt, and are experts at keeping their sex lives separated from their love lives. For some reason, cheaters need to taste forbidden fruit to keep a romantic high. Never do they think about the reality awaiting them on the other side of that forbidden bedroom door. Sunny, there are seven B'S that destroy relationships: Booze, bars, broads, blow, bills, betrayal and bullshit.

"Booze causes aggressive lies. When Meeko drinks, he doesn't have to be responsible for his actions. He likes the atmosphere of a bar and the fact that everyone is drinking right along with him. He likes broads admiring and flirting with him, and this tells me it makes him feel young, sexy and handsome. He loves the thrill of getting away with something. Blow or cocaine, lets him escape reality and feel free. Bills allow him to pretend he's rich and that makes him feel powerful around those who have less. Betrayal means getting over on someone. He's deceiving himself and others, creating guilt, self-contempt, and inner turmoil—forcing him to distance himself from everyone he loves through guilt. Meeko uses threats and anger to keep his power. He knows fighting will eventually burn out the opponent, and this is the only way he can justify his dishonesty to himself.

"It is evident that you understand this lesson, so use the experience to heal the damage. Meeko fears sensitivity and keeps his feelings numbed as an excuse to continue his callused ways. In reality, he has no true power. His empowerment comes from stealing the energy of strangers.

"In time you will divorce Meeko and return to your career, and someday you will seriously pursue the medicine ways. Now go home and think over what I've said."

When Sunny arrived home Meeko was not there, so she decided to take action by straightening out her finances. She called Kate to see about booking another tour, but was advised to wait until spring.

Disappointed, Sunny went to the Medicine Wheel to pray. Shortly after she returned to the house Meeko called. He told her he had checked into the drug and alcohol rehabilitation program at the Veterans Administration Hospital.

Feelings of frustration washed over Sunny as she hung up the phone. Once again, she was being forced to take over all the responsibilities.

Sunny felt a small glimmer of hope when, a week before Christmas, Meeko returned home waving a check and dragging a good-sized pine tree.

"Sweetheart, I sold three paintings while I was in the hospital. We're going to have the best Christmas ever!"

Sunny was cordial but distant, unwilling to set herself up for more emotional stress. Meeko ignored her attitude and excitedly spent the afternoon stringing up lights, then begged Sunny to help him decorate the tree.

Late that evening he made them each a cup of hot buttered rum, and they sat together on the sofa watching the Christmas lights cast shadows across the snow-covered lawn. The serenity of this winter wonderland seemed almost magical.

"Do you think it would be possible to recapture the beauty we once had?" questioned Meeko. Sunny smiled and said nothing, but was impressed with his creative faculties and positive attitude. "Let's go shopping tomorrow and fill the house with Christmas presents." Sunny reluctantly agreed.

It was the first time since the affair that they had been out together, and Meeko insisted on a celebratory lunch. Sunny became discouraged when he drank steadily throughout the meal. She was filled with despair when he continued drinking that evening and for days thereafter.

At last it was Christmas Eve.

"You went to the hospital to stop drinking! Why did you start again?"

"Sunny, please let's not fight. I refuse to be unhappy during the holidays, and I promise I'll quit after New Year's. I know I'm drinking too much, it gives me the courage to believe that everything is all right between us. Let's go to that party we've been invited to tonight. I'll just have one sociable drink and be on my best behavior. I promise I won't get drunk."

When they arrived at the Christmas party, Meeko went directly to the bar to mix himself a tall bourbon on the rocks. He downed it quickly and mixed himself another while talking to a friend's daughter and her college friends who were home for the holidays.

Within the hour, Sunny heard loud music coming from the recreation room and went to see what was going on. She found Meeko dancing sensuously with the young girl. When at last Meeko looked in her direction, he smiled sheepishly and said, "The master is showing these kids how it was done in the fifties." Seeing the contempt in Sunny's eyes, he quickly released his partner.

Humiliated, Sunny left the room to spend time with their friends. An hour later one of the girls walked into the sitting room inquiring of Meeko's whereabouts. Sunny went upstairs to the bathroom, where she found Meeko with his gold straw, four lines of coke and the college girl.

"Meeko, what the hell are you doing? It's time we leave."

"I don't want to go home," he insisted, pulling two lines up his nose.

Sunny looked on in disgust, as Meeko loaded his syringe, pumped up a vein and shot up, then passed the syringe to the girl who followed suit.

Sunny coldly insisted on going home. In angry silence, she vowed to herself that Meeko had embarrassed her for the last time.

No sooner did they arrive home than Meeko left, saying, "I gotta make a score, I'll be right back."

Feeling deeply disappointed and hurt Sunny watched the car disappear, then prepared for bed.

The following morning when she awakened and saw that Meeko had not returned, she stoically prepared Christmas dinner for the small group of friends they had invited to the house. When Meeko showed up around eleven o'clock, attempting to explain his whereabouts, Sunny snapped at his every remark.

Meeko refused to acknowledge her nasty attitude, and as the guests began to arrive, he poured himself a drink, lit a joint, and sat down at the dinner table with Sunny and their guest.

Sunny brought out the food and joined the dinner party, covering her hurt with polite smiles.

When the last guest had gone, she quietly unloaded her gun and went to find Meeko. Finding him asleep in the spare bedroom, she positioned the barrel against his temple and pictured his gray matter splattered across the pillow.

Meeko's eyes opened in terror at the feel of the cold steel barrel nuzzled hard against his temple.

Sunny smiled wickedly then methodically pulled the trigger. "One. Two. Three."

As the clicking sounds exploded in Meeko's head, he slowly took her wrist and removed the gun from her hand. Sunny smiled as he moved around the room cautiously, showing the greatest of respect.

"Sunny, Shung' tells me that you need to go back to work. I think that's a good idea."

"Why? Are you afraid I'll kill you?" she asked, following him into the family room.

"No," said Meeko, and went to the bar to mix himself a drink.

"This has been one helluva Christmas Day." Sunny pulled a large butcher knife from under one of the pillows on the sofa and threw it at him.

Meeko glanced into the mirror behind the bar just in time to see the knife speeding toward him, and threw up his hand to deflect it.

"Take that as a warning, Meeko. One more drug deal and I'll turn you and your friends in to the narcs."

"You try it and you'll get yourself killed. I know I was wrong to stay out all night, but please let's not ruin the holidays."

Nodding in feigned agreement, Sunny got up and mixed Meeko another drink. As she handed it to him, she asked, "Hey, what's that rat poison doing behind the bar?"

Meeko looked at her suspiciously. "Sunny, you didn't put anything in my drink, did you?"

"Maybe, maybe not."

Meeko poured out his drink then dumped the rat poison down the drain. "You know, you're getting dangerous."

Seized by an impulse for destruction, Sunny yanked the Christmas tree to the floor, breaking all the decorations. She proceeded to tear open the presents and shred the contents into bits. Using great restraint, she then wrapped up the dinner leftovers and took off for Ida's house to see Shung'.

"Shung', I won't take another day of this abuse. I want to leave him, but I'm afraid to go back on stage. My logical mind and my stupid self-pity are whipping my ass. Dear God, what could I possibly be learning from all of this pain?" Sunny rested her weary head in her hands and sobbed. "I'm a zombie living on coffee and pills. I can't sleep and I'm catnapping my life away. I'm terrified of my dreams and afraid of what the future holds. Nothing seems real to me."

"Sunny, I've heard that Meeko has brought a medicine man from Rosebud into town. He's having a *Yuwipi* ceremony in your home tomorrow evening. I want you to stay here tonight and I'll go back with you tomorrow."

Late the next afternoon Sunny and Shung' returned to find many people in the family room waiting for the ceremony. Meeko was helping with preparations. After the pipe was smoked, Meeko brought the medicine man a hot coal. Taking it from Meeko, he placed it on his tongue, coughed and spit it out. "Watch what you're doing! You just burned me!"

Sunny watched in amusement, then looked over at Shung', who nodded her head, smiled slyly as a fox, then left. As his helpers wrapped the medicine man in a blanket and tied him up, Sunny recognized the slip knot and knew the ceremony was staged. As the lights went out Lightning Man and Gourd Man appeared, but again Sunny sensed trickery.

Following the ceremony Meeko insisted that the medicine man and his helpers stay for a few days. Sunny didn't want them in her home, but to keep the peace she allowed them to stay in the basement.

While vacuuming the family room the next afternoon, Sunny noticed several small pieces of quartzite lying on the carpet. Curious, she took them to a geologist friend. Once he had examined them he laughed, demonstrating how rubbing the pieces together would make flying sparks.

"Well, there's the medicine man's Lightning Man," Sunny chuckled.

She then asked a friend in the police department to run a background check on the people in her house and was shocked to learn they were ex-cons. She arrived home to find beer cans and traces of cocaine lining her dining room table.

She confronted her visitors, saying, "You're jailbirds!"

Shaking the police records in Meeko's face, she railed, "Look! These people have served time as convicted murderers, thieves and whores."

"Judging another is not the way of the Red Road," said the medicine man with a stern face.

"Breaking the law isn't either," Sunny countered, holding out the quartzite. "How dare you make a mockery out of a sacred ceremony! I was trained Medicine, and you're a joke! Get out of my house or I'll have the police remove you!"

"Nephew, this woman is no good. Get rid of her. I'll find you a decent woman! Sign over your car to me as payment and I'll pronounce you divorced!"

"You charlatan! You take that car and I promise I'll take one of yours."

Meekos's lips were tight and his rage was beyond speaking. Suddenly his mind snapped and he was back in Vietnam. He knocked Sunny to the floor and grabbed her grandmother's pipe, throwing it across the room. As it bounced off the wall, it broke into pieces. The medicine man urged Meeko and the others to hurry. They quickly got their things and raced from the house.

Mortified, Sunny dropped to the floor in total disbelief unable to understand the terrible thing that had just happened. For two days she sat holding the broken pipe, mourning the loss of the most sacred thing she owned. Not knowing what to do, she called Shung' and told her what had happened. Shung' demanded she come at once.

By the time she arrived the stones were waiting for a sweat. As they left the sweat, a redheaded woodpecker flew near. Shung' borrowed Ida's truck and they followed the woodpecker across roads, ditches and many farm fields. When it landed in a pine tree, Shung' stopped the truck, allowing Sunny to do what she must do. She sat on the ground crying and praying as she dug a hole under the tree and buried her grandmother's pipe. In heartbroken silence they returned to Ida's in silence.

Sunny sadly drove home thinking about the woodpecker. The redheaded woodpecker was the favorite bird of the sun, and was also connected to the rhythm of Mother Earth. Her grandmother had used this particular species of woodpecker to gauge weather predictions. Shamans used its power to ride the drumbeats to other dimensions. Woodpecker stimulated the mind to a new way of life and was used by shape-shifters. Its pecking sound warned one not to jump into a situation until you had all the facts.

Woodpecker was now telling her it was time to follow her life's destiny. Sunny called Shung' to share this new information and asked her to please come over for a visit. When she heard the crunch of tires in the driveway, she went to the door and happily escorted the medicine woman into the house. They shared a cup of coffee and some sweet rolls.

"Will you look at this?" Sunny handed Shung' the bag of quartzite.

"Hmmm, I guess he didn't trust the above powers. Looks like he brought the power of *Wakinyan* in the form of foolishness." She laughed heartily and set the bag aside. "Sunny, don't judge that poor soul. Let him be at peace with his illusion. None of us are perfect. It takes courage to be imperfect, and that's what helps us recognize the truth and power of spirit. Mockery of Medicine will get you killed. Who knows? Maybe there will come a day that he will become a good servant to *Wakan Tanka*.

"Forget about him, Granddaughter. I can feel the dark murky waters tumbling and slithering around in your mind. You must rid yourself of this awful hatred and conquer the dark ones that are attacking you. I'll help you smooth out the wrinkles of your mind. You mustn't let anything change the course of your destiny.

"Let Raven call you back to your future. Trust this dreamer until you can feel true passion return to your life. Follow the destiny of your grandmother's precious sacred bundle, and step behind her on the Medicine road. Remember, a true dreamer can never look back. Once you take this step, you can never share yourself completely with another earthly being.

"True love desires the spiritual growth of another. I'll protect you on this journey if you promise me that you'll take Meeko's harsh lessons as a true love. Listen to me and I will walk with you until you have completed your destiny. You will be allowed some physical pleasures along the way, but know it takes strong discipline to walk the spirals of the Sacred Circles to attain this medicine power."

"Shung', if it will remove my pain, I'm ready to feed my soul to the hungered beast of my ignorance. I swear I will do what you ask! I'll dance with the wind until I reach every spiral, and I'll find my way back to harmony and balance. I promise I'll make myself worthy of picking up Cheering Woman's Sacred Medicine Bundle."

"Sunny, I'll hold you to your word. It's time you to step back into the sacred Sundance circle. If you do this, you'll become as powerful as life itself. If you don't, then know your sorrow will kill any hopes of your becoming the one to carry Cheering Woman's sacred bundle. These are not my rules, it's just the way it is."

"Oh, Shung, why didn't I listen to you? I can't believe I wasn't there for myself."

"Sunny, your mistake was loving beyond yourself. You simply locked your heart away from others and didn't realize how badly a lost love can hurt."

"I know. Life was much easier when I let my shields rest at my side. I promise, Shung', I'll remove every mask of illusion from my face. I'll walk free with the wind of truth and I'll come to you in the right way."

After their evening sweat, Shung' informed Sunny that she was leaving to prepare the spring training camp. "I'll see you in about three months."

Sunny promised she would be there and fervently hoped that she could keep her word.

For the next two weeks, Sunny sat among the Stone People in the Medicine Wheel, trying to release her feelings of anger and her desire for revenge from her heart. But somehow she could not, and gave in to bad medicine, cursing her enemies.

First, she focused on Meeko's heart and mind, capturing them in her dark circle. Next, she touched Karl's fourteen-year-old daughter, seeing her as a hooker. She envisioned Danny's wife leaving him for another man, and Lawrence's most expensive stud horse, cutting its hind legs so badly on barbed wire that it could no longer mount. Finally, she vowed to expose the medicine man and fulfill her promise and claim the car.

As she waited for her bad medicine to take effect, she opened up the power to destroy by offering blood to the spirits that would open her dark side. The spirit of *Round Face Man* appeared, ready to do her bidding. With haughty arrogance, she offered a sacrifice to the sacred fire.

As she entered the house the phone was ringing. Sunny picked it up and recognized the voice of the medicine man. She smiled as he told her his son had wrapped his car around a telephone pole and was in the hospital.

"Please, Sunny, I ask you to stop your bad medicine," he pleaded.

"That's the breaks, medicine man. Wanna try for seconds?"

The medicine man handed Meeko the phone. "This crazy woman refuses to make peace."

Meeko furiously demanded she stop, but Sunny merely chuckled and hung up the phone.

Meeko moved the medicine man and his groupies into an apartment in downtown Billings. After weeks of women, drugs and booze, they were evicted, and Meeko was left with the bill. Devastated over having been hoodwinked by his medicine friend, Meeko spiraled into a deep depression. Within a week he had overdosed, causing a heart attack, and was placed in intensive care at the Veterans Administration Hospital. Shortly thereafter, a doctor called to inform Sunny of Meeko's condition.

She rushed to the hospital and when she saw Meeko's coma-like state, she slapped him hard across the face and began to beat his chest. "You'll never escape from me, and you won't die on me either! I'll kill you first!"

Meeko's eyes flew open, and when he saw it was Sunny, he rolled over moaning, "Not You!" Alarmed the doctor called security to have Sunny escorted from the hospital, instructing her not to see his patient again.

During his recovery, Meeko called constantly, but Sunny refused to answer the phone. One day she stopped by the post office to pick up her mail and found a letter from Meeko. Written on the outside of the envelope, was: Read this letter on a happy day.

Sunny opened it and read:

> Today is March 19th, 1984, and I want to burn this day into my memory because I know that my life will take a change to whatever, but without you, it doesn't matter anymore. Sweetheart, I wish you would take my calls, but since you will not, I will write you this letter and tell you of my feelings because I can't seem to get your attention any other way. I'm about to go crazy with all this pressure.
>
> I just don't know what to do. If I leave the reservation, all my hopes will go up in smoke. If I don't straighten up I will lose my wife. Please come back to me. I will try to handle this pressure and I promise that I will stop the things that cause you to lose your temper. I can't go on like this much longer. I have no self-respect or honor left. I sit and cry for the good times that we have shared.
>
> I know we can get back to those days. Sometimes I sit and look at all the things around me, and find only the memories of the happy times, which hurt worse than the sad ones. I know I have lost you and I beg you to let me return to our shared happiness. Is that too much to ask? Is love just a word to describe the pain that can never be eased once it has gone?
>
> I must need these harsh lessons or I wouldn't have made it so hard on myself and those around me. I know in the past I've done things wrong, and now I suffer the consequences of those actions. You know the real me can see the beauty in a sunrise or a sunset. You know I understand the peace when touched by a warm breeze. My question is, why can't I feel the warmth of your smile? I tried very hard to become something that I was not meant to be. But, My Sweetheart, even murderers can sometimes make parole. Why can't I? I have seen no prison more cruel than the prison that I have built for myself.
>
> And now listen to the soul of my heart. Once long ago, there was an Indian man who thought life was for many things. It promised love and laughter for living and for dying. The one thing this man did not allow in his life was the crossing of another's path. So, one day, when the Indian man began to feel his niche in life, he became too generous in his existence with others. He began to realize that

life seems to be for paying homage to those who deserve it and punishing those who do not respect the sacred gift of life.

Although I had been alive for many years, my life began when I first took you in my arms and gave birth to all the special thoughts which still remain about you and with you. I worship my lovely wife, and there has never been a drop of moisture fallen, that I have welcomed more than those from my lady's eyes on our wedding day. The happiness you've brought to me will live forever. These memories are burned into my mind. I will always envy those that have found and cherished a real love.

Well, as you know, I'm in the hospital because of my abuse with drugs and alcohol. You were right, the medicine man is a crook. He has stolen everything from me. His son got drunk and wrecked my car. He didn't have a driver's license and my insurance refuses to pay. As you predicted, it was three o'clock one afternoon when he wrapped the car around a telephone pole. I'm sure you know that you've scared the hell out of everyone on the reservation. It was kinda funny watching all of them run from your power.

Soon the Spring Equinox will return and I hope to spend my time rebuilding a place for myself in this world. I wish I could make it mean more to me than it does. My life is now a question in itself. The world is a place to experience the purpose of all creation, and I know that I was not meant to spend my life just going through the pains of this hurt.

Am I really worth so very little that a few minutes on the phone is too much to ask from you? I have looked at the world around me and found that I am no worse than any other. But if this is so, why are all those others able to laugh and be grateful for their very existence? Could I really be so naïve that I do not understand why I was born? Maybe the future will bring me happiness, but will I be able to recognize it or enjoy it when it arrives?

Sunny, I must go to a place where people live without spending so much time hurting others. I can no longer compete in this kind of world. I can no longer hurt anyone like I have hurt you. I have to try to find whatever is left of my honor and cling to whatever direction that Wakan Tanka will give me.

I will always love you. Don't throw me away, wait for me. I will return when I am ready to give you the love that you deserve. I love you.

Meeko

Sunny folded the letter and stuck it in her purse. When she arrived home she phoned Meeko at the hospital. Both cried for what they had lost, even though they knew there was no coming back together.

"I have listed the house, filed for divorce and placed a lien on the business. As you know we're broke, so I'll be heading south to visit my cousins, Pete and Peck to cut a dope deal."

"Sunny, no! Why in hell would you do this?"

"Just business. I need the money! I've experienced enough hurt from you to last for ten lifetimes! I hate your lessons, Meeko, but I know I will love the woman that comes out of this mess."

"Sunny, wait until I'm out of the hospital! The doctor says if I don't stop the drugs and booze, it'll kill me, and it will be my heart. Please, I know our marriage is over, but if you'll stay with me until we're both back on our feet, I promise there will be no more affairs, and we can try to rebuild our relationship."

"Meeko, don't try to stop me or I'll destroy you."

Within a few hours, Sunny had packed the motor home and she and ShaTonga were on the long drive back toward financial independence.

Sunny hoped to complete her financial goal without Shung' knowing, in time to meet her on the agreed upon date for her spring medicine training.

Sunny prayed to Creator promising that if he would let the spirits protect her on each run, she would only deal in drugs for three months, then quit. Although she knew the business and felt comfortable with her decision, she prayed that Sam would ride with her on these long hauls.

Pete and Peck fronted Sunny five kilos of pure uncut cocaine and another two keys of crystal meth. She first made peace with the spirit of each package then asked the drug entity for its help and protection. Disguising herself so she would not be recognized, she steeled herself to ward off what trouble might arise and began to deliver the drugs from coast to coast, never entering the same state twice.

At the end of her three months on the road, she headed for Aspen, Colorado relieved to know this was her last run. She had accomplished her financial goals, but the life of a drug dealer had made her ruthless.

It was three in the morning when Sunny arrived at her Billings home, to find the 'Sold' sign still up and a light on in the house. Carrying a loaded sawed-off shot gun, she stepped inside to find Meeko asleep on the sofa with the television blaring. She stared with shock at the shadow that seemed to stretch across the room like a long bony finger of death.

After Meeko awoke, they spoke kindly but distantly for a long time. Then Sunny told him she was leaving on another trip.

"You need to stay here so we can work things out. I'm really sorry for what I've done. Please tell me you still love me." When she did not reply, he followed her to the motor home and as she started the engine, he asked, "Where are you going?"

"None of your damn business!" she spat back at him as she backed out of the driveway. Sunny pressed on the brakes and slid the window back. "See you around," she smiled as she closed the window and headed toward the open road.

She drove all night and at day break she stopped to pick up some breakfast to take to Shung'.

Sunny was shocked to see the lowly shack that Shung' called a training camp. Noticing Shung's truck was there, she opened the door and was stopped in her tracks by a pack of vicious wolves that rushed her from underneath the house. She dashed back to the motor home for safety and seeing no sign of Shung', Sunny waited several hours, then left and checked into the nearest motel.

Each day she went back, and each day the wolves were waiting. This went on for four days. On the fifth day, Sunny decided to cross the barrier of wolves, thinking defiantly, 'If this is my day to die, then let it be so!' As soon as she stepped from the motor home, the wolves came out again in full force.

"Here! Here! Get away you fools and let the idiot pass." Sunny smiled to see Shung' standing in the doorway looking like a wild woman.

"Sorry, I'm a little late. I needed to take care of some business."

Shung' did not answer as she stepped off the porch to relieve herself. Sunny was appalled as she watched Shung' pee in the yard, then wipe herself on her skirt. She followed Shung' back into the house.

"Taking care of business, huh? Do you think that I don't know your every thought and action? You've become bad medicine. You've hurt an innocent fourteen year old child. A wife has left her family for another man. The tendons of a stud horse were cut, and it can never be used as a breeder. A medicine man's son was hurt in a car wreck. Meeko ended up in the hospital because you couldn't fix yourself and decided to hurt everyone! Now you come back to me after a drug run and expect me to accept these bad things you've done. I don't think so!"

Shung' picked up her rifle and slung it over her shoulder. "I don't want to talk to you right now. I'll be back in a few days. If you're still here, I might talk to you."

On the second day of the medicine woman's absence, Sunny was excited about her plans to refurbish Shung's two-room shack in hopes of earning her forgiveness. She replaced all the screens and a few broken windows, painted the exterior, put in a new bed, laid new linoleum on the kitchen floor and stocked the cabinet with canned goods. When she was finished, Sunny felt proud of what she had accomplished and was sure Shung' would forgive her when she saw these wonderful gifts.

On the fourth day, Sunny was having coffee outside with some of Shung's students under the arbor when she saw Shung' dragging a deer up the hill. She ran to help, but Shung' shooed her away with a stern look and pulled the deer into the yard. Still refusing Sunny's help, she skinned it out and cut it up, throwing the scraps to her wolves. Once the meat was cut into strips and placed on the drying rack, Shung' took the hide and shoved it in a wooden barrel of salt-brine.

Without a glance toward Sunny, she went to the river and bathed the blood from her body. As she walked naked back to the house, Sunny ran to her with a towel, saying, "I can't wait for you to see what I've done."

Shung' stepped into her kitchen and roared in anger, "How dare you come into my home and make it over for your comfort! You fool! You call this a gift? You've crossed one boundary too many! I'm through with you!" With her hunting knife Shung' slashed every screen, kicked out the new glass in her windows, tossed the bed into the yard, demanded that the linoleum be stripped, and threw the canned goods across the floor. Still enraged, Shung' got into Sunny's face, screaming at her as she backed her out of the house by poking and pushing her in the chest.

Terrorized, Sunny tried to justify her actions. Shung' refused to listen.

"Don't lie to me and stop lying to yourself! If I wanted that shit in my home, I would've gotten it! But no! You took it for granted that I'd forgive you if you came with gifts. Well, I'm not stupid and I'm far from gullible. You've taken all the sacred teachings and used them to deal drugs. You're nothing but a bragging piece of shit! I should stuff your ass down the toilet and flush it. Humph! Look at those phony painted fingernails, and who in the hell are you trying to impress wearing those fancy jeans and cowboy boots? The money you have on your back would feed a family of four for a month. Sunny, I'm sick of you and I don't want you around here! So, why don't you get out?"

Shung' turned her back on Sunny and headed for the back yard. Sunny followed close behind apologizing, "I'm truly sorry. I thought it would be nice for you to have comfortable living quarters."

"God, are you just stupid?" Shung' grabbed a wolf turd from the ground and shoved it into Sunny's hand. "Girl, you act like shit! You think like shit! You might as well smell like shit! Go ahead! Put it down, so I can run your ass off of my property."

Sunny sat under a large tree and cried, devastated over Shung's reaction. She knew Shung' would dismiss her as an apprentice if she put the wolf turd down or made one more mistake. By late that night, Sunny had figured out what she must do to please Shung'.

The following morning Sunny heard a new group of students arrive, filled with excitement at the opportunity to study with a medicine woman for the next six weeks. Sunny went to the river for a bath. Thinking it would please Shung', she removed her Patti Nails and all her makeup, dressed in old jeans and worn-out sneakers, and took a seat with the new group. However, to her great embarrassment Shung' screamed, "Get out of my circle and sit under that tree until I say different!"

Sunny meekly did as she was told and listened from afar to Shung's teachings for the rest of the day.

The standoff between them continued for three weeks despite Sunny's every attempt to win Shung's favor. She chopped wood, cleaned, cooked, and paid for everyone's food. Each morning before daybreak, she ran ten miles in the hills before joining the morning sweat, repeating this routine before the evening sweat. After the sweats, she would help the fire keeper clean the lodge and reset the Old Man Four Generations fire pit. At the end of each day she was exhausted yet still determined that she would again apprentice under Shung' no matter what it took.

One day Shung' said abruptly, "We need deer meat. Go get one."

Without a word, Sunny picked up the rifle and left. She set up camp in a patch of bushes near the water. That night she prayed for a deer to come so she could fulfill Shung's request. Early the next morning, she heard some deer come to water and after tracking them, shot an old male that was isolated from the herd. When the deer dropped,

Sunny performed the sacred rite for taking a life, gutted the animal and transported it on a large dead branch back to Shung's camp. There she cut up the deer and placed the meat strips on drying racks. After placing the hide inside the barrel of salt-brine, Sunny walked over and sat under a tree to have a cigarette.

A smiling Shung' brought her a cup of coffee and sat down next to her. "Ah, Ms. Sunny Beam, I see you're learning to respect Medicine. You did good, but it's time for you to go back to your world. You need to learn discipline of mind and body to understand the importance of respecting another's boundaries. It's up to you, but I want you to go back to the beginning of your training with your grandmother and relearn everything she taught you.

"Remember, it was Cheering Woman who gave you a good name. I want to make sure you understand its meaning so you can carry that name into your future with integrity. So, *Ezonzon Wi Cha Nah He*, get packed and go collect some more green paper. Don't return to me until you have graduated from your infidelity experience. By then you should be a far wiser person. I hope you become wise enough to keep honorable principles and love without harm. Build your faith in Creator until you understand the limitless power of love. Deny yourself nothing in life. Find your happiness so you can express all that you are.

"Life is merely a school for you to learn and grow. Everyone builds strength when forced to face their darkest hour. You cannot live life to its fullest if you keep hiding in the shadows of another's existence. Your battles with confusion showed you had no belief in *Wakan Tanka* and you judged everyone by your lowly principles. Never compromise your principles again. You think you've faced demons? Wait until you learn to walk between worlds. Learn to love yourself and risk all to build your faith from life's experience. Don't bother to come back until you've accomplished what I've asked for."

"Oh, Shung', please don't send me away! From the very beginning of my marriage, I saw Meeko stifling my spirit but I was too afraid to do anything about it. I wouldn't have survived this experience without you. It was my lack of trust that caused the trouble between us. Shung', I'm sorry I didn't tell you everything, but I had to do what I had to do to survive. Believe me, I'll change and I promise I'll find my pathway back to myself."

"Sunny, I didn't tell you to hurt others! I didn't tell you to sell dope. I told you to respect yourself and all life forces. How can I respect you when you choose to turn to bad medicine? I'm sure Cheering Woman has turned over in her grave a thousand times with your shenanigans. Let's hope you've learned that your life is the most precious gift you will receive. I've helped all I can, now it's up to you to take control of your emotions. How can you follow the old ways if you have no faith or commitment to yourself? This banishment will force you to get in touch with your feelings and rebuild your belief in *Wakan Tanka*. Before you can have strength and courage, you must awaken the unborn you and come to terms with your life as a woman.

"It's time to take your destiny in your own hands and begin making peace with your bad experiences. Until then, you will never experience the power of good medicine.

So, Granddaughter, you are now the keeper of your keys. Take this opportunity to go back to the beginning of your life and fix the damage you've caused others. Find the dreams that will make you happy. Now go! That is all I have to say."

Shung' escorted Sunny into the house and forced her to pack.

Her eyes filled with tears, Sunny drove away. Her last view of Shung' was standing with her wolf pack on the old dilapidated front porch. Wiping the tears from her eyes, Sunny transformed her feelings of frustration and anger into determination. "I will be back, Shung', she called out. I will be the best damn pupil you have ever taught. You wait and see, Shung'! You just wait and see! I'll be back!"

Sunny Returns to Sundance

Driven by humiliation and rejection, Sunny was determined to regain the strength needed to return to the stage and prove her self-worth. She flew to New York and once again, hating the expectations placed on her by others, she confronted them feverishly. Kate was very supportive but could only watch the heartbreak that seemed to dog Sunny's life.

Sunny's existence became an endless routine of eating, sleeping and working. She traveled extensively throughout the world and her fame grew, but her personal life continued to deteriorate. Riddled with doubts and fears, she became a confused and unfulfilled woman, desperately searching her past for answers to the many questions that remained hidden behind a wall of futility.

Sleep had become just a word. Many mornings Sunny lay watching the sunrise while exploring many disturbing questions that had no answers. As she tried to reach the core of herself, she would ask: Who am I? What am I? What is the purpose of my birth? Sunny pondered these questions over and over until fatigue drove her to desperation.

In all this confusion, Sunny feared she was approaching the borders of insanity. Trapped behind this barrier of despair, she would drop to her knees, pleading to *Wakan Tanka* to help her return to the old teachings to find her heart. But try as she might, Sunny felt disconnected from Creator and knew her prayers were useless words. Tired of living with these tortuous, serpentine thoughts, Sunny cried out from the essence of her soul:

"Oh Coyote, Coyote, Coyote! How you walk on my mind, yet I can only hear your echoes in my pain. My lost soul cries out in unbearable loneliness. Oh Coyote, am I a fool that consistently just catches my own tail?" But within her heart, Sunny knew she was the biggest trickster in her life.

One evening when she had finished her last show on the island of Fiji and was waiting for the elevator to go to her room, her chest tightened and her heart began to pound rapidly. Filled with terror, Sunny knew she was being engulfed in a full blown panic attack. She dug into her handbag and pulled out a fistful of pills, swallowing them as best she could. Getting no relief, she raced through the lobby and headed to the beach, hoping to escape whatever was trying to take her life. She ran until exhaustion took over, then stood gasping for air in the blackness of night—alone, so very alone. She thrust her fist to the sky, frantically challenging *Wakan Tanka*:

"I've tried hard to follow a good way, but the knowledge to get there escapes me. I hate myself for letting life cut such deep wounds into my soul. I can't take any more! What have I done to bring such wrath upon me? I'm tired of this struggle and I beg you, give me life or give me death! Release me from this agony, or take back your breath of life and let me breathe no more! Oh, Great Spirit, if you refuse me then take pity on my soul and stop this pain."

The only answer she heard was the sound of waves breaking on the shore. In a fit of rage, Sunny defiantly walked into the ocean, allowing her body to sink into the murky darkness. She entered a long tunnel and peace came over her. A light beckoned her onward and she heard a gentle voice say, "Go back, my child. It is not yet your time."

Sunny yearned to stay where she was until she found herself surrounded by many remorseful earthbound souls who had taken their lives. Realizing she too would become one of them and suicide was not the answer to her problems, she backed away from the light.

From far above, Sunny watched as a black man lifted her body from the water and placed her on the beach. As her soul re-entered her body, she began to vomit profusely and gasp for air. Slowly becoming aware, she opened her eyes to find a crowd had gathered and some were taking pictures. Fearing her career would be ruined, she stared into the eyes of the black stranger, mutely begging him to cover her face as she was put into an ambulance.

In the emergency room, a staff doctor examined her and found she was in good physical health, but expressed concern over her mental state. Afraid her suicide attempt would become public, Sunny appeased him with lies, saying, "I just swam out too far and wasn't strong enough to get back to shore."

The next morning she was released from the hospital and was relieved to see the story was not in the newspaper. She returned to the hotel and was walking to the elevator when the mysterious black man approached her.

"Hey, lady! I'm the one who saved your life. I'm thankful you're all right."

Sunny opened her purse and thrust five twenty dollar bills at him stating, "I suppose this will keep you quiet!"

The gentle stranger pushed her hand aside, then answered in a sweet voice, "No thank you, lady. But please get some help." He turned and walked away.

Dumbfounded, Sunny watched as he quickly vanished into the crowded street.

Three days later as Sunny was boarding a plane for Australia, she searched the crowd and was thrilled when she saw the mysterious stranger waving to her. After the plane lifted into the air Sunny, haunted by the stranger's presence, stared out the window vowing she would unlock the painful door to her troubled soul.

Upon her arrival in Sydney, she was greeted with great fanfare and quickly escorted to a waiting limousine. The driver handed her a packet of information about places she might like to visit, then drove her to Kings Cross where she checked into the hotel and met with the staff from the St. George League Club to prepare for the press party that evening. Within the week, Sunny was performing before packed houses, once again using the stage to hide from the reality of her life.

During the day she spent her free time visiting the zoo. One morning she spotted a group of koala bears chewing on eucalyptus leaves high in a gum tree. She called softly to them. A guard tapped her on the shoulder and informed her she was not to touch the animals.

When the guard was out of view she mind-linked with one of the koalas. It soon crawled down the tree and onto her shoulder. As she stroked its soft fur, a little paw reached out and touched her hair. As they stared into each other's eyes with great curiosity, the koala bear ever so gently removed her red hair ribbon, then slowly inched back up the tree with its bounty. The magical connection with this foreign animal rekindled a flame of warmth in Sunny's heart and life suddenly felt better. She continued to visit her new little friend, always leaving a red ribbon as a token of their friendship.

Sunny became an avid runner and continued her endurance training in a nearby park. She was curious about the aboriginal people she met there and soon had made friends with a few of them. They were inquisitive about this American Indian and insisted she was an Apache with Samantha eyes. They were shocked to learn that she did not know John Wayne personally. Sunny soon found she had much in common with these new friends of hers. Each day they met to discuss their shared knowledge of the subtleties of nature's teachings. One day they suggested that Sunny meet their elders on a walkabout. Since Australia was at the end of her tour, Sunny was intrigued with the idea of going on a walkabout with the native people.

Sunny was amazed at how easy it was for her to understand the aboriginal way of life, whether it was eating, gathering food or praying. She loved the barren openness of the terrain and soon found she had reconnected to the sensitivity of Mother Earth and this was beginning to free her troubled mind.

The gentle aboriginal people understood her needs and reaffirmed to her that the sacredness of living a good life was the only way to feed her soul. For the first time, she was beginning to replace the broken pieces of her old sorrows and walk back to her heritage, knowing that would be where she would find her face.

Sunny sadly bid these magnificent people goodbye and graciously thanked the elders who had so kindly helped her find the thread of truth that led her back to becoming the dreamer that her grandmother had predicted so long ago.

Ever searching for her soul, Sunny boarded a plane for Mexico City, where she was met by José, an elderly man who was to become her guide and interpreter to the many places they would visit on her journey.

Sunny was driven by her quest. Each place she visited held a different key to the old sacred knowledge that was so deeply ingrained in these lost cultures. She no longer felt as inept, and soon was walking peacefully amongst the relics of the old ruins. She examined many of the crumbling statues that still held onto the past even though they had almost been conquered by time. This place had once been a flourishing civilization, and Sunny wept over the lost knowledge, hoping that someday it might be rediscovered.

Sunny felt her mind slip away as she sat among these old sculptured figures. She envisioned many books that were bound with golden leather, falling gracefully from a misty sky. Instinctively she knew that they contained the old knowledge that had been lost for centuries.

Sunny continued to travel from country to country searching for ancient knowledge. She discovered one of her past lives and found it was filled with the study of old Medicine. She cried with joy when she realized her need to explore was broadening her comprehension and healing her pain.

She and José traveled through the isolated areas of Central America, filling her with a richness of old past memories. Each place seemed to provide her with another thread to weave into the tapestry of herself and allowed her to learn the oldest philosophies about Mayan numbers and calendars. Sunny began to understand the true meaning of time, space, measure and dimension.

One day as she reflected back on Shung's words, she burst out laughing. Here again, the seeds that her beloved teacher had planted were walking strongly on her mind. She could still hear Shung' say: "Time is mankind's worst enemy. Time eats up everything, that is if you look at it in a three-dimensional space. But if you speak of time in multidimensional levels, then you have the ability to go beyond time and space as we know it."

Shung's voice rang inside her head. "*Sku'ya*, stop limiting yourself. Travel to another time and space with this newfound knowledge. That is the only way you will learn about the billions of universes that have existed throughout all eternity."

Sunny closed her eyes, breathed slowly and there sat Shung'. "Can Bear become Buffalo? Can Coyote become Eagle? Can you become the person you were born to be? The knowledge you are seeking will not be withheld from you if you come from your heart. True power comes from focused attention and your belief system can only be attained through patience and perseverance. Apply what you know and quit trying to force your growth."

Slowly Sunny began to realize how hard Shung' had struggled to teach her and felt ashamed that she had been such an unwilling apprentice. Feeling guilty over her past behavior, Sunny finally appreciated the gift of a caring medicine teacher.

After that everything began to talk to Sunny, proving to her that she was standing in the center of her power. No longer was she afraid to walk the web of faith back to the old Grandmother's Lodge. How patient the spirits of the grandmothers had been in their willingness to guide her precarious walk through those bad times. This knowledge helped her give in to the spirits of limitless power. Through her diligence in Shadow World, she went beyond time and space and entered into the multidimensional levels of spirit where she found many things that were not of this world. Having nothing in this world to compare these things with, Sunny found she could not comprehend many of their meanings.

Feeling a need for greater understanding, she asked José to take her deep into the jungles of Guatemala. They came to a quaint little village where Sunny met an old medicine woman. The language barrier made direct communication impossible, and she relied heavily on sign language and José interpretative skills. As they spoke at great length of her spirit travels, Sunny accepted the simple fact that life was based upon all structures of the heavens.

One day while sitting with the old medicine woman, Sunny realized something was being lost in translation. In an attempt to grasp the meaning of what the old woman was saying, Sunny used her ability to read expressions and body language, but still had difficulty connecting to the medicine woman's thought process. Since she had nothing to compare the old woman's visions to, she tried imagining Shung's interpretation of what she was experiencing and heard Shung's voice:

"Don't starve in poverty like you did as a child. Be yourself. Take it all in and feel it as if you were wearing it like your skin. Become soft and pliable yet strong. Let her words embrace your mind and let them expand beyond time to become limitless, timeless. Find the space within to embrace the motion of your existence. Think of how wonderful it is that life's necessities have become one of your gifts of power. Whatever they demand from you, know they are merely building a stronger foundation on which to support the simplicity of a meaningful life. Use your inner and outer senses of sight, sound, taste, touch and smell. Let the essence of all life take you to unknown dimensions. Sunny, use these gifts as a lesson to develop your growth."

Sunny smiled as she explored the many available passages to the spirit world. She knew that free will marked the path of a dreamer and realized that once she stepped upon this path, she could never turn back. She became an advocate of self-discipline in every thought, action and deed. Unexpectedly her life was spiraling upward from the smallest of things. She ate ravenously from each experience to gain its knowledge, and it mattered not whether it came from throwing a stone, a bird flying overhead or a simple walk with nature. Everything she encountered was a reminder of who she was and what she was becoming. The sadness of her early life and marriage eased away, confirming Shung's words.

She and José decided to venture into San Salvador to spend a few days strolling the beaches. Each day she sat alone on the beach watching the sun go over down. One evening as she idly played with a small seashell, she held it close to her ear and heard the ancients whispering of the power rising on each wave coming from the oldest of ocean floors.

So many wonderful things were happening to her! Sunny felt her innocence return as she reflected back on her first vision quest. It had been a time of innocence that had allowed her to ride the shaft of an eagle's feather. It was her Grandmother who had anchored her to the solar and star systems. Finally that seed of knowledge was beginning to bear fruit. When she awakened the following morning, Sunny found herself once again in love with life. It seemed the more she visited the poverty-stricken areas of Central America, the stronger her childhood memories with her grandmother became. These old memories released her from years of suffering and pain. She continued to gather her power, hoping that someday she would step upon the Warrioress' journey and carry the integrity and honor of all that she was becoming.

Sunny felt the seeds that had been planted so long ago crack open with a pulsating heartbeat from another time and speak of the infinite numbers as being the sacred language of *Wakan Tanka*. She knew that her grandmother had taught her beyond doubt that the touch of *Wakinyan* was always near, opening many levels and transforming her understanding into multidimensional thinking that was now touching her very existence.

Sunny loved watching her dreams dance forward, helping her see the flaws that had been so cleverly hidden, waiting for the right time to unfold. Each day she prayed to the spirit helpers to let her understand every symbol and message contained in the sacred language. She grew stronger in all that she saw, touched, heard and felt. This gave her a support she had never known possible.

Months passed and Sunny's journey led her to Costa Rica where early one morning she was awakened by the sound of a steady, drizzling rain. Sunny finished her breakfast then dressed warmly for her daily walk along the deserted beach. As she strolled along, she thought of how each storm held millions of tiny rain spirits bonded together as one. Why did humans feared such bonding, she wondered. Why couldn't the human race be as the raindrop tribe, working together to accomplish one purpose?

As these thoughts walked on her mind, Sunny felt a chill and sat under a group of large trees. As she sat wrapped in a blanket huddled against a tree trunk, she watched the slow, drizzling rain and reflected on one of Cheering Woman's old stories. She remembered her excitement when her grandmother had described the birthing of the Rain Spirit Clan back on Turtle Island.

She could still feel that same urgency in each raindrop, the need to complete its journey as quickly as possible and return to *Wakan Tanka*. She remembered her grandmother cautioning her to always show the raindrops great respect since they could spare little time to speak with others if they were to complete their purpose in life on time. She thought of their urgent need to fill the rivers, lakes, ponds and little brooks and saw the integrity of their life-giving purpose. Sunny felt very secure as she realized the total dependency of all life came from these sacred Rain Spirits. She could hear their faint, anxious whispers all around her as their wetness disappeared into the ground, continuing their journey for the good of all.

One small yet extremely powerful raindrop caught her eye as it twisted and turned, finding its way to the corner of a leaf. It seemed as though this droplet was held in a small, invisible bag. Intrigued, Sunny watched it increase in weight and disconnect from the leaf. Like magic it fell to the ground in slow motion and burst open, leaving a faint wet mark by her bare feet.

Suddenly, a tiny voice echoed from deep inside. "When you learn to walk between two raindrops, you will know that shape-shifting is based on the transition of molecular matter."

Taking this thought Sunny began to break down the life cycle of a raindrop. Rain falls, the sun heats it and creates a mist that rises. A raindrop must be careful never to collect debris from the atmosphere, otherwise its weight will pull it back to the earth's floor. Like all life, even a raindrop can teach us about the karmic wheel.

After dinner Sunny usually went to bed early so she could take advantage of more adventurous morning hours on the beach. Once she had gathered her newly found treasures of the day, she would go back to the hotel and spend a lazy afternoon lying in a hammock, experiencing the beauty of the heavy afternoon showers, pondering the thought of her co-existence with a raindrop. Could this be the power of unity within all things? Does it prove the concept of reincarnation? Suddenly Sunny realized life just is. The human spirit makes the same journey as a raindrop. And so it is.

Sunny knew it was time to change the things that had influenced her life in a bad way. Why continue to walk through the dark forces of life's bitter fights? Must lessons that cause turmoil be our destruction, or can they also create growth? Does it take abuse for us to truly know we have learned from the subtleties of nature's greatest teachers of duality? Realizing she too must continue her journey just as the raindrop, she accepted that life was a gift and therefore her freedom.

Sunny knew she had witnessed the subtleties of true medicine power. She felt humbled and thankful for the experience shared by one special raindrop which had bathed her spirit in the knowledge of rebirthing the Self.

Despite this new knowledge, Sunny soon found it took greater discipline than she had ever known to ride with the winds in the invisible worlds. But during the next three months of hard work, she discovered that she no longer walked alone and finally understood the true meaning of *Mitakuye Oyasin*, all my relations. Exhilarated with her progress, Sunny began to understand what it meant to embrace life and she saw the world through different eyes. It was time to fulfill her vow and return to Shung' to pick up her grandmother's medicine bundle. If she hurried, she could reach the reservation in time for Sun Dance.

She packed all the gifts she had gathered and said goodbye to José, then drove to Panama City and caught a plane to Rapid City, South Dakota, where she rented a car and drove to Rosebud. As she rounded the last curve near the BIA building, she chuckled when she saw the only phone within twenty miles was still standing at the edge of the road, desperately in need of repair. The road had seemed much wider when she was a child. She rolled down the window to capture the sweet fragrance of the plains and breathed in the wonderful aromas, allowing the moment to engulf her soul. She looked toward the horizon to see the dark clouds of a typical summer afternoon, and knew another rainstorm was readying itself to dance across the Dakota plains.

Sunny rounded the last curve and pulled to a stop at the barred gate. Willie, wearing a red beret, walked up to the car smiling.

"Hey, Cuz, long time no see. You're a little late. I guess you're on Indian time, huh? Got the road blocked off to keep out the nosy wannabes." He laughed as he tied a red flag onto the antenna of her car. "We placed the Sundance tree in the ground this morning. Sorry you missed it."

About that time another car pulled up behind Sunny. Willie lifted the bar to let Sunny pass, saying, "I'll find you in camp. We'll talk tonight."

"Sure thing, Cuz," she answered, pulling into the parking area. Sunny took her new handpainted shawl and wrapped it around her shoulders then walked to the Sacred Sundance Circle. As she approached the Sacred Cottonwood Tree, she felt its awesome presence, and in that moment was overwhelmed by the joyous spirit of the many colorful prayer flags flying in the soft wind.

After extending her arm to the intercessor for a flesh offering, Sunny walked over and embraced the Tree of Life. She felt it breathe under her touch and move like human flesh. She cried with gratitude for the gift of this experience and lay her head against the tree, listening to its gentle heartbeat as tears of happiness rolled down her cheeks. Oh yes, she was glad to be home!

When Sunny left the circle, she walked past the area that was established for the sundance pledgers and recognized many sundance brothers and sisters as they came near to welcome her back to their sacred circle.

She heard a voice behind her, saying, "Welcome back, Sunny. It's been almost three years since you've been home."

Sunny turned to face Meeko and as their eyes met, their souls once again intertwined and they knew that love still flowed between them.

Meeko offered to help Sunny get settled. After walking to the car in silence, Sunny filled Meeko's arms with her camping equipment and the many gifts she had brought for the elders. "I'm camped in a beautiful place near the river. Can I put your tent next to mine?" he asked. Sunny agreed and as they reached the area she saw Shung' beading in front of a small open fire.

Shung' saw Sunny and put down her beadwork. She picked up a cracked mug and filled it with black coffee then sat back down, smiling as Sunny approached.

Sunny placed a huge package on the ground in front of Shung', then with bowed head took the coffee cup and knelt down in front of her. Shung' thrust her chin forward, signaling Meeko to go away. Sunny sipped her coffee in silence until Shung' handed her a piece of fry bread, as she considered what to say.

"Granddaughter, it's been a long time." Shung' sniffed the air around her. "Well, you don't smell like shit and you don't look like shit, but I wonder if you still think and act like shit?" Shung' patted Sunny lovingly on the head, mending the rift between them.

Relieved that Shung' had forgiven her, Sunny answered, "I've worked hard to clean up my shit. But I'll be happy to carry a wolf turd around for the rest of my life if it pleases my *Unci*." She smiled and lay her head on Shung's knee.

"Yes, I know, Granddaughter," answered Shung', stroking Sunny's hair. "I saw you arrive, and I'm happy that you're home."

Handing the package to Shung', Sunny asked, "After Sun Dance, can I return and finish my training with you?"

Shung' nodded yes and opened her gift, a large bull buffalo robe. "Are you ready to pick up your medicine bundle?"

"I'm ready to do what you tell me."

Shung' handed the robe to one of her apprentices to take into her tipi. When Shung's expectations were not met immediately, she snatched the sacred buffalo hide away and placed it behind her chair on the east wall.

During the afternoon, many people stopped by to admire this sacred gift and Shung' took great pride in honoring Sunny for having given it. She had the rest of her apprentices serve food and coffee while she entertained her guest with stories of the past experiences with her most unruly pupil.

Sunny felt she was back in the family circle once again. The talk turned to the latest gossip on the reservation regarding the BIA, new births, divorces, murders, deaths, names of those who were serving time in prison and those who had graduated from college. Sunny enjoyed the dry sense of humor that prevailed, even though she knew most were having great difficulty in coping with the humorless, poverty-stricken life of the reservation.

It was almost noon when Sunny joined Meeko at the river bank, where he had set up her tent a comfortable distance from his. As she approached, Sunny noticed he was carving a red clay pipe. Meeko set it aside, "God, Sunny, you look great! There's an extraordinary inner beauty that you didn't have the last time I saw you."

"For the first time in my life, I feel at peace," answered Sunny pulling up a lawn chair and sitting down.

"What made you come home? I was beginning to worry that you'd forgotten about your people."

"Meeko, I needed time to think about my life. You should've known that I was born to the blanket and I would always return."

Feeling uncomfortable he teased, "Well, I kinda thought you had gotten tired of listening to the old Sundance leaders yelling in their gravelly voices, 'Sundancers! Get out of those blankets before you smell like an old bear!' as they walked along kicking our feet."

Sunny reached over and smacked him affectionately. "You bet I did, hope it happens again this year."

"I'm sorry you missed going with us to get the tree. See those four little girls over there? They're the ones who were chosen for the ceremony. They were all so proud to have earned the right to have the sacred red circle painted in the middle of their little foreheads. I helped the little one hold the ax so she could get her four licks on the tree, and believe me, she took her part in that ceremony very seriously. When I stepped in with my ax, the little one came close to me and whispered, 'Please be careful, because I don't want the tree to feel any pain.'

"Sunny, it took at least fifty men to bring that tree back to the sacred circle. Before we stood her up, everyone came forth and placed their prayer ties and Sundance ropes in it. When we stood her up and the wind touched her, she came alive with all the people's offerings. I painted the Red Road from the base of the trunk to the first branch and I felt her join the people in ceremony. I was so touched that I knelt down beside her in humble appreciation and gave thanks for her life.

"Oh, I forgot! I was surprised when I received the Sundance skirt you sent me in the mail. I love it and I'm wearing it this year. But I must ask, did you deliberately do all that beadwork to weigh me down during those four long days on my feet?"

"Meeko, I intentionally made it heavy. I wanted you to suffer for all the hard lessons you gave me. But if you see it as a problem, I'll take some of them off."

"No! No! I was joking. I think it will be the most beautiful skirt on the field."

The day ended quickly and the smell of food drifted across the campground making them hungry. After eating, they sat silently watching the darkness cover the peaceful sky and listened to the insects rejoice in the night's arrival. All around campfires danced to the rhythm of the stars.

Meeko stoked the fire. "I know how you love the smell of cedar, so I brought this log especially to welcome you home." He carefully placed it on the fire and once it was burning, both sat watching its beautiful flames. Meeko placed a pot of coffee on the open fire. "Pretty, huh? I hope you realize I will always feel closer to you than to any other."

As a lonely night bird sang in the lazy stillness of the evening blending with the gentle voice of the river, Sunny's mind drifted back to her childhood days and she knew she had made the right decision in coming home.

Meeko took off his shoes and stretched out on the ground, wriggling his bare feet in the cool, rich soil.

"I got here about three weeks ago to help prepare everything for the Sun Dance. It seems to have healed my soul."

"Meeko, I came back to finish my Sun Dance vows and hopefully pick up my medicine bundle."

"I've moved back to the old homestead. Still paint a little. You know what still bothers me? I thought your love for me was so strong that no matter what I did, you'd never leave. I could intellectualize why you left, but when I felt your heart leave me, I couldn't handle the reality. The terror of being without you caused deep depression and an unforgettable loneliness. I still have problems accepting that you'll never come back. I know that when I lost you, I lost my soul and I'm still just an empty shell. Sunny, I've missed you terribly. Would you consider running away with me? We could go live on a mountaintop, far from the world."

"Hell, no! You've got to be kidding. It took me too long to find my soul. I've learned if I'm to ever love another he must understand the true meaning of love. I once wanted all the things that you are now offering, but time has taught me those things must be found inside myself. I keep my life simple, and most importantly, I work on my relationship with myself. I will always love you, Meeko, but not at the cost of losing myself. I do miss what we once had, but life goes on, and we'll both survive. We'll always be connected in spirit but never again in flesh."

"Sunny, there is no other for me. I know I destroyed our journey together. You are still my life, and that's why I'm pulling twelve buffalo skulls this year. Maybe it will help me find my way. Shung' has known for two years that you'd be picking up your medicine bundle this year. That's why I came—so we could Sundance together for our fifth and final year. Sunny, when I look at you, I'm amazed. I'm proud of your strength." He reached over to take her hand and added, "Thank you for forgiving me. Someday maybe you'll return to the reservation to live."

"Meeko, I'm happy that I've experienced reservation life, but I'm also glad that I no longer live here. I'm tired of being rejected as a breed, and I no longer need that kind of pain. I've experienced too much sorrow in life, but I love the woman that crawled out of those horrible experiences."

Shung's voice came through the dark. "Will you two shut up! I'm trying to sleep!"

Both giggled quietly as Meeko whispered, "You know, Shung' can be as grumpy as an old badger. We'd better get some sleep. You know the old ones will be up before sunrise."

As they crawled into their separate tents, Wicahmunga called out, "Both of you better stay in your own tents tonight. Remember, I'm watching you."

Up early in the morning, Meeko stoked the fire and while the coffee was boiling he began making breakfast. When he saw Shung' and Wicahmunga walking toward their campsite, he tapped on Sunny's tent to let her know that Shung' was on her way. Dressing quickly, Sunny stepped out of her tent just in time to see Wicahmunga walking toward Meeko with a contemptuous look on her face. Sunny giggled, recalling how a single word from her could make Meeko cringe.

"Well you dog of a dog, I hear you'll be pulling buffalo skulls this year. Maybe the heart of a buffalo is in there someplace." Wicahmunga playfully poked him in the ribs. "Do you remember when you were three years old and pissed on me? My dress smelled so bad that I had to throw it away. I just might help you this year if you buy me a new dress," she snorted, punching Meeko on the arm. "Have you told Sunny that you're living with that fat Rachel at Granbear's old homestead?" She turned to Sunny. "Don't talk to that dog turd! His head is so far up his ass, he can't see nothing! I don't care if they pierce him clean through, all they're going to find is a big, crusty buffalo chip." Wicahmunga cackled as she vanished toward the river.

"I swear that woman's my worst nightmare."

"Don't talk like that about Wicahmunga," said Shung'. "I just might let her help me in the Sundance ceremony. When Shadowhawk pierces your back with those eagle claws, I don't think you'd like to lay your head in her lap."

Meeko and Sunny enjoyed the teasing atmosphere and both felt good. When Meeko handed Shung' a plate of food, she took a bite of the meat and said, "This meat is so stringy I think it must be collie."

Meeko laughed and tasted it, agreeing it definitely held memories of dog meat. Once the morning meal was completed, Meeko cleaned up the campsite as everyone went their separate ways to prepare for the upcoming ceremony. Sunny spent the morning with the grandmothers while Meeko sat with Shadowhawk making preparations to pull the twelve buffalo skulls.

Afterwards Sunny went to the river to bathe, then ventured about the camp visiting with old friends. On her way back, she noticed that Old Wolf was sleeping in front of Shung's tipi. She smiled, remembering how Old Wolf always lay in front of the doorway to keep intruders away from Shung'. She was glad to see Old Wolf tending to her duties, completely engrossed in snapping at the pesky flies.

Seeing Shung' was busy, she suggested to Meeko they go for a walk. They removed their shoes and waded across the river. As they climbed the steep embankment on the other side, they noticed Old Wolf was following close behind.

Walking through the trees to a clearing, they stopped and stared at the never-ending fields of swaying grass that stretched as far as the eye could see. As they continued on, they noticed a disturbance in the tall grass and saw it was Old Wolf sniffing the bushes. All of a sudden she pounced on a bush that was covered with butterflies. As they scattered everywhere one landed on Old Wolf's nose. She crossed her eyes then spun in a circle, trying to remove the intruder. Meeko and Sunny laughed as they stretched out on the ground, gazing in awe at the myriad of colorful butterflies dancing in the air.

Meeko jumped up and captured a yellow butterfly. Cupping it gently in his hands, he offered it to Sunny. "Take this butterfly as a token of the love that we will always share. It is the butterfly who teaches us the beauty of simplicity." Meeko gently kissed Sunny on the cheek.

"Sunny, in the beginning our time together was very beautiful. It was not you but me who destroyed our relationship. I know that I can never heal the damage, but I want to say again how sorry I am for hurting you. Somehow I had forgotten that real love is as fragile as a butterfly. If you hold it too tightly, you'll take away its power to fly in beauty. If you hold it too loosely, it never knows you care. I destroyed the sensitive beauty of the butterfly in our relationship, and this one came to remind me that my heartache comes from my own stupidity. I threw away the only thing of value in my life. Since then, I've learned that love can only be shared if held with gentleness. Do you remember the old legend about the silence of the butterfly?"

"Yes, but tell me again. I love hearing you tell your stories."

As they moved to a spot under a huge tree, Meeko began the tale.

"Once long ago when Great Spirit was building the worlds, he accidentally gave a voice to the butterfly. When some jealous birds heard butterflies singing their songs, they started to complain bitterly. Seeing the discord between these two nations of flying ones, *Wakan Tanka* transferred all the sweet songs back to the bird nation. Looking again at the butterfly nation, *Wakan Tanka* decided they should remain silent but tell their story through colorful designs. When Creator's job was completed, all the butterflies had stories painted on their wings.

"I too am working hard to regain my beauty, and I hope *Wakan Tanka* will let me sing my song again for you. Sunny, I've learned love can never live between two people unless it is nurtured as the most precious gift one can ever receive from another human being. I still pray our love will be renewed someday."

"Meeko, the love we once shared gave us both a great strength and many wonderful memories that will last from life to life. Your love protects me from giving mine away too freely. So you see, Meeko, it is you who still holds my heart."

"And you are my heart. No matter where we go in life, we'll always be together. I believe the butterfly came to demonstrate that our love will never slip too far away. And no matter the distance between us, we'll always remain close," reminded Meeko.

"Yes, that was wonderful time, but that time has passed, and we now have different priorities in our lives."

"My sweet soul mate, I'm so sorry. I've often thought of what could have been, and I wondered why it was necessary to suffer such a horrible ending. Maybe we had to part to complete our birth purpose. I do hope we can heal the damage between us. No matter where you are or who you're with, I will always be your husband and you will remain my wife."

Sunny nodded and lay back in the grass. Spotting a bird's nest high in a tree, and hearing no sound, she climbed the tree. Finding the nest empty she collected a few hawk feathers, then proudly showed off her bounty.

Teasingly, Meeko tried to take them from her, but Sunny dashed off laughing. Both being natural runners, they headed across the field and as Meeko drew closer, he tackled her to the ground.

As they rough-housed Meeko held her close and kissed her hard on the mouth and as always, Sunny responded like a hungry animal. As their passion blazed, they began to strip off their clothes and devour each other. Suddenly, Meeko pulled away.

"We both know better than to do this before a Sun Dance. We must remain pure in order to enter the circle in a sacred manner."

"Meeko, you're right, that was sheer lust. We both know that real love is wanting the spiritual growth of another."

"Sunny, I know my love for you will never die because I see it in the swaying branches of a tree, a budding flower and even a freshly fallen snowflake. I pray for that beauty to return because you are the passion that brings life to my soul. Just as the sky covers Mother Earth, I need your love to cover me so that my soul can feel the warmth of your sun."

"Meeko, it was hard to leave, but to live I had to say goodbye. I will always love you and remember you as one of my best teachers. You made me look at the broken pieces of my life that I had always refused to see."

"Sweetheart, I thank you for still loving me during that process."

From nowhere, Wicahmunga appeared. Startled, Meeko jumped up, quickly pulling Sunny to her feet. With extreme harshness, Wicahmunga marched them back to the campground to find Shung' sitting by her fire. She glanced up, her eyes gravely suspicious, but Meeko reassured her, saying, "*Unci*, nothing has happened. You may rest assured neither of us would ever break our vows of celibacy before a Sun Dance. I would never destroy Sunny's opportunity to pick up her medicine bundle."

Wicahmunga plopped down on the ground. "I followed them all day. What he says is true, but they were teasing each other."

"I accept their word, Wicahmunga, and I thank you for standing by their truth. I may be old, but I know neither of you would ever betray your pipes. Now Meeko, go to the men's Sundance tipi. Shadowhawk is waiting for you."

Sunny handed Shung' the hawk feathers. "*Unci*, I found these today. I offer them to you for a consideration. I need to learn more about the above people so that I can soar high and learn to shape-shift."

"Take her feathers, but I wouldn't teach her if I was you! She's not worth it! Make her pay through the nose," scorned Wicahmunga.

Sunny dismissed Wicahmunga's remark and continued:

"*Unci*, What I am about to say, I don't say lightly. During all my travels for the past few years, I've learned to appreciate and understand the reverence that must be offered to Medicine. I've worked hard to find my direction—which was back to you. I never understood how powerful you are. I've come to know that you've always been my teacher. I ask once again to learn how to become a servant of *Wakan Tanka*. If you accept me, I will maintain integrity and honor in how I use this old knowledge. I will give you my complete trust without ever questioning you again. I know with your guidance and my commitment to obey, I can earn the right to walk as a dreamer. I don't deceive myself with thoughts of becoming Medicine or trying to be like you, but simply choose to become an extension of all your teachings. Please consider my request and know that I will accept your final decision."

Shung' sat quietly in thought a long time before answering. "Sunny, I've never dismissed you. I sent you away, not because I was angry, but to force a commitment from you. I've walked on your dreams ever since you left. Know that if I accept you, there is no turning back."

"Don't take her back. She's a breed and there's nothing but problems with those kind of people."

"Shush, Wicahmunga. Go get that big white box from the tipi."

Snorting in anger, Wicahmunga did as Shung' requested. She glared at Sunny as she handed her the box, saying, "You don't deserve this," then sat down, anxious as a child on Christmas day to find out what was inside.

Sunny lifted the lid and saw a beautifully beaded white buckskin dress with boots, headdress, belt, cuffs and bag to match. With tears in her eyes, she gently caressed the pieces with the greatest of respect. "Oh, Shung', I don't know what to say except that I'll treasure these forever."

"I made that dress for your Sun Dance. The spirit world tells me your happiness will come when you have walked the many uncharted highways in the sky. I know Great Spirit has guided you this far, so allow the above powers to continue directing your inevitable destiny.

"It's time to stop fearing rejection. This dress will prove that you no longer need to be accepted by anyone but yourself. When you've completed this Sun Dance, I want to know you have accepted yourself." Shung' handed Sunny two eagle feathers. "Wear these in your sage wreath so Eagle will claim you. The women's *Inipi* starts in a few hours. We'll talk more after the Sun Dance."

It was long before daybreak when Sunny came out of the last sweat and entered the women's lodge to prepare for her first day in the Sundance ceremony. Once dressed, she came out of the tipi to find Meeko. His face was painted with Bear medicine and two red-tipped eagle feathers were attached to his sage headband, representing his time spent in Vietnam. He handed her a piece of sweetgrass with a red-tailed hawk feather attached.

"Sweetgrass is a gift from the spirits. Let it keep your medicine as sweet as it smells."

Sunny smiled a silent thank you. She felt a great pride knowing they were again dancing together.

As they stood in line waiting to enter the Sacred Circle, Sunny observed the uniqueness of each dancer's attire. All the dancers had eagle bone whistles hanging around their necks waiting to be awakened. The men were adorned with the powers of Eagle, Buffalo, Bear or *Wakinyan* in their paints and Sundance skirts. The women wore white dresses fastened at the waist with colorful shawls. For the next four days everyone was prepared to pull down the above powers for the people. Sunny felt a strong bond with all the Sundancers, and for a moment it was as though she had stepped back four hundred years in time.

Flags flew gently at each doorway as first light touched the horizon, announcing to the drummers and singers to set the rhythm for the Sun Dance to begin. Barefoot, the Sundancers entered the sacred circle in step with the high-pitched voices of the singers. The Sundancers placed their filled pipes onto the pipe altar with a silent prayer, asking the above powers to come join them.

In unison, two hundred and forty-seven Sundancers moved in a clockwise manner onto the field. As they began to open their first sacred circle, the dancers wove a certain spell of holiness upon the land. A soft wind joined them and assisted in awakening the prayer banners that were hanging from the Tree of Life. With each step they took, the dancers blew their eagle bone whistles, creating a power from within to help build the vortex of an invisible tipi.

As they danced, the spinning energy rose higher and higher, connecting the tipi in the sky to the one on the ground. The Sundancers' faces expressed a devout holiness, reflecting their desire to journey to *Wakan Tanka*. The dancers stared without blinking at *Wi*, the Sun Chief, until he no longer existed as they reached their arms up to the Great Spirit. The drummers carried the heartbeat of *Maka Ina*, while the singers held the resonance of every soul, driving the dancers to ride this power as one.

The onlookers sitting around the arbor were captured under this awesome spell. They knew everything was in balance and harmony as the dancers rode the vortices in earnest prayer for all the children of the world.

On his fourth and final day without food and water, Meeko walked to the center of the sacred circle with two large red circles painted on the upper part of his back. As he lay down on the bed of sage the *Unci* placed a piece of sage in his mouth, saying, "Bite down hard, Grandson. Lean on *Wakan Tanka*, then you will feel no pain, but only love from the Great Spirit."

The intercessor cut two slits into each of the red circles and pushed the piercing sticks through Meeko's skin. Meeko struggled to his feet as the helpers tied the twelve buffalo skulls in a long string to his back. Walking strongly from the Tree of Life, Meeko blew his eagle bone whistle and began his first round on his journey around the large sacred circle. The people raised their voices in prayer to the Great Spirit in support.

On his final round, Meeko stumbled under the weight of the massive skulls and dropped to one knee. He put his hand to his brow and prayed hard to keep his focus.

Sunny left the other dancers and walked to stand at his side in silent prayer. Shung' joined her, and placed a hand painted shawl around her shoulders. "Pray, daughter, pray!"

One of the medicine men saw this and walked over to Meeko. "Get up, Brother! You're a Sioux and we Sioux don't feel pain! Call on Eagle and ask for the strength of his heart. Now follow the pipe and get to your feet!" His voice was curt as he fanned Meeko off with an eagle wing.

Meeko remained on the ground and both women saw he was not going to move. Again the medicine man yelled in anger, "I want this man on his feet!" Reaching down, he coiled the ropes around his hand and yanked with all his might as he spat, "I said get to your feet."

Meeko groaned and tried to get up. The blood ran profusely from the newly torn wounds as the medicine man continued to hold the ropes taut, forcing him to rise.

Again Meeko went down on his knee. Shung' and Sunny saw the agony on his face and looked at the medicine man in disgust. Sunny went to his side and whispered, "Sweetheart, pull in your power. You must complete this last round with honor. Go inward and gather your strength. Call upon *Wakan Tanka*! Let the Great Spirit take you beyond this robe of flesh."

Sunny cried openly as she began to pray: "*Hau*, Tunka'shila, touch him. Let him feel your strength and your all-encompassing love."

Shung' gently fanned Meeko's back with her eagle feather wing. "Grandson, take my strength and let's run this circle with our past grandfathers and grandmothers. Talk to the old ones—they will give you the power to deal with this physical pain. *Wakan Tanka* is with you. Lean on this love and walk as a proud man of great honor around this last circle."

Meeko struggled to rise again and again and mumbled, "I can't."

Sunny's eyes blazed with rage and through clenched teeth she whispered, "Meeko, you will get up, even if I have to drag your blanket ass the rest of the way around this circle."

For a moment Meeko looked at her with hatred, then suddenly a great anger at her disrespectful words rose within and he struggled to his feet, determined to endure even if it cost him his life.

Shung' saw and quickly selected twelve children from the arbor, placing each one on one of the buffalo skulls.

Sunny stood steadfastly by Meeko, her eyes cast down, praying relentlessly to *Wakan Tanka*. Suddenly she looked up to see seven golden eagles circling overhead. She motioned for Meeko to look up. He saw the eagles and heard their soft whistling voices calling to him. Meeko's strength returned and suddenly he was on his feet, lunging forward. Pow! Pow! Pow! Pow! His skin tore free!

Meeko had broken away from his burden and was running free as the wind to complete his final round. Sunny and Shung' ran behind him, filled with great pride as many friends and family stepped forward to follow them back to the sacred Sundance Tree. The women rose from their seats and trilled as they passed by, bringing tears to the eyes of all who witnessed this miracle.

Tired but exhilarated, Meeko leaned on the Sacred Tree and prayed humbly. The medicine man cut off the excess skin and placed a special herb into the torn wounds to stop the bleeding then wrapped the flesh in a red cloth, which he handed to Meeko before walking away.

By noon the number of Sundancers was diminishing as the sun beat down hard on their exhausted bodies. Sunny mourned the loss of many Sundancers who fell because they could no longer endure the pain.

Sunny felt herself enter into another world and fly through the sun. She walked to the Sacred Tree to offer up her flesh. Shadowhawk pierced the four red circles marked on her upper arms and inserted eight eagle feathers. Sunny willed herself not to bleed as she returned to her place in the circle.

A runner brought burning sage on a piece of bark to smoke off her wounds. Sunny continued to dance strong for two hours, allowing the high-pitched voices of the singers and the beat of the drums to connect her to the above powers as she left her body.

Then she returned to the Tree of Life where Shadowhawk stood waiting. He swiftly drew the feathers one by one through the flesh of her arms. Sunny's face held a peaceful look as she ran the circle with the speed of a deer, no longer on this earth. As she completed the round, Sunny returned to the Sacred Tree and humbly gave thanks to *Wakan Tanka* for allowing her to complete what was in her heart.

By four in the afternoon the annual Summer Solstice Ceremony had ended. The few Sundancers that were able to finish left the sacred circle knowing they had fulfilled another commitment on their pipe.

The people had always considered those that finished a Sundance to be holy and believed they could heal with their touch. Meeko and Sunny smiled at each other in a gentle way, then went to stand in the healing line to serve those who had a need.

Many people stepped forward to let the Sundancers lay their hands on their heads for a healing. They offered the Sundancers gifts of feathers or sacred articles to show their appreciation for their dedication. As they left the healing line to dress for the giveaway, Meeko and Sunny felt a love for the people far beyond what exists between a man and a woman. And so it Was.

Meeko and Sunny shared many tender goodbyes with the Sundancers before they returned to their campsite. As they sat in exhaustion, Meeko gently touched Sunny's shoulder, saying, "Thank you for the support." He handed her the small red bundle that held his flesh. "Take this so that I'll be with you always."

Touched by his gift, Sunny held it close to her heart and handed him her small bundle of flesh in return, knowing this exchange was done with pure love and honor. Sunny and Meeko watched the sun disappear below the horizon before joining the others that were sitting around Shung's campfire. After eating, everyone spent the evening discussing the last four days.

"Maybe I'll come and visit you someday," said Meeko.

"That would be nice," answered Sunny.

"I'm glad to see you two are finally healing the damage between you," reminded Shung'.

The cleanup crew finished their work and came over to join them, hoping to hear one of Shung's old stories about the Sundancers of long ago.

Willie approached with a big smile on his face. He sat between Sunny and Meeko. "Hey, guys. You two danced strong this year. Boy, I hope you'll come back next year. Did you know Grampa Old Raven is having a peyote ceremony tonight? You wanna come?"

Meeko accepted but Sunny declined. As night unfolded, she watched the shadowy figures reflected on the tarp wall of the peyote tipi. The water drum for the ceremony began. Sunny listened until the campfire burned down to soft embers, then retired for the night.

Early morning as the warm sun caressed Sunny's cheek, Meeko poked his head in her tent. "Get up, sleepy head." He handed her a fresh cup of coffee and told her about the healings in the peyote ceremony. They spent the next two days healing their bodies, and on the third morning they broke camp and loaded their cars to go home.

"Will I see you again?" asked Meeko.

"Who knows?" replied Sunny.

"We could change all of this if you'd let it happen."

"Meeko, I'll never jeopardize my beliefs or principles for any man again, but I want you to know that I'll always help you."

"Oh, Sunny, you are my heart. If you refuse me in this life, I'll surely die. Please let my handsome looks detain you for another day." Meeko smiled his most winning smile.

"Meeko, please stop this nonsense. You know I can no longer share a physical love with you."

"Then, if I die before you, I'll wait for you on the Other Side; and if you go before me, will you please guide me to the Other Side and into your loving arms?"

Sunny buried her head deep into his chest. "That goes without saying." Sadly, she got into her car and turned onto the highway.

Meeko jumped into his truck and followed alongside, forcing her to slow down.

"I love you! Please, let's go play one more day," he pleaded.

"No, Meeko, maybe if I pray hard enough I'll find myself a good man."

"But Sweetheart, there's no man that can give you the magic that I can. You'll never love another man in this lifetime. We've entered and returned from the maze of life's mysteries, but I know I can make you come back to me." He pulled his truck closer, forcing her to the side of the road. He got out and sidled up to her door. "Wanna stop and get a cup of coffee?"

She threw up her hands in exasperation. "Meeko, you don't want coffee, you want to stop this parting."

"Ah yes, my love. That's true. You see, I carry the power of the night and I understand the language of a woman. I know your inner secrets and they speak to me through the whispers of your beautiful body. The oldest of the old ones have walked on my mind and they have shown me that my arrow is no longer broken. It is straight and strong and headed for your heart. I beg you, please free me from this prison and take me back into your life."

"Oh please, great warrior, let me pass. I beg you to remove this barrier from my life," she teased.

"Never! We've fought too many battles together. We're the free thinking people in this world, and we must stand together so we can help each other fight the battles within ourselves."

"Fool, we'll always battle. If we live long enough to reach old age, that is."

"Ah yes, My Sweetheart. Can this fool call you for a date on your seventieth birthday and maybe have a roll in the sack?"

"It's a date. But in reality, I think you're nothing but a figment of my imagination."

"Ah yes, and what a potential we harbor as we write our crazy life scripts in our imaginations. Look at the nasty characters we've created for each other. When we finish this chapter doesn't it make sense that another should begin? Sweetheart, you know life is boring when we're apart. You need me as much as I need you. This time I promise it'll be different."

"Oh, Meeko, stop! I've learned enough from your school of hard knocks. What I need is a world that holds no harsh words, lies or deceptions."

"Sunny, we're both afraid of being vulnerable, but we can still share a common dream and rebuild a life together."

"Meeko, the loss of our marriage has shown me that when I allowed you to abuse me, I surrendered my integrity. Today I walk freely as an individual spirit."

"Sunny, I know we're still connected, it's you who inspires me to develop my greatest abilities. My strength comes from the real beauty of our love. I believe true love is about helping one another enhance their power."

"Meeko, I do love you, but my attention is now focused on other things, and I refuse to be distracted from my spiritual growth. I know our spirits bind us together, but I now live my own life."

Seeing Shung's truck in the distance, Sunny leaned over and softly kissed Meeko in a lingering moment of tenderness.

"Promise me that I'll see you again."

"Maybe." Then Sunny tearfully pulled behind Shung' and headed down the highway.

Meeko leaned against his truck crying openly as he watched her car disappear over the hill. He had never felt so alone in his life. He reached into the glove compartment for his bottle and took a stiff drink before starting his long drive back to Fort Peck. Using his loneliness for Sunny to qualify his drinking, he continued to nurse his bottle to numb out his feelings. Great Spirit knew how much he wanted Sunny, but somehow time had eaten up the promise of their shared dream.

By nightfall he found himself less than two hundred fifty miles from Fort Peck. He saw two hitchhikers in the beam of his headlights. Meeko popped on the high beams and recognized Jim and his brother Bobby from the reservation. As Meeko pulled over, they threw their bags into the back of the truck and climbed up front with him. "Are you headed to Fort Peck?" Meeko nodded. Glancing at his gas gauge, he decided to pulled into the next truck stop.

While waiting for their food to be served, Jim asked, "Got a cigarette?" Meeko passed his pack and Jim took out two cigarettes, saying, "I'll take one for later," then passed the pack to Bobby who did the same.

Jim lit his cigarette. "Where you been, Brother?"

"Sun Dance."

"Good. We've been to *Paha Sapa*," said Bobby.

Meeko passed around his bottle and as they continued their journey they discussed Indian politics and the new policies being enforced by the Department of Interior. When the bottle became a dead soldier, Meeko tossed it out the window.

"I got some good smoke. You want some?" Jim asked. Rolling a joint, he lit it and passed it around.

Meeko took a hit and handed it back, saying, "Good shit."

"Yeah. Me and my brother grow it."

"Well, you definitely know how to be good farmers," answered Meeko taking another hit.

It was quite late when they arrived at Fort Peck. Meeko pulled to the side of the road to let them out, then waited until they retrieved their bags from the back of the truck. "See you around," said Meeko as he continued his drive through town. He noticed the bars were closed, but there were a few dark, shadowy figures sitting on the curbs waiting for them to open. What a fucking morbid place, Meeko thought. He was tired but happy when he opened the door to find Rachel, his common-law wife and their two Old English sheepdogs, Tanka and Tankshee. After petting the dogs and pouring himself a drink, Meeko told Rachel about the last few weeks. When she asked if Sunny had been at the Sun Dance, he answered, "Yes, and she was as lovely as ever. Rachel, I'm tired. We'll talk more tomorrow."

Rachel knew he would not again speak about his encounter with Sunny.

For the next few months, Meeko painted feverishly until he had completed enough art work for another show. With nothing to keep himself busy, Meeko's life had once again become boring and he filled his emptiness by hanging out at the local bars. He and Rachel fought constantly over his drinking, keeping things in a constant state of turmoil.

During a heavy rainstorm one night, Meeko awakened soaking wet. Hung over and shivering from the cold, he knocked the dogs from the bed and staggered toward the window. "Goddamnit, Rachel! How many times do I have to tell you to keep this fucking window closed when it's raining?" Obediently Rachel got out of bed, closed the window and quickly changed the bedding. Meeko reached under the bed for his bottle and took a sip before crawling back under the dry covers.

Early the next morning Meeko awakened, still angry, and sat staring out the window at another gray, rainy day. Restless and in the mood for a fight, he drove to the Watering Hole and sat at the end of the bar where he ordered bourbon with a water back. As he nursed his second drink, he overheard some oil men talking about him.

"Keep your voice down. That crazy Indian is sitting right over there! Hell, I hired that bastard once, and he flew so close to the ground that I thought he was trying to kiss the sagebrush good morning. I'm not kidding! I nearly shit my pants that day. I'm glad I got his pilot's license jerked."

Meeko rose from the bar stool and slowly walked over to their table. "Now, Art, you know that's not true. But you did shit your pants, and ever since then you've been using one of the turds in your back pocket for an identification card."

The others roared with laughter as Art stood up to challenge him. Meeko shoved him back in his seat. "See you around, Art. Call me when you need a new turd." Everyone in the bar knew Meeko had been looking for a good fight, and as he left they let out a sigh of relief.

Meeko continued to prowl from bar to bar looking for a fight. Around midnight he returned to the Watering Hole and within fifteen minutes a full-blown barroom brawl was in process.

When the sheriff arrived and saw Meeko, he was furious. "You fucking Blood, I'm tired of this shit. You're going to the detox center!"

"Sheriff, I'm not going anywhere unless it's to my grave."

The sheriff pulled a gun on him and demanded Meeko get in the car.

"Fuck you, man! That gun doesn't scare me! Go ahead, pull the goddamn trigger!" Meeko rushed at the sheriff, grabbed the barrel of his gun and put it to his own head. "Where are your fucking balls? Pull the goddamn trigger!"

"You fucking blanket ass! Let go of my hand!" yelled the sheriff as a deputy stepped forward and hit Meeko from behind.

As he crumbled to the floor Meeko threatened, "You're a dead man. "

He was taken to the detox center and awakened three days later to find himself in a straitjacket. He knew he was heavily sedated and could only hear muffled voices surrounding him.

Meeko shook his head to rid the cobwebs from his brain. "Where am I?"

"You're in the detox center," answered the doctor.

"Bullshit! Get me out of this fucking jacket!" Meeko struggled violently to get free. The doctor administered another shot and within seconds, Meeko lay silent and helpless.

When his behavior did not improve, the doctor had him flown to the Veterans Hospital in Denver for evaluation. Meeko was immediately placed in the psychiatric ward for close observation and treatment.

Each time the sun went over down on another day, Meeko's fears would slowly turn into raging terror, and it became necessary to keep him sedated to cope with his withdrawals. Once he was able to sleep without drugs, he was moved to a less restrictive ward. When forced to attend group therapy, however, he became sullen and withdrawn.

During the midnight shift change, two staff members heard a bloodcurdling scream. They entered Meeko's room to see he was once again fighting the invisible demons of his past. Thinking he was a captive back in Vietnam, Meeko raced to the door trying to escape. When he found it was locked, he held the staff hostage. As another staff member peeked through the window to see if help was needed, Meeko charged at him, breaking the glass.

Cut and bleeding, Meeko began to trash the room as he fought with his invisible world. At last, in sheer exhaustion he fell to the floor crying as the two male nurses sedated him, put him in a straitjacket and moved him to a padded room to await transfer back to the lock-down ward.

Meeko refused to eat and his massive weight loss made him physically weak. He spent his days staring out the barred windows, trying to remember what had taken place. He knew his spirit had taken leave of his body and was desperately afraid a step-in was now in the process of taking over his soul.

"How long have I been here?" he asked the one person he trusted, a nurse who reminded him of Sunny.

She handed him his morning pills and began to straighten his bed. "About three months. Your wife and the doctor think it's best for you to stay here for a while longer. I suggested that she bring your art supplies, maybe painting will help you feel better." The nurse deposited a bag of paints and canvases along with his mail before leaving the room.

Meeko looked through the art supplies and threw them across the room. Fumbling through his mail, he smiled when he recognized Sunny's handwriting and the familiar cologne always sprayed on her letters. Taking the large lavender envelope, he carefully opened it, and read:

Dear Meeko,

I'm writing this letter as I sit by a lake. I wish you were here to share in this regal beauty. Three days after the Sundance, Shung, Wicahmunga and I arrived at the training camp about twenty miles outside of Brownsville, near the Blackfoot reservation, and I've been here ever since. The winter has been very cold, but spring is almost here and this place is absolutely beautiful. It's nestled in a valley on a river near snowcapped mountains. The mornings are magnificent. The tall pine trees hold back the warmth of the sun until almost noon. I walk to the lake each afternoon and spend time with my thoughts. At times I can see my entire life's reflections rise to the surface of the lake as if it were a mirror of who I truly am. This is the most powerful and inspirational place I've ever encountered. The ever-changing activity of nature is simply awesome. The birds and animals that I have come to know are no longer wild and are accepting my presence. Each day that I encounter these sacred beauties, it puts a smile on my face.

In these dream-like moments, I wonder how long a person can refuse her destiny. I think of mankind's ideas and realize we're not so unique. It makes me wonder about the individuality of any one thought. But as my thoughts become visible to me, I look at the power of my free will. I'm slowly beginning to realize how wonderful it is to have the choices of what to act upon. It would be impossible to count the number of times that I've sat here and wished that I had done things differently with my life. I know Shung' has given me the time and direction to look back upon my previous experiences. It's so easy to blame someone else for our circumstances rather than accept the consequences of what we have chosen to do. I have a peace that I have never known. It seems I'm beginning to look at the world with fresh eyes, and it's awesome.

I've learned so much by being with Shung', but I'm worried about her health, especially her heart. Next week I'm taking her to Nevada to live with me so I can make sure she has a good doctor.

I've received another oil contract with regard to drilling on our property. I think we should talk about this before either of us sign it. By the time you receive this letter, I should be in Nevada. Call me and let's see what works best. Enclosed are the pictures I promised, along with some old ones that you might enjoy.

By the way, Wicahmunga now refers to me as a mean-ass cobra who wraps herself in the finest of silk. Can you imagine? She says I earned the name because I refused to drive her into town during a blizzard to get her soda and candy. Oh, well. What the hell, maybe she's right.

Love you, Sunny

Meeko smiled at Sunny's uncanny ability to know when he was in trouble, and was not surprised that she had timed her letter perfectly. Here he was at the lowest ebb in his life, and Sunny had walked back to him through a simple letter.

He looked at the pictures for hours, desperately missing the life they had shared. Each time he tried to answer her letter, he never got beyond the first paragraph. At last he decided to express his feelings by painting.

The following morning Meeko set up his easel and using his imagination, began to paint all that she had written about.

The next time Rachel came to visit she was surprised to find Meeko painting feverishly from an old photograph of Sunny and she felt his sense of magic returning. She sat for a long time waiting for him to acknowledge her presence, and when Meeko did not look her way, she left, knowing there was no longer a place for her in his life.

Meeko continued expressing himself on his canvasses, trying hard to heal his pain. Each time he asked to be released from the hospital he was refused. He became angry at the doctors' control and packed his things determined to return to the reservation without their permission.

He felt free as he walked up the dirt road to his house. The dogs ran to him, barking in greeting and he stooped down to pat their heads. "Hi, guys." He hugged his old friends with great affection.

Rachel saw them coming and immediately went to the stove to make Meeko a plate of food. As he set down his bags Rachel blurted out, "Sunny called."

The hair stood up on Meeko's arms. "Did you tell her anything?"

"No, but the phone number is over there on the pad." Meeko went to the table and noticed the area code was in Nevada.

"Are you going to call her?"

"Not now, maybe later," he answered, dismissing the subject. "Does the truck still run?"

"I guess. Joe stopped over last week and put in a new battery."

Without a word Meeko got up from the table and loaded the dogs into the back, then headed into town. He stopped at the liquor store and purchased a package of beef jerky and a quart of bourbon. He fed the puppies bits and pieces of the jerky as he drove from bar to bar.

Still restless, he went to the old graveyard. He walked through the graveyard brushing snow off the headstones of his many ancestors, until he found Renna's and sat down to think. Breaking the seal on his bottle, he took a drink then offered one to Renna as he watched the dogs run and play. He thought of Granbear and their shared dreams. He thought of Sunny and their shared dreams. He thought of the many people he had disappointed in life and began to cry over his many failures and wasted years. Time had eaten up his life. He had been given many chances, and now he had to accept the fact that his life was coming to an end.

Glancing at his watch, he realized it was almost closing time at the Watering Hole and decide to join his old drinking buddies for a round. When he heard the bartender say, "Last call," Meeko knew another night of his life had slipped away into oblivion. He staggered out the door. Tankshee, Little Sister Dog, was waiting for him and stayed close by his heels demanding that she ride home in the front seat.

Meeko was near oblivion and many times swerved off the road. When he finally pulled into his front yard, he collapsed over the steering wheel where he slept until the sun awakened him the following morning. Guilt ridden and suffering from a terrible hangover, he entered the house. Rachel remained quiet as she served him breakfast, then fed the dogs.

Meeko silently went to his art room and began to paint obsessively. By the end of the day he had four paintings started. As the days slowly rolled into weeks, Sunny's face came alive on every canvas. When he had finished the last one, he went to the phone and dialed her number. When he heard her voice, he could not bring himself to speak and gently placed the phone back in its cradle, then left the house.

Meeko had been on a three week drunk when Rachel went in search of him. She found him passed out at Renna's gravesite and somehow managed to get him into the truck and drive him home. By the following day Meeko had sobered up somewhat and was sitting at the table, when Rachel said, "Meeko, what you're doing is no good. You must either let Sunny go or go to her."

"I know, Rachel. But I can't."

"Well, you have to do something. Sunny is a good woman and I think you should call her."

Meeko shoved his plate back and went to the phone. When Sunny answered, he said, "Hey, pretty lady. What're you doing?" For a moment there was silence.

"Meeko, it's good to hear from you. Are you okay?"

"I'm good, very good. I miss you. After the Sun Dance I came home and drank my way through another twenty-five paintings. I think they're good, but I want to bring them down and get your opinion."

"Oh, that would be wonderful. When do you plan on being here?"

"Oh, in a couple of days, if it's all right with you. I'll call you when I get there."

"Sounds great. Talk to you then."

Meeko went to find Rachel and as he walked into the bedroom he found her packing his things. Without a word she shoved his suitcase toward the door and left the room. Meeko shrugged his shoulders and pulled his hide bag from under the bed, then carefully packed his canvases in it and zipped it shut.

Not a word was said as Rachel drove him to the airport. When Meeko got out of the car he asked her for two hundred dollars, offering to return it after he had sold a few paintings. Rachel hesitated, but when she saw the hurt look on his face she believed his promise to repay her and gave him the money. Meeko smiled and took the money. Before he said goodbye, he made sure she would stay at the house and take care of his dogs.

By the time he arrived in Denver to change planes, he was feeling apprehensive over the trip and called Sunny to let her know when he would arrive. While waiting for his flight, he went to the bar to have a drink to settle his nerves. By the time he arrived in Las Vegas, he was once again inebriated.

When Sunny saw him staggering around the baggage area, her face hardened.

"Hey, baby, met some friends on the plane. Had a couple of drinks to celebrate my new art show. Aw, don't be mad at me. I'll be okay after a cup of black coffee," he promised, his words slurred.

Sunny signaled for a skycap to load his bags into her car and with few words she drove home, letting Meeko nod off to sleep. When they arrived, Sunny took him to his room. "Get some sleep. We'll talk later."

Meeko slept until late afternoon then joined Sunny, Shung' and Wicahmunga on the patio. I'm sorry about this afternoon, ladies," he mumbled as he pulled out a chair and sat down to pour himself a glass of iced tea from a pitcher sitting on the table.

"I saw you! I saw you! You bum! You're nothing but a stinking drunk!" Wicahmunga got up and hit Meeko over the head with a tabloid she had been reading.

"Please, Wicahmunga. Since my divorce I've learned what it is to live as a man who once knew beauty and is now ruined because of his deceptive ways. I live with this pain and sorrow. I drink to forget. I know each of you look for the good things in life, but in my case, my past has hindered any hope for my tomorrow."

Tempers flared between Shung' and Wicahmunga until Sunny yelled, "Both of you stop!" Then looking directly at Meeko, she said, "Meeko, I'm not judging you. Your life is yours—not good, not bad, it just is. You can live your life as you see fit, but you will not drink while you're in my home."

"I'm sorry. I promise I won't drink anymore while I'm here. Sunny, I know that I've become a piece of shit. But so what? You know I'm an alcoholic. I know your faith is strong and you've always reached for the brass ring, but I don't have enough faith to do the same. I have many cloudy days in my life, and I drink to stop the pain."

"Oh, stop it! It's time to get off your pity potty and start being responsible. The only person that's ruining your life is you. It's your choice. Why not start using that brain of yours to do something constructive, rather than being so compulsive? Surely you realize why I hate alcohol. It was you and Sam that taught me what I don't want in my life, and that's what inspires me to grow beyond my trailer trash background.

"Meeko, I've worked hard to heal those deep wounds inside of me. I've found that life without peace or beauty can be disastrously sad. I've found life is not about things. The real beauty of life is simply a quiet time filled with beautiful sunsets and sunrises. It's the birds singing, it's the bees collecting pollen, it's a flower blooming, it's the first green leaf on a tree in spring, it's the simple things that prove the worth of a day. So don't tell me about all your bad breaks, and stop your 'poor me' shit. You are who you are because of your choices in life."

"She's right," added Wicahmunga. "You're nothing but a coyote in heat. You think you're so clever, but I've known that you're dumb since you were a little boy. You're nothing but an idiot. Don't you know that people are supposed to think before they do things?"

"Oh, all of you, shush! I'm doing something very important." Shung' went back to watching the cloud formations overhead. Everyone remained quiet until Shung' spoke. "Meeko, did you ever think about what clouds teach?"

"Not really. But I like watching the pictures they make in the sky."

"See, I told you he's stupid. He's like a deer. He never looks up," snorted Wicahmunga.

"A cloud has no direction unless it uses the wind to travel. If you walk through life like a cloud, you will have little to say about the direction your life takes. Meeko, come sit with me and I'll tell you about the life span of a cloud. Did you know it takes a strong thought to disperse a cloud?"

"Ha! The only cloud he knows about is his clouded mind from another hangover."

Meeko chuckled at Wicahmunga's words, knowing they were true. He walked over and sat next to Shung'. She did not believe in idle chatter, so he decided to pursue the subject of a cloud. He knew it was up to him to take her riddle apart before he could ever understand the spiritual meaning behind her words. Everyone quietly joined in the study of a cloud, but within an hour they drifted their separate ways.

Meeko awakened late the next day. On his way to the kitchen to get a cup of coffee, he found a note from Sunny leaning against the pot:

"Sorry I missed you. I had an early appointment. Enjoy your day, we'll be back sometime this afternoon. Love, Sunny."

Disappointed that he had missed her, Meeko made himself breakfast and decided to explore Sunny's home. The place seemed too big for just one person. He began to search for clues of another man in her life. Venturing into her office, he found a picture of himself from long ago, and was satisfied there was no other man. Finding nothing else to do, he went for a swim. As he lay in the sun, he thought with envy about Sunny's financial success without him.

The sound of a car horn startled Meeko awake. He jumped up to see Sunny getting out of her car, her arms filled with groceries and he ran to help.

"Meeko, when you're through bringing in the groceries will you light the grill so we can have a cookout?" Asked Shung'. "Wicahmunga, will you make the salad while Sunny and I prepare the rest of the dinner?"

"No! No! No! No! Let Sunny make the rabbit food. I want to do the fire. You know that old drunk knows nothing about building a happy fire."

Shung' threw her hands up in the air in disgust, and without another word everyone went about their assigned chores. Meeko had cleaned the grill and was putting a match to the charcoal when Wicahmunga sneaked up behind him.

"You're making an angry fire. The fire hates you, and I hope it burns you, just like the sun. See, look at your skin, it's too dark. I know your mother wasn't that dark. And your father wasn't that dark and none of your kin are either. Humph! You're either an impostor, or you need a bath." Without warning, she shoved Meeko into the pool and cackled with glee as he climbed out, cursing at her.

"Goody, goody, goody! I gave the asshole a bath. Tee hee, I'm glad you lost your sunglasses," she said, then ran away hoping he would chase after her.

"Goddamnit, Wicahmunga! You get back here and help me find my glasses." When she did not respond, Meeko dove into the pool and retrieved them from the bottom. When he came out he stormed into the house and began to chase after her.

"Help! Help! Help! Meeko's trying to rape me!"

When he finished explaining to Shung' and Sunny what had happened, Wicahmunga came out of her hiding place and in complete innocence denied his accusations, swearing he'd been drinking and had fallen into the pool. Shung' and

Sunny roared in laughter as Meeko continued to chase her, hoping to throw her in the pool.

"That woman is my worst nightmare! I swear if she has her way, she'd kill me just to entertain herself."

After the trauma was over and everyone had settled down, Sunny and Shung' put the steaks on the grill, while Wicahmunga sat at the table, waiting to be served like a special guest. As they ate, Wicahmunga continued her playfulness, stealing bites of Meeko's food. When they were finished eating, she immediately went to the kitchen and cleaned everything before joining the others on the patio to enjoy the lazy afternoon. Finding the sun too hot for their comfort, they retreated into the cool house where Meeko unpacked his new paintings.

Sunny was moved by their beauty and remarked, "Meeko, this is some of the best work you've ever produced. If we put together a showing, I think things can happen for you."

"Don't do it! His work is shit! They won't sell. Give him some crayons and make him start all over," yelled Wicahmunga with wicked glee as she scrutinized Meeko's work.

"Shung', is there any way you can stop their bickering?"

Shung' gave both a stern look.

"Well, maybe the white folks will like them, but I've seen better on outdoor shit houses.

"Wicahmunga, will I ever do anything that pleases you?"

"Nope."

After Shung' left, Wicahmunga moved close to Sunny and pinched her, whispering, "Tattletale, tattletale! Why don't you mind your own business? You know better than to meddle in my business." And for the rest of the day, few words were exchanged between them.

She called several friends and art dealers, all of whom expressed great interest in seeing Meeko's work. Thrilled with their interest, Sunny began preparations to set up an art show in her home. Sunny spent the next few days making a guest list and calling each one to invite them to the art show. She contacted a lighting company who provided the lighting to depict the story Meeko was expressing. Meeko viewed the eloquent display, humbled by the fact that Sunny had given him another chance for success.

On the day of the show the catering people arrived at three o'clock to set up for the evening festivities. Wicahmunga sneaked around making sure they did everything right. Around six that evening everyone dressed and sat on the patio, except Wicahmunga who hid in the bushes to make sure she was the first to see all the guests arriving.

At seven o'clock, Sunny welcomed her first guest. By nine o'clock the party was lively, and she had introduced Meeko to the most influential people in the city, all of whom seemed to greatly admire his work.

Meeko remained aloof and seated himself at the open bar, belting down one bourbon after another while talking with the bartender. Sunny noticed he was getting drunk and discreetly asked the bartender to help her get Meeko to his room.

It was quite late when Sunny finally closed the door on her last guest. She turned to Shung' and held up a fistful of checks. Since it was late they cut their conversation short and bid each other goodnight. Sunny went up the stairs, hesitating for a moment outside the guest room. When she heard loud snoring, she decided to wait until morning to speak with Meeko about the sale of his paintings.

It was late the following morning when a sullen Meeko joined everyone for breakfast on the patio. Staring defiantly at Sunny, he poured a shot of bourbon in his coffee.

"I don't like your phoney friends. They're too damn high-and-mighty for my taste."

"Meeko, why is it that no matter what I do for you there's always a fault after the fact? Maybe you don't like my friends, but I know you sure as hell love their fucking money." She threw the money on the table. "Last night was an opportunity for you! But no! God forbid you'd show any appreciation for a thing that I do for you!"

Meeko gritted his teeth in rage. He got up and shoved his chair back then slammed his cup down on the table, breaking it. Infuriated, he grabbed the money, called a cab and stormed out of the house.

All three women sat in stunned silence. Sunny started to cry.

"Let it go, Sunny, let it go! He's just a drunk and it's not your problem," said Shung'.

By the time Meeko arrived back at Fort Peck, he had run through most of the money and immediately went in search of his friends to invest the rest in drugs. When he arrived home, he threw the money he owed Rachel on the floor as he walked past her without a word. He went directly to the bathroom, tied off his arm, shot up and waited to reach a euphoric state. As he spun out of control, Meeko knew he had overdosed, and he lay paralyzed on the floor, hoping never to awaken.

He began to share his dope and fixings with anyone who would party with him, which drained him financially and forced him to live on the streets. Often Rachel found him lying among the garbage cans in the rat-infested alleys behind the bars. She would take him home and try to get him help, but nothing would subdue his need for another fix. Each time his government check arrived, he would disappear until he was broke. Destitute and helpless, Rachel was forced to apply for commodities.

Some weeks later Meeko awakened in an alley, choking on his own vomit, shaking out of control. He tried to get to his feet, but found he was unable to move. A freezing rain was coming down. He struggled to his feet only to find he had lost his shoes. He dug through the garbage cans with no success, trying to find something that would help ward off the cold. As he staggered from the alley, he checked his pockets and found he was penniless.

When he rounded the corner and saw his reflection in the window it scared him. There, facing him, was a stranger with a swollen, bruised face that had blackened eyes sunk deep into his head. His shredded clothes and matted hair were covered with dried blood. At first Meeko did not recognize this tired old man's face. But when he realized he was looking at himself, he knew he had become another Renna. With this stark, harsh truth searing his brain, Meeko began his long struggle to get home, knowing his worst fears had become a reality.

The strong, ever-blowing winds of the plains joined the slow, drizzling rains pounding against his frail body. "This fucking filthy reservation is destroying me." He unzipped his pants and pissed in the street, then continued aimlessly down the highway. As he staggered along, Meeko lost his balance and fell into a ditch. Hopelessly he got to his knees and reaching up to the dark, clouded sky, he begged, "Oh, *Tunka'shila*, what have I done with my life? One part of my mind is clear on what I must do, yet the other side of me is consumed with total terror! What have I done?"

As he got to his feet, a group of reservation whites passed and one leaned out the car window.

"Hey, let's hit that sonuvabitchin' drunken Injun."

They swerved close enough to splash him, but when they saw it was Meeko, one shouted, "Holy shit, man! That's Meeko! Let's get the fuck outta here! He's nuts!"

Meeko remained in this weakened state until he reached the yard where he fell face first into a puddle. He called out pitifully to Rachel who, crying, ran to help him. Once inside, she covered him with blankets and gave him a cup of hot soup. She filled the tub with hot water then gave him a bath and helped him dress in clean clothes.

"Rachel, I know that I've destroyed everyone that has come into my life because I'm hooked bad on drugs and alcohol. But that's not all I have to tell you."

"I know Meeko, " she cried, holding him and rocking him like a baby. "I know. Just be quiet and settle down. The doctors told me that you're HIV positive. Have you told Sunny?"

"No! And you must promise me that you won't ever let her find out." Meeko, pulled away from her and begged for another drink.

Rachel poured one and handed it to him. "Meeko, if you love Sunny the way you say you do, then tell her. Or I will."

Exhausted, Meeko lay across the bed, burning up with fever. Two days later he was diagnosed with double pneumonia, which quickly evolved into full-blown AIDS.

In a weakened state, Meeko struggled against the disease, his body slowly dwindling. Each day he grew weaker until he was nothing but loose skin stretched over skeletal bones. The pain was far worse than he had ever known, and he begged for something to make it stop. Knowing that he was dying, Rachel kept him well supplied with alcohol and drugs.

Realizing his time was drawing near, Meeko phoned Sunny. When he heard her voice he started to cry.

"Sweetheart, I've got something very important to tell you. Creator knew what he was doing when he took you away from me. I know he did it to save your life for something good. You see, my love, I've known, but denied for over a year what I'm about to tell you. My love, my love, I'm so sorry for the heartache I've brought to you. I'm dying... I have AIDS."

Sunny waited for the impact of his words to pass. With a broken heart, she asked, "My one love, are you sure?"

"Yes, my beautiful lady, it's true. When I had my last checkup at the VA hospital where I was treated for Agent Orange contamination, they informed me that I was HIV positive. I was offered treatment but I refused and decided to do it my way. I refuse to be a fucking guinea pig in the name of science. I was going to tell you when I came to see you, but I couldn't. Please don't worry. *Wakan Tanka* has given me many chances to live a good life, but I wouldn't listen. I'm sure that you're okay, but will you please get a test for my peace of mind? Call me and let me know you're all right?"

"Meeko, I've been tested every time I go in for a checkup. I'm okay. Now tell me, my only love, what can I do for you?"

"Sunny, there's nothing anyone can do. Let me handle this in my own way and please, My Sweetheart, don't get involved with my decision. Just love me and be there for me."

"Are you out of your fucking mind? Shit, Meeko! I can't just sit here and do nothing."

"Easy, my little *Sku'ya*. All I ask from you is to love me and to be there for me, no matter what happens. Sell the rest of my paintings and send the money to Rachel."

"My love, they're already sold. Tell Rachel I'll get the check in the mail today."

"Sunny, I'll ask Rachel to send you the rest of my work. If you'll sell them for me, it'll help us survive."

"Meeko, I'll be happy to do that. Now tell me, how are you doing?"

"I'm dealing with great pain and many regrets about my wasted life. My bullshit has finally caught up with me. I called to tell you my time is near. You see, Sweetheart, last week I heard my death song."

"Oh, no! I'll come to you!" Sunny began to cry.

"Please don't. I'd rather you not see me like this. My memories of the love we had twelve years ago will be my strength in these final days. You know you are my only love and I want you to know that you were the best thing that ever happened to me. Sunny, you are and always were, a good person. Don't ever forget that. Since my visit with you, I've been writing you letters every day. Rachel will mail them to you when I've gone to the Other Side.

"I called today because it was time. I know in my death, as in my life, you will be there for me. Why I always fought you, I'll never know. But now I know that love and games do not build a life for anyone. My past has become the curse of my existence. To get through this transition, I'm asking if you'll let me call you every day. I had little honor in life, but now I ask you to help me have honor in my death. And one more request, My Sweetheart. When the time comes for me to take my journey to the Other Side, will you keep my soul for one year?

I know I didn't help you in this life, but I promise I'll return and help you from the Other Side. Sunny, I honor the love we shared. Now let me go home in peace, basking in your love. That would be my greatest strength and the only thing I need to heal my soul."

"Yes. No matter what world you are in, Meeko, I'll always be with you." Sunny hung up, knowing that the old problems that had rested between them had been resolved and their circle of one was slowly closing.

A few days later Meeko awakened to another gray dawn and got out of bed feeling at peace for what he was about to do. He took an old blanket and gathered all of his sacred things, then carefully tied them into his backpack. He kissed Rachel goodbye and left the house. As he turned onto the highway he glanced back at the old homestead and felt a sadness for all the things that he had not yet accomplished.

After driving as far as the terrain would allow, Meeko got out of the truck and trudged the last few miles to the top of the mountain where Granbear had given him his earlier training. Standing at the top, he looked down over the still valley and let his heart embrace the things that he held close. In the far distance he saw patches of snow beginning to melt under the warmth of the spring sun and felt at peace. He reached down and patted the ground, saying, "Everything is good. Everything is balanced." He smiled, remembering these were the same words spoken by Granbear on their first trip to this mountain. As he stripped to the waist and opened his medicine bundle, he thought of Granbear's teachings and the beauty they had shared in his younger years.

Meeko sang a preparation song as he carefully made an altar of freshly gathered sage and topsoil in the center of a circle he had drawn. With his digging stick he carved a half-moon shaped mound in the soil and placed red, yellow, black and white ceremonial flags into the ground around it. He covered the altar with a deerskin and placed his sacred articles upon it. He placed his pipe and eagle wing next to his bear knife then sat down in front of his altar.

Meeko removed his hair ties while singing an old war song and attached two eagle feathers to his hair. He painted the lower part of his face black with a yellow lightning bolt across the bridge of his nose. Taking a handful of soil from *Maka Ina*, he offered it to the four directions and once satisfied that everything was in balance, he sang his pipe filling song while loading it.

"*Hau, Wakan Tanka*, Great Mystery, forgive me for what I am about to do. I have listened to you, but I did not hear your many subtle messages. I've walked my lifetime out of balance. I feel as if I am two people living in one body. These two souls are in conflict, and my head has fought this battle far too long. Rather than fight anymore, I am sending both of us back to you.

"My heart grieves that I have failed my destiny and those who have dared to love me. I know I have disrespected the sacred body that you gave me. Now I choose to give my flesh back to Mother Earth."

Meeko continued to lament as he picked up a buffalo skull and offered it up to Father Sky. A mass of dark, billowy clouds had gathered overhead and took the form of many spirit helpers. A white buffalo calf, a grizzly bear and the Three-legged White Wolf walked toward him, beckoning him to join them. Suddenly he felt his heart fill with courage.

"Oh, *Tunka'shila*, hear my prayer. You have shown great patience with me, and I thank you. Let my life's story remain in the hearts of the people in a good way. Let them see the value one must have in trusting his soul. I plead for all people to cherish their life, which is the greatest sacred gift received at birth."

Meeko smoked his pipe and offered the ashes to the four winds. He picked up his hunting knife and cut four deep lines across his chest.

"Oh, Sweet Spirit, I'm coming home. Please welcome me. Help me reach the deep sleep so I can sing your great song from my soul. Oh, sweet Mother Earth, keep me warm and let me feel your comfort as I lay cradled in your body. Touch me tenderly as you cover my body with yours. Oh, *Tunka'shila*, let me touch your sweet face in this twilight time as I begin my journey back to you. Help me as I offer all that I am to you, Great Spirit."

Meeko plunged the blade deep into his chest, ripping it open. As his last offering to Creator, he tried to pull his heart from the gaping hole before slowly slumping forward and falling across the earthen altar.

A burst of brilliant blue light took the form of an eagle and rose from the center of the altar. The spirits of Red Rope and Granbear reached out, taking Meeko's hand as they soared high above. Flying, flying, flying, Meeko looked down and saw his tired and worn-out body. For a moment he felt a sadness, but as he drew nearer to the light he knew his soul was free and he was on his way to the Other Side, far Beyond the Pines.

In another place Sunny felt a jolt of electricity pierce through her and she felt Meeko touch her hand. As she screamed out, a shimmering red rose slowly materialized in the palm of her hand, then vanished. She knew Meeko had taken his life and was making his journey back to the spirit world.

Sunny cried out and ran to Shung'. Shung' and Wicahmunga were just coming out of their morning sweat. Sunny blocked their pathway, hysterically trying to explain what she had just experienced. Shung' grabbed her arm, saying, "Easy, child. Settle down. Come, let's go to the house and talk about what you have seen."

As they gathered quietly around the kitchen table to listen to Sunny's experience, Wicahmunga jumped up from her chair. "I'm not listening! Meeko wouldn't do that! I'll put a spell on you if you accuse him of such things."

Shung' knew Sunny's words were true and comforted her. "My sweet child, I am so sorry you have experienced another devastation, but whatever was his truth, you must accept this was his decision."

"Shung', what if it was just my imagination? Will you please go to the Other Side and see if he's there?"

Although Shung' already knew the truth, she called to Wicahmunga to help her darken the room and set up the ceremony. When Shung' was in Shadow World for over an hour, Sunny knew her vision had been true.

Shung' returned from Shadow World and sat quietly with a saddened face. "What you saw was true. Meeko has left his robe of skin on the top of a mountain behind the old homestead. He tells me you will soon receive many letters from him that will explain everything."

Sunny lay her head on the table and wailed, feeling as though her life force wanted to join his. Shung' quietly picked up the phone and called Rachel to tell her where to find Meeko's body.

At four o'clock the phone rang. Shung' answered and after a short conversation with Rachel, she hung up the phone. "They've found his body. They're bringing it down from the mountain now. It is best that people remember him in a good way. I told Rachel to take the body to the funeral parlor to arrange for a closed casket ceremony."

Sunny continued to wail as she listened to Shung's words. She went to the kitchen, took out her scissors and cut off her hair to begin her mourning ceremony. Finding her pain too confining, she left the house and walked aimlessly into the desert, lamenting Meeko's death. Finally she sat down in exhaustion, wailing as she cut flesh offerings from her arms and legs.

For four days Shung' and Wicahmunga sat on the patio helplessly listening to Sunny lament her grief. Both were saddened, but knew they could not go to her since she had chosen to honor his death in the old way.

Right after sunrise on the fifth morning, Shung' and Wicahmunga saw Sunny walking to the house. As she entered, Shung' saw her many cuts and made a hot herbal bath. She bathed Sunny carefully while taking a closer look at her wounds. She instructed Wicahmunga to bring the special salves. They spread the medicines on her open wounds and put her to bed. Wicahmunga brought her a cup of soup and insisted she drink it, then both ladies stood in prayer at the foot of her bed. Weak and saddened, Sunny lay still in the darkened bedroom.

It was late when everyone retired for the night. When the phone rang early the next morning, Shung' answered it quickly, to find it was Rachel telling her that Meeko was being buried the that afternoon. When Shung' told her about the funeral, Sunny glanced at the clock and realized there was no way she could get there in time. Again she left the house to spend time alone in the desert.

Shung' and Wicahmunga understood her loneliness. But as weeks passed and Sunny's depression had not lifted, Shung' became concerned. Each day, Sunny would walk to the mailbox hoping to find the letters from Meeko, and would return to her room, disappointed.

At last they arrived in a large envelope. Quickly she sat down, ripped it open and read:

My Dearest Sunny,

Day one: Today, I write this letter in the hope it will answer all your questions and help heal the turmoil that you are suffering. Please understand that I took my life because I refused to live under the circumstances of my illness, and could not deal with any more emotional pain created from my guilt. Forgive my irresponsible ways in life as well as in death. Please don't judge me for these things.

Sweetheart, don't cry for me. What happened to my life had nothing to do with you. It happened because of the poor choices I made. Who knows better than I, that my destiny was truly written in the stars? Remember how we always looked to the North Star to feel the presence of the other? Then look up now, Sunny, and know, I am still with you.

I want you to accept my death and get on with your life. Bad or good, it was I who made all the decisions, in life as well as in death.

Please allow me this right. My lovely, lovely Sweetheart, accept that I had an incurable disease that was taking my life. The pain and suffering was more than I could handle. My mental anguish was paralyzing. I relate this to all the pain that I have created for others. I have made amends for most of my wrongdoings, so please accept that I am happy with my decision. I thank you for all the phone calls that supported me during this devastating time. You helped me regain my belief in *Wakan Tanka*. I know hindsight is twenty-twenty, but I must tell you that if I had my life to live over, I would spend every minute of the day with you. But we both know my weaknesses would make this impossible. Again, I must say you are a wonderful and caring person, and without you I would have never lived this long.

Day two: Today, let me digress back to the lethargic atmosphere I embraced during my prison time. I can see how that time helped me accept the presence of all life. Remember I told you one of the inmates was a medicine man? It was he who taught me to stop blaming others for my problems and to bear the weight of my own self-destructive nature. Oh, my love, I am so sorry. I've shared so little with you, but today, I come from my heart to express a truth. Did you know that I could never match your abilities nor was I willing to put forth the effort to try? All that is left in me is the sadness from never telling you this before. The pain that I have created for you is incomprehensible to me. Oh how I wish I had done things differently.

Day three: Today, I am thinking about us. There was once a tender spot in your heart for me. I took it and made it callused, now there are nothing but the scars to look to for tenderness. I know that I will always love you, and I also know we can never be together again in this life. Your temper and imagination became my worst enemies, yet my truth was always my weakest offering to you. Since this dreadful disease struck me down, it has been impossible for me to count the number of times that I have wished things had been different between us. Above all, I wanted you to know that your words were never wasted on me. It was you who gave me the enchantment of life that still is a part of everything I see. When I sit with the twinkling stars at night, I always see that same brightness shine from your eyes. When I listen to music, I think of the birds singing their songs of happiness when we were together. I will always love you, and I cannot imagine what it will be like to never see you again.

I think of Mother Earth and Father Sky, and everything tells me that I am their child which proves my reason for living and dying. Remember how we once collected stones in our many travels? Even they have always taught me to read who I truly was. It was this old knowledge that I sought in the Stone Nation that gave me peace.

But it was your voice who spoke my name as I rode on the whispers of the winds during our time together. It was you who showed me the joy of a gentle touch. I will forever see you as a mischievous child always playing on the rainbow's edge. Why even yesterday, I saw your happiness in a little bird that was sitting on my window ledge. I must again thank *Wakan Tanka* for allowing me to study the wisdom of Socrates. It was he who helped me grasp the true wisdom of the concept of a soul and proved to me that the Great Spirit demands we relinquish all that we are before we can learn the true beauty offered along our life's journey.

Day four: Today my mind is screaming for recognition of the many shared moments that I so cherish. The memories of the times we walked among the flowers and you helped me hear the tiny high pitched voices of their sweet laughter. I remember you once asked me what it would be like to ride on the back of a bumblebee. Ah, my sweet *Sku'ya*, your beautiful ways and thoughts leave little to anyone's imagination.

You are my strong woman, but sometimes, I worry over your hell-bent inspirations. I know you understand it could mean your destruction or construction, but my God, woman, what a belief system in the above powers you have!

Do you know one of my greatest apprehensions? I fear your fascination with unstable people and, I fear they may lead you toward romanticism. I beg you never to listen to their potential dreams. I fear you might try to save another irresponsible little boy like myself who could dangerously rule your life. Please listen to me, My Sweetheart, get rid of any man who has any addictions like myself because he will drag you away from your destiny. I beg you to keep those pretty feet on the ground and remember, I hope to remain the most handsome and charming man you will have ever known in this lifetime.

Day five: I was thinking over your father's advice when he spoke once at great lengths with me about you. He was right when he said you were highly impressionable, so listen to your father's words and please be aware that your emotions can recoil and spring back on you. Please excuse my rambling but my mind seems to come and go. Did I ever tell you how I love the way you act quickly upon your ideas? And I know you will do this for the rest of your life. Forgive me for my concerns, but hear my words, Sweetheart. I know you will always win if you use the same efforts toward your material wealth as you do your spiritual wealth. Did you know that I found my security in the power of your will? Never, never let that die for another's useless fears.

Day six: Today I'm suffering with terrible pain, but when I think of our many shared dreams it seems to ease a little. Ah, to have those days again. Please know my dreams were destroyed because of my low self esteem and fear of success. It was never anything you did. But rest assured my problems will no longer exist when I leave this earthly body. I promise when I return to the Other Side, I will protect and guide you so you can complete those dreams that you want to accomplish. Now, again I remind you, please keep my soul and when you release it a year from now, know I will come to you with a clear mind. Remember when we once promised each other that whoever died first would return and prove life existed after death? I Promise I will return as proof that life is eternal.

Day seven: Today, I simply share my beliefs of who I am. I was never as special as you thought. You were the unique one. Sunny never lose your individuality. Remember it was you who taught me that it was my thoughts that made my reality. My dear sweet one, continue to walk your every thought and please do not mourn for me. Like the eagle, know I am merely releasing my soul to fly with the above powers. My love, my love. Keep strong in your faith. I know you will accomplish your birth purpose. I will see you when you complete your life/death circle and this gives me a great comfort knowing that we will be together again. Put my death behind you quickly and go back into the world and build that cornerstone you need for your success.

Please, my dear lady, live a good life and always stay a free soul. I loved you in life and I will love you in death. I apologize for being a heavy burden in your life, but know I will help you complete your destiny as soon as I arrive on the Other Side. You see it is you who gives me the strength for what I am about to do. Be happy and please accept my decision. Don't mourn for me. Be happy that I am free from this earthly bondage. Pray for me. I'll be waiting for you when you decide to cross over.

I love you, Meeko

Sunny held the tear-stained letters close to her heart, feeling the pain in Meeko's words. As she entered the house she collapsed on the floor, wailing. Wicahmunga ran to see what was the matter and when she saw Sunny, she knew the letter had come. Wicahmunga picked it up and ran to Shung'. "Hurry, read this! Maybe it will tell us why Sunny is lying on the floor crying."

Shung' read the letter to Wicahmunga and both women cried over the sorrow and losses that were between these two young people. Shung' wiped her eyes on her apron.

"Wicahmunga, take this letter back where you found it and bring Sunny to me."

"I'm an old woman. I can't pick her up!"

"Oh, for God's sake, Wicahmunga."

Shung' put the letter into her pocket and went to Sunny. But when she saw her curled into a fetal position on the floor, she realized there was nothing she could do but sit and nurture Sunny through this trying time. Around noon Shung' was able to coax her into the kitchen and as they sat with Wicahmunga at the table, she poured Sunny a cup of herbal tea to help her sleep. She placed the food in front of her.

"Eat, my child, eat!"

Sunny picked at her food until Shung' saw she was not going to eat and suggested she get some rest. "Tomorrow we will start working on conquering this pain."

Submissively, Sunny followed her upstairs and curled in a fetal position on the bed. Shung' gently covered her with a blanket then sat beside her in the darkened room.

Sunny slept fitfully, too vulnerable to be alone. She knew time and space were folding in on her, and in a panic she began to beg for her sleeping pills. Shung' feared the old habits would return and she would use them to escape, rather than heal the problem. Yet she did not want to be unfair to Sunny, since she needed something to free her mind from this terrible loss. Going to the medicine chest, Shung' took two pills and a glass of water to her.

"Here. Sleep, my child, sleep."

From that day forward Sunny slept almost around the clock, refusing to leave the room. Early one morning three weeks later, Shung' walked into the bedroom and opened the drapes demanding that Sunny get out of bed. But no matter what Shung' said, Sunny refused to get up and her mind became even more consumed with Meeko's death.

After several more useless attempts, Shung' refused to wrestle another day with Sunny's self-imposed pain. In a fit of anger, she dragged Sunny from the bed and forced her downstairs. Wicahmunga could not understand why Shung' was being so gentle with Sunny.

"Humph, look at her. She's too messed up to think. All we're doing is sitting around watching her pop pills and sleep. I say we throw her pills away and leave here."

"Shush, Woman! She needs time. Now apologize!"

Wicahmunga scowled for a moment at being corrected, then slowly removed her juniper berry necklace from around her neck and placed it on Sunny.

"Wear these! They'll stop you from being lost in the darkness that lies between your ears. These beads will stop those screaming nightmares, then maybe we can all get some sleep!"

But Sunny had taken too many pills and heard nothing as her head fell onto the table in exhaustion. Wicahmunga and Shung' carried Sunny back to bed and waited by her side until she awakened for another pill. An hour later Sunny tried to get out of bed, mumbling for more pills.

"There are no more! I flushed them down the toilet," stated Shung' flatly.

Sunny reached for the phone, but it was not there. "Where is my phone?"

"I removed all of them from the house. You will not call the doctor for more." Shung's voice was cold.

Sunny stumbled from her bed and went searching throughout the house for her medication. She became angry when she found that Shung' had emptied all of her secret hiding places. Returning to her bedroom, Sunny threw herself on the bed in despair.

Wicahmunga rose to her feet. "Sit up! I am talking to you! See those beads around your neck? They're more powerful than those damn pills. Now, listen to me! Here's the deal. Those beads represent a triangle and it takes in all the trees, the animals and the Stone People. Maybe this will keep your mind in balance long enough to get your head clear." Sunny reached up and touched them gently. "Now, don't think those are a gift! When you're better, I want them back." Wicahmunga caught a hard look from Shung' and retracted her statement, saying, "Well, maybe if you'll try to get well, I'll teach you how to make your own."

Sunny smiled weakly, as she continued fingering each bead. And once again, protocol had been established between the three ladies. Shung' sat down on the side of the bed saying, "It's time to leave this sadness behind and get beyond the grief and depression. If you want to honor Meeko, then honor his request. Let me teach you the ceremony for the keeping and releasing of the soul. If you will do this properly, who knows, maybe I'll consider letting you pick up your Grandmother's medicine bundle very soon. After all, you can become a medicine person in one year if you follow these old beliefs."

Sunny agreed. She understood the dedication and the tremendous responsibilities she must undertake in the coming year, if she were to do as Meeko had requested. There would be sweats and the pipe must be smoked three times a day for the purification of his spirit. She almost wished she had not agreed to do this. But within a week Sunny felt better about it. She knew all the loving prayers she sent to *Wakan Tanka* would keep Meeko's memory alive in the hearts of all those who loved him, and this was a good thing.

The following morning she began the preparations for the keeping of the soul ceremony. As she beaded a buckskin bag, Sunny thought of how few people followed the first rite on the pipe anymore. When the bag was completed, Sunny lined the bottom with freshly picked sage then took a lock of Meeko's hair and a piece of his flesh from their last Sun Dance and placed them inside the bag. Then taking three sticks, she tied them together with rawhide to make a ceremonial stand.

The next day at sunrise, Sunny gathered these things together and went to her rose garden. As she set up the tripod, she hung the bag near the top facing South, and every day thereafter she continued doing her work to maintain her commitment to Meeko. Every three months, she lovingly lowered the bag on the tripod, knowing the time was approaching to prepare for the releasing of Meeko's soul.

One night as she lay in bed reflecting on the upcoming ceremony, she heard a whisper and saw Meeko standing at the foot of her bed.

"My lovely bride, I told you I would come and prove there was life after death. Guess what? I found out where the bathroom is," he said with a grin and vanished into Sunny's bathroom.

She screamed with fright at his presence then broke into laughter. Finding she could no longer sleep, she sat on the side of the bed and smoked a cigarette, knowing no matter where life would take her, there was life after death.

Sunny waited until sunlight to share the vision with Shung' and Wicahmunga. Wicahmunga looked at her in a knowing way. "Humph, so you're just finding that out? That silly fart has been hanging around here for months."

The next day Shung', Wicahmunga and Sunny drove into the mountains to release Meeko's soul. Once camp was established they began to drum and sing the old ceremonial songs. Many small balls of blue light circled around them and Meeko's joyful face appeared, coming directly from the sun that was surrounded by a large bluish haze. Sunny cried joyous tears knowing Meeko had made a safe journey back to *Wakan Tanka*.

Medicine Woman

On the drive down the mountain Sunny reflected on how hard the past year had been and how much commitment and devotion it had taken for her to achieve the depth entailed to earn the first rite on her pipe. When they arrived home she was told it was time to return to the reservation for Meeko's traditional giveaway. She immediately called Rachel and told her they would be there within the week to complete the rite of the keeping and releasing of the soul.

Sunny, Shung' and Wicahmunga gathered the necessary ceremonial herbs along with the needed sacred objects, then left Las Vegas on their long, leisurely drive back to the Fort Peck Indian Reservation. As they arrived at Shung' home, many people were waiting to greet them. As Wicahmunga got out of the car she joked, "Well, we're back on the rez. I wonder if they've cooked up enough dog meat to welcome us bloods home?"

"Yeah I was wondering about that too," chuckled Shung'.

"Oh my God, that's sick. When are you two ever going to stop trying to gross me out?" snickered Sunny.

The women stretched their aching bones and laughed boisterously as Shung' teased, "Sunny, when will you ever get a sense of humor?"

Sunny quickly unloaded the bags, saying "I'm going for a drive, I'll be back before sundown." As she drove away Sunny rolled down the windows, delighted to once again experience the freedom and openness of reservation life. Anxious to visit all the places that held fond memories of her life with Meeko, she drove to the place where she had first met the demon. Relieved when she did not feel its presence, she drove to the dam and strolled across its walkway, thinking of the many nights she and Meeko had spent there studying the stars. As she drove away Sunny was consumed by emptiness, knowing what they once cherished was no longer.

She arrived at Auntie Lizzie's and was surprised when Shadowhawk opened the door. Auntie Lizzie, hearing Sunny's voice, excitedly welcomed her home. They visited over lunch, and Sunny was happy to learn that Shadowhawk and Auntie Lizzie had remarried.

Sunny returned to Shung's at seven o'clock and was delighted to find the Bear Clan gathered in the warmth of a family circle around the kitchen table, happily discussing the latest births and marriages. As the night grew late, final plans were made for Meeko's giveaway.

Early the following morning everyone gathered at Rachel's, and by late afternoon all of Meeko's belongings and the many gifts given by the Bear Clan were laid out for the evening giveaway. At twilight the old grandmothers took their places. They gave great thought to each item to make sure it would meet the needs of the less fortunate people that lived on the reservation. When the last gift had been given away, food was served and the people took turns sharing their personal experiences with Meeko while he was on Mother Earth. Some stories were sad, while others were humorous, caring and comforting. By the time the guests had departed, everyone knew that Sunny would be staying at Shung's, and they promised to spend time with her before she returned home.

While Shung' comforted Rachel, Sunny walked through the unpainted three-room house fighting back tears at the sight of Meeko's pitiful surroundings during his last heartbreaking days on Mother Earth. The worn-out linoleum, broken couches and rickety chairs reminded her of the harsh poverty she had known as a child. To help out Rachel financially, she purchased several of Meeko's paintings which hung precariously from newspaper covered walls. After wrapping them lovingly in blankets, she packed them in the car.

When Sunny returned to the house, Wicahmunga sidled near and shoved an earring into her hand, saying, "When Meeko was a kid, he gave this to me. I want you to have it." Shadowhawk observed them then joined them in laughter as he gave Sunny the matching earring, bringing to her mind the story of when Meeko had given the earring to Wicahmunga to escape her wrath. They all chuckled when Sunny removed her earrings and gave them to Wicahmunga to pay the debt for her gift. Wicahmunga reacted in her usual suspicious manner. She studied the earrings closely before putting them on, then stared at her reflection in the mirror, sarcastically remarking that they looked much better on her than Sunny. Everyone laughed in agreement.

The following morning Sunny picked up Cousin Willie and drove to the mountain peak where Meeko had taken his life. As she sat in silence overlooking the valley, Sunny could feel Meeko's presence. She and Willie smoked the sacred red pipe and when the ceremony was completed, Sunny offered the ashes to the winds and said her last goodbyes. For the rest of the afternoon the two walked over the land touching every stone, bush and tree, giving thanks to them for helping Meeko get ready for his journey home. Willie stood atop the biggest boulder reflecting on Sunny's sorrow and said affectionately, "Rachel gave him a nice funeral. A lot of people attended, including his pilot friend Jake, some Vietnam buddies, a few fellow inmates and even your cousins Peck and Pete. Boy, do those guys know their booze and drugs."

"I know," Sunny said, her mood lightening.

As they headed down the mountain Willie said, "Got something I want to talk about. You know how good Meeko was at figuring things out. I was wondering if you'd take over and help us fight a few legal battles with Uncle Sam?"

"I'll think about it. Right now I've got too much on my mind, so let's drop the subject!"

"Hey, don't get pissy with mc. I'm only trying to remind you of your obligation to the people," chided Willie, softening his tone to keep from ruffling her feathers. They had little else to say as they drove back in silence to Wolf Point. Sunny dropped Willie off at the nearest bar then continued on to Shung's.

Two weeks of living on Indian Time had passed far too quickly. Sunny, Shung' and Wicahmunga packed the car and left on their long drive back to Las Vegas. During the drive home they talked extensively about Meeko's wonderful giveaway, until Shung' said, "Sunny, I'm proud of how you've earned the first rite on your pipe. Usually when a person completes this rite they are Medicine. I know it's been a long and hard journey, but it has taught you the responsibilities of your higher purpose in life.

"It's good that you've learned the difference between real values and unreal evaluations of life. You have a noble soul, and you must never again abuse Medicine like you did when you left Meeko. Your analytical mind accepts that real wisdom comes from life's experiences, but you must always remember that appearances can be deceiving. You've made many mistakes, and I'm happy that you had the heart to correct them. I know you're lonely for Meeko, but now that we've released his soul, the circle between you can be closed. I think it's time to pick up your grandmother's medicine bundle and earn your medicine pipe."

"Oh, Shung', are you sure I'm ready? There's so much I don't know."

"Sunny, nothing is beyond your comprehension. Once you understand how *Wakan Tanka's* powers work, you can connect to the magical secrets of the Red Road. To continue your spiritual growth, you must look to your finer qualities and guard against the limited thinking of others. Sometimes you will be called upon to protect the rites of the pipe. To do this, you must become as hollow as its stem. I know that in time you will walk with a smooth rhythm, all the while enjoying the beauty that you behold."

From the back seat, Wicahmunga snorted, adding, "She can't do it. Her ego is too big, and besides, the spirits will never recognize her with all that makeup smeared on her face. Shung', make her pull over. I have to pee."

"Oh, shit," said Sunny in disgust as she pulled the car to the side of the road. Wicahmunga got out and scurried across the field. Sunny and Shung' laughed as they watched her squat down behind a small bush, trying to hide her big butt.

Once they were back on the highway, Shung' continued, "Sunny, look over the years, and see the many hard challenges that you have met and conquered. Look at your childhood and the heartbreak you suffered when you lost your marriage. Consider all the inappropriate behaviors you have changed. You see, Grandchild, you have knowledge of many things. It was your experiences that taught you to give the proper respect to every energy force within the universe.

"When we get home, I want you to practice moving more freely through the many dimensions of time and space as I teach you to perform some of our sacred rituals. Many of my teachings will come to you in a very subtle manner, and you are to never discuss these with any person who is not Medicine. The key to this journey is being able to walk with the consciousness of all living things and having the ability to travel between worlds," concluded Shung'.

"Yeah, big deal. She'll never learn anything! She's too stupid, and she's still a bad person. Everyone knows she has bad blood. It probably goes all the way to her bones! Humph, she can't speak, let alone think in our language. All she understands is how to confuse people with her contrary English. So how can she ever learn our old language when she's so wrapped up in her fear-ridden English words? I don't understand why she insists on using English anyway, it's full of lies and junk."

"Oh, shush, woman!" demanded Shung'. "Never mind Wicahmunga, Sunny. You must remove all the masks that you hide behind and go back to your heritage to find your face. It is your actions that allow you to understand the integrity of walking in honor. Think of our ways of teaching and you will see the subtleties of truth in everything. Most people don't grasp the mystery of Great Spirit's all-knowing power, otherwise they wouldn't need to display their identity in their jewelry and clothing. Power does not reside in objects. The power of Medicine is in the depth of the person and how they connect to the energies that flow from *Wakan Tanka*.

"Eons ago, the above people came here and built many temples and sacred places for teaching the future generations. We were taught to face the West in prayer in order to collect a flow of energy to develop our immortal souls. As you know, we still use these same powers to become true Skywalkers. Once you accept the duality in all things, you will know how to respond to the above mysteries of the sun, moon and stars. Doesn't it stand to reason that if the above powers influence our weather, seasons, plants and animals, then surely they must also affect humans? It is these powers that cycle us through time, space, measure and dimension. Our sacred rituals depend upon this heavenly knowledge. If we do not acknowledge these gifts, then how can we maintain our earthly survival?

"Everything relates and is connected to the whole. Each life force has its own time, tone and rhythm that is constantly influencing our lives. We must become good observers of the sky to understand the sacred calendars left long ago by the old medicine people. The Great Mystery gave us mathematical designs among the stars, to help us integrate our earth knowledge into the predictable sky language and know when it is time to perform our sacred rituals. Only then can a Skywalker spiral the inner and outer vortex that let's them connect to all that is."

With total frustration Sunny complained, "Oh, God, Shung', I never realized how much I didn't know. How can I ever accomplish these things when half the time I can't grasp a thing you're saying?"

"Be careful, Shung'! I don't trust her, and besides she always tries to trick us with her big words. I told you she was dumb! I once asked her about Grandmother Spider and she didn't know the answer! I warned her that it was Grandmother Spider who wove the web that held all the planets and stars in place and she didn't understand one word I was saying."

"Yes, you did, Wicahmunga. And you also told me that if I ever got caught in her web, I would never escape until I learned all the spider knowledge. I'm sure you hoped I would get caught in her web and be eaten."

"Well, maybe I did, and maybe I didn't. All I know is you're just a breed, and you can never tell what your kind of people are going to do."

"That may be true, sister, but if she does get caught, I believe it will be you who will have to go and free her. In fact, I think it's time you teach her all the symbolic designs of the sacred language and their meaning," smiled Shung' smugly.

Wicahmunga adamantly bemoaned her fate until she fell asleep. Soon Shung' was asleep too, allowing Sunny to drive several hours in blessed silence. As the lights of Las Vegas loomed on the horizon, Shung' stirred, climbed into the front seat, lit a cigar and poured herself and Sunny a cup of coffee from the thermos.

"Shung', it seems that my life has been one battle after another. I've fought my whole life trying to survive, get an education and become someone. I've fought to have a home. I've fought to have love. I've fought to get closure on Meeko's death, and now I'm fighting to find out who I am. God, I'm so tired!"

"Sunny, those old experiences will someday become the strength that will build your power. This is what makes wisdom, so be patient with yourself. One day you will know all that I'm saying."

At last Sunny pulled into her driveway, thankful to be home. She left Wicahmunga sound asleep in the back seat as she and Shung' went inside to turn on the lights. When Sunny returned to get their bags, she reached over and gently shook Wicahmunga to wake her. Startled, Wicahmunga grabbed her purse, screaming, "Quit trying to steal my money! Get your hands off me! I wasn't asleep. I was just resting my eyes."

"Then why was all that snoring falling out of your mouth?"

"Better my mouth than my ass," Wicahmunga retorted, crawling out of the car.

The two of them walked to the house. Before they went to bed Shung' reminded Sunny that her training would start at dawn. Just before sunrise the three sat at the table discussing the upcoming day. "Wicahmunga, take Sunny for a walk into the desert and teach her the meanings of the old calendar symbols, then let her spend the rest of the time in Shadow World."

"Humph, her soul is too dirty to travel between worlds. If she gets lost, I won't go and get her."

"Is that so, Wicahmunga? You are responsible for her errors, and you will go bring her back."

"I won't do it! I won't do it," yelled Wicahmunga, getting up from the table and running out the back door.

Sunny enjoyed a hearty laugh at Wichamunga. Shung' smiled, saying, "Don't worry. She'll be back. Wicahmunga is a wise and good soul, but she's the most cantankerous old woman I've ever met. You're smart not to argue with her. Now go follow her around until she acknowledges you, but conduct yourself respectfully. After all, she is Medicine."

Carrying a blanket, a carton of Wicahmunga's favorite cigarettes and a bundle of herbs, Sunny went in search of the old medicine woman. She found her pouting under a tree. Sunny spread the blanket and sat facing her quietly, waiting for permission to speak.

"I don't want to do this for you, since you're not smart enough to learn, but I'll do it for Shung'. And if you piss me off, I'll quit," snapped Wicahmunga.

"I'll be on my best behavior."

"Then give me the tobacco and herbs like you're supposed to!" Sunny did as instructed, whereupon the old woman studied the carton of cigarettes, opened it carefully and counted to make sure there were ten unopened packs. Satisfied that she was not being cheated, Wicahmunga closed her eyes and sat in silence for a long time.

"Since your mind is so limited, I'll speak about the sun's pathway. I hope you know that a sun is a star and a star is a sun. Don't ask me why! It just is. So I'll teach you with simple words. All those religious societies have to write their stories down 'cause they can't remember anything, just like you." She paused waiting to be acknowledged for her brilliance.

Sunny nodded sweetly in understanding so Wicahmunga would continue.

"A certain number of clustered stars make different designs and shapes as they move around in the sky. If you know their meaning they will tell you how they affect your life. Humph, you should already know this stuff. After all, *Wakan Tanka* expects us humans to at least be as smart as the animals and the green things." Sunny was afraid to speak. She sat quietly with her head bowed while she listened to Wicahmunga complain about the inability of a breed to learn anything.

"Give me a chance," pleaded Sunny.

"No, you little twerp, but you better listen to every word I say 'cause I ain't gonna repeat it. Everything is born from the sacred zero and that's *Wakan Tanka*. If I go to the first pole in the *Inipi*, it's the sun. That means build your own power and quit trying to steal mine. If I go to the second pole, that's *Taku Skan Skan*. That means to get your ass moving in your life and leave mine alone. If I go to the third pole, that's *Maka Ina* and you're supposed to know all that. You think you can build Old Man Four Generations fire pit, so you should know the fourth pole, that's Inyan, the Stone People. Everything that I mentioned is connected to everything else. So those four powers are one."

"I think I understand."

"You shut up! I didn't give you permission to talk."

Wicahmunga, picked up her talking stick to remind Sunny to be silent. She used the stick to draw a circle in the dirt representing the sky map and began to point out the hidden secrets in the celestial wonders.

"I once read a book that called energy a scalar wave. Ain't that funny? See this? It has no beginning or end. I hope you can measure from the earth to the above powers without using a stupid ruler. If not, you'll have to figure out your own way to measure the movements in the heavens.

Sunny, a bewildered look on her face, timidly answered, "Okay, I'll try to follow exactly what you said."

"That's it! Your expression lied! Try means NO! Now be quiet! I can't think with you talking." Wicahmunga paused for a moment, then begrudgingly added, "You can't see the wind because it's invisible. But you know it exists because you feel it and see it moving things around. Right?"

Sunny nodded, waiting for Wicahmunga to make her hidden point.

"That's knowing the visible and invisible powers that always make things change. Well, life says the same thing. Everything moves around. Okay? We live in a solar system along with other planets. We know that an eclipse or a meteor shower talks to all of Mother Earth's relatives as it dances among them. The sun is the center of our solar system and is constantly throwing off bits and pieces of itself that touch us with messages of wisdom. So you better learn to listen. Now look up and think about all this stuff. And you better remember what happens to our solar system, happens to us.

"Everything is born from the sacred womb of life. Everything affects the whole of the universe, which proves we are all related and we can't survive without each other. Life and matter are created by different energies of thought. When a girl has her first moon, she births the power of her will and begins her journey to become a woman. Most women become giggling, twittering twats. Men have two heads, and they usually think with the little one. Humph, humans are so stupid about their bodies that they multiply like rabbits, then before you know it their kids are having kids. Ah yes, sex is the strongest drive in the human race, and we don't have enough common sense to keep it under control. But you watch! They'll stay out of control playing with their pee pees until the whole world goes hungry. My, such ignorance. Dumb! Dumb! Dumb!

"Long time ago the original people were vegetarians and the plant people fed them. Then this sex disease got out of control and too many people were born, causing everyone to nearly starve to death. The hoofed ones felt sorry for these human nincompoops and gave their lives so the people could live. I once heard you tell Shung' that you're a vegetarian because you don't like to kill things. Well, that's a lie. When you eat, you kill. If the mouth doesn't do it, the stomach acids will. Humph, I just tell my body to take what it needs and get rid of the rest. That's my simple prayer to take care of my body."

Sunny laughed so hard that she had to hold her aching stomach as tears streamed down her face.

"You think that's funny, huh? Well, so do I. But it's a truth. The human animal only thinks with its crotch or its stomach. Yeah, sensitive people have feelings, but they don't listen to their gut. We humans are bad predators. Waste! Waste! Waste!"

"For a moment Sunny, think back on how your mind flew away when Meeko died. It took strong Bear and Cougar courage to kill that craziness. See, life is like a cat-and-mouse game. Everybody plays with the truth but no one ever seems to get the fact that everything is born with a purpose. Chances and choices operate in every moment of life to help you accomplish your birth purpose. We're nothing but a bag of water just proceeding through time from one life to another. I wonder what we'll become when *Wakan Tanka* finishes the great masterpiece of the human race. I know it takes a clear head to understand the purpose behind life. Now if you ever get that far, maybe you'll see the bigger picture. That is, if you ever learn how to pay attention and remember what you've heard."

Sunny smiled appreciatively, and for the first time realized that Wicahmunga was truly a *contrar* medicine woman.

"What are you grinning about, you witless turd? Well, that's all I have to say. I've talked so much that I'm losing my voice. Go to Shadow World and see if you can find the animals painted in the stars, then take all that into time and space. When you can prove to me that you got it, then I'll teach you the next four powers. Now go away and leave me alone. Let nature talk to you." Wicahmunga walked away in a huff all the while grumbling to herself about her poor, damaged voice.

Sunny's enthusiasm rapidly vanished, however, because by the following morning, Wicahmunga was once again complaining to Shung'. "Don't make me spend another day with that breed. She's stupid and I don't like her! Why should I be stuck teaching that blockheaded fool?"

Shung' glared, then threatened, "Wicahmunga…"

"Shung'…Oh, all right. If I gotta, I gotta. But I'm gonna take my own good time."

For two hours, Sunny obediently followed Wicahmunga as she dawdled through the desert. When they had circled back to the patio, Wicahmunga plopped down in the porch swing singing at the top of her voice. Sunny knew the lesson was over for the day. She calmly closed her eyes and relaxed in the warmth of the sun while practicing her Shadow World technique.

Wicahmunga suddenly stopped singing and yelled, "You twit! I caught you stealing my energy!" Disturbed by the racket, Shung' dashed from the house in time to hear, "You lazy bum! You don't know shit about energy, and you better leave mine alone."

Sunny got up defensively from the chaise lounge. "Shung', I didn't steal a damn thing from that woman!"

With a thundering voice, Shung' demanded the attention of both women. "I dare either of you to open your mouth," she bellowed, invoking the fear of all that was holy in them. "Sunny, you know better than to play her game. I know both of you understand that the universe is filled with pure, unadulterated energy and it is given freely to all those who come with a good heart! Wicahmunga, why in the hell are you using trickery to confuse and create these dilemmas?"

"Cause that's how I teach," murmured Wicahmunga apologetically.

"That's it! The game is over! There will be no more lessons today," directed Shung', disappearing back inside the house. Unable to contain herself any longer, Wicahmunga giggled and stuck her tongue out as she shook a threatening finger in Sunny's face.

Sunny left the patio in a total rage and walked for miles into the desert trying to decide what she could do about the situation. A red-tailed hawk flew overhead, called to her and vanished back into the sky. Sunny shielded her eyes from the sun's glare, hoping to get a another glimpse of Hawk as she continued her walk in the desert. She noticed Hawk was circling overhead again and as she sat down to ponder its presence, the hawk landed in a nearby bush. She focused on its beautiful shimmering feathers until their eyes met and she immediately realized that where the mind travels, so does the energy. The answer was simple. She would no longer allow Wicahmunga to control her mind.

The hawk flew south, while Sunny reflected on Hawk's teachings. Hawks were masters of timing. They were shy, but fiery-tempered and almost impossible to train. They flew high, selected their prey and swooped down on their unsuspecting victim, killing and eating it on the spot.

Well, well, Wicahmunga. I now understand how you are teaching me. You will no longer ruffle my feathers. I don't care what you say, I'm not guilty of stealing energy, and you will never intimidate me again with your prejudice and your nasty words. I know my heart is in the right place, and I can feed warmth to my inner self and accept your knowledge without fear. Sunny knew she had disconnected herself from the emotional control that Wicahmunga had forced upon her. She felt good about this lesson from Hawk.

Sunny saw Shung' approaching and ran to greet her. "I've found my answer. I know Wicahmunga's knowledge is given from the heart, no matter how it's presented. Her methods of teaching are unusual, but they are very real. I'm no longer upset with her."

Shung' embraced Sunny, proud that she was finally standing up for herself. "Sunny, think back to when you were on stage. Didn't you use trickery and instincts to win over your audience? Didn't it become second nature to you? If you watch Wicahmunga's manipulative ways, you can appreciate her amazing abilities. She is unique and she is strong Medicine. She will force you to know all that you are. Have you considered that she is deliberately testing your will and possibly your Medicine potential? Maybe her lifestyle is not on as grand a scale as yours, but I do think she's getting to the core of your ego. So, if energy is born from your attitude, why blame her for your weaknesses?"

"I was afraid that if I showed any disrespect, you would dismiss me as an apprentice," confessed Sunny.

"Ah, be careful of your thoughts. I never said I'd dismiss you if you upset Wicahmunga. I told you to accept everything that is around you, but I never said to let her abuse you. Sunny, know what you are trying to accomplish and let your common sense guide you as you question these lessons. When you stop qualifying, comparing and judging, you might be able to see that Wicahmunga is forcing you to a higher purpose. Look back at your marriage. Was that a failure, or was it two loving souls who came together to help each other grow spiritually?

"If Wicahmunga gives you enough aggravation, maybe it will force you to become the warrioress that I know you are, so you can survive in the world of Medicine without me. She's forcing you to see how others control you through your emotions. I say she is demanding that you stop placing expectations on yourself and others. You know energy can be easily taken from an indecisive person, but not from a knowledgeable one. So why not enjoy the wild beauty in Wicahmunga's spirit? Look around you. Do you see any plants in this desert trying to be like a hothouse plant? Listen to the buzzing of the insect world and feel their energies intermingle as they continue their productive lives. Wicahmunga is merely trying to teach you how to see real beauty," smiled Shung', stretching her arms expansively to make her point.

"Now stand up to Wicahmunga and you'll see that she'll stop aggravating you." Shung' and Sunny headed back to the house. "By the way, there's nothing to eat. We can either go shopping or you can give me a gun so I can go get us some food." Shung' laughed heartily at her own joke as they approached the patio.

Wicahmunga rose from her chair and immediately got into Sunny's face, yelling at the top of her voice, "Gimme your car keys. I'm going to town!"

Sunny laughed and answered, "Hell no! You're not driving my car! Besides you know you can't drive on the street."

Wicahmunga stepped back and smiled, pleased with Sunny's new attitude. "Oh, you think you're a warrioress, now? To me, you're still nothing but a little shit and I think you owe me for all the aggravation you've caused me!"

Sunny smiled, "Not only will I take us shopping, I'll take us out to lunch to celebrate my new way of thinking."

Dressed in their finest clothes, Wicahmunga and Shung' chattered excitedly all the way to the casino. As they entered the gambling area they huddled close to Sunny gawking at its vastness, lush décor, and buzz of activity. Sunny stopped at the cashiers cage to get fifty dollars worth of quarters then showed them how to play the slot machines. When they were happily engrossed, she left them to visit an old friend. Upon her return she was shocked and a little embarrassed to find Wicahmunga banging on her slot machine as she argued loudly with it, accusing it of stealing her money. Sunny feared an arrest and quickly handed Wicahmunga more quarters, extracting a promise from her to be quiet. This eased the situation, and shortly Sunny suggested they forget about gambling and go for a fine lunch. Both women agreed, delighted to be able to experience their first meal in a fancy hotel.

No sooner were they seated than Wicahmunga began to complain vehemently about the fact that the menu was written in French. "How am I supposed to read this thing?" she grumbled, hurling the oversized menu to the floor. Sunny calmly picked it up and ordered for everyone. Lunch was otherwise uneventful, which pleased her— until the check arrived.

"This place may be pretty, but they're nothing but a bunch of fancy highway robbers."

Sunny breathed a sigh of relief as they left the casino. When she tipped the valet, Wicahmunga complained again about the hotel thieves and threatened to get a job parking cars.

Their special outing over, the three women stopped at the grocery store. Each went her separate way, selecting favorite foods which Sunny paid for at the checkout stand. Sunny was pleased that her relationship with Wicahmunga had begun to mellow.

After the groceries were put away, Wicahmunga insisted on making coffee so she could share her favorite sweet rolls with Shung' and Sunny on the patio. She filled a tray with hot sticky buns and coffee, along with two bowls of melted butter. As they sat dipping their rolls and sipping their coffee, they spent the afternoon entertaining each other with stories of their casino adventure.

It was long after sundown when the subject turned to Medicine. Sunny attentively listened to Shung' and Wicahmunga speak at length about the many responsibilities of being a medicine person. The responsibility of what they were saying caused her to feel twinges of apprehension, and she was happy when her guests decided they were exhausted and needed to retire for the night.

For the next two weeks Shung' and Wicahmunga spent their days watching Sunny closely to see if she was applying her new lessons. Early one morning Shung' instructed Sunny to begin going alone into the desert to become more aware of all that was around her. Sunny soon found these trips were bringing a deeper clarity to her awareness. With this understanding came the realization that the learning process was accumulative and would come to her in due process. For once she truly understood that a person without awareness could never find the higher meaning of Self, or define their true spiritual identity. Sunny felt good about this sudden insight.

On this day she returned from one of her many walks and went to the kitchen to get a glass of cold lemonade before joining Shung' on the patio. "I see you're making peace with your new challenges," smiled Shung' as Sunny sat down.

"Oh, yes, thanks to Wicahmunga. What a wonderful, unique lady. Not only has she challenged my very existence, she's made me take a negative situation and turn it into a positive experience."

"So, are you saying that Wicahmunga has shown you how to take negative energy and make it work for you?"

"Yes, in many ways," laughed Sunny. "I remember that whenever she picks up a lemon, she always says, 'When you have lemons come into your life, all you can do is make lemonade.'"

"Once a person gets clear about their direction in life, it's easier to connect to the ever-flowing energy of the heavens. I am happy you've decided to stop reacting when your emotional body gets pushed around. That tells me you're starting to reevaluate situations instead of immediately giving up your power. Now that you're aware of your addiction to traumas and dramas, let's hope you leave those old patterns behind. Never allow another to place doubt in your beliefs or sway your emotions into a caretaking position. I'm glad to see that Wicahmunga's guidance has strengthened your faith in yourself and helped rid you of your emotional selfishness. Ah yes, fighting for fairness has forced you to raise your vibration to a higher spiritual level. I think you're finally ready to start some serious studies of the above worlds," decided Shung' as she and Sunny went to prepare dinner.

After they had eaten, Shung' and Sunny picked up their blankets and headed out into the darkness of the desert, leaving Wicahmunga to watch her favorite television shows. Reaching a spot where no artificial lights could distract them, they sat quietly focusing on the moonlit shadowed desert. After a while Sunny mentioned the strange sounds coming from the desert's night creatures.

"Sunny, you're witnessing natural laws at work. Feel the energies coming from these creatures. You must connect to their way of life before you can learn about their subtle powers." Shung' took her talking stick and drew a circle on the ground. "All of Mother Earth's night children follow and value the natural laws. It gives them a structure to build a safe and productive life. To speak with them, you must learn how each one communicates. Once you have this understanding, you will have developed the sensitivity to have a relationship with all of *Maka Ina's* night children. For example, think of the sky nation. If a bird circles overhead one, two or three times, then each circle will create a different meaning. No matter how things appear to you at first glance, they may not be true unless you consider the subtleties of the complete message.

"Ah, there's always many things to consider. The daytime, the nighttime, the seasons, the colors and each sound must fit into every circle of thought. Add your collective perceptions together then review what you have seen, smelled, felt and heard. Then you will know how to use this sacred knowledge in your everyday life. After all, the universe is created from circles, designs, symbols and energy. It is very important for a pupil to learn the symbolic, sacred language of *Wakan Tanka's* night children."

Shung' continued making designs on the ground as she explained, "A circle is forever ongoing. Just as the sun guards each day with warmth and love, it too was born from a circle. Look at the many shapes of the human body. Some are round, some are flat and some are square. Those with square bodies are dependable and good organizers of time. They have built a stable foundation for themselves as well as others."

As she drew another design on the ground, Shung' continued, "Look at this triangle. See how it points upward? This tells me that I'm equal in all things and I have the gift of wisdom which can only come from my inner sensitivity. If I choose to turn it upside down, then I would read it to mean I am a creative person with confidence and reasoning which is guided from a spiritual point of view. See this rectangle? It's standing on end. This tells me it's time for focused concentration. If it were on its side, that would tell me to draw power from my experiences in life to develop a stronger will. In other words, I'm telling you to go deeper in thought so you can become aware of the meaning in all the designs of life.

"And there is much more. Think about people who can feel power but have no clue about what they are feeling. Watch how people try to find power to get a quick fix for their identity. Look at those who collect and wear Indian jewelry. Look at the museums that hold the bones of our forefathers and so many of our traditional artifacts. People unconsciously feel that kind of power. They know something is different, but they don't understand why these things attract them. Think of our ancestors and how they painted symbolic meanings on their tipis, clothes, tools, weapons and even their cooking utensils. Surely you can see that life is art and art is life."

"I hate people like that, Shung'. What are they trying to prove by collecting these things? Why don't they study the Indian way and find out why we do things the way we do?"

"Because it would take too much precious time from their busy lives, and they don't want to work for anything. Everything on earth is told in the stars, but like the deer, no one wants to look up. Father Sky is filled with star clusters that make sacred designs. That's why we look to the heavens to determine when it's time for our ceremonies. We must follow the sky maps in order to fulfill our lives in a sacred manner. Someday you will walk in balance between worlds and know that you are walking a good way. What is above is below, and what is below is above. That is, and always will be, the only pathway to connect you to *Wakan Tanka*."

"Shung', you make it sound so beautiful and simple, but it's so immense that it confuses me."

Shung' thought for a moment, then answered, "Granddaughter, let's approach this another way. Reach back to all of our sacred stories and investigate the aspects of what they say to you morally, then think of their effect on you in this three-dimensional world. Mother Earth demands that measure is placed between two linear points, whereas the skies teach us that movement in design is hidden within a sacred geometric language. This means there are many different ways to think about dimension, space and time. Think of these things and you'll truly understand the meaning of Indian Time."

"Oh God, Shung', my brain is frying. This is awesome, but totally confusing," said Sunny, holding her head dramatically in her hands.

Laughing, Shung' answered, "Ah yes, *Sku'ya*, the celestial wonders stretch our minds, because they hold the secrets to all that exists in our universe. Sometimes it may seem as though it's beyond your abilites to learn, but you'll never know what you can accomplish unless you're committed to hard work.

"Ah yes, the sky gives us much to ponder in very subtle ways. Just remember the onion. When you peel one layer by layer, it sometimes makes you cry, but that's how you get to the core of hidden knowledge. All these seeds that I have planted in your mind tonight hold wisdom, but it is you who must water them and hold them close in warmth to make them grow. And as you know, Sunny, wisdom is accumulative." Shung' folded her blanket and motioned for Sunny to start their long walk back.

"The next time you travel to the above worlds, ask one of the spirits to share the sacred symbolic language of the traditional shaman with you. But never go beyond what you know, or you could be captured and possibly never return. Heed my warning, and if you disobey, don't expect me to help you. I believe in teaching slowly so that you get the depth that only comes from accumulative knowledge."

As they approached Sunny's house the next morning, they smelled wonderful aromas coming from the kitchen. Wicahmunga had already set the table on the patio, and she immediately appeared with a beautiful tray of breakfast foods. As the ate they shared many new findings of their desert trip then went to bed for some well needed rest.

That evening Wicahmunga insisted she join them on their nightly studies. As the three women walked into the darkness of night, Sunny pondered the greatness of this vast universe. She could not fathom its size because it went well beyond her imagination. Shung' looked up and remarked, "Ah, on a moonless night it seems the stars sit so close to the earth that you can almost hear them whispering their wisdom as they travel through the unknown places of deep space. Look at their wonderful patterns of motion as they attempt to guide us along their sky highways of swirling energies. Nothing is ever locked in one place. Everything moves within its own group and makes a yearly journey around the sun just as the earth."

"I know that," snorted Wicahmunga. "But there are those that can, and then there's those like Sunny, who can't."

"Shush, Wicahmunga!"

"Did you say that no matter whether a thing is above or below, everything exists within its own dimension, space and time, and that's what you're calling measure?" asked Sunny.

"Yes. Think of how the past affects the present to create our future. Do you realize how precious our ancestors' teachings are? We must revere the old ones for giving us these wonderful roots to grow from. It's the past that gave us this valuable information, and that's the secret of connecting with the above and below time clocks to keep our relationship with *Wakan Tanka*. This sacred gift teaches us about the many different time calendars that tells us when to perform our sacred ceremonies. It is the solstice and equinox rituals that help all life become renewed and purified. This keeps us connected to the above powers so we can understand the possible futures that are going to materialize in the upcoming seasons. Isolation from this knowledge keeps us from understanding *Wakan Tanka's* bigger plan. For life to exist, everything must co-exist within Creator's perfectly designed structure," stated Shung' as they prepared to leave.

"Shung', she'll never get it. I say she's too stupid for this kind of training. Don't you know she doesn't understand the true meaning of Indian Time?" laughed Wicahmunga, walking ahead of them in complete boredom.

Ignoring Wicahmunga, Sunny asked, "Shung', when do you think I can learn to travel though space and time?"

"When you accept that you can! The next time I strip you from your earthly bondage, I will show you boundless worlds that exist far beyond Mother Earth. Once you accept their existence, I think it will whet your appetite enough to keep you traveling for the rest of your life. Right now, I want you to eat this knowledge until I'm satisfied that you understand what I'm giving you."

Two years had come and gone. Sunny had continued her training and was now spending every waking moment learning and sketching what she had found in the sky. She was consumed with the above and below maps of the powers that directed all life, and she had learned to recognize the sacredness in all of the rituals under the watchful eyes of Shung'. This night she had finally completed her last sketch that showed the connection between the above and below powers. She went to Shung' for final approval, and for the next two days Shung' studied both maps carefully as Sunny waited with bated breath. Finally on the third day she called to Sunny.

"Well, Granddaughter, your maps correlate to the time for the upcoming ceremonies. It's time to place your knowledge on the deerhides."

As *Wi* touched the horizon the following morning, Shung' and Sunny had just finished their morning pipe ceremony and were ready to work on the earth and sky maps. Sunny had gathered the necessary supplies and pinned her sketches to the wall, pleased that her two years of hard work had met with Shung's approval. With guarded pride, Shung' watched her enthusiastic pupil carefully apply her new knowledge to the deerhides.

Without warning, Wicahmunga stormed into the room and began to scold Sunny. "Those hides cost me money, so don't you dare make a mistake or you'll have to pay me for them!" Sunny tossed the hides aside and jumped up from the table, grabbing Wicahmunga and mauling her in a huge playful bear hug. "You fool, what do you think you're doing? You touched me! Get your hands off me! You barbaric shithead!"

Shung' broke into laughter, saying, "Stop this nonsense! When are you two ever going to quit denying the love that rests between you?" Growling like an old bear, Wicahmunga ran from the room all the while ranting about Sunny giving her a disease. Sunny chuckled and calmly went back to the table to continue her work.

After several more weeks of laboring arduously at the drafting table, Sunny stood up and stretched her cramped muscles, saying, "Oh Shung', I still have problems understanding all this galaxy stuff. There isn't enough time in one life to learn the depth of all this knowledge. No matter what I try, it seems everything changes constantly, yet stays predictable."

"Sunny, we're only puny humans. We are all one in the big plan of the Great Mystery, and you're whining about nothing. We are seeded by the stars and that's a fact. So, stop obsessing and accept that the above powers affect Mother Earth. We have always performed our sacred rituals by the measures of time, space and dimension which are found in the movements of the heavens. When the above and below maps line up, we know it's time to perform another sacred ritual. These are the rules and they're cut in stone.

"It was the wise *Pte Oyate*, Buffalo Nation, that first used the sky knowledge. Each year they collected more information until they had made many calendars to pass on to their future generations. The old people always said the past is the present is the future, and everything has its potential, purpose and reason for existence. For example, when Meeko died his soul traveled back through the Big Dipper to the invisible space of the spirit world where Blue Woman, the ancient grandmother guards the entrance. This birthing chamber guides every soul into its earthly life. When that soul embraces the circle of death, it returns to her. If we have lived a good life, she will gently direct us back to the spirit world. If our life on earth has been destructive to others as well as ourselves, she will then push us off the clouds, forcing us to wander alone on the karmic trail looking for our soul. Sometimes this takes many earthly journeys, but

Wakan Tanka is patient with his children and will let us stay on the karmic trail until we get it right.

"I remember a story my grandmother once told me. One night, there were two Plains women who sat together watching the stars. Each woman fell in love with a different star and dreamed of someday marrying it. Every night thereafter the women would gaze at the heavens with such intense desire that they were eventually whisked away from Mother Earth to live among the stars. They soon found their beloved stars were kind of like humans, except bigger, stronger and smarter. The women's dreams came true and they were promptly married to their beloved starmen.

"They lived happily for several years, learning the ways of the star people. Each day the women went to the fields to gather food with the others. Both star husbands warned their earth wives not to pull up any of the wild turnips. One obeyed her husband's wishes, while the other disobeyed his request.

"Each day when this woman went to tend the fields her curiosity grew. In time she became heavy with child and she began to miss her mother and family. She spoke of this to her dear friend who warned her not to break her husband's rules. But she disregarded her friend's advice, and one evening she slipped away to the wild turnip patch. She grabbed the leaves of a large turnip and pulled. It came out of the ground with ease, leaving a large gaping hole. She peered down through the hole at the world below and she saw her village and her people. A grave loneliness crept over her, and she wanted desperately to return to her people to have her baby.

"She replaced the turnip to hide the hole and began to secretly collect turnip leaves, which she wove into a long rope. One night when she thought the rope was long enough to reach *Maka Ina*, she took it to the turnip patch, quietly lowered it through the hole and began her journey home. The closer she came, the more excited she was until she discovered her rope was too short to reach the ground. She was too tired to climb back to the stars, and feeling the hopelessness of defeat she let go, falling to earth.

"Her people saw her near-dead body and ran to her side. The women began to wail in grief. Before she died a boy child was born. Everyone saw he was very different from all the other babies. He grew from an infant to a full-grown man in just a few days. He was very kind and wise, speaking often about his earth mother and star father. The people called him Falling Star. To this day he belongs to no one, yet serves everyone. They say that Falling Star still travels from tribe to tribe, teaching star knowledge to all those who want to learn. They say he is a holy man, and if you call on him in the proper manner, he will come to help you learn about his people.

"Sunny, to become a Skywalker is not easy. I can only teach you what I know to be true. It is you who must find the seeds of star knowledge from deep within and make the transition to empower your skywalking abilities. But rest assured, someday you will sit with the old people in the Grandmother's Lodge in the sky, and they will teach you about your star ancestors."

"Humph, I don't care how much they teach her about the star ancestors, she's no relative of mine! She'll never be smart enough to talk to my star relatives."

"Hmmm, I bet I am related to you!" challenged Sunny, playfully chasing after Wicahmunga, who ran to her bedroom and locked the door.

From that day on, Shung' and Wicahmunga left Sunny to her nightly star studies. Sunny accepted that it was her responsibility to utilize the collective knowledge of her two teachers to discover the teachings of the hidden sky powers. After three months with little progress, Sunny knelt to pray. "Oh, *Tunka'shila*, I've worked hard and I've kept my promise. I know that you are the master of all, but please, *Wakan Tanka*, have mercy upon this slow-learning child. Show me what I need to know to find the key to the sky powers. Help me understand these millions of cosmic doorways so that I can enter them in the proper way."

Night after night Sunny sat alone in the desert hoping to attain her solo star journey. Each time she failed, she returned to Shung' for more answers. Shung' merely posed more questions for her to think about, always adding, "Sunny, what you're trying to accomplish is very difficult. This type of learning takes much patience. When you're trying to gather the whole mind of Mother Earth and Father Sky, you must trust the harmonic sounds of the star seeds implanted in you long ago. When you accomplish this, your mind will merge with the resonant frequencies of all life forces, no matter where they are located in the universe. There are many subtleties that must be understood before you can move into the shadows of other worlds. This kind of depth takes years of centered patience before your mind can merge with the vastness of all these new realities."

As Sunny continued to struggle with Shadow World technique, Shung' observed her lack of focus and called her to the patio where she and Wicahmunga were waiting. "Sunny, the only way that you'll ever be able to learn Shadow World is by doing. There are no shortcuts. Relax the body. Still the mind. Control the breath. Remove all thought and disconnect from your emotional body. That is the only way you will understand what I am teaching. Think about all the sacred places in the world. Since you know that *Paha Sapa* is the heart of all that is, go there."

Shung' took Sunny's hands and their minds linked. Sunny found herself standing in the center of the Black Hills. She saw its sacredness rise into a regal beauty, surrounded by the plains which had become a sea of swaying grass. Without warning she became a blade of grass. Shung' unexpectedly dropped Sunny's hands, causing her to jerk back into her body, saying, "That's how you find the spirit of all things. The spirits will talk to all those who come from the heart and are seeking their way. You must have different eyes to look upon the sacred. There is no power greater than that of the spirits who protect our sacred *Paha Sapa*."

Wicahmunga chimed in, "If she had learned about the history of the animals she'd already know this. I bet she doesn't even know that it's the animals who let the people live. Humph, I bet she doesn't know the patience they have as they wait for the human to grow a good heart."

Sunny was frustrated by her lack of knowledge and felt Shung' and Wicahmunga's demands were impossible. Maybe it was time to quit. Just as she rose and prepared to leave, Shung' caught her attention, saying, "There's another sacred place called Devils Tower."

"No! Let me tell the story," interrupted Wicahmunga, launching into another history lesson from long ago.

"In the beginning of time, there lived a young girl who was given a spirit power to take the form of *Mato*. She loved this power and eventually her ego and pride got so big that she reveled in controlling others. Soon she was constantly chasing her seven sisters, demanding they obey her or she would devour them. One day after months of imposed slavery, the sisters refused to serve her any longer.

"When Bear Girl heard this, she spewed with rage and chased her sisters unmercifully. They ran for their lives, but when they realized there was no escape, they climbed to the top of a huge boulder and prayed to the spirit world to help them escape her revenge.

"But Bear Girl had the power of smell and easily followed them. As she came closer and closer to where they were hiding, the earth began to shake and she began to tear up everything in her pathway. The sisters were scared to death and pleaded to *Wakan Tanka* for help. Suddenly the boulder began to rise upward toward the sky. And anyone with half a brain knows that this really happened, because you can still see Bear Girl's claw marks embedded in Devil's Tower. If you look for the Pleiades in the buffalo's head you will see those seven stars still huddled together.

"So, dog turd, if you'll let go of your ego, those seven little sisters will teach you about the sky people," warned the wise Wicahmunga, squinting her eyes until they became narrow slits.

"All right, I know that neither of you would tell me a story unless you were demanding that I clear my head of another problem," responded Sunny.

"You got that right, girl. I told you the story, dummy, to show you that you're just like Bear Girl. I worry that once you have a little power, you'll try to destroy people. Your ego is so big that I doubt if there's enough space left in that brain of yours to learn anything. But who knows, you may accidentally learn something in spite of your stupidity."

"Sunny, it's your impatience and your need for recognition that are holding you back," stated Shung'.

"Then what can I do?"

"Learn by humility, you twerp, and start showing respect and consideration for all things. And you can start by showing that respect with me!" Wicahmunga handed her an empty glass, silently demanding a refill. Defiantly, Sunny went to get Wicahmunga's tea. When she returned, she sat down angrily.

"Easy, Sunny," counseled Shung'. "If you don't heal your need for recognition, how can you serve *Wakan Tanka*?" These words cut deep, and Sunny knew if she didn't rid herself of her inflated ego, once again her training would stop.

Feeling lonely and isolated with this problem, Sunny began to spend long nights in Shadow World to rid herself of her ego. She thought of Meeko and all of the natural laws they had broken. She felt great sorrow for having used her medicine training in such a bad way. How could she have been so cruel to take and abuse such a sacred gift to punish others just because her life experiences had been harsh? She knew the only way to continue her training with Shung' was to reflect back on these life teachings and forgive herself with love and honor for this terrible behavior.

Why hadn't she listened? But it was not too late. Day after day she prayed over her ruthlessness until she recognized the damage that she had caused others through evil. Slowly Sunny began to honor these past experiences and to accept the fact that her life would have good as well as bad times. After all, life was just a training ground to achieve spiritual growth. With this came the realization that Shung' would not allow her to learn any more about medicine until she became totally aware of the ramifications that came from every thought, action, word and deed.

Armed with this new awareness, she went to Shung' and told her what she had found in Shadow World. Shung' smiled, saying, "That's good news, Granddaughter. It's time you apply that knowledge in your everyday life. When you can walk your thoughts and know that what you say is true, then you are truly becoming a good human being. I am proud of what you've accomplished. Wicahmunga and I will be leaving in the morning to go home. I want you to call Kate and go back to work. Someday when you're ready, I'll see you again."

Early the next morning, Wicahmunga had just finished bringing down the last of the bags when Eddie drove up in his truck. Little was said as their bags were loaded onto the truck and they pulled out of the driveway. Sunny stood sadly at the door watching them leave. Reluctantly she called Kate, and within a week she was on a plane to New York, preparing for her return to the stage.

Once back into the spotlight, Sunny became more aware of what Shung' had been trying to teach her. She knew she was cold and demanding with the crew. How was she ever going to apply what she had learned from Shung' in this business?

She could hear Shung's voice in her head, "Diffuse the situation! Stop creating confusion! Stop your temper! Stop your cruelty!" But how could she, when management was constantly manipulating her with lies and deception? No matter what she tried, she was continually being stripped of her of honor and integrity. Her disposition darkened and her temper flared. There was no way in hell she could have a spiritual life in this world of chaos.

How could she ever follow her beloved teacher's lessons? The only time she was safe was when she was on stage performing. As time progressed Sunny recognized that her ego was being fed by the admiration and worship from her audience. She needed time alone to work things out. She called the hotel manager and asked him to please make the steam room available to her after hours. She went there each night and used her imagination to build Old Man Four Generations fire pit. In her mind she saw herself carrying the stones down the grandmother pathway to meet grandfather. She saw herself place each stone into the sacred altar of the *Inipi*. Each night she would mentally complete the entire four rounds, and in time she was once again controlling her life with kindness. As her peace slowly returned, Sunny began to call Shung' for support and this helped her maintain a strong walk on the red road.

A year and half later, Shung' called to say it was time for Sunny to come home. "My little mutt, meet me in Cheyenne in two weeks." Sunny hung up the phone, thrilled that her tour would be over in ten days.

It was early spring and still chilly in Wyoming, and Sunny looked forward to seeing the budding new growth piercing through the snow banks as the seasons fought to maintain their time on Mother Earth. The day her show closed she hopped on the first flight to Denver where she picked up a rental car to drive to Cheyenne.

It was a happy moment when Sunny at last embraced Shung'. But the medicine woman had little time for displays of affection and was in a hurry to get on with more important things. They spent the night in Cheyenne and the next morning loaded the car with enough camping supplies to last a week. As they left the motel Shung' mentioned that she had received the new below and above maps Sunny had sent, and was quite pleased with the growth they showed.

"I like the way that you've used your Medicine Wheel training to apply the earth knowledge to find how it is connected with the stars."

"I went back to Grandmother's stories and recalled the power of each gatekeeper on the Medicine Wheel. Then I connected them to the animals that live in the sky. It was Bear and Cougar that helped me see more clearly what I needed to do to stay on the good red road. Little did I know when you sent me back to work, that I would need these two animals to survive in the manipulative world of show business.

"It was Bear that made me set strong boundaries against management, and Cougar reminded me to stay detached from my emotions so I could see through all the control issues that were keeping me in a state of confusion."

"It made me very sad to send you away, but I knew if I didn't you would always come to me for your answers. You needed to learn to stand up for yourself, and so I did to you exactly what Cheering Woman did to me so many years ago to build my confidence."

As they drove along in silence, Sunny wondered what new mystery her medicine teacher was preparing for her to experience. As if reading her mind, Shung' informed Sunny they were headed for Medicine Mountain to see one of the oldest and most sacred Medicine Wheels. She went on to speak in great length about the old world calendars and the secrets that lay hidden within each stone of the Big Horn Medicine Wheel.

The winds blew a constant blanket of powdery snow across the roads, sometimes blinding Sunny's view. By late afternoon they finally arrived in the vicinity of the Big Horn mountain range. Sunny could not believe the vastness of the landscape before her. As far as she could see the beautiful, silent land was covered with a soft white blanket of freshly fallen snow. They saw herds of deer and elk scattered across the terrain. As they reached ten thousand feet, the women smiled at one another knowing they had finally reached the end of their journey.

Sunny parked the car and popped the trunk, taking out their warm clothing and blankets before joining Shung' on the long walk up the mountain. As she followed Shung' along the old trail, Sunny noticed many tobacco ties fastened to tree branches. When they reached the top, both were short of breath and thankful the cold wind was dying down. Sunny set up the tents while Shung' built a warm fire and made a pot of coffee. When the campsite was established, they sat near the fire curled up in blankets as they drank steaming cups of coffee and caught one another up on what had been going on in their respective lives.

As the darkness of night slowly engulfed them, Shung' pointed out the stars as they appeared in the sky. The moon was full and Sunny could easily observe the placement of the stars as they presented themselves in the heavens. Finally Shung' spoke:

"Do you see the seven sisters in the buffalo's head? Look further toward the Milky Way and you'll find three stars aligned in the belly of the buffalo. Well, long ago when those three stars appeared a certain way in the sky, it told the medicine people that the stars were lining up with the sacred places on Mother Earth and it was time for ceremony. Now look over there. Do you see Aldebaran? That tells us it will be twenty-eight days until Rigel makes its presence. Then in another twenty-eight days we can see the presence of Sirius in the tail of the buffalo."

Sunny was awestruck by the way the words seemed to flow like a melody from Shung's mouth.

"This is the oldest Medicine Wheel in North America. The ancient ones knew how to use the stars for guidance on Mother Earth. The sky has always told us when the season's will change, when to plant, when to fish, when to hunt and when to have ceremony. I hold great honor and appreciation for these sacred teaching left by the old medicine people."

As they entered the Medicine Wheel Shung' offered tobacco and gave thanks for the ancient knowledge placed in the simple stone designs that lay at their feet. She spoke to Sunny about the great importance of the outer circle of the Medicine Wheel, then explained how each stone kept the records of the moon, planets and stars. She explained the significance of the stones in the inner wheel and how they could bring about changes in an individual's life, reminding Sunny again of the importance of their correct placement.

"All of these sacred things teach us to live and perform within exactness in our ceremonies, just as our forefathers did long ago. Sunny, it's time to alter your mind and focus on the center circle. Feel the true meaning of humility and appreciation, then step into that center with your mind and let your energy flow with you as you travel northwest until you reach the altar of *Wakinyan*. Stay there until you meet his alter ego, the likable giant. When you've made this connection you will understand that an ego destroys real power."

Glad that she had practiced daily on this exercise, Sunny closed her eyes and did as instructed. A swallow appeared on her mind screen and slowly turned into the good-natured giant. She watched him shape-shift into *Wakinyan*, the Thunderbeing. Sunny felt his touch and was thrilled to know *Wakinyan* had finally accepted her as his pupil.

It was two hours before Sunny left the Medicine Wheel. Shung' spoke as she approached, "Sunny, it's good to see you've gotten rid of your fear of seeing spirits. I take great pride in seeing you stay focused in an altered state for long periods of time. I now know that you can visit Shadow World with your eyes wide open. Now bring me your latest maps and let's see if your star placements are as correct as I think they will be."

Shung' threw a log on the fire as Sunny unrolled the two maps. Shung' examined the them carefully, noting with pride they matched perfectly. Sunny felt pleased by the medicine woman's approval and as she quietly rolled them up again, Shung remarked, "I see you've spent many hours on those maps. Come, let's have a good meal together and we'll spend the rest of the night studying the shadows of *Hanwi*."

Sunny hugged Shung' respectfully, saying, "Thank you for allowing me to spend some time alone with you."

"And I with you, Granddaughter. I've missed you around here."

As the sun touched the horizon with first light, Sunny awoke to a cloudless sky and a chilly morning. She dressed warmly then joined Shung' for a hearty breakfast. Wrapped in blankets, both women huddled close to the fire, waiting for the sun's rays to warm another beautiful day in the raw nature of Wyoming. Within minutes the fiery ball of the sun gazed down on Mother Earth as the crisp morning air swept across the untouched terrain, giving the place a sense of spiritual purity.

Sunny was filled with excitement knowing this day would bring her many adventures before the sun went over down. She was deeply moved to see each ray of the sun touch the Stone People as it painted its way to the center of the sacred Medicine Wheel. She knew it was time to follow the solar clock as a Skywalker and walk in a proper manner upon Mother Earth.

Shung' was well aware that Sunny's heart was open and felt good that her apprentice could finally see the sacredness in all things. Smiling, she thrust her chin forward, motioning for Sunny to join her in another walk around the ancient circle. As they moved from stone to stone around the Medicine Wheel, Shung' described the hard work it had taken to build this eight-hundred-year-old structure which looked simple to the untrained eye, yet contained all the heavenly patterns.

"Keep in mind, Sunny, each of these stones carries its own knowledge. Each stone also works in unison with the others, connecting to the twenty-six or more above and below dimensions." The two women talked for hours about the visible and invisible ever-changing power that lay hidden deep within each stone.

"Shung', I could stay here for the rest of my life and never learn all the secrets that are hidden in these stones."

"Ah, yes. Everything in time, and everything takes time—and time eats everything. We skins don't measure time like white people, we just enjoy it."

It was almost three in the afternoon when they trudged down the mountain to continue their quest. Two days later they reached the vicinity of *Paha Sapa*. They saw Harney Peak in the distance among the granite and stone, stretching high above the timberline. Sunny smiled as she recognized the home of *Wakinyan*.

"Can you feel his power?" asked Shung'.

"Ah Shung, I can feel the very essence of his power," beamed Sunny.

"Long ago our elders would come here to seek a vision to gain their medicine powers."

As they continued their drive and dark clouds began to accumulate overhead, Sunny's mind slipped back to thoughts of *Wakinyan*. She could envision him flying from the top of this great summit, shooting lightning bolts from his one eye as he traveled across the world eradicating destructive human thought. Suddenly a loud clap of thunder jolted her back to reality.

"That is *Wakinyan's* voice warning us to walk cautiously in his area," reminded Shung'. "Many of our ancient prophets climbed that peak and I have lived to see many of their predictions come true. Turn here!" commanded Shung'. "I want to show you something."

Veering south toward *Paha Sapa*, they entered a grassy area and parked. Shung' led Sunny up a trail to a remote spot known as Wind Cave. She peered inside, then crawled though the small entrance and motioned for Sunny to join her.

Sunny leaned inside just far enough to hear a loud sigh coming from somewhere deep within the cave. Stepping back, she answered, "No, I have no desire to go in inside. I've heard of too many people that went in and never came out."

But Shung' had already vanished into the bowels of the cavern and did not hear. Sunny called out again and again but there was no reply. An hour later she reappeared, scolding, "Stop yelling before you break my eardrums!" As they walked back to the car, she remarked, "Sunny, sometimes I wonder what I'm going to do with you and your senseless superstitions. I swear that you act just like Sam, and you know how limiting that is. I brought you here to experience the doorway to the *Pte Oyate's* history, so that you can understand that good principles are timeless.

"My word, Granddaughter, we would never have had the great buffalo herds without the underworld. It was Buffalo who gifted the people with survival when they first emerged onto middle world. The old people once said that when the buffalo first came into our world, they were so small that you could almost hold them in the palm of your hand. But when they took first breath, they grew to the size they are today. It was through this miracle that the plains became filled with Buffalo who always took care of the people's needs.

"Look around. Can't you feel Buffalo's spirit in these bountiful grasslands? Long before the white man came, buffalo herds spread across these plains as far as the eye could see. When the white man killed them off the spirits grew very angry, and the *Pte Oyate* let the herd dwindle to almost nothing to always remind the people of the horrible thing the Europeans had done to our nation.

"Ah yes, this was shameful. For some reason the white race has little regard for the betterment of the people—a situation that has destroyed the harmony among all races. Why even within our own culture, there is little social bonding left between tribes and clans. Our oldest of prophets say that someday people of all races will come together and the buffalo herds will return to the land, bringing back the sacredness to all of *Wakan Tanka's* creations." As they drove off Sunny noticed that Shung' seemed as pure as an innocent child, which seemed to be a direct result of their mysterious journey.

It was nearly dark when they approached the little town of Hermosa. Shung' insisted they continue driving until they reached the group of high-cropped hills off in the distance. When they had reached their destination, Sunny stopped the car and Shung' started out across an open field with Sunny close behind. In the darkness, Sunny tripped over a rock. Cursing vehemently, she began to massage her skinned knee.

Annoyed by Sunny's immature behavior, Shung' scolded, "You certainly are impatient with yourself. If you can't feel where you are, then I suggest you buy a flashlight."

"Shung', I'm tired and hungry. What's the purpose of this stop?" grumbled Sunny.

Shung' turned around and stared coldly at Sunny, "Wait a minute, girl! You came to me to learn these ways! Are you trying to tell me how I should teach you? If so, then I'll stop right now! You anger me with your impatience when you are overly tired. You don't have a clue how to be one with the land on a dark night. Maybe you need to go back to New York and re-establish your survival instincts!" snapped Shung', picking up her pace as she walked away.

Sunny could hear Shung' mumbling under her breath, "How can this be, Grandfather? I'm an old woman and my health is failing, yet you give me a spoiled brat to contend with, and all she does is whine, whine, whine!"

Sunny knew she had breached the unspoken agreement between pupil and teacher. Fearing that she would be shunned for the rest of the trip, she caught up with Shung' and apologized profusely in an attempt to bring back the closeness between them. As they crested a barren hill, Shung' eased the tension by speaking of the radiant full moon and of the brothers and sisters of the solar system. Soon they sat down to watch the sky nation move across the heavens.

"Sunny, everything in life has its own time," began Shung' once again inspired to teach. "It was our ancestors who first observed the vibrating waves from *Wakan Tanka's* heavens shower down and bathe the earth with new information in hopes that the people would learn to accept the flow of knowledge that came as a sacred gift from above.

"Look at the North Star. Remember what your sweet grandmother said before she died? 'Sunny, when you are afraid or lonely, look up to the North Star and you will always find me there watching over you.' Now look directly above the North Star and you will see *Wakinyan*. Move your eyes slightly to the right and you will see the Salamander. Let your eyes wander westward and you see the Turtle. Right beneath the turtle is the rack of Elk. Now just above the elk the sky tells us it's time to gather the red willow bark and mix our sacred tobaccos for our pipes. If you look to the South you can see groupings of other animals. Below them is the Snake.

"Remember when Cheering Woman taught you about the sacred racetrack around *Paha Sapa*? Well, that too appears in the sky. Look to the East and you will see Bear Lodge. Next to that is our Old Man Four Generations fire pit. Move your eyes over to the Big Dipper, and we're back where we started. This is the sacred circle that joins the below and above worlds. Now do you see how simple it is to connect the sky powers to Mother Earth and use this knowledge when loading your pipe?"

The sun was beginning to peer over the hill when Shung' and Sunny made their way back to the car.

"Shung', I can't tell you how sorry I am for my impatience."

"Well, you can be very opinionated. If you could keep your mouth shut and just accept, it would make both of our lives easier. Everything comes in time, Granddaughter. C'mon, I'm hungry," replied Shung'.

About ten miles down the highway, they came to the town of Sturgis where they checked into a motel and immediately ordered food to be sent to their room. Sunny felt grungy and turned on the shower, but just as the water got hot, Shung' stepped deftly around her and into the tub. Sunny giggled, knowing that Shung' had just put her in her place.

When room service arrived Sunny set the tray of food on the table, where it greeted Shung' as she stepped out of the bathroom fresh from her shower. Then Sunny showered and joined her for a leisurely meal. A gentle kindness seemed to once again envelope them. After a long nap, they walked leisurely into town.

It was nearly sundown when Shung' suggested they return to the motel to do their evening pipe ceremony. After offering the ashes to the four winds, they crawled into their beds and bid each other goodnight.

Sunny stared out at the moon and felt at peace. She liked where she was with her life, and fell asleep with the thought that her mysterious trip with Shung' would be to her benefit.

Early the next morning Sunny awakened to find Shung' already up and sitting by the window with a pot of coffee and some sweet buns. As she crawled out of bed to join her, Shung' said, "Sunny, I like it that you are committed to praying daily with your pipe. That's what has finally connected you to the spirit world. You are gathering new strength. Last night when I touched your mind, you were peaceful." Shung' poured herself another cup of coffee and continued, "Granddaughter, it's nice to see you emerging into your power. You are becoming a blossom on the Tree of Life just as Cheering Woman predicted long ago. I'm glad to see that you have finally learned that power comes only through silence and deeper understanding."

"Shung', nothing can express my sincere thanks for all you have done for me. Without you, I would have never found the meaning of *Hau, Mitakuye Oyasin*. For the first time in my life, I know in my heart that I am truly related to all living things and no one but myself can ever again separate me from *Wakan Tanka*. It was your teachings that gave me the understanding of all our sacred ceremonies."

"Sunny, you're thinking more like your grandmother everyday. I remember how I cried when I felt her presence the day that you pledged your commitment as a five year Sundancer on the sacred cottonwood tree. Each year for five years thereafter, I saw her dancing by your side from sunrise to sundown. I saw many spirits come to help carry your heavy burdens as you gazed into the heart of the sun. That last year when I feather pierced you, everyone heard and saw seven golden eagles circle the field seven times. That's when I knew you had placed your trust in *Wakan Tanka's* love."

Early the following morning they left the comforts of the motel and pulled onto Highway 90 heading north toward Bear Butte. They had driven for about two hours when Shung' informed Sunny that they would be meeting Wicahmunga and Eddie there. "They've been there for the past two days preparing things for us. When we finish what we came here to do, I think we should spend a few days in the Badlands."

"Oh, no! I remember once when Meeko and I had a flat tire there and had to spend the night. I swear those stones changed into forms I never thought possible. Every time I go there, I hear eerie cries and chants echoing through those eroded canyons. It's like walking with bad *Wakanpis*."

"I've heard many people say that," noted Shung'. "Remember the story about the battle between *Unktehi*, the monster, and *Wakinyan*? Oh, it was a terrible time when *Unktehi* turned on the people and flooded the land. As far as the eye could see, the people, animals and green things were under water. Old *Wakinyan* knew the sun's rays were like golden teardrops and he called upon *Wi's* powers to suck up the moisture and dry out the land.

"The old people still speak of seeing Bone Woman roaming over the Badlands, gathering all the bleached bones from that terrible battle. Once she found all the bones, she restructured the bodies and used her power to breathe life back into them. They say that once life returned to the animals they ran a short distance, then looked back for a moment to thank her. With her help the earth slowly became filled again with the songs of birds and the sounds of the four legs journeying across the land. Sometimes you can hear Bone Woman calling out to all those that need her, particularly in the Badlands."

"Shung', I've heard those stories since childhood. I don't care who gathers the bones as long as I'm not out there after dark."

"Oh, you're such a poop!"

When they came close to Bear Butte, Sunny asked, "How long are we going to be here?" Shung' poured two cups of coffee and handed one to Sunny.

"Oh, just a few days. Do you remember how Bear Butte got its name? There was this great battle between *Mato* and *Unhcegila*, the Mastodon. They fought for days until Mother Earth's body was bare to the bone and *Mato* was torn to shreds. *Mato* knew he was dying and walked away. Now Mother Earth witnessed this battle between these two powerful beings, and when she saw *Mato* stumble and fall she cried out in pain, then slowly covered her great warrior child with her own body. You can still see the outline of *Mato* lying on the ground.

"Sunny, think of all those great warriors that still live and protect the Badlands. Some of our most powerful medicine people have come to Bear Butte to lament for a vision to gain their powers."

After driving some distance, Sunny arrived at the conclusion that Shung' had more on her mind than giving her another history lesson. As Sunny parked the car she saw Eddie and Wicahmunga waving from the top of a hill and knew she was there for ceremony of some kind.

Eddie and Wicahmunga met them part way down the hill and helped carry their things to camp. While Sunny set up her tent Wicahmunga scrutinized her every move.

"Betcha don't know why you're here! Betcha! Betcha!" cackled Wicahmunga.

"No, and I don't care."

"Oh, you will!" Wicahmunga left to help unload firewood from the back of Eddie's truck. Shung' motioned Sunny to join her.

"I heard you fussing with Wicahmunga again. Evil begins with a bad mood, so be careful what you do. I want you to find the love in your heart to understand and appreciate those who have given of themselves to help you. As we both know, throughout your life you have consistently bounced between madness and wisdom. If it wasn't the red race calling you a no-good breed, it was the white race branding you as a heathen. You've always thrived when you've been forced to explore all that you can be. These painful conflicts have enabled you to find your identity within both races.

"You were ten years old when you did your first *Hanblecheyapi*, and it was Cheering Woman who gave you your spiritual name. Look at how many years you've worked to earn the right to carry the name Wind Wolf Woman. Does not the wind speak to you? Does not your voice speak to the wind?

"You once asked me to teach you medicine. I have done this. You are ready for the next step. Now it's time to trust your abilities as Medicine. It is time for your 'little death' *Hanblecheyapi*, the one that will challenge everything that you are or ever hope to be. It's the most honest route and the hardest to travel. Let *Wakan Tanka* guide you to your Grandmother's bundle."

"The 'little death' *Hanblecheyapi*? Are you sure I'm ready?"

"Why do you question me? Think back on the many times that Cheering Woman brought you here to speak with the spirits. Sunny, it's time to stop wrestling your inner demons and fight the battle for your spiritual freedom. Take this shovel and walk the land until Mother Earth tells you where to dig. When you find the place, dig a four by seven foot pit that is four feet deep. I must go now."

Sunny picked up the shovel and walked until sundown, but the land did not speak to her. That evening she sat alone wrapped in a blanket as she watched dark shadows fill the space around her. Knowing that when the time was right she would find her sacred place, Sunny relaxed and went to Shadow World. Surrounded by darkness she fell asleep, comforted by an inner feeling that something good was going to happen. Immediately she was transported to a plane of perpetual existence where she witnessed the prelude to her present life unfold in all its many dimensions.

She saw two sealed souls—a female and a male—preparing for another mortal life on Mother Earth. They seemed to understand that the purpose of this life would be to rediscover their oneness in the infinite power of *Wakan Tanka's* timeless embrace. They knew this mortal life would be but a brief glimmer in the earthly experiences needed to complete the evolution of their souls. But since time is meaningless to those who live forever, they did not mind. Sure of their love, they vowed that neither would rest nor find contentment until they found each other again.

A gentle breeze swirled in the vibrational folds of the females soul's transparent gown, whirling soft colors around her. She began to dance gracefully in tempo with the wind's playfulness, while gliding effortlessly over the grassy knolls of nature's rebirthing chambers. She listened with delight to the muted giggles coming from the new blades of grass under her footsteps as she drifted to the male soul's side. The two intertwined in the magic of the moment which held a delicate sadness.

"For some time your spirit has seemed distracted. When do you think your mortal birth will occur?" queried the male soul.

"Soon, I think."

The male soul was not yet prepared for another mortal life and was apprehensive about their upcoming separation. Collecting his thoughts, he said, "Perhaps. I know this lifetime is crucial for you, but our love is the indispensable source of my power. For many lives we have been joined as one in the red race. This has brought us much sadness. Are you strong enough to carry such a burden alone while experiencing another life with these people? Why not wait until I too am ready, so that I can help in this endeavor?"

Gently brushing her hand across his lips, she answered, "I want to go alone so there will be no attachment to another. In this way the unfolding of my soul will be less encumbered."

"What can you accomplish as a mortal woman if the old traditional ways have not changed? You have already suffered many hardships on the mortal plane to prove your worthiness to walk as a medicine woman."

"I have suffered many defeats, but I continue to flourish with each life experience. In this forthcoming life, I know that I must strive to learn emotional detachment. It is the red race that challenges my growth with the most severe lessons. The family I have selected is well qualified to plant the seeds of traditional knowledge. My life with them will serve my purpose, and as I grow into womanhood, I will find those I need to complete my earthly journey," she answered as the wind embraced them with invisible arms.

The female soul gently brushed a few strands of hair from his face as they pondered their upcoming separation. For a brief moment the breezes ceased, and both felt the power of stillness that only the wind can convey.

"I see you have made your decision," he said. "A mere mortal female would be powerless to attempt this monumental undertaking alone. I will prepare immediately to join in your endeavors, so that I can help you balance your power as we walk with honor among a proud people."

His words caused a grave sadness in the female soul. After a multitude of lifetimes together, it seemed he was still patronizing her. Yet she also knew he truly wished to support her mission and help catalyze her growth.

In anticipation of their imminent separation, they decided to visit the Garden of Beauty to rekindle the love between them and the Hall of Records to assess their past lives. Strolling past the twilight edge of immortality, they paused at the entrance to a vibrant garden, watching in wonder as electrifying life forces performed a ballet of undulating floral rebirthings around the archway. As they stepped inside, the two souls saw a maze of roots spread beneath the soil, while above ground they saw multitudes of blooms in a kaleidoscope of hues. Since nothing is hidden from a pure heart, they readily perceived each flower's secret through its mystical aroma and unique beauty.

Suddenly they overheard a little blue mountain flower whisper shyly to her lofty yellow and brown brother, the sunflower, "Why do you follow the blazing hot sun?"

"I am preparing for my return to the Great Plains," said the sunflower, gazing at the bright orb overhead. "We sunflowers symbolize commitment to the spiritual journey of Sundancers. Perhaps our devotion to the sun will teach others to seek this enlightenment within themselves."

The male soul playfully brushed his eyelashes across the female soul's cheek. As he moved to touch his lips to hers, a yellow butterfly with magnificent wings accented in designs of black emerged from their lips as an expression of the sacredness of their special touch. The clouds separated, allowing the tenderness of the moment to be sealed forever in time and space.

The yellow butterfly alighted gently on the female soul's shoulder and, like the breath of a newborn, lifted into flight, carrying on its wings the message of touch. In response, a voice preceding all sound spoke, creating an eternal echo:

"The power of touch shall always be felt by those who are aware of their spiritual consciousness. This gift can be shared only by beings who hold pure love in their hearts."

The two souls continued along the flower-lined pathway, which now bordered a winding river. As the male soul reached down to admire a red rose, it fell into his cupped hand. He lifted it to the female soul's nose as a token of his everlasting love.

Inhaling its intoxicating aroma, she declared, "May we forever savor the beauty and delicacy of the red rose."

"Love is merely accepting what is," the male soul reminded her as he placed their undying love into each petal so it would live forever. Then, from between his fingers, he let the petals drop one by one into the clear waters, saying, "From this time forward, let it be known that whenever a rose is given to another, its presence will re-create this moment in all of its loveliness."

Silently they watched the petals drift on soft waves, tumbling toward the Sea of Souls, where they burst into gigantic sprays of color.

"Let the red rose hold forever this moment of our love," the male soul added, idly tracing a rosebud on the female's hand.

The impact of this moment was so great that it caught the attention of Flora and Iris, Queens of the Flowers, who declared:

"Let the red rose be the symbol of eternal love and let its timeless message always remain hidden within each petal."

The two souls continued their stroll, lingering at a spot where rocks tumbled toward the water's edge. The couple, appreciating the need for refinement in their own rebirthing, watched the rocks tumble returning to Mother Earth as smooth river stones.

The male soul paused and pointed upward ever so gently. There sat a lone night bird, singing serenely as it waited for others to join in its soulful melody. The song soon exploded into a rhapsody that accompanied the roar of the cascading waterfall nearby.

Stirred by this orchestral magnificence, the hearts of the two souls joined in the oscillating dance of sight and sound as the waterfall exuded a luminous rainbow that stretched into infinity. As they crossed over an ethereal bridge of color and tone, the two souls heard cries of sadness coming from earthbound souls far below.

They turned to see a castle-like structure, its towers ascending like rockets from granite mountains at the edge of a vast, clear lake. The glistening white of the granite fused with crystalline brilliance, melting into liquid golden rooftops that gave a glorious splendor to the awesome birthing of this palatial structures.

Emerging from a path hidden between hanging cliffs and deep, narrow canyons, the lovers made their way along the transparent cobblestones that led to the Hall of Records. They shaded their eyes from the intense brightness, aware that souls without a pure heart could be blinded. Because they had evolved enough to master interdimensional control and see through every cell of their heavenly bodies, their vision was not impaired, and their faces reflected the radiance of the pure etheric power surrounding them.

As they arrived at the Hall of Records, the male soul agonized over what was to come. "I hope the Sacred Seven realize how important it is for me to be with you when you return to the mortal plane," he said, referring to the council members who oversaw the destiny of souls waiting to be reborn on Mother Earth.

"Have faith, the right decision will be made," the female soul said encouragingly. "And no matter what is decided, it is written in the stars that we shall always be as one. Since the beginning of time we have been sealed souls, joined to fulfill a single purpose."

The rebirthing chamber of the Hall of Records was a large yet intimate space, containing a luminous floating table. At the table sat six members of the Sacred Seven, their forms composed of pure energy. The seventh, suspended from an ethereal void high above, was Sakowin, the Master. The seated members extended a warm greeting to the two souls. Sakowin simply nodded, signaling the start of the council's inquiry into the souls' rebirth.

Waja, the Independent One, inquired, "Before you reach a final decision on this rebirth, are both of you comfortable as self-contained spirits?"

Numba, the Balanced One, offered her expertise, saying, "Can spiritual freedom be experienced in a mortal life? Can the soul maintain its spiritual foundation when faced with the hardships of earthly limitations? Spiritual freedom is an individual choice, and both spirits must have adequate balance and harmony to accomplish this goal."

Yamni, the Mother of Creativity, rose from her seat noting, "When a soul returns to experience another mortal life, it must remember that the spirit is not flesh. Its earthly birth must contribute to the spiritual growth of all humankind. It is therefore necessary for each soul to retain the awareness and freedom needed to demonstrate pure love. Only then can it drink from the cup of sweetness promising limitless devotion in spiritual love. To attain this beautiful gift of shared love, each of you must surrender to the other."

Topa, Mother of Foundation, added reflectively, "If the male soul is to be reborn at this time, he would have only a short earthly interim, for he is not ready to return." Then she addressed the female soul. "Knowing that you will lose your counterpart, can you withstand the pain of being alone as a mortal? You would need to develop a certain detachment from him during this earthly experience if you expect to accomplish your purpose."

Zaptan, Father of Change, added, "As each of you face your individual challenges, you must encourage others to aspire to enlightenment, for only then can you bask in the beauty of spiritual freedom."

After a moment of silence, Sakpe, Father of Service, proclaimed, "Each soul must offer unselfish service to humankind. Otherwise both will stray, losing themselves in this earthly life."

Sakowin allowed the two souls to absorb the council's wisdom, then inquired from above, "Am I to understand your wish is to return to mortal life?"

Both nodded.

"The Sacred Seven have spoken," Sakowin continued. "You must remember that balance and harmony are necessary if you are to help guide future generations of humankind. Your mortal births require each of you to set aside your personal goals in the interest of serving your purpose of birth."

Lowering his eyes in respect, the male soul, responded, "Kind Ones, I do not question your collective wisdom. However, I feel I must return and share another mortal life with this female soul."

Silence reigned in the Hall of Records as Sakowin stated, "We counsel souls, not make their choices. Let us search through the pages of time before you make your final decision."

A gigantic book materialized before them and the pages flipped open, revealing in holographic form, the sealed souls' past life experiences.

The first page showed a young Mandan girl, Isda, whom the female soul recognized as an earlier manifestation of herself. While watching this scene unfold, she once again became young Isda. She recalled the death of her mother and the medicine training she had received under the watchful eyes of her father, *Mato Topa*, Four Bears—a leader and medicine man of the Mandan Sioux nation who commanded respect from every tribe.

The image faded and the scene advanced to the year 1836. Leaders of the seven Sioux nations were sitting around a council fire discussing the weaknesses developing among their people. As they passed the pipe and prayed, they reflected on the white man's betrayal. Captivated, the two souls watched as their people were given warm blankets to ward off the bitter cold unaware that they were contaminated with smallpox. As illness began to ravage their camps, they soon realized this gift was part of the white man's ploy to weaken their nations. Thereafter they agreed that to survive the white man's deceit, the Sioux tribes must stop fighting among themselves and join together as a single nation.

The two souls watched *Mato Topa* prepare to offer in marriage his most precious gift—Isda, known as Light Eyes because of the unusual gray color of her eyes, a sign that she had been born to medicine. He proposed her marriage to Wieasta, a well-known Sioux warrior. This marriage was designed to bind together the Sioux nations.

However, Isda's three brothers considered the union unwise and their silent glares showed their disapproval. Aware of their displeasure yet haunted by dreams of another time and place, Isda accepted her destiny. It was agreed the wedding would take place during summer solstice.

As the day approached, Wieasta arrived with a group of warriors on magnificently groomed war ponies. Dressed in their finest leathers and feathers, they presented an impressive display of power and strength. While the warriors set up camp apart from the rest of the tribe, Wieasta boasted to them of his many triumphs in battle and of the strong medicine powers his future woman possessed, stating proudly that he was sure their union would bring power and hope to all the tribes.

Isdsa watched from a distance. Threatened by his arrogance, yet drawn to his handsome looks, her soul seemed strangely awakened by his words.

Every tribal member helped with the ceremonial preparations by gathering stones, sage, sweetgrass and wood. Soon fires glowed throughout the camp and the medicine people were busy constructing many sweat lodges. The women made gifts of honor, all the while whispering among themselves about the fact that at the age of nineteen Isda was very old for her first marriage.

The following morning two medicine Dog Soldiers were chosen to set up tipis—one for ceremonial purposes and another for consummation of the couple's union. Late that afternoon the food was cooked, causing the people to rub their bellies in hunger as they hurried to and fro finishing preparations and exchanging jokes and playful banter in anticipation of the ceremony. All except Isda's three brothers thought she was very lucky to be accepted by such a great warrior and provider.

As the sun appeared above the horizon on the day of the wedding an apprentice handed Iron Woman her eagle fan and pipe. This strong medicine woman began the ceremony by cleansing the sacred circle with sage and sweetgrass. When this was done she lit her pipe, letting the smoke billow into mounds of white clouds as she offered her prayers to the six directions.

As Wieasta and Isda entered the circle, Iron Woman smoked them off with sage, blessing them and wrapping a buffalo robe around their shoulders to signify their joining. Once the ceremony was completed, they faced the East to offer the marriage up in prayer to be sanctioned by *Tunka'shila*.

The grandmothers took Isda to the ceremonial lodge to teach her the duties of a married woman, while outside celebrations lasted far into the night.

As dawn was breaking, Wiesta appeared in the doorway. Bending down, he gently touched his sleeping bride, saying, "Come, woman, it is time for us to sanction our marriage. The couple silently crept toward the pathway of the deer where, in keeping with tradition, the children were eagerly awaiting their appearance. Jumping out of their hiding places with delightful yells, they chased the couple down the pathway.

Isda and Wieasta joined in the fun. "Run toward the marriage tipi," Wiesta whispered. "I will lead the children astray." Isda watched him vanish down the trail, then hurried along in high spirits. When he at last arrived at the marriage tipi his arrogance gave way to shyness, and he timidly began to build their first fire.

Feeling awkward herself, Isda reached for a leather pouch and headed for the river, saying, "I will get water for us."

Just as she lowered the bag into the river, her three brothers darted out of the nearby woods on horseback, riding fast toward her. Her oldest brother, with fire in his eyes, pulled back hard on the reins and slapped his lance across his chest shouting savagely, "Our father's age has clouded his judgment. This marriage has taken away my birthright as the future leader of our people." With that he lunged forward, driving his lance through Isda's chest. As he slowly removed it, he watched Isda crumble to her knees then fall to her death in the water.

As the image in the book faded, the female soul, remorseful that this mortal life had not been fulfilled, identified Isda's murderer as her own beloved male counterpart.

Another hologram appeared, revealing a battle on the Great Plains. Too many treaties had been broken, and every man, woman and child was filled with fear and rage. The people wanted to stop the white general known to them as Yellow Hair from taking the land, killing the buffalo and desecrating their burial grounds. Many tribes had attempted to defeat Yellow Hair, but this time the Sioux nations were fighting as one.

As the battle progressed, the female soul, now known as White Hawk, heavy with child, bounded laboriously across an open field. A yellow-haired man galloped toward her on horseback and ran her to the ground. With one swipe of his long knife, he opened her stomach, exposing the fetus. The anguish of that terrible moment held mother and child captive until they were hurled back to the Other Side.

Both the female soul and her male counterpart recognized that he was the unborn child and both re-experienced the sorrow of their long-ago demise.

As the scene faded, a new hologram began to take shape. The third scene portrayed the European political powers of 1890 as they shaped history, this time ravaging the New World like locusts. The male soul, now as the warrior Medicine Cloud, together with the female soul, known in this lifetime as Amba Hawi, were moving from their assigned reservation to the Virginias.

Because of his ability to speak the white man's language in addition to many Indian dialects, Medicine Cloud had been appointed scout leader for the new white nation. This occupied him for many moons, forcing him to leave Amba Hawi alone. During this time she used her employment as a servant to gather information from Virginia's political and social circles to assist Medicine Cloud in his secret endeavors.

One evening a sympathetic white friend named Daniel brought Amba Hawi news of a plan to kill Medicine Cloud. The two agreed to leave immediately and warn her husband of the threat.

"We will travel in darkness," said Amba Hawi, tying a bundle of supplies to a traveling stick and handing it to her informer.

As Daniel ran toward the barn to saddle the horses, Medicine Cloud appeared from the shadows, announcing with controlled rage, "You were in my home without my presence and alone with my woman!"

"We were getting ready to come find you," Daniel stammered. "There are white men planning to kill you." But his explanation failed to penetrate his friend's suspicious mind.

"You have dishonored me," Medicine Cloud growled. Stepping forward, he plunged his hunting knife deep into Daniel's chest letting the body dangle from its blade. When death had finally taken him, Medicine Cloud pulled the knife free, wiped it clean on the white man's clothing and returned it to its sheath, continuing on silent footsteps toward the kitchen.

Amba Hawi, startled by his sudden presence and glad he was safe, rushed to his side. "They are planning to kill you. We must hurry! Everything is prepared, and Daniel is saddling the horses," she cried, handing him blankets.

Angrily tossing them aside, Medicine Cloud shouted, "Have you forgotten you are an Indian, woman? How could you allow another man in this house during my absence?"

Shocked at his reaction, she replied in Sioux, "We are not in Indian country! Here we abide by the white man's laws, and besides…"

Medicine Cloud stopped her in mid-sentence, grabbed her hair and pulled her close, growling, "You will never again dishonor any man." With one quick stroke he slit her throat, watching her eyes register shock as she fell to the floor. Assured she had taken her last breath, he calmly walked out of the house, never to return.

For years Medicine Cloud ran from the law, but eventually he was captured and imprisoned for life. The abuse, beatings and hard labor of prison added fuel to his smoldering hatred for the white man, and he was often kept in solitary confinement. There, the more he reflected on the injustices dealt against his people, the further he sank into despair. Ultimately, futility took its toll and he turned to the memories of his long ago love for Amba Hawi to help him endure his loneliness and pain.

As an old man, plagued by the white man's lung disease, Medicine Cloud was allowed to roam freely within the confines of the prison. On one of his early morning walks he became so racked with fever and coughing that he had to lean against a wall for support. Sweat streamed from each pore of his body, and his spirit lingered between life and death. Medicine Cloud knew that before he could re-enter the spirit world, he must release all hatred from his heart and ask forgiveness for his cruel deeds.

Slowly he returned to his cell and sat on the edge of his cot, immersed in thoughts of his beloved Amba Hawi whom he had so brutally murdered. Filled great heartache, he mumbled, "I wonder if there is ever an end to this harsh school of life. Why is so much suffering necessary? Why do I always have to learn the hard way?

A spasm of coughing caused blood to trickle from his mouth. Knowing his time had come, he lit his pipe and softly prayed for a safe journey back to the spirit world, saying:

"*Hau, Wakan Tanka, Tunka'shila*, I humble myself before you in my last earthly hours. Let my return be peaceful after I devote these last moments to memories of the beauty my life has held. As a youngster, I was inspired to sing my song from the soul. Yet in this impending hour, I wonder if I have become a light that shines to your satisfaction. I look now to the smiles your many beautiful creations on Mother Earth have placed upon my face.

"I seek your knowledge and ask for the strength of your love. Let me fly back to you as a warrior, with your wisdom waving my warrior's banner so I may hear and feel my heart again. I, Medicine Cloud, reach to your power and beg you to cleanse my soul. Let my black thoughts, which hang in dark clusters, fall like last year's leaves to the ground. Let me once again run freely in the open fields and feel the warm sun as I roam Beyond the Pines. I ask for a warm place, because I have lived with the coldness of humankind's snow-covered heart. I ask to be forgiven for the pain I have cause others, so that my soul can know freedom as I ride back to the twilight shadows of the deep sleep. Whatever eternity has written, let it be so."

The lights grew dim as Medicine Cloud fell backward onto the bed, choking on his spittle, while before him glowed the radiant spirit of Amba Hawi.

"It is time. I have come to help you return," she said lovingly.

As the morning sun raced across his face, a warm peace enveloped him and he faded from the earthly plane.

As the book closed, the corners of its sacred pages burst into flames. In the silence of the moment, the male and female souls understood their destiny once again.

Dropping humbly to his knees, the male soul pleaded, "It is imperative that I return to the mortal plane! I must never again doubt this shared love that rests between us."

Sakowin answered, "This is not our decision. You have seen your past lives and their limitations. Are you ready to reach beyond these restrictions in another mortal life?"

The male soul grasped his counterpart's hand tightly in his. "Oh Sacred Seven, I must return and prove the worthiness of the love I have for this soul. I beg you to give me protection against my earthly frailties."

The female soul interrupted, "If this is his aspiration, I offer my assistance to help lighten his burden."

"Then it shall be written in the pages of time," announced the Sacred Seven in unison.

As their words echoed throughout the rebirthing chamber, the wolf kingdom, feeling the purity of the female soul's promise, gathered around the couple in a circle of light. A female timber wolf stepped forward, saying:

"We have known this female soul for many lifetimes, and once again, we hear the unity of Wolf coming from her heart. We will support and nurture her in this endeavor. In return, we ask that she remains free from her counterpart's emotional burdens. To become one with us, she must walk with pride, honor and dignity."

From deep within her heart the female soul nodded her acceptance.

"To awaken our gift from within, you must develop a quick yet sensitive mind. Otherwise this gift will remain dormant. As Wolf you will suffer humiliation, poverty, rejection and a severe lack of understanding from the human race. You must always visit us in the shadowed darkness of night to receive our future guidance." With these words the silent howls of the pack permeated the very essence of the female soul.

The Sacred Seven remained silent, acknowledging this gift. Then Sakowin addressed the female soul:

"Wolf is the sacred teacher on Mother Earth. It is time for the two legs to share with Wolf the need for survival. Your mortal life will be with the Wolf Clan people. They will teach you the duality of all Wolf's traits. This will take much time and effort to accomplish. Therefore the Sacred Seven will gift you with a seven year extension to your earthly life."

Turning to the male soul, Sakowin declared:

"Young soul, I see you have made your final decision. Since life is but a moment in immortal time, become a mirror to yourself. The word 'I' is what separates you from the all. Erase this word from your heart so you may transcend its distorted reflections. Cease being torn between the pleasures of flesh and spirit. Release the tortures of your past lives, and allow no doubt to dwell in your earthly memories. Follow truth, not the illusions cast by shadows of fear. Sorrow is the yearning to return to infinity, and real love is the spiritual growth of another. If you accomplish these things, you will have completed your destiny and the 'I' will be no more."

Once again facing the female soul, Sakowin stated:

"Become as a water droplet. Search every river and stream for truth. Let the divided and undivided become as one and demonstrate a love that is spirit rather than physical. Let me remind you this life force is given to you in a state of purified energy. When you return to the spirit world, bring this energy back as pure as it was given."

Knowing those words would soon become her reality, the female soul humbly whispered, "Oh, Great Holy One, since we are joined souls, I want to free myself from this bondage. I offer the seven year extension of my earthly life to the male soul."

"Let this soul be released from her karmic fate," commanded Sakowin. As his words resonated throughout the universe, the Sacred Seven dissolved into nothingness, leaving the two souls standing alone in the Hall of Records.

Knowing the shock of a rebirth would shroud their memories, they burned their love deep into their hearts. When they reached the Crest of Time, the male soul asked, "My Love, how can I be assured of finding you?"

"Search for me in the rays of the sun as it reflects my name. Now, he who holds my heart, tell me how will I find you?"

"Search the fields for the yellow butterfly so that you will remember the touch of my lips, and look for a red rose painted on my left hand."

The male soul reached for the hand of the female soul, but it was too late; she had already stepped into the light of passage. Her soul burst forth like a blazing star, burning with a brilliant flame as she sped toward mortal life.

As the male soul watched, the spirits of all roses shed their morning dew and a tear of happiness was born in his eyes.

Knowing he was unprepared for an earthly birth, the male soul realized that his reunion with the female soul would be lost forever if he did not hurry. A wave of great urgency forced him toward the Sea of Souls, where many souls were waiting in line to be rebirthed to the earthly plane. The male soul pleaded his dilemma to the hearts of all the waiting souls, but was denied entrance. In desperation, he approached a sullen soul standing a little away from the others, saying, "If you allow me to join in your mortal birth, I will extend your earth life seven years. You may do with these years as you wish."

The hearts of both souls understood and agreed. Instantaneously the two joined souls hurled as one into the blackness of space searching for the body that would house them on Mother Earth.

Sunny opened her eyes just as the sun was breaking on the horizon. Was this a dream? Could it be true? I need to talk with Shung'. She unwrapped the blanket from around her body, her face streaked with tears of happiness and joined Shung' and Eddie for breakfast. After eating she asked Shung' to join her on a long walk.

"I've been to the Other Side and was shown many of my past lives with Meeko," Sunny began. She went on to explain how she and Meeko had been intertwined souls through many lifetimes.

"Cheering Woman spoke to me of this long ago. She always knew this man would be in your life. Without this relationship you would not be who you are today. This vision confirms to me that you are ready for the little death ceremony."

When they returned to camp Sunny picked up her shovel and continued her search for the right place to dig her pit. This time an inner knowing led her to the base of Bear Butte where she began to dig. Shung' and Wicahmunga joined her with their shovels and within a few hours the preparations for Sunny's little death ceremony had been completed.

The three women returned to camp, where Eddie had the *Inipi* ready. Silently they entered the sweat and Eddie took his place as Fire Chief. After the sweat Sunny cut a hole in the center of an old sheet and slipped it over her head then started her walk to the pit which was to be her home for the next four days and nights.

Everyone gathered close as Sunny climbed inside. With smiling faces they sang a protection song and Shung' offered prayers for Sunny to have a good vision.

"Pull the dirt in around you and leave it loose," instructed Shung'. Sunny turned to face the West and began pulling the dirt around her. When her body was half covered, Shung' said, "Place your arms to your sides." Then ever so gently, she and the others placed the remaining loose soil around until all but her head was covered. "Now move your body around until you are comfortable." Sunny did as instructed. When she looked up at everyone she saw tears of joy flowing down their cheeks.

One by one they wished her well on her vision quest. Eddie bent down and kissed her cheek, saying, "You are like my own child to me. I know you will do fine. My prayers are with you, Granddaughter."

Wicahmunga, still crying, held Sunny's face in her hands and kissed her on both cheeks.

Then Shung' sat on the ground and held Sunny's head lovingly and sang an eagle song as she tied a small eaglet plume into her hair. "My little *Sku'ya*," she said softly when the song was finished. "I have given you all that I am from a loving heart. Listen closely to the spirits and they will help you gather your power.

"I'm going to cover your head so your senses will not distract you from your purpose. But first, take one last look around at all the beauty that will be with you. Listen to the voice of the land and let it carry you to the heart of your identity. Let Mother Earth embrace your body close to her bosom as the spirits feed your soul.

"Your little death will take you to many dimensions of reality. Use your time well as you sit in the womb of *Maka Ina*. She will help you make your transitions through the dimensions of time, space and measure. Keep in mind that knowledge is neutral and allow your thoughts to direct you in how it is to be used.

"If Medicine is to be your future, then begin shaping this future with a heart filled with love, and connect to everything you know. Respect and discipline will be your primary tools through this process. Take all that is and build a strong spiritual foundation as you bring your past into the present and observe what *Wakan Tanka* has in store for your future. It is time for you to dedicate your life to the Great Spirit. In order to be a vessel for *Wakan Tanka* you must give your all.

"I'm going to walk away now. You were born to do this and it is time." With these words she placed a black hood over Sunny's head. "Let your spirit fly as free as the eagle, granddaughter. Ride with him on the winds."

Sunny listened to her teacher's departing footsteps until they faded into nothingness. The hood made her feel strangely isolated and she tried to peer through the black cloth, but could see nothing. After a few hours her body began to ache and Sunny wished she could change her position. The afternoon was hot and she marveled at how Mother Earth cooled her skin while sweat dripped from her brow. She began to reflect back on her childhood innocence and relive many happy memories of her days with her grandmother.

The thought of Cheering Woman's many sacrifices for the people brought tears to her eyes. Her thoughts turned to Sam. It was he who had taught her to have the courage to stand up and take command of her destiny. And her beloved Meeko, why hadn't she been able to see the soul purpose of their marriage? There were so many clues. For the first time her memories of these special people in her life held no sadness or pain, and she realized that without them she would not be who she was today.

As the sun slowly disappeared over the horizon, Sunny delighted in the changes that were taking place within and around her. As night touched the land she felt the quickness of the temperature change and smiled at the feel of the cool earth against her skin. And everything was good. But when the blackness of night closed in on her, she began to question the unknown and the more deafening the silence became, the tighter her fears gripped her mind.

Suddenly she heard the sound of horses galloping toward her. Fearing they would crush her, she screamed out for Shung' but there was no reply. Her senses were more acute with her head covered and she could identify the intruders as a herd of wild mustangs. Sunny knew she was in a vulnerable position and she prayed for Bear to protect her boundaries. One of the mustangs approached her and began to sniff about her head. She commanded it to leave. The horse nuzzled her hooded head, snorted and then casually trotted away. Sunny thought about Horse's message and knew she was being told to adapt quickly so that her trip to the spirit world would be speedy.

Sunny continued to be disturbed by the many unfamiliar sounds around her until she recalled that Cheering Woman had once told her that whistling drives away bad spirits. Sunny whistled till dawn, but all she got was a dry mouth—no sleep and no vision.

As the shadows of night vanished and the light of day touched her, Sunny enjoyed basking in the warmth of the morning sun. By mid-afternoon, sweat poured down her forehead, stinging her eyes. A few soldier ants crawled over her neck, biting her without mercy. Her whole body tingled, as though pierced with needles. Sunny fought the desire to dig herself out of the pit as she focused her thoughts on her hatred of failure.

As if to test her fortitude, a swarm of sweat bees began buzzing around her head. Although she twisted her head from side to side to ward them off, she was stung on the neck and the top of her head. Nearly mad with frustration and discomfort, she screamed for help, but the only reply was the echo of her own voice.

Suddenly she was torn from the earth's floor and flung to where, she did not know. In that moment, Sunny realized that if she was to survive she must fight for some stability. Desperately she began to search for a safe place. She saw an open doorway and raced through it into the arms of Meeko. Filled with relief, she asked, "Where am I?"

Red eyes glared back at her. Knowing this was not Meeko, she tried to struggle free. Without warning she fell down, down, down into a bottomless pit covered with debris. She clawed desperately at the earth, trying to find something to grab onto. But what seemed like earth was nothing but sky patterns, and she continued to fall.

As her mind ran wild with terror she looked up to see a big bear staring down at her. She was frightened of the bear's presence until she heard a soft, soothing voice say, "Let your mind go beyond this ordinary world, far beyond death." With these words Sunny began to feel more calm and she begged the sacred *Mato* to help her fight this enemy. Suddenly many bridges appeared in the shape of a grid and Sunny found herself running back and forth in her confusion over which bridge to cross. Looking across one of the bridges she saw Bear and ran to safety.

As the hours passed, Sunny continued to lament, begging for a sign. She thought of the four parts of her soul and remembered the *Sicun*. If the *Sicun* represented her intellect and the essence of her mind, then why was it not helping her relate to the sixteen powers of the *Inipi* so she could get rid of her fears?

In frustration, she cried out, "Oh, *Tob Tob*, bear with me during this time. I have a need. Please help me connect to *Wakan Tanka*, the power of all." Suddenly she heard someone singing in a language that she had never heard, yet completely understood. She tried to comprehend its significance, but it meant nothing to her confused mind.

Sunny slept little that night. She no longer feared the unknown, but still a vision did not come.

The next day passed slowly, accented only by occasional winds. As darkness approached, Sunny was exhausted and ready to give up. She wished she were home, lying in the sun by the pool, gazing at the glorious colors of spring. Thoughts of spring transported her back to childhood, and suddenly she found herself running through the fields, watching the clouds fly swiftly overhead. She could see her grandmother's garden. The flowers and herbs that she and her grandmother had planted were dancing with the wind.

She heard Cheering Woman call out, "*Sku'ya*, come sit on the blanket with me. Feel the beauty of life all around us. Feel its spiritual value. You will see that the circle of life has no beginning or end. Your *Hanblecheyapi* is not just about you, it's about all the animals, the flying ones and all the growing things. Open your heart and let their sweet voices guide you."

Shocked to attention, Sunny listened intently as her grandmother continued, "Think back on your woman training. Remember how excited you were to finally learn how to stitch a beautiful quilt? Remember how much you enjoyed beading your soft leather pipe bag?"

Cheering Woman held out their Ropes of Hope, saying, "See, here's mine and here's yours. *Sku'ya*, watch closely as I intertwine them, so I can help you in this quest." As the soft ropes began to intertwine they blended together and swirled around Sunny's body giving her a pleasant tingling sensation. "Fly, Little One. Fly with me," said Cheering Woman as she vanished into nothingness.

Guilt gnawed at Sunny as she recalled the many times she had silently fought her grandmother to escape from learning the sacred teachings. She marveled at how her life had encompassed so much pain and so much beauty from those old lessons. How hard she had worked to fulfill her dreams, and how rewarding it had been to receive many eagle feathers in honor of her good deeds.

For awhile longer she basked in warm memories of her life with Cheering Woman. From out of the blue, she heard the sound of wings overhead. Sunny looked to see many eagles flying overhead. Looking across the plains she spotted another sitting on a high rock. How can this be? I see the winged ones and yet, I supposedly cannot see through the hood.

A black owl not of this world let out a strangled screech as it landed near her face. Sunny, knowing the owl was an underworld servant, gasped. Her apprehension diminished as she watched the owl become two dancing flutes. Each note of the flute seemed to enter her body and she found herself singing words she did not know but fully understood. During this rapturous moment Sunny sang until she no longer had a voice.

From somewhere far in the distance, Sunny heard loud drumbeats and she chanted, "Oh drums, I hear you talking. Oh drums, I feel you walking," while in her heart she danced, keeping time with the beat until the sound faded and silence consumed her.

A shining white horse rode forth and Meeko, in all of his glory, dressed in the finest of white leather, quickly dismounted. She melted in his arms as he embraced her lovingly, and once again they stood together on the bridge dropping rose petals into the Sea of Souls. In that instant, Sunny remembered her soul's purpose on earth.

Meeko looked deep into her soul and said, "My Sweetheart, reach back and draw our ancestors into you. Bring that honor from the past and let this be your strength. Summon this power to you and think of it as your future to come." With these words he vanished.

No sooner had Meeko disappeared, than his great-grandfather rode forth with many warriors by his side. Granbear slipped from his paint and smiled, saying:

"I have walked many miles with you. As Bear Clan, Daughter, you have earned the right to celebrate life, and you should give thanks to *Wakan Tanka* for that life. Soon you will face the moon of the strong cold, and I will be riding by your side. Before you join us on the Other Side, you will see the moon when the green grass grows and the ponies shed their hair. When the strawberry moon arrives, look for the moon that ripens. When the moon of the wild rice shines high above, look for the moon that tells the changes of the seasons. I will come to you when the moon of the falling leaves appear. I am Granbear. We are one."

Suddenly Granbear was gone and she heard the warning growl of a large grizzly. Sunny watched as a bear appeared and rapidly grew to such stature that its body seemed to encompass the universe. He took her to somewhere in the underworld, a place she did not know. The bear held her between his paws, pummeling, biting, hitting and clawing until her blood and skin were scattered everywhere. Sunny felt as if she had been skinned alive, much like a tree stripped from its bark.

Bear carried Sunny to the river where he bathed her and took her to a cave where he fed her many strange roots. Then Bear began to make a shield, and when it was finished he placed it inside her body as he remolded her from the inside out to prepare her for her true mission in Medicine.

Everything vanished into darkness. Dawn came over and over again, but the sun did not rise. Four comets flew past and she watched as the Bear Clan nation was birthed from the stars. Sunny joined them as they danced with the moon.

A silver disk appeared and took her far beyond the sun where she saw many separate worlds that were all joined to Mother Earth. Fearing she might become lost in space and time, Sunny searched the sky to find the North Star, knowing it would help her maintain her connection to Mother Earth.

Sunny gyrated through the future to the year 2070. There was no sun, no moon or stars and even the seasons could no longer be recognized. The directions had been changed and no one knew where to find the West, North, East or South.

Mother Earth loomed before her in total darkness amidst an angry wind that blew fiercely through the hot darkness like a wild, angry ghost dancing with fervor to bring the survival of all life forces to a halt. The wind continued its uncontrolled chaos, splitting Mother Earth's body into wide, gaping canyons and topless mountains.

The trees were already dead, their bleached trunks and branches lying upon the terrain like scattered kindling. Huge boulders had been ripped from the soil, smashing to pieces as they rolled across the earth. Mother Earth had been raped, and she was a dying planet. There was no day or night, only the ever-moving sands, hiding what once was, then exposing what had once been hidden.

Their were no signs of racial prejudice among the few remaining people. Only hunger mattered in their desperate struggle for survival. Middle-aged men and women tended meager crops, while the elders and the wounded waited patiently at the sacred watering holes to collect a few precious droplets of life-giving water. The strongest children roamed over the desolate landscape armed with digging sticks as they searched through the rubble for whatever usable materials they could find. When the people came together to rest, an old medicine woman would tell them stories of the long-ago people and how life once was on Mother Earth.

Sunny found herself sitting among a group of children who listened with spellbound reverence as the old story teller spoke:

"Long ago the people did not appreciate *Wakan Tanka's* sacred gift of life. Over the generations, they became too comfortable with man-made laws and forgot about the natural laws of *Wakan Tanka*. They took their freedom and their luxurious way of life for granted, ignoring all of Creator's warnings that appeared in the sky.

"They were so in love with money that they destroyed the tree nation and forced the animals to live in the steel-and-concrete jungles that covered Mother Earth. As a result of this terrible behavior the rich became richer, while the less fortunate suffered from poverty and hunger in a land that was plentiful.

"As time went on, many people lost their homes and possessions. Many children vanished from the face of Mother Earth, never to be found. In those times, both parents had to work to provide food and shelter for their children. The corrupt lawmakers remained aloof to the needs of the people, giving the masses a mere pittance for their labor, then taking it all back in taxes.

"Back then it was mandatory that all children attend schools to learn how to function as future workers in the government system. The leaders of the world continued their worship of power and money, using their manmade laws to benefit their greed as they sucked the life out of Mother Earth's body.

"Slowly and too late the people saw their power had leaked away. Honor and integrity were no longer valued and the streets were rampant with those who would steal, kill or rape for a mere morsel of food.

"At last our forefathers began to rage against these powerful fraudulent leaders, and around the world the downtrodden races cried out to *Wakan Tanka* and stood up as one against government corruption.

"For centuries the power people of the land continued to keep humankind under control with hunger and germ warfare. The day came when Mother Earth was in such a weakened state that she could no longer fight back and she began to plead with the winds, the water and the air for help.

"*Wakinyan* heard her plea and roared in mocking laughter at the stupidity of humankind. He sent lightning bolts raging across Mother Earth, ravaging all that was left with fire. The world was an inferno. As the air ignited and seared their lungs, the two legs and the four legs found it impossible to breathe and hysteria ruled the land.

"The people began to run around frantically to where they did not know. The winds danced along with the fire across barren hills. Mountaintops blew off and crumbled into dust that swirled over the ground. Ashes spewed upward for thousands of feet, masking the planet with thick heavy darkness.

"Mother Earth shuddered, heaving the water from her ocean beds as new shorelines were cut. Little by little her body split open like ravenous jaws and she began to devour herself. It was a terrible time.

"Dry river beds stretched for miles under a blanket of acid steam. Those who survived stood by helplessly watching Mother Earth slowly die. The stench of decay was everywhere. The ever-blowing winds kept up until Mother Earth became a barren dust bowl and it seemed as if insanity ruled!

"Then one day a small light appeared in the sky and the sun was reborn. Within days the blazing heat had sucked the few remaining ponds, rivers and lakes dry. As the steam rose the sun became a flaming red ball spinning in the midst of meaningless space.

"I was a child during those horrendous times, and I remember them well. A new generation of survivors roamed the land. Death protruded from their eyes, their hearts crying out for someone, anyone, to share in a moment of companionship.

"Mother Earth had become a dangerous place and only a few were brave enough to chance leaving their place of safety. When it became a necessity for these brave ones to go into the unfruitful land to hunt for food, the others, knowing the heat of the sun could kill, gave them what little clothing they had to cover their bodies.

"Throughout these years of hardship the people found their greatest strength came from prayer and sacred rituals, and in time they began to rebuild their lives. The wise people came to the realization that if they were to live they must have a ceremony to bring back the rains. They gathered together those who could remember the old ceremonies in hopes that they could appease these destructive forces.

"At last they located a determined young medicine woman who had the power to lead dancers through the invisible dark worlds. She agreed to perform the old Ghost Dance, and after weeks of training, she chose the strongest dancers from all races.

"The ceremony began on a gray, humid morning. The dancers entered the sacred circle determined to bring balance and harmony back to Mother Earth. The most enlightened ones moved toward what they instinctively felt was the West Door, praying humbly to *Wakan Tanka* to have pity on the people of *Maka Ina*.

"For hours these eagle dancers spun round and round the center of the circle where the sacred cottonwood tree should have been. The chanting and the prayers grew stronger and louder as they begged *Wanbli Gle'ska* to come and help them challenge the harshness of nature.

"The other dancers moved with the rhythm of Mother Earth trying to reach an altered state as they stood in the North, East and South doorways forming the outer ring of the sacred circle. The dancers knew their sole purpose was to pull down the powers from the above while begging *Wakan Tanka* to forgive the ignorance of their forefathers.

"Days melted into nights and still they danced, but their pitiful cries were not heard. Some fell from sheer exhaustion and were forced to leave the circle. Knowing the dance must go on if they were to live, the men, women, children and even the old people, took the places of the fallen dancers.

"The Eagle dancers in the West were like Dog Soldiers, determined to complete the ceremony even if it meant their death. They fought to hold the rhythm of Mother Earth's heartbeat, moving incessantly on bleeding feet as they cut a deep circle into her body.

"Pitiful cries rang out from parched and bleeding mouths as the people begged *Wakan Tanka* to release the moisture from the sky. Seeking, ever seeking to find the Red Road in the above world, they danced until they stepped beyond all spiritual parameters they had ever known.

"But the winds continued. In desperation they joined hands and mind-linked with their beloved Mother Earth. They saw she was captured in a grotesque web of darkness. Each dancer grabbed a strand of the web and tugged relentlessly to rescue her from its grip as they all prayed for the life-giving rains to come. Onlookers saw their struggle and joined them in prayer determined to force the sky to bring forth its cleansing moisture.

"Again *Wakinyan's* voice thundered down and he shot his lightning bolts among the dancers. Then thick dark clouds gathered overhead and the wind stood still as *Wakinyan's* thunderous voice was heard everywhere.

"The first raindrop, a jewel more precious than any diamond, fell in the center of the circle. As the dancers dropped to their knees in thanksgiving, sheets of rain began to pour down.

"Their eyes filled with tears of happiness as they humbly filled their hands and whatever containers they could find with this precious gift. It continued to rain and within hours, the rivers and lakes were overflowing and water was running across the land.

"All at once the rains stopped and stillness held the land. The people gazed with awe as a huge beam of light penetrated the sacred circle. A powerful booming voice invited the people to enter the cylinder's core. Some were afraid and withdrew to the safety of darkness, while most submissively entered, never to be seen again."

As the old medicine woman finished her story, she studied the children's faces searching for the few passionate ones who could learn to keep the old ways. With smoldering eyes she filled her sacred pipe then smoked it slowly. When she was finished, she said:

"We are the descendants of those few that chose to remain on Mother Earth. What I say is sacred knowledge to be forever remembered and passed on to our unborn children. We must teach the coming generations the sacredness of their planet and prepare them to become the caretakers of Mother Earth.

"Our children's children will build a new and sacred world. Show them how to share freely with others so all may one day live in peace and harmony. You must always walk the Red Road, which leads to the doorway of the central sun. Let this sun light the flame in your soul and become one of its resonating rays. This will allow you to listen to your heart."

She got up slowly and draped a seed necklace around each child's neck as a reminder to keep the old teachings hidden in the sacred ceremonies. When this was done, she said, "Value these old ways, and never deny yourself the power of Eagle. If you allow this terrible history to continue repeating itself, then know that Eagle will hunt you down and devour the entire human race." A gentle smile crossed her face as tears of sadness filled her wise old eyes.

The old woman approached Sunny and looked deep into her heart, saying, "Look around you. These pitiful little islands that we now inhabit were once the Great Rocky Mountains of Colorado. Isn't it sad what your generation has done?"

The door of Sunny's vision closed and she found herself back in the pit. She wondered if the necklace of seeds still hung from her neck. Her thoughts were interrupted by the sound of footsteps approaching and she realized that Shung' and Wicahmunga had been nearby all the time, protecting her with their powerful ceremonial prayers.

Ever so gently Shung's weathered, wrinkled hands removed the shroud from Sunny's head and lovingly encircled her face. Eddie and Wicahmunga carefully laid out a bearskin with an eagle feather tied to the upper right side. Wicahmunga placed two sacred rattles and a drum on the bearskin as Shung' picked up a shovel and began to dig Sunny from the pit, all the while singing an old sacred song. The three lifted Sunny from the pit and lay her upon the bear robe. Shung' lit a piece of white sage, smudged Sunny off and softly proclaimed:

"Let it be known throughout time, space and dimension that this woman walks strong with the old medicine ways just as her grandmother predicted long ago."

She then placed an unusual necklace of seeds around Sunny's neck and decreed:

"It has taken many years for you to become *Ezonzon Wi Cha Nah He*, Sunlit Soul, the name your grandmother gave you at birth. Now that you have met, seen and faced all that you are, walk strong, Daughter of the Sun, as *WIND WOLF WOMAN*.

If you like this book and want to purchase one for someone else, please check with your local bookstore or use this form:

Name _____

Address_____

City_____ State_____ Zip_____

E-mail Address_____

Wind Wolf Woman _____ copies @ $24.95 U.S. each $_____

Nevada residents, please add applicable sales tax $_____

Shipping: $3.50 U.S. per copy $_____

Total enclosed $_____

For more than five copies, please contact the publisher for quantity rates. Send completed order form and your payment to:

Taté Publishing
701 Kenny Way, #1
Las Vegas, NV 89107
Fax: 702-878-4185
E-mail: info@windwolfwoman.com

Credit card orders via our web site at www.windwolfwoman.com

If you like this book and want to purchase one for someone else, please check with your local bookstore or use this form:

Name _____

Address_____

City_____ State_____ Zip_____

E-mail Address_____

Wind Wolf Woman _____ copies @ $24.95 U.S. each $_____

Nevada residents, please add applicable sales tax $_____

Shipping: $3.50 U.S. per copy $_____

Total enclosed $_____

For more than five copies, please contact the publisher for quantity rates. Send completed order form and your payment to:

    Taté Publishing
    701 Kenny Way, #1
    Las Vegas, NV 89107
    Fax: 702-878-4185
    E-mail: info@windwolfwoman.com

Credit card orders via our web site at www.windwolfwoman.com